Quantitative Business Analysis

The Wiley/Hamilton Series in Management and Administration

Elwood S. Buffa, Advisory Editor | University of California, Los Angeles

Quantitative Business Analysis

DAVID EUGENE SMITH
San Jose State University

John Wiley & Sons
Santa Barbara   New York   London   Sydney   Toronto

A WILEY/HAMILTON PUBLICATION

Library of Congress Cataloging in Publication Data

Smith, David Eugene, 1941–
   Quantitative business analysis.

   (The Wiley/Hamilton series in management and administration)
   1. Industrial management—Mathematical models.
2. Operations research. I. Title.
HD30.25.S63   658.4′033   77-23299
ISBN 0-471-80405-3

Printed in the United States of America.

10   9   8   7   6   5   4   3   2   1

This book was copyedited by Irene Elmer, designed by Bruce Kortebein and set in 10 point Times Roman by Santype International. Kathy Trainor designed the cover, the illustrations were prepared by Etc. Graphics and printing and binding was by Quinn and Boden. Chuck Pendergast and Jean Varven supervised production.

About the Author

David Eugene Smith is a professor of Business
Administration at San Jose State University. He received
his B.S. and M.S. degrees from San Francisco State
University and his M.B.A. and Ph.D. from the University
of Santa Clara. He joined the Marketing Department of
Marketing and Quantitative Analysis at San Jose State
University in the fall of 1969 where he teaches marketing,
quantitative methods and future studies.

To Patricia

Preface

In schools of business, the instructor of courses in quantitative analysis has a major problem. Students enrolled in these courses typically have both a wide diversity of educational needs and a wide diversity of quantitative sophistication. To satisfy these students, an effective text can be neither too quantitatively sophisticated nor too cursory in its presentation. Quantitative Business Analysis was written to solve this problem.

The text is intended to be highly readable and thorough in its coverage. It emphasizes the student's conceptual understanding. Concepts are presented with sound logic and causal reasoning in the context of applied illustration. The mathematical prerequisites have been kept to a minimum. The student needs only a reasonable background in basic algebra. A previous introduction to probability will be helpful, but it is not required. For students who lack this introduction or would like a review, Chapter 2, Quantifying Uncertainty, provides the required background.

Prepared primarily for use in schools of business, the text has been structured to provide flexibility in covering the topics. It is suitable for a survey course or for a full year sequence. To make it more adaptive, the material has been grouped into four major topic areas: decision theory, mathematical programming, inventory and queuing theory, and simulation. As illustrated in Figure p. 1, each area can be considered independently in the selection of topics. Appendix sections and specially designated chapters represent optional material. Frequently more technical, the optional material provides select extensions for a more thorough coverage. These sections can be excluded without loss of continuity.

A general guide for topic coverage is provided in Table p. 1. In a full year sequence, the entire text can be covered comfortably. For a survey course, the topics listed in column 1, Table p. 1 represent a useful selection. This list will require modification depending on the level of the students' background, the amount of supplementary material, and the depth of coverage.

I would like to express my appreciation for the helpful suggestions provided by the reviewers and most particularly to Elwood S. Buffa, University of California, Los Angeles for his comments. In addition, a very special and well-deserved thanks to Janet Anaya, San Jose State University, for typing the entire manuscript, proofing the calculations in the illustrative examples, and classroom testing the materials.

David Eugene Smith
March 1977

Contents

DECISION THEORY

INVENTORY AND QUEUING THEORY 457

SIMULATION   573

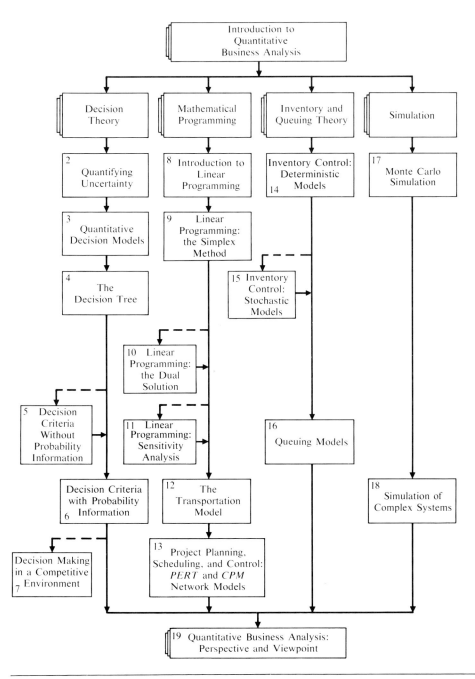

FIGURE P.1

Organization of Topic Coverage

	Survey Course	Two Semesters	Two Quarters	Three Quarters
1 Introduction to Quantitative Business Analysis	✓	✓	✓	✓
2 Quantifying Uncertainty	✓	✓	✓	✓
3 Quantitative Decision Models	✓	✓	✓	✓
4 The Decision Tree	✓	✓	✓	✓
5 Decision Criteria Under Uncertainty Without Probability Information	—	✓	—	✓
6 Decision Criteria Under Uncertainty with Probability Information	✓	✓	✓	✓
7 Decision Making in a Competitive Environment: Game Theory	—	✓	—	✓
8 An Introduction to Linear Programming	✓	✓	✓	2nd Quarter ✓
9 Linear Programming: the Simplex Method	✓	✓	✓	✓
10 Linear Programming: the Dual Solution	—	✓	2nd Quarter —	✓
11 Linear Programming: Sensitivity Analysis	—	✓	—	✓
12 The Transportation Model	✓	2nd Semester ✓	✓	✓
13 Project Planning, Scheduling, and Control: PERT and CPM Network Models	✓	✓	✓	✓
14 Inventory Control: Deterministic Models	✓	✓	✓	3rd Quarter ✓
15 Inventory Control: Stochastic Models	—	✓	—	✓
16 Queuing Models	—	✓	✓	✓
17 Monte Carlo Simulation	✓	✓	✓	✓
18 Simulation of Complex Systems	—	✓	—	✓
19 Quantitative Business Analysis: Perspective and Viewpoint	✓	✓	✓	✓

TABLE P.1

A General Guide

1

Introduction to Quantitative Business Analysis

Man is a decision maker. Throughout life, in every action, decisions are fundamental. They are unavoidable. The success or failure of an individual, of a society, or of mankind depends directly on the ability of individuals to render rational, intelligent, informed decisions.

Man lives in an environment of decisions, an environment of choice situations. His environment of choice is analogous to a decision to move on a chess board. The only major difference is the greater complexity: the board is not as finite, the pieces not as distinguishable or as few in number, the rules not as clearly defined. Nonetheless, each move opens future opportunities, forecloses others. The player has no small stake in the outcome of the game.

An individual really has no rational choice but to choose, and to choose wisely. For not to choose is itself a choice, and not always the most desirable one. Some choices are more important than others, some more abstract and less clearly defined. Yet each choice will affect all other choices—the whole being a transient continuum weaving past to present, unfolding the future. If man is truly concerned with controlling his destiny, concerned with success rather than failure, he must masterfully learn the process of how to make better choices, how to make better decisions.

THE DECISION PROCESS

While making countless decisions each day, an individual seldom if ever gives any conscious thought to the process by which decisions are made. All decisions, however, have essential elements in common. The more clearly these elements can be understood, the more easily the decision maker can properly perceive, formulate, structure, and analyze a decision environment. With this understanding, the more easily the decision maker can make better choices, better decisions.

The essential elements of any decision are:

(1) *the problem:* a conceptualization of a choice situation; the discovery of a situation providing an alternative selection;

(2) *information:* the input into the system; a store of value; a store of symbolic models, images, and processes; a medium of transference;

(3) *the value system:* a standard for measurement; the assignment of meaning to alternatives;

(4) *decision models:* the analysis or synthesis of information; the process of using information in terms of the value system to evaluate and ultimately sort alternatives;

(5) *the decision:* the selection of an alternative, the objective and output of the decision process.

The decision process, unfortunately, is not as easily conveyed as this simple list would suggest. The essential elements often vary in order and in importance. For example, in the discovery of a problem, the decision maker conducts a cursory, preliminary exploration of the decision environment. The decision maker must *decide* whether to become more fully involved in the decision process. This initial inquiry requires each of the essential elements—information, a value system, a method of analysis, and an alternative selection.

If this preliminary investigation is sufficiently promising, the decision maker begins a more formal involvement in the decision process. The initially perceived problem will typically contain subproblems with subproblems of their own. Each subproblem, again, may require each of the essential elements.

Information is indispensable at every stage. At times, desired information may not be available. It may be too costly or too time consuming to obtain. Especially for group decisions, an appropriate value system may be difficult to define. The means of analysis may vary substantially in formal sophistication at different stages throughout the decision process.

The decision process is complex—possibly as complex as man's perception of reality. Basic to any decision, however, are the essential elements in all of their varied forms.

The Problem: A Choice Situation

The first essential element of the decision process is *the discovery of a problem.* A problem may be defined as the *conceptualization of a choice situation.* It is the awareness of possible alternative courses of action that offer a different level of satisfaction. It is often the realization of the difference between what is and what could be.

Once a person realizes that there are better alternatives, he or she tends to be compelled to action. Not to select a better course of action is to forgo obtainable gains. To forgo an obtainable gain is to suffer a real *opportunity loss*. In turn, this perception of potential loss creates a state of psychological disequilibrium motivating the person to action, to further inquiry, to a more deliberate consideration of the other elements of the decision process. Irresistably, as a result of a personal striving for a better life, an individual's perception of potential transforms that person into a decision maker.

Information: The Medium of the Process

Information plays an encompassing role in the decision process. It constitutes the only input into the system. It helps the decision maker to perceive the choice situation. Information clarifies the decision maker's perception of future environments and the definition of alternatives. It serves as a store of past experience. And as a store of past correlates between cause and effect, it contributes to the evolution and transformation of the value system. Information is the manipulative ingredient used in the analysis. It constitutes the output of the entire decision process.

The decision process can be conceptualized as an information-gathering, storing, processing, and producing system. Information serves as the catalyst and the medium of the system. *The decision process synthesizes information into choice—into action.*

The Value System: A Standard for Assigning Value

In the process of selecting between alternatives, the decision maker assigns perceived worth or value to the alternatives. This is done by referring to a *value system* that serves as a master guide for scaling relative value. *The value system gives meaning and quantification to the alternatives.* It serves to guarantee a decision consistent with the decision maker's objectives.

The value system, therefore, is central to the process of defining and selecting alternatives. It clarifies the real meaning of each alternative and of the selection between alternatives. It assigns value to and sorts alternatives.

Decision Models: The Analysis and Synthesis of Information

Once clearly defined and value weighted, the alternatives are analyzed. *The analysis consists of synthesizing the relevant information in terms of the value system to evaluate and sort alternatives.* The process of analysis is commonly termed a *model.* It focuses on the *search for optimality.* It restricts alternatives, evaluates alternatives, and sorts alternatives.

The Decision: Selecting an Alternative

Alternatives provide the structure or framework for the decision process. The problem begins with the perception of valued alternatives. The alternatives are then defined and clarified in terms of probable future environments. With a value system and through analysis, the alternatives are systematically restricted, evaluated, and sorted. This process of identifying, clarifying, restricting, evaluating, and sorting alternatives is performed to allow the selection of the best alternative. *The selection of an alternative is the reason for the entire decision process.*

The Decision Process: A Complex Transient System

The decision process is highly complex. Any attempt at a complete description would be as exhausting as it would undoubtedly be lacking. Figure 1.1, however, provides a simplified illustration of the relationship and interaction of the essential elements.

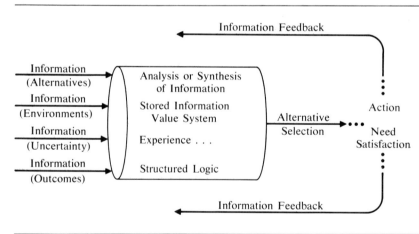

FIGURE 1.1

The Decision Process

The decision process is a dynamic, evolutive, need-satisfying system. It is an information input, information-generating, information-utilizing, and information output system. It functions to identify, clarify, restrict, evaluate, and sort alternatives. It converts perception of choice into action, into need satisfaction.

DECISION MODELS

In different decision environments, different elements of the decision process become strategic. At times, the discovery of a problem may be the most critical. At times, some vital information may not be readily available or even obtainable. The alternatives may be unclear or too numerous. Especially in social decisions, the definition of an acceptable value system may often be, at best, quite vague. An acceptable means for analysis may not be known, may not adequately fit the unique problem, or may be too tedious, costly, or time consuming. Any of the essential elements of the decision process may be critical to a best alternative selection.

While each essential element is required to solve a problem, this text will consider most of these elements as givens. Throughout the text the decision environment and the specific problem will be clearly defined. Relevant information will be provided or will be calculable. The proper value system will be supplied or will be sufficiently determinable. The text will focus predominantly on a single element—the development and the application of *models* to help a decision maker select an appropriate alternative.

Decision models can be sophisticated expressions of formally structured logic or loosely structured impressions of cause and effect. Language, symbols, and logic are all decision models. Thoughts are decision models. Decision models represent any attempt to describe, explain, or predict reality. They represent mechanisms for coping with the complexity of the real world. They generally provide a simplification of reality. Ideally they abstract from the rich complexity of the real world the essential behavior with a few significant relationships. And as simplifications, they help a decision maker to *understand* the behavior of the complex real world. They help a decision maker to define, restrict, sort, evaluate, and select purposeful behavior.

Since the scope of decision models is as inclusive as man's thoughts and perceived realities, this area of inquiry must be restricted. The text will focus on the development of formal quantitative decision models for application to business and economics.

QUANTITATIVE MODELS IN BUSINESS AND ECONOMICS

With the evolution of man's knowledge, a parallel evolution of decision models has occurred to help a decision maker to cope better with the decision environment. Accelerated by increased understanding, all areas of human inquiry appear to evolve, some more rapidly than others, along a continuum from the extreme of a pure art to that of a pure science. As more is known, the decision environment can be more easily described, explained, and predicted. It can be more easily understood and therefore dealt with. Through time, experience and experimentation tend to produce hypotheses, guidelines, and principles. These eventually evolve into the more scientific forms of theory, laws, and truths. And in the process of this movement, very loosely structured qualitative decision models tend to evolve into more highly structured quantitative decision models.

In the broad area of business and economics, there has been a similar evolution. During and after World War II, problem solving moved from an art to more of a science. Pragmatically, as a type of problem justifies the need for a better solution, quantitative models have evolved to help decision makers to make better decisions. And in the wake of this evolution, a wide assortment of powerful quantitative decision models have developed.

People have always been vitally concerned with the allocation of scarce resources. The problem area is universal. The problem invades every human endeavor. It occurs whenever restricted resources are allocated among competing activities to accomplish an objective. Examples are numerous: the allocation of men and machines to produce products; the blend of refined crudes for gasoline; the routing of goods from factories to warehouses; the location of a new plant; the selection of a portfolio; or the assignment of work groups to projects. Fortunately, the quantitative model of *linear programming* has evolved to facilitate the optimal allocation of resources.

A second major problem area has been the planning, scheduling, and control of complex new projects. Included in this area would be the construction of a new apartment complex, a shopping mall, or a sports stadium, or the development of a new product. On a more massive scale are projects like the Polaris weapons system, putting man on the moon, the B-1 bomber, or a space platform. To prevent delays and to allow a timely economic completion, these projects must be extensively planned, scheduled, and controlled. Quantitative models have evolved that minimize completion time with the incorporation of time-cost tradeoffs. The primary models are the Program Evaluation Review Technique (PERT) and the Critical Path Method (CPM).

With the size and complexity of present day organizations, another common and important problem area has been the maintenance and control of inventories. With inventory policy a function of the supply, the demand, and the review period for ordering, quantitative models have been developed that economically balance the costs of too many or too few items in inventory. These models constitute inventory theory.

Another almost universal problem area is waiting lines. Virtually everywhere people or items wait for service at service facilities. A person need only look around to discover a waiting-line problem: the check-out counter of the grocery store; the elevator; the traffic on the freeway, or the tennis courts on Saturday morning. Airplanes wait for runways, machines wait for repair, and commuters wait for buses. Any time there is waiting for a facility, a potential waiting-line problem exists. Waiting-line or queuing theory has evolved in response to this type of decision environment.

An individual, an organization, or an entire country often encounters competitive situations. An organization's product, promotion, distribution, and pricing strategies all reflect competition. Missile employment capabilities, detente, the SALT arms agreements are competitive strategems. Game theory has evolved as a conceptual framework for strategy selection.

With countless decisions today dependent on events tomorrow, decision makers have been increasingly concerned with measuring the uncertain aspects of a decision environment. The impact of uncertainty on decision making is often so prevalent and basic as to go unnoticed: the chance of good weather for a weekend trip; the chance of breaking a leg skiing; the chance of getting a raise; the chance of a drop in the interest rate, or the chance of an income tax audit. The uncertainty of events influences the decision maker's choice. Probability, statistics, and stochastic models descriptively define and measure uncertainty. Methods have been developed to incorporate chance into the analysis of a decision environment.

As social roles become more complex and more highly interrelated, there is a parallel need for better models to cope with problems involving highly complex, dynamic, interrelated feedback systems. Computer simulation models are increasingly serving as a powerful tool in this problem area. Simulation models have been constructed that can dynamically interrelate all resource and information flows for marketing systems, production systems, financial systems, and entire organizations. They allow a decision maker to consider the inter-related repercussions on the entire system of a change in any component of the system. A change in inventory policy, the selection of new plant location, or a new promotional strategy can be tested in a matter of minutes. Moreover, not only have entire organizations been successfully simulated, but a first generation of simulation models has been constructed to study the dynamic systems behavior of the major forces affecting man in the world environment. The world implications of population, natural resources, capital investment, the food supply, and pollutants can all be studied in man's quest for a higher quality of life on a finite, populous globe.

The quantitative models that help decision makers to resolve these major problem areas are the subject of this text. They constitute the substantive part of the discipline commonly called *Management science* or *operations research*. Less widely used synonyms are quantitative business analysis, operational analysis, operations management, operations engineering, industrial engineering. decision analysis, and decision sciences.

QUANTITATIVE MODELS IN THE DECISION PROCESS

Before examining the development and application of quantitative models, their role in the decision process requires consideration. Quantitative models typically focus on only part of the vast complexity of the real world. They provide a simple and efficient representation of a part of the overall decision environment. And since they consider only part, they alone do not provide a complete basis for the decision. They only serve as often invaluable aids in the decision process.

Most real-world problems are extremely complex. To gather all the information regarding the decision environment would be an indefinite task. The decision maker is forced to take only *part* of the complex fabric of the real world—to take only an *abstraction*. Information is then gathered in regard to this part. Pertinent variables are isolated, relationships are formed, alternatives are separated from uncontrollable states, and models are developed to synthesize the relevant information. An optimal solution is then produced for part of the overall problem—for the abstraction.

An optimal solution for a part is generally not enough: the whole problem must be considered. Usually, however, the whole problem cannot be easily quantified. Quantitative data may not be easily obtained. The analysis may not be readily amenable to objective modeling. Adjustments still must be made for the rest of the decision environment—for the other information not included in the abstraction. Most frequently, these adjustments must be made in a less objective, less quantitative way. The decision maker must rely on his or her rich resource of personal experience to consider all other informational components judgmentally. Wisdom, intuition, judgment, a feeling are the terms that most commonly apply to the required adjustment of the abstraction back to the real world.

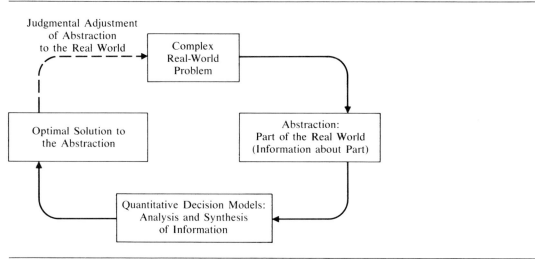

FIGURE 1.2

Adjusting Quantitative Decision Models

The role of quantitative models in the entire decision process is illustrated in Figure 1.2. They very efficiently analyze the abstraction and generate an optimal solution to this part of the problem. The rest of the relevant information

Introduction to Quantitative Business Analysis

must then be considered to complete the process—to provide the final decision. Quantitative models are valuable tools. They rarely serve as an end in themselves.

SUMMARY

A person who desires to make better decisions needs to become aware of the decision process. The more fully a decision maker understands this process, the more easily he or she can consistently make better decisions. The decision process contains five essential elements: the problem, information, the value system, decision models, and the decision. Depending on the decision environment, any of these elements may become strategic to a proper decision. Although all elements are essential to any decision, this text focuses primarily on the development of quantitative decision models for application in business and economics.

Through man's search for a better way, quantitative models have been developed in all human endeavors. The field of business and economics is no exception. Formal quantitative models have been developed that provide a decision maker with optimal solutions to such major problem areas as: the allocation of resources; the planning of new projects; the control of inventories; the selection of strategy against opponents, and the coordination of large-scale, interrelated, feedback systems.

The development of quantitative models for business and economics occurred primarily after World War II. While developments and applications have grown tremendously, quantitative models still have not successfully evolved to solve all problem areas. Typically, they only provide an optimal solution to part of a more complex decision environment. In many situations, however, they are indispensable to the decision maker. Through time, with continued development, quantitative models will increasingly serve the needs of man.

2

Quantifying Uncertainty

Probabilities are fundamental to decision making. They measure the likelihood of uncertain events or environmental states. They quantify uncertainty.[1] Since most decision environments contain uncertainty, probabilities become an unavoidable aspect of the decision-making process. Just as cost and profit information are often indispensable to an alternative selection, under conditions of uncertainty, the uncertainty must be measured—probabilities must be assigned.

Probability concepts and probability theory constitute a discipline in themselves. This chapter provides only the basic fundamentals needed for model building and decision making. For readers already familiar with probability concepts, the material should be primarily a review. For readers with little or no earlier exposure to probability, enough background is provided to meet the requirements of the rest of the text.

This chapter also provides a new approach to certain probability problems. Models are introduced to structure the calculation of probabilities from a decision environment. This will remove the apparent uniqueness of actually similar problems. Complex probability problems can be solved by a simple step-by-step procedure.

The last part of this chapter provides tools for structuring probability information. It will tie together concepts described earlier and demonstrate the ease with which all of the probability components of a decision environment may be obtained.

---

[1] Uncertainty is used as a *general* term that includes the category sometimes referred to as *risk*.

PROBABILITY DEFINED

Depending on the decision environment, the concept and calculation of probabilities will vary. The following section will define several concepts of probability under varying conditions.

Probability: The Classical Definition

The classical definition of probability is one of the oldest and most frequently used means to calculate probabilities objectively. It assumes a known *probability space*, containing a number of *equally likely*, *mutually exclusive*, and *collectively exhaustive* events. Such events are commonly referred to as *elementary* or *simple* events. Given a known probability space of elementary events, the probability of an outcome is defined as *the ratio of the number of elementary events favorable to the outcome* (N_f) *divided by the total number of elementary events* (N_t). Symbolically,

$$P(\text{outcome}) = \frac{N_f}{N_t}.$$

The probability of one particular elementary event (θ) in a *population* of n becomes:

$$P(\theta) = \frac{1}{n}.$$

If the outcome were to contain x elementary events, the probability would be:

$$P(\theta) = \frac{x}{n}.$$

The classical definition of probability is not really too foreign or too complex. It is a formal statement of common logic. For example, if asked the probability of rolling a four with a fair die, most people will intuitively reply, "one in six." When asked why, they tend to offer the following logic. There are six possible outcomes. Only one can occur at a time. Each outcome has an equal chance of occurring. The outcome *four* is one of these possibilities. Therefore, the probability must be one out of six, or the ratio 1/6.

This reasoning parallels the classical definition. The possible outcomes from the roll of a die are known. They form a known probability space of six outcomes:

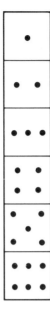

Each outcome has the same chance of occurring: they are *equally likely*. Only one outcome can occur at a time: they are *mutually exclusive*. All outcomes or possibilities are considered: they are *collectively exhaustive*. In essence, the outcomes represent six *elementary events* on a known probability space. The probability of a single elementary event is:

$$P(4) = \frac{1}{6}.$$

The classical definition isn't so unfamiliar after all.

Probability: The Relative Frequency Definition

One major difficulty in applying the classical definition to a decision environment is the assumption of a known *probability space* or known *population*. In many situations the probability space or population will not be known, and the classical definition cannot be applied.

If the population is unknown, however, a sample can often be taken to define the population. The larger the sample, the more information gathered, the more closely the estimated population will resemble the true population.

Once a large enough sample has been taken to represent the true population, something resembling the classical formula can again be applied. From the sample an estimate of the probability can be expressed as:

$$P(\text{outcome}) = \frac{\text{number of favorable outcomes } (n_f)}{\text{total number of outcomes } (n_t)}.$$

The probability of an outcome becomes the *relative frequency* of the sampled events.

The larger the sample, the more closely the constructed population will mirror the actual population, and the more closely the relative frequency will approach the classical counterpart. As the sample (n) increases, the relative frequency will measure the true probability more accurately. And in the limit, the relative frequency will provide an exact assessment:

$$\lim_{n \to \infty} \frac{n_f}{n_t} = \frac{N_f}{N_t} = P(\text{outcome}).$$

For example, a large warehouse contains several thousand finished products. The true percentage of good items is 90 percent. The percentage of good items in the population is unknown. The probability of selecting a good item is desired.

A single item is sampled and found to be good. With this *limited* information, a logical assessment would be:

$P(\text{good item}) = 1.00.$

However, a decision maker will hardly feel confidence in a statement based on so little information. A larger sample will be desired.

As the randomly drawn sample is increased to one hundred, the following information becomes available:

92 good

 8 defective.

The relative frequency probability assessments will be:

$$P(\text{good}) = \frac{92}{100}$$

$$P(\text{defective}) = \frac{8}{100}.$$

Intuitively, the decision maker's feeling of confidence is greatly increased.

Statistically this increased confidence is warranted. As the sample size increases, the relative frequency will rapidly begin to stabilize around the true probability value. As the sample size increases, the probability of getting a relative frequency that differs significantly from the true value decreases rapidly.

Interestingly, for this sample of 100, the probability that the relative frequency will differ from the true probability value by more than .05 can be calculated as less than 7 percent. If the sample is increased to 400, this probability decreases to less than .0003. For a fairly large sample, the relative frequency provides an accurate probability assessment.

Probability: A Subjective or Personalistic Assessment

In many decision environments, probabilities are required when the probability space is unknown and experimentation is impossible. Neither the classical nor the relative frequency definition can be applied. Yet if a decision must be made, the uncertainty must be measured. The decision maker must somehow derive the required probabilities.

Many required probability assessments fall into this category. What is the likelihood that the stock market will rise 40 points next month; the likelihood that you will get an A on the next examination; or the likelihood that you will break a leg skiing? Such probability assessments serve as the basis for countless decisions daily. In such a situation, quantitative information is not always readily available. The decision maker must consciously and subconsciously weigh and relate whatever information is available. The decision maker is frequently forced to rely heavily on information accumulated through past experience to *subjectively* or *judgmentally* assess the likelihood of events.

The adequacy of such *subjective* or *personalistic* probabilities might be questioned. Important information may be overlooked or inappropriately considered. The defense for subjective assessment is pragmatic. If probabilities are essential to a required decision, some form of probability assessment must be made. A subjective assessment will be better than no assessment. Moreover, objective information is often not obtainable. Furthermore, even when it is obtainable, the time and cost of acquiring objective information may be excessive for the decision maker. A decision maker must frequently rely on personal wisdom and wealth of experience to express the probability of events explicitly.

Probability: A General Definition

A probability may be loosely defined as *the chance that an event will occur*. If there is a clearly specified known probability space, a probability becomes *the ratio of the number of favorable elementary events over the total number of elementary events*. In a sampling or experimental situation, a probability becomes *the relative frequency of an event as the number of trials gets sufficiently large*. Where objective information is unavailable, a probability will be *the subjective sum of a person's past experience, feelings, or intuition*.

In general, then: *A probability is a summarization of information quantitatively measuring the chance that an event will occur*.

In this definition an important concept is that a probability is a *summarization or composite of information*. This information can be *objectively* derived either from a known probability space or from a relative frequency of sample events. It can also be *subjectively* assessed from personal knowledge or experience. In each case, a probability is information that expresses in a single *statistic* a measure of the uncertainty.

To define probability as information is to view it from a different perspective. Instead of being a possible end in itself, it becomes a quantitative measure to be used in the decision process.

FUNDAMENTAL CHARACTERISTICS OF EVENTS

The calculus of probability is concerned with measuring the uncertainty of events. Several important characteristics of events simplify computations. They exist when two or more events are:

(1) equally likely,

(2) mutually exclusive,

(3) independent,

(4) dependent, or

(5) collectively exhaustive.

If two or more events have the same probability, they are *equally likely*:

$$P(e_1) = P(e_2) = P(e_3) = \cdots = P(e_n).$$

If a fair coin is tossed, heads and tails will have the same probability. They are equally likely events.

Two events are *mutually exclusive* when they cannot occur simultaneously. That is, if one occurs, the other cannot occur:

$$P(e_1 \text{ AND } e_2) = 0.$$

For example, if a fair coin is tossed and a head appears, a tail cannot appear on the same toss.

If the occurrence of one event in no way affects the probability of the other, the two events are *independent*. In this case, the probability of e_1 given e_2 has occurred (expressed as $e_1|e_2$) will be the probability of e_1:

$$P(e_1 \mid e_2) = P(e_1).$$

For example, if a fair coin is tossed twice, the probability of a head on the second toss (H_2) is not affected by the outcome of the first toss:

$$P(H_2 \mid H_1) = \frac{1}{2}$$

$$P(H_2) = \frac{1}{2}$$

$$P(H_2 \mid T_1) = \frac{1}{2}$$

If the occurrence of one event affects the probability of another, the events are *dependent*. If e_2 is dependent on e_1, then:

$$P(e_2 \mid e_1) \neq P(e_2).$$

Information about the occurrence of e_1 changes the probability of e_2. Consider a deck of 52 cards containing four aces. If one card is randomly drawn from a well-shuffled deck, the probability of an ace is:

$$P(A) = \frac{4}{52}.$$

If two cards are drawn sequentially without replacement and the first one is an ace, the probability of an ace on the second draw becomes:

$$P(A_2 \mid A_1) = \frac{3}{51}.$$

The first draw has affected the probability of the second: the events are dependent.

A set of events is *collectively exhaustive* when it includes all the events on the probability space. The sum of their probabilities will be one:

$$\sum_i P(e_i) = 1.$$

If one card drawn from the deck represents an event, the entire deck of 52 cards represents the collectively exhaustive set.

BASIC PROBABILITY RULES

The calculation of probabilities from a known probability space containing *elementary* events can, at least theoretically, always be derived from the basic classical formula:

$$P(\text{outcome}) = \frac{N_f}{N_t}.$$

At times, this formula can be difficult to apply. For even simple sampling procedures, the exact expression of the probability space may be difficult to conceptualize, let alone enumerate. In such cases three probability statement rules significantly facilitate calculations

OR and AND Statements

There are two basic types of probability statements: OR statements and AND statements. OR *statements are used to separate different samples that represent ways to obtain a desired result.* AND *statements are used to separate the individual events within a sample.* For example, if a fair coin is tossed twice, the probability of one head becomes:

$P(\text{one head}) = P(\text{head AND tail OR tail AND head}).$

The OR separates the different samples that represent ways to obtain the desired result (one head). The AND separates the individual events within the sample: head AND tail. Specific rules apply for both OR statements and AND statements.

OR Statements: $P(A$ OR $B)$

In calculations involving OR statements, a solution can be obtained by applying the following general probability rule:

(1) $P(A$ OR $B) = P(A) + P(B) - P(A$ AND $B).$

While this rule is applicable to all OR statements, there is an important special case. If the events are *mutually exclusive*, they cannot occur at the same time. The event A AND B will be impossible: $P(A$ AND $B) = 0$. For mutually exclusive events, the rule becomes:

(1′) $P(A$ OR $B) = P(A) + P(B).$
     mut. exc.

When this special case exists, the probability rule is simplified to substituting a *plus for OR.*

AND Statements: $P(A$ AND $B)$

The second general probability rule applies to AND statements:

(2) $P(A$ AND $B) = P(A)P(B\,|\,A).$

This rule also contains an important special case. If the events are *independent*, the occurrence of one will not affect the probability of the other. Therefore, if events A AND B are independent, the $P(B \mid A)$ will be $P(B)$. The *joint probability* becomes:

(2′) $P(A$ AND $B) = P(A)P(B)$.
   indep.

In this special case, the AND is equivalent to *multiplication*.

Conditional Probability: $P(A \mid B)$

The third probability rule applies to the *conditional probability of A given B*: $P(A \mid B)$. It can be derived directly from the joint probability rule:

$$P(A \text{ AND } B) = P(A)P(B \mid A),$$

or stated another way,

$$P(B \text{ AND } A) = P(B)P(A \mid B).$$

Dividing by $P(B)$:

$$\frac{P(B \text{ AND } A)}{P(B)} = P(A \mid B).$$

Since $P(B$ AND $A)$ and $P(A$ AND $B)$ both indicate the same joint occurrence, $P(A$ AND $B)$ can be substituted for $P(B$ AND $A)$. The conditional probability rule becomes:

(3) $P(A \mid B) = \dfrac{P(A \text{ AND } B)}{P(B)}.$

If the events are independent, the rule only verifies the definition of independent events:

$P(A \mid B) = \dfrac{P(A \text{ AND } B)}{P(B)}$
indep.

$ = \dfrac{P(A)P(B)}{P(B)}$

$P(A \mid B) = P(A).$
indep.

The rule is designed, however, to apply to *dependent events*. To avoid the common error of cancelling probabilities, as in the case of independent events, the conditional probability for *dependent* events might be better expressed as:

$$P(A \mid B) = \frac{P(A \text{ AND } B)}{P(B)^*}.$$

The asterisk emphasizes that $P(B)$ contains all of the ways to obtain B.

For example, B occurs jointly with A_1, A_2, or A_3:

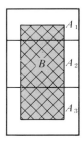

The probability of A_1 given B becomes:

$$P(A_1 \mid B) = \frac{P(A_1 \text{ AND } B)}{P(A_1 \text{ AND } B) + P(A_2 \text{ AND } B) + P(A_3 \text{ AND } B)},$$

or

$$P(A_1 \mid B) = \frac{P(A_1)P(B \mid A_1)}{P(A_1)P(B \mid A_1) + P(A_2)P(B \mid A_2) + P(A_3)P(B \mid A_3)}.$$

More compactly expressed as Bayes' formula:

$$(3') \quad P(A_1 \mid B) = \frac{P(A_1)P(B \mid A_1)}{\sum_j P(A_j)P(B \mid A_j)}.$$

APPLYING PROBABILITY RULES: SOME EXAMPLES

Almost everyone has initial difficulties in applying probability rules. This is usually either because they exaggerate the number and complexity of the rules or because they consider each problem as unique. To correct part of these misconceptions, *only three rules are required to calculate probabilities*:

1. Classical formulas: $P(\text{outcome}) = \dfrac{N_f}{N_t}$

2. OR statement: $P(A \text{ OR } B) = P(A) + P(B) - P(A \text{ AND } B)$

$P(A \text{ OR } B) = P(A) + P(B)$
mut. exc.

3. AND statement: $P(A \text{ AND } B) = P(A)P(B \mid A)$

$P(A \text{ AND } B) = P(A)P(B)$
indep.

Complex problems may require the use of more than one rule. In these cases, a model will be presented shortly that allows a logical step-by-step solution.

To assure the reader's comfort in applying the calculus of probability, a number of increasingly difficult examples will build to the mastery of the general case. The following problems all assume the rack of 15 pool balls illustrated in Figure 2.7.

If one ball is randomly drawn, each of the 15 outcomes will be *equally likely*, *mutually exclusive*, and in combination *collectively exhaustive*. They define a *known* probability space of *elementary events* satisfying the classical definition. The balls have two important characteristics. They are numbered consecutively from one to 15, and those with numbers above eight have a white stripe.

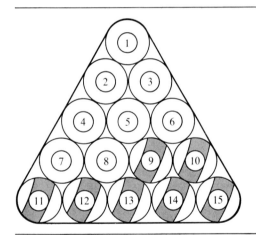

FIGURE 2.1

Each of the following problems will be solved in two ways. First it will be solved using the *basic classical formula*. Then it will be solved using a *probability rule*.

Problem 1
If a single ball is randomly drawn, what is the probability of drawing either the one or the 15 ball?

Quantifying Uncertainty

(1) $P(\text{event}) = \dfrac{N_f}{N_t}$

$P(1 \text{ OR } 15) = \dfrac{2}{15}$

Two items are favorable to the desired event and there are fifteen items in total. The probability is 2/15.

(2) $P(A \text{ OR } B) = P(A) + P(B)$
   mut. exc.

$P(1 \text{ OR } 15) = P(1) + P(15)$

$$= \frac{1}{15} + \frac{1}{15}$$

$$= \frac{2}{15}.$$

The two events are *mutually exclusive*. If one item is drawn, the one and 15 cannot occur at the same time. The special case can be applied: OR becomes plus. With reference to the probability space, note also that the 1/15 probability for $P(1)$ and $P(15)$ was derived from the basic classical formula N_f/N_t.

Problem 2
If a single ball is randomly drawn, what is the probability of drawing an even-numbered ball?

(1) $P(\text{event}) = \dfrac{N_f}{N_t}$

$P(\text{even}) = \dfrac{7}{15}.$

Seven items out of 15 are even. The probability of drawing an even item is 7/15.

(2) $P(\text{even}) = ?$

The outcome, even, is a *compound event* consisting of a number of *simple* or *elementary events*. To solve this problem, first list one way of obtaining the compound event:

$P(\text{even}) = P(2.$

Next write OR and then a second way of obtaining the compound event:

$P(\text{even}) = P(2 \text{ OR } 4.$

Add another OR and repeat until all the ways are listed:

$$P(even) = P(2 \text{ OR } 4 \text{ OR } 6 \text{ OR } 8 \text{ OR } 10 \text{ OR } 12 \text{ OR } 14).$$

The next step is to remove the OR statements. Since the simple events are mutually exclusive, the ORs become plusses:

$$P(even) = P(2) + P(4) + P(6) + P(8) + P(10) + P(12) + P(14).$$

Referring to the probability space and using the basic classical formula, substitute the specific probabilities:

$$P(even) = \frac{1}{15} + \frac{1}{15} + \frac{1}{15} + \frac{1}{15} + \frac{1}{15} + \frac{1}{15} + \frac{1}{15}$$

$$= \frac{7}{15}.$$

Problem 3

Given that a ball is striped, what is the probability that it is even numbered?

(1) $P(event) = \dfrac{N_f}{N_t}$

$P(even \mid striped) = \dfrac{3}{7}.$

The given information restricts the probability space to striped balls only (Figure 2.2). Of the seven striped balls, three are even. Using the classical formula, the probability will be 3/7.

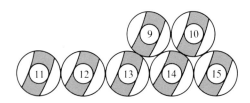

FIGURE 2.2
Given Striped

(2) $P(even \mid striped) = \dfrac{P(even \text{ AND } striped)}{P(striped)}.$

From the probability space,

$$P(\text{even} \mid \text{striped}) = \frac{\frac{3}{15}}{\frac{7}{15}}$$

$$= \frac{3}{7}.$$

Of the 15 balls, three are even and striped and seven are striped.

The probability of even AND striped in the numerator can also be solved using the AND statement rule:

$$P(A \text{ AND } B) = P(A)P(B \mid A)$$

$$P(\text{even AND striped}) = P(\text{even})P(\text{striped} \mid \text{even})$$

$$= \frac{7}{15} \cdot \frac{3}{7}$$

$$= \frac{3}{15}.$$

The two probability components are obtained by referring to the probability space.

Problem 4
If one item is drawn, what is the probability that it is either even or striped?

(1) $P(\text{event}) = \dfrac{N_f}{N_t}$

$$P(\text{even OR striped}) = \frac{11}{15}.$$

There are seven even and seven striped balls. Of these, three (10, 12, and 14) are both even and striped. Counting all possibilities no more than once, 11 of the 15 are either even or striped.

(2) $P(A \text{ OR } B) = P(A) + P(B) - P(A \text{ AND } B)$

$$P(\text{even OR striped}) = P(\text{even}) + P(\text{striped}) - P(\text{even AND striped})$$

$$= \frac{7}{15} + \frac{7}{15} - \frac{3}{15}$$

$$= \frac{11}{15}.$$

The *joint probability* of even AND striped prevents any double counting.

Problem 5

If a ball is randomly drawn *and* replaced, and a second ball is then drawn, what is the probability of drawing the eight ball both times?

As soon as a problem becomes slightly more complex, the basic classical formula becomes difficult to use. It is a counting procedure that requires the definition and enumeration of the probability space. The probability space for this sample of two is no longer the simple set of events shown in Figure 2.1. It becomes the significantly expanded probability space in Figure 2.3.

1,1	1,2	1,3	1,4	1,5	1,6	1,7	1,8	1,9	1,10	1,11	1,12	1,13	1,14	1,15
2,1	2,2	2,3											2,14	2,15
3,1	3,2	3,3												3,15
4,1	4,2		4,4											
5,1	5,2			5,5										
6,1	6,2				6,6									
7,1	7,2					7,7								
8,1	8,2						(8,8)							
9,1	9,2							9,9						
10,1									10,10					
11,1										11,11				
12,1											12,12			
13,1												13,13		
14,1	14,2												14,14	14,15
15,1	15,2	15,3											15,14	15,15

FIGURE 2.3

The Probability Space for a Sample of Two

$$(1)\ P(8\ \text{AND}\ 8) = \frac{N_f}{N_t}$$

$$= \frac{1}{225}.$$

As becomes quickly apparent, the basic classical formula is not suitable for all problems. For example, if a sample of four with replacement were being considered, the probability space would consist of 50,625 elementary events.[2] The enumeration alone would preclude the use of this formula.

Using the probability rule:

(2) $P(A \text{ AND } B) = P(A)P(B)$
indep.

$$P(8 \text{ AND } 8) = P(8)P(8)$$

$$= \frac{1}{15} \cdot \frac{1}{15}$$

$$= \frac{1}{225}.$$

The probability rule provides a direct solution.

THE PROBABILITY OF COMPOUND EVENTS

The foregoing problems demonstrate the separate application of the OR and AND statement rules. Many decision environments, however, require a combination of rules to determine the probability of a *compound event*. With the aid of a *procedure* or *model*, the probability of a compound event can be obtained fairly easily. The model will allow a systematic, step-by-step application of the already familiar OR and AND statements.

The probability of a compound event can be determined as follows:

1. Indicate one way of obtaining the compound event, separating each simple event with AND statements.

2. Write OR after this one way. Then list all other similar ways, separating them with OR statements.

3. Use the probability rules to remove the OR and AND statements. Remove the OR statements first.

4. Refer to the probability space and determine the probabilities for each simple event.

5. Perform the calculation.

------

[2] For a sample of size 10 with replacement, a full enumeration would consist of 15^{10} or 5.76×10^{11} events.

The procedure structures the compound event into subcomponent OR and AND statements. The subcomponents can then be solved by applying a single probability rule.

For example, two containers hold both good (g) and defective (d) items (Figure 2.4). Two items are randomly drawn from one of the containers. A selection from container 2 is twice as likely as from container 1. What is the probability of getting one or more defective items?

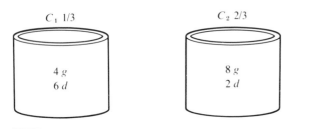

C_1 1/3

4 g
6 d

C_2 2/3

8 g
2 d

FIGURE 2.4
The Probability of a Compound Event

Following, step by step, the *probability model for compound events*:[3]

(1) P(one OR more defectives) $= P(C_1$ AND g AND $d)$

(2) P(1 OR more defectives) $= P(C_1 \cap g \cap d$ OR $C_1 \cap d \cap g$
OR $C_2 \cap g \cap d$ OR $C_2 \cap d \cap g$
OR $C_1 \cap d \cap d$ OR $C_2 \cap d \cap d)$

(3) remove OR:
P(1 OR more defectives) $= P(C_1 \cap g \cap d) + P(C_1 \cap d \cap g)$
$+ P(C_2 \cap g \cap d) + P(C_2 \cap d \cap g)$
$+ P(C_1 \cap d \cap d) + P(C_2 \cap d \cap d)$

remove AND:
P(1 OR more defectives) $= P(C_1)P(g \mid C_1)P(d \mid C_1, g)$
$+ P(C_1)P(d \mid C_1)P(g \mid C_1, d)$
$+ P(C_2)P(g \mid C_2)P(d \mid C_2, g)$
$+ P(C_2)P(d \mid C_2)P(g \mid C_2, d)$
$+ P(C_1)P(d \mid C_1)P(d \mid C_1, d)$
$+ P(C_2)P(d \mid C_2)P(d \mid C_2, d)$

(4) P(1 OR more defectives) $= \dfrac{1}{3} \cdot \dfrac{4}{10} \cdot \dfrac{6}{9} + \dfrac{1}{3} \cdot \dfrac{6}{10} \cdot \dfrac{4}{9}$

$+ \dfrac{2}{3} \cdot \dfrac{8}{10} \cdot \dfrac{2}{9} + \dfrac{2}{3} \cdot \dfrac{2}{10} \cdot \dfrac{8}{9}$

$+ \dfrac{1}{3} \cdot \dfrac{6}{10} \cdot \dfrac{5}{9} + \dfrac{2}{3} \cdot \dfrac{2}{10} \cdot \dfrac{1}{9}$

---

[3] For convenience, the intersection symbol $\cap$ will be used for AND.

Quantifying Uncertainty

$$(5) \quad P(1 \text{ OR more defectives}) = \frac{146}{270}.$$

The model allows a solution as simple as the simple subcomponent parts.

CONDITIONAL PROBABILITY

Once the decision maker understands the computation of a compound event, the calculation of conditional probabilities is not difficult. A *conditional probability* can be separated into a *joint probability* and the *probability of a compound event*:

$$P(A \mid B) = \frac{P(A \text{ AND } B)}{P(B)^*} \cdot \frac{\text{joint prob.}}{\text{Prob. of compound event}}.$$

The numerator can be evaluated by the joint probability rule $P(A \text{ AND } B)$. The denominator can be evaluated separately as the probability of a compound event. The conditional probability contains two separate parts, each one solvable by the *known* procedures.

Conditional Probability: The Logic

Before proceeding with the computational process, it is helpful to examine the logic of conditional probability. Refer again to the example of 15 pool balls. This time the balls are identified as either solid or striped, and either light or dark colored. There are eight solid balls, four light and four dark. There are seven striped balls, three light and four dark. Figure 2.5 represents the probability space.

SL	SL	SL	SL		
SD	SD	SD	SD	S	solid
StL	StL	StL		St	striped
StD	StD	StD	StD	L	light
				D	dark

FIGURE 2.5
The Probability Space

Given that a ball is light, the problem is to determine the probability that it is striped. In terms of the *conditional probability rule*:

$$P(St \mid L) = \frac{P(St \text{ AND } L)}{P(L)}.$$

The *given* information restricts the probability space of all events to a subset of the given events. Given a light-colored ball (L), the probability space of all balls is restricted to the subset of light-colored balls (Figure 2.6). Given the *subset*

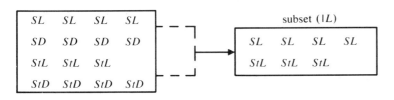

FIGURE 2.6
A Subset of Events

of events, the probability of a striped ball is derived by counting the number favorable divided by the total number. Of the seven balls in the subset, three are striped. The probability of a striped ball, given the subset of light color, therefore becomes:

$$P(St \mid L) = \frac{3}{7}.$$

In terms of the conditional probability rule, a ratio provides the same result. The probability rule again:

$$P(St \mid L) = \frac{P(St \text{ AND } L)}{P(L)}.$$

The denominator represents all of the ways of obtaining a light-colored ball—that is, all of the ways of obtaining the given subset of events. The numerator represents one of the ways of obtaining a light-colored ball—one unique set of the subset:

$$P(St \mid L) = \frac{P(\text{unique set of the subset } (St \text{ AND } L))}{P(\text{subset of events } (L))}.$$

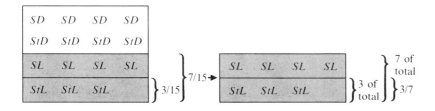

FIGURE 2.7
The Unique Set of the Subset

In terms of the initial probability space, the probability of the subset of events (*L*) can be derived by counting:

$$P(\text{subset of events } (L)) = \frac{7}{15}.$$

There are 15 items. Seven of them are light. The probability of selecting one item in the subset is 7/15. The probability of the unique set (*St* AND *L*) is:

$$P(St \text{ AND } L) = \frac{3}{15}.$$

Three of the 15 items are striped and light. The probability of the unique subset is 3/15.

The probability of the unique set in terms of the total subset will be the ratio of the two:

$$P(St \mid L) = \frac{\frac{3}{15}}{\frac{7}{15}}$$

$$= \frac{3}{7}.$$

The numerator represents the number of ways, in terms of the total population, of obtaining the unique set (*St* AND *L*). The denominator represents the number of ways, in terms of the total population, of obtaining the given subset. The probability of the unique set within the subset must be the ratio of the number of ways of getting the unique set over the number of ways of getting the subset (Figure 2.7). In essence:

1. The given information restricts considerations to a subset consisting of 7/15 of the entire population.

2. The unique set is part of the subset and consists of 3/15 of the entire population.

3. Of the 7/15 of the total, the unique set is part, and it is 3/15 of the total.

4. The unique set must be the ratio of 3/15 to 7/15 or 3/7 of the subset.

Conditional Probability: A Computational Procedure

A conditional probability can be systematically derived from the probability rule:[4]

$$P(A \mid B) = \frac{P(A \text{ AND } B)}{P(B)^*}.$$

For example, assume the two containers of good (g) and defective (d) items represented in Figure 2.8. A single item will be randomly drawn from one of the containers. The initial probabilities of drawing from the specific containers are 4/5 and 1/5 respectively. If an item is drawn and found defective, what is the probability that it came from container 1?

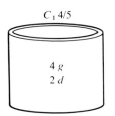
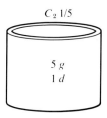

C_1 4/5

4 g
2 d

C_2 1/5

5 g
1 d

FIGURE 2.8
$P(C_1/d)$

Expressed as a condition of probability, the problem becomes:

$$P(C_1 \mid d) = \frac{P(C_1 \text{ AND } d)}{P(d)}.$$

The numerator contains one unique way of obtaining a defective item. The denominator contains all of the ways.

The major difficulty is the calculation of the denominator. It can be treated, however, as a separate problem:

$$P(d).$$

---

[4] In $P(B)^*$, the * just emphasizes that there are a number of ways of getting B.

Being a compound event, it is solved by applying the probability model described on page 27. Indicate one way of obtaining the compound event; indicate all other similar ways separated by ORs; remove the ORs and then ANDS obtain the probabilities from the probability space, and perform the computation. Specifically,

(1) $P(d) = P(C_1 \text{ AND } d)$

(2) $ = P(C_1 \text{ AND } d \text{ OR } C_2 \text{ AND } d)$

(3) $ = P(C_1 \text{ AND } d) + P(C_2 \text{ AND } d)$
$ = P(C_1)P(d \mid C_1) + P(C_2)P(d \mid C_2)$

(4) $ = \dfrac{4}{5} \cdot \dfrac{2}{6} + \dfrac{1}{5} \cdot \dfrac{1}{6}$

(5) $ = \dfrac{9}{30}.$

Given the denominator, the entire problem can be easily solved:

$$P(C_1 \mid d) = \frac{P(C_1 \text{ AND } d)}{P(d)}$$

$$= \frac{P(C_1)P(d \mid C_1)}{P(d)}$$

$$= \frac{\frac{4}{5} \cdot \frac{2}{6}}{\frac{4}{5} \cdot \frac{2}{6} + \frac{1}{5} \cdot \frac{1}{6}}$$

$$= \frac{8}{9}.$$

In fact, since the numerator is *always one component* of the denominator, the numerator can be taken directly from the calculations for the denominator:

$$P(C_1 \mid d) = \frac{P(C_1 \text{ AND } d)}{P(d)}$$

$$= \frac{P(C_1 \text{ AND } d)}{P(C_1 \text{ AND } d) + P(C_2 \text{ AND } d)}$$

$$= \frac{\frac{8}{30}}{\frac{8}{30} + \frac{1}{30}}$$

$$= \frac{8}{9}.$$

Since the numerator is part of the denominator, a *simplified procedure* can be used to obtain the denominator. A model for solving conditional probabilities is:

1. Express the problem in terms of the conditional probability rule.

2. To determine the denominator, write the numerator followed by OR and another way.

3. The other ways will contain the same type of events and the given event. Write the given event preceded by AND and the other event(s) similar to those preceding AND in the first way.

4. Using the probability rules, remove the OR and AND statements, ORs first.

5. Derive the probabilities from the probability space.

6. Calculate the solution.

This procedure or model separates the problem into easily solvable component parts. Applying the procedure to the preceding problem:

$$(1) \quad P(C_1 \mid d) = \frac{P(C_1 \text{ AND } d)}{P(d)}$$

$$(2) \qquad\qquad = \frac{P(C_1 \text{ AND } d)}{P(C_1 \text{ AND } d \text{ OR }}$$

$$(3) \qquad\qquad = \frac{P(C_1 \text{ AND } d)}{P(C_1 \text{ AND } d \text{ OR } \_\_ \text{ AND } d)}$$

$$\qquad\qquad = \frac{P(C_1 \text{ AND } d)}{P(C_1 \text{ AND } d \text{ OR } C_2 \text{ AND } d)}$$

$$(4) \qquad\qquad = \frac{P(C_1 \text{ AND } d)}{P(C_1 \text{ AND } d) + P(C_2 \text{ AND } d)}$$

$$\qquad\qquad = \frac{P(C_1)P(d \mid C_1)}{P(C_1)P(d \mid C_1) + P(C_2)P(d \mid C_2)}$$

$$(5) \qquad\qquad = \frac{\frac{4}{5} \cdot \frac{2}{6}}{\frac{4}{5} \cdot \frac{2}{6} + \frac{1}{5} \cdot \frac{1}{6}}$$

$$(6) \qquad\qquad = \frac{8}{9}.$$

A second problem will add clarity. Two work bins contain good (g) and defective (d) finished products (Figure 2.9). A worker takes an item from bin 1 and transfers it into bin 2. Later an item is drawn from bin 2 and found to be defective. What is the probability that the worker initially transferred a defective item?

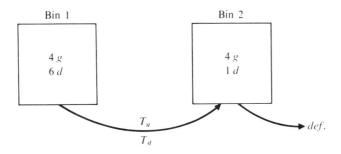

FIGURE 2.9
$P(T_D/d)$

The probability of initially transferring a defective item (T_d) is 6/10. Given that a defective item was drawn from bin 2, the probability of T_d will be increased. What is the effect of this added information on the prior probability?
Following the procedure:

(1) $P(T_d \mid d) = \dfrac{P(T_d \text{ AND } d)}{P(d)}$

(2) $ = \dfrac{P(T_d \text{ AND } d)}{P(T_d \text{ AND } d) \text{ OR}}$

(3) $ = \dfrac{P(T_d \text{ AND } d)}{P(T_d \text{ AND } d \text{ OR } \underline{} \text{ AND } d)}$

$ = \dfrac{P(T_d \text{ AND } d)}{P(T_d \text{ AND } d \text{ OR } T_g \text{ AND } d)}$

(4) $ = \dfrac{P(T_d \text{ AND } d)}{P(T_d \text{ AND } d) + P(T_g \text{ AND } d)}$

$ = \dfrac{P(T_d)P(d \mid T_d)}{P(T_d)P(d \mid T_d) + P(T_g)P(d \mid T_g)}$

(5) $ = \dfrac{\frac{6}{10} \cdot \frac{2}{6}}{\frac{6}{10} \cdot \frac{2}{6} + \frac{4}{10} \cdot \frac{1}{6}}$

(6) $ = \dfrac{3}{4}.$

Using this procedure, complex problems can be solved systematically.

THE REVISION OF PROBABILITIES WITH ADDED INFORMATION

A probability has been defined as *a summarization of information measuring the chance that an event will occur.* Unless there is a known probability space, some relevant information will not be available. Probability assessments based on samples or on personal experience will be inaccurate to the extent of the incomplete information. They can be improved, however, by incorporating additional information into the initial summarization.

This process is familiar to everyone. On a potentially rainy morning, suppose you need to decide whether or not to wear a raincoat. You will need to assess the probability of rain. In so doing, you may consider the past week's weather, yesterday's weather, and the weather forecast, and then add a final look out the window. All of these factors may contribute to your final probability assessment. A significant change in any relevant factor, a raindrop or sunshine, will cause you to adjust your earlier assessment.

The Revisions of Prior Probabilities by Bayes' Theorem

The process described above is *subjective*. There is also an *objective* procedure for revising probabilities. This procedure is the *conditional probability rule*, or *Bayes' theorem:*

$$P(A_1 \mid B) = \frac{P(A_1 \text{ AND } B)}{P(B)^*},$$

or

$$P(A_1 \mid B) = \frac{P(A_1)P(B \mid A_1)}{\sum_j P(A_j)P(B \mid A_j)}.$$

A set of computations will demonstrate how additional information is incorporated into the initial assessment to adjust a probability. A production process is either in control or out of control (Figure 2.10). If it is in control, 2 percent of the items the process produces will be defective. If it is out of control, the defective items will increase to 20 percent. On the basis of past experience and a conversation with the night foreman, the production manager subjectively assesses a .70 probability that the process is in control. To confirm his initial feelings, the production manager selects a finished product from the production line, tests it, and finds it good. What is the revised probability that the process is in control?

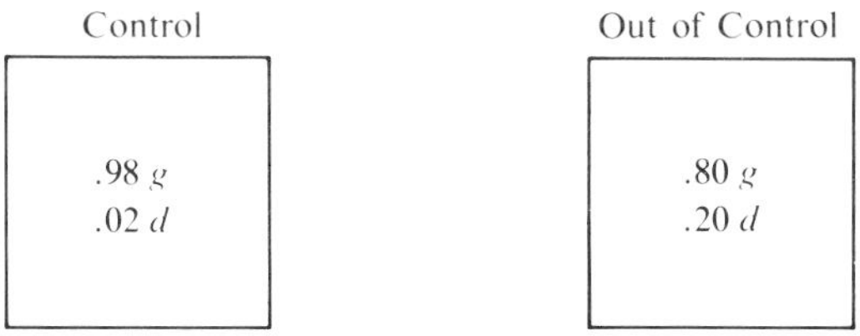

Control	Out of Control
.98 *g* .02 *d*	.80 *g* .20 *d*

FIGURE 2.10

The Production Process

Stated as a conditional probability:

$$P(\text{control} \mid \text{good}) = \frac{P(\text{control AND good})}{P(\text{good})*}$$

$$= \frac{P(c \text{ AND } g)}{P(c \text{ AND } g) + P(oc \text{ AND } g)}$$

$$= \frac{P(c)P(g \mid c)}{P(c)P(g \mid c) + P(oc)P(g \mid oc)}$$

$$= \frac{(.70)(.98)}{(.70)(.98) + (.30)(.80)}$$

$$= .741.$$

The *prior probability* of .70 has been adjusted to a *posterior probability* of .741.

The production manager then takes a second sample. This item is also good. The new assessed probability of control will be:

$$P(\text{control} \mid \text{good}) = \frac{P(\text{control AND good})}{P(\text{good})*}$$

$$= \frac{P(c)P(g \mid c)}{P(c)P(g \mid c) + P(oc)P(g \mid oc)}$$

$$= \frac{(.741)(.98)}{(.741)(.98) + (.259)(.80)}$$

$$= .778.$$

With a sample of two good items, the probability has been adjusted from .70 to .778.

A probability is a summarization of information. Bayes' theorem allows the objective addition of information to a prior sum to form an adjusted *posterior* sum:

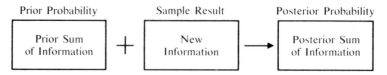

Prior Probability	Sample Result	Posterior Probability
Prior Sum of Information	+ New Information	→ Posterior Sum of Information

In this way probability assessments can be continually updated as additional information becomes available.

A Tableau to Revise Prior Probabilities into Posterior Probabilities

The incorporation of information to adjust prior probabilities can be accomplished more systematically by using a *tableau*. If E_1 represents the event to be adjusted, and Inf_1 the specific added information, the basic formula for adjustment becomes:

$$P(E_1 \mid Inf_1) = \frac{P(E_1)P(Inf_1 \mid E_1)}{\sum_j P(E_j)P(Inf_1 \mid E_j)}$$

$$= \frac{P(E_1)P(Inf_1 \mid E_1)}{P(E_1)P(Inf_1 \mid E_1) + P(E_2)P(Inf_1 \mid E_2) + \cdots + P(E_n)P(Inf_1 \mid E_n)}.$$

These same components can be arranged in a tableau (Table 2.1).

Events	Prior Prob.	Conditional Prob.	Joint Prob.	Posterior Prob.
E_j	$P(E_j)$	$P(Inf_1 \mid E_j)$	$P(E_j)P(Inf_1 \mid E_j)$	$P(E_j \mid Inf_1) = \dfrac{P(E_j)P(Inf_1 \mid E_j)}{P(Inf_1)}$
E_1	$P(E_1)$	$P(Inf_1 \mid E_1)$	$P(E_1)P(Inf_1 \mid E_1)$	$P(E_1 \mid Inf_1) = \dfrac{P(E_1)P(Inf_1 \mid E_1)}{P(Inf_1)}$
E_2	$P(E_2)$	$P(Inf_1 \mid E_2)$	$P(E_2)P(Inf_1 \mid E_2)$	$P(E_2 \mid Inf_1) = \dfrac{P(E_2)P(Inf_1 \mid E_2)}{P(Inf_1)}$
.	.	.	.	.
.	.	.	.	.
.	.	.	.	.
E_n	$P(E_n)$	$P(Inf_1 \mid E_n)$	$P(E_n)P(Inf_1 \mid E_n)$	$P(E_n \mid Inf_1) = \dfrac{P(E_n)P(Inf_1 \mid E_n)}{P(Inf_1)}$
$P(Inf_1) = \sum_j P(E_j)P(Inf_1 \mid E_j)$				

TABLE 2.1

Tableau for Revising Probabilities

A set of calculations will clarify the use of the tableau. To compare the process of adjustment using a tableau with the process using Bayes' theorem, reconsider the previous problem (Figure 2.10). There are two possible events: the production process is either in control (c) or out of control (oc). A prior probability assessment has been made: $P(\text{control}) = .70$. An item has been sampled and found to be good. The adjusted prior probability is sought. Table

Events E_j	Prior Prob. $P(E_j)$	Conditional Prob. (likelihoods) $P(Inf_1|E_j)$	Joint Prob. $P(E_j \text{ and } Inf_1) = P(E_j)P(Inf_1|E_j)$	Posterior Prob. $P(E_j|Inf_1) = \dfrac{P(E_j)P(Inf_1|E_j)}{P(Inf_1)}$
Control (c)	$P(c)$	$P(g|c)$	$P(c)P(g|c)$	$P(c|g) = \dfrac{P(c)P(g|c)}{P(g)}$
Out of Control (oc)	$P(oc)$	$P(g|oc)$	$P(oc)P(g|oc)$	$P(oc|g) = \dfrac{P(oc)P(g|oc)}{P(g)}$
$P(g) = P(c)P(g|c) + P(oc)P(g|oc)$				

TABLE 2.2

The Tableau Format

2.2 illustrates the tableau format. Table 2.3 contains the computations. The new adjusted probability—the probability of control given that a good item was selected—is represented by the posterior probability of .741.

Events E_j	Prior Prob. $P(E_j)$	Conditional Prob. (likelihoods) $P(Inf_1|E_j)$	Joint Prob. $P(E_j \text{ and } Inf_1) = P(E_j)P(Inf_1|E_j)$	Posterior Prob. $P(E_j|Inf_1) = \dfrac{P(E_j)P(Inf_1|E_j)}{P(Inf_1)}$
Control	.70	.98	.686	$\boxed{.741}$
Out of Control	.30	.80	.240	$\boxed{.259}$
$P(g) = .926$				

TABLE 2.3

The Revised Probabilities

The production manager then selects a second good item. This added information can be incorporated into the assessment by letting the posterior probabilities become the new prior probabilities and repeating the process (Table 2.4).

Events E_j	Prior Prob. $P(E_j)$	Conditional Prob. (likelihood) $P(Inf_1 \mid E_j)$	Joint Prob. $P(E_j \text{ and } Inf_1) = P(E_j)P(Inf_1 \mid E_j)$	Posterior Prob. $P(E_j \mid Inf_1) = \dfrac{P(E_j)P(Inf_1 \mid E_j)}{P(Inf_1)}$
Control	.741	.98	.72618	.778
Out of Control	.259	.80	.20720	.222
$P(g) = .93338$				

TABLE 2.4

Revising the Revised Probabilities

If additional samples were taken, the posteriors would become the priors for the next calculation. The tableau provides a systematic procedure for incorporating additional information. It facilitates the process of probability adjustment.

THE PROBABILITY TREE

A *probability tree* provides a systematic means of structuring the relevant events of an uncertain environment. It structurally represents the direct relationships among all events. It provides a clear and precise definition of the total environment.

To construct a probability tree, the decision maker begins by forming a *chance fork*. This represents the first mutually exclusive set of temporally related *chance events*. Each chance event is represented by a *branch* with the associated probability for that event. At the terminus of each branch the decision maker forms a new chance fork. In turn, they contain the next set of related chance events represented by branches. And at the new termini, the branches form new chance forks with new branches. With each relevant event, a *tree* structurally defines the relationships among all the events and their associated probabilities.

To demonstrate the construction of a probability tree, the recent production process example will be reintroduced (Figure 2.10). The initial probability that the process is in control is .70. If it is in control, the process will produce

2 percent defective items. If it is out of control, 20 percent of the items will be defective. Two items are sampled and both are found good.

The *first* relevant event is the state of the process. This is represented by a chance fork with branches representing the two associated chance events:

Chance   Chance Branches
Fork   of Events

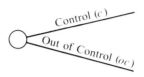

The *second* relevant event is the first sample result. It will form a new chance fork with resulting branches. In turn, this is followed by a chance fork with branches for the second sample. With probability information, Figure 2.11 illustrates the probability tree of all possibilities.

Path Probabilities

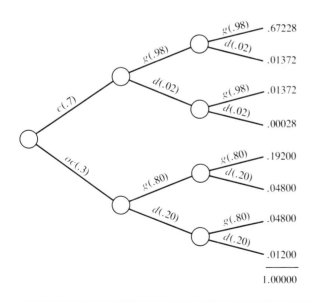

FIGURE 2.11
The Probability Tree

The *path probabilities* represent the *joint probabilities* of all the chance events along the connecting branches. For example, the probability that the process will be in control and that both samples will be good is:

$$P(c \cap g \cap g) = P(c)P(g \mid c)P(g \mid c)$$
$$= (.70)(.98)(.98)$$
$$= .67228.$$

The path probabilities give the likelihood of all possible combinations of the three events. They form a collectively exhaustive set of the sample space with a total probability of 1.00.

The completed tree simplifies probability calculations considerably. Consider the calculation of a compound event: the probability of one defective item. The hardest part of such a calculation is to list all the ways of obtaining the event. A probability tree makes this simple. As indicated in Figure 2.12,

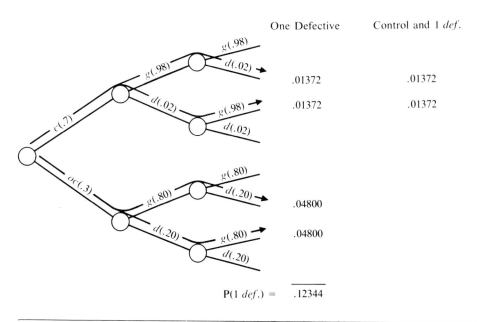

Path Probabilities

FIGURE 2 12

Probabilities from a Probability Tree

Quantifying Uncertainty

there are four ways of obtaining one defective:

$$P(1 \text{ defective}) = P(c \cap g \cap d) + P(c \cap d \cap g) + P(oc \cap g \cap d) + P(oc \cap d \cap g).$$

Summing the associated path probabilities:

$$P(1 \text{ defective}) = .01372 + .01372 + .0480 + .0480$$
$$= .12344.$$

Calculation of a probability tree also facilitates the conditional probabilities. For example, consider the probability of control, given one defective in the sample of size two:

$$P(c \mid 1 \text{ def.}) = \frac{P(c \cap 1d)}{P(1d)}.$$

Considering the denominator first, Figure 2.12 indicates four different ways of obtaining exactly one defective. Of these, two are associated with control in the numerator. The probability becomes:

$$P(c \mid 1 \text{ def.}) = \frac{P(c \cap g \cap d) + P(c \cap d \cap g)}{P(c \cap g \cap d) + P(c \cap d \cap g) + P(oc \cap g \cap d) + P(oc \cap d \cap g)}$$

$$= \frac{.01372 + .01372}{.01372 + .01372 + .04800 + .04800}$$

$$= .2223.$$

By a formal structuring of the situation, the probability tree allows a decision maker to perceive easily all relevant relationships and possible outcomes.

THE JOINT PROBABILITY TABLE

Another valuable tool for calculating probabilities is the *joint probability table*. Decision making in an environment under uncertainty may require considerable probability information. The joint probability table efficiently localizes all relevant information. It contains all joint probabilities and all marginal probabilities. Moreover, it allows the systematic computation of all conditional probabilities.

Reconsidering the production process problem (Figures 2.10 and 2.11), the format for the joint probability table is expressed in Table 2.5. There are two categories of events: the *process state* (C, OC) and the *sample result* (0 def, 1 def, or 2 def). The body of the table contains the probabilities of all joint relationships between these two categories of events. In the margin of the table, *marginal probabilities* represent the probabilities of the separate events.

Process State	Sample ($n = 2$), Number Of Defectives			Marginal Probabilities
	0 *def.*	1 *def.*	2 *def.*	
Control (C)	$P(C \cap 0d)$	$P(C \cap 1d)$	$P(C \cap 2d)$	$P(C)$
Out of Control (OC)	$P(OC \cap 0d)$	$P(OC \cap 1d)$	$P(OC \cap 2d)$	$P(OC)$
Marginal Probabilities	$P(0d)$	$P(1d)$	$P(2d)$	1.00

TABLE 2.5

Format for Joint Probability Table

Table 2.6 represents the joint probability table, complete with probability values. The separate joint probabilities can be computed from the probability rule:[5]

$$P(c \cap 0 \ def.) = P(c)P(0d \mid c)$$
$$= P(c)P(g \mid c)P(g \mid c)$$
$$= (.70)(.98)(.98)$$
$$= .67228.$$

Process State	Sample ($n = 2$), Number Of Defectives			Marginal Probabilities
	0 *def.*	1 *def.*	2 *def.*	
C	.67228	.02744	.00028	.70000
OC	.19200	.09600	.01200	.30000
Marginal Probabilities	.86428	.12344	.01228	1.00000

TABLE 2.6

The Joint Probability Table

Once the joint probabilities have been determined, the marginal probabilities can easily be assessed as the probability of a compound event. For

---

[5] The probability of control and one defective is easily calculated by referring to the probability tree in Figure 2.12. The tree indicates that there are two ways of having control and one defective:

$$P(C \cap 1d) = P(C \cap g \cap d) + P(C \cap d \cap g)$$
$$= P(C)P(g \mid C)P(d \mid C) + P(C)P(d \mid C)P(g \mid C)$$
$$= (.7)(.98)(.02) + (.7)(.02)(.98)$$
$$= .02744.$$

example, the marginal probability of control is the sum of the row joint probabilities:

$$P(\text{control}) = P(c \cap 0d) + P(c \cap 1d) + P(c \cap 2d)$$
$$= .67228 + .02744 + .00028$$
$$= .70000.$$

The marginal probability of zero defectives is the sum of the associated column joint probabilities:

$$P(0 \text{ defectives}) = P(c \cap 0d) + P(oc \cap 0d)$$
$$= .67228 + .19200$$
$$= .86428.$$

Once constructed, the joint probability table provides a wealth of information. Moreover, it simplifies conditional probability calculations to a single division. Symbolically, the probability of control, given zero defectives, is:

$$P(c \mid 0 \; def.) = \frac{P(c \cap 0d)}{P(0d)} .$$

The numerator is a joint probability; the denominator, a marginal probability. The required values can be obtained directly from the table:

$$P(c \mid 0 \; def.) = \frac{.67228}{.86428}$$

$$= .778.$$

Similarly,

$$P(oc \mid 0 \; def.) = \frac{P(oc \cap 0d)}{P(0d)}$$

$$= \frac{.19200}{.86428}$$

$$= .222.$$

All other conditional probabilities can be derived as easily (Table 2.7).

State (S)	$P(S|0def.)$	$P(S|1def.)$	$P(S|2def.)$
Control (C)	$P(C|0d) = .778$	$P(C|1d) = .221$	$P(C|2d) = .023$
Out of Control (OC)	$P(OC|0d) = .222$	$P(OC|1d) = .779$	$P(OC|2d) = .977$
	1.000	1.000	1.000

TABLE 2.7
Conditional Probabilities

The Joint Probability Table

PROBABILITIES FOR A DECISION ENVIRONMENT

As a final consideration, the complete set of probability information will be determined for a decision environment. This will tie together several important concepts and demonstrate the ease with which essential probability information may be obtained.

Consider a decision environment where three workers (W1, W2, and W3) are producing a similar product. Of the total daily output, the three workers produce 50, 40, and 10 percent respectively. The quality of the individual production also varies. Worker 1 produces only 2 percent defective items. Worker 2 produces 4 percent defectives and worker 3, 10 percent (Table 2.8). All finished products are stored in a large warehouse. A single item is randomly selected from those produced. The objective is to determine all the probability information for the decision environment.

The first step is to structure the relevant events by constructing a probability tree. The first event is the worker who produces the item. The second event is whether the item is good (g) or defective (d). Since the worker's production precedes the selection of an item, Figure 2.13 represents the resulting probability tree.

	% of total output	% defectives
Worker 1	.50	.02
Worker 2	.40	.04
Worker 3	.10	.10

TABLE 2.8

Basic Characteristics of the Decision Environment

Path Probabilities

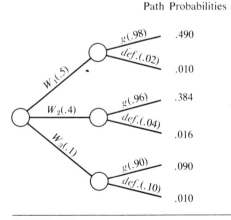

FIGURE 2.13

The Probability Tree Structure of the Decision Environment

The second step is to construct a joint probability table (Table 2.9) based on the information in the probability tree:

Producer	Quality		
	good	defective	
W_1	$P(W_1 \cap g) = .490$	$P(W_1 \cap def.) = .010$	$P(W_1) = .500$
W_2	$P(W_2 \cap g) = .384$	$P(W_2 \cap def.) = .016$	$P(W_2) = .400$
W_3	$P(W_3 \cap g) = .090$	$P(W_3 \cap def.) = .010$	$P(W_3) = .100$
	$P(g) = .964$	$P(def.) = .036$	1.000

TABLE 2.9
Joint Probability Table

Each of the joint probabilities represents one of the path probabilities on the probability tree. The marginal probabilities are obtained simply by addition.

This leaves only the conditional probabilities. With the joint probability table, these are easily derived. For example, if a good item is selected, the probability that it was produced by worker 1 is:

$$P(W_1 \mid g) = \frac{P(W_1 \cap g)}{P(g)}.$$

Reading the joint probability numerator and marginal probability denominator from the joint probability table:

$$P(W_1 \mid g) = \frac{.490}{.964}$$

$$= .508.$$

The joint probability table makes conditional probabilities accessible through a single division.

With the probability tree and joint probability table, the uncertainty of a decision environment is fully structured and uniquely defined. Information regarding uncertainty is made readily available.

SUMMARY

In decision making under conditions of uncertainty, the uncertainty must be measured. The decision maker must understand the concepts and calculation of probability. This chapter provides the necessary basic foundation.

Although probability is always the measure of the chance or likelihood of an uncertain event, the concept and calculation of probability can take several forms. The classical definition assumes a known probability space of equally likely, mutually exclusive, and collectively exhaustive events. A probability is calculated as the ratio of the number of events favorable to an outcome divided by the total number of events. The causal reasoning corresponds highly with intuition and logic.

If the probability space is unknown, however, the classical definition can no longer be strictly applied. In this case, a sample can be taken to define the unknown population. From the sample information a probability is estimated, using the relative frequency definition: A probability is the ratio of sample results favorable to the outcome divided by the total number of outcomes. In the limit, as the sample approaches the total population, the relative frequency estimate approaches the classical counterpart.

In many situations the probability space will be unknown and sampling will be impossible. The decision maker must then rely heavily on personal experience to estimate, subjectively or judgmentally, the probability of events.

More generally, whether it is *objectively* derived or *subjectively* assessed, a probability is *a summarization of information that measurably expresses uncertainty*. As such, it is essential to decision making under uncertainty.

The objective calculation of probability is facilitated by two simply applied rules: the OR statement and the AND statement. For compound events a probability model systematically breaks down the complicated situation into easily solvable OR and AND subcomponents. Moreover, the often troublesome conditional probability can be derived by the division of two components: an AND statement in the numerator and a compound event in the denominator.

Conditional probabilities add an important dimension to the measurement of uncertainty. They allow the adjustment of probabilities based on additional information. If repeated adjustments are required, a tableau for revising probabilities can be used to facilitate the computations.

The probability tree and the joint probability table are both valuable tools for measuring uncertainty. The probability tree systematically structures the complete sample space for the decision environment. It provides a clear and precise definition of the relationships among all events. The joint probability table conveniently assembles relevant probabilities. It contains joint, marginal, and, by an appropriate division, conditional probabilities. These two tools provide the decision maker with a ready access to essential probability information.

Boot, J. C. G., and E. B. Cox. *Statistical Analysis for Managerial Decisions*. New York: McGraw-Hill Book Co., 1970.

Chou, Y. L. *Statistical Analysis with Business and Economic Applications*. New York: Holt, Rinehart, & Winston, 1969.

Clelland, R. J., J. deCani, F. Brown, J. Bursk, and D. Murray. *Basic Statistics with Business Applications*. New York: John Wiley & Sons, 1966.

Dixon, W., and F. Massey, Jr. *Introduction to Statistical Analysis*. New York: McGraw-Hill Book Co., 1969.

Feller, W. *An Introduction to Probability Theory and Its Applications*. Vol. 1. New York: John Wiley & Sons, 1968.

Freund, M., and F. Williams. *Modern Business Statistics*. Englewood Cliffs, N.J.: Prentice-Hall, 1969.

Hamburg, M. *Statistical Analysis for Decision Making*. New York: Harcourt, Brace, Jovanovich, 1970.

Hoel, P. G., and R. J. Jessen. *Basic Statistics for Business and Economics*. New York: John Wiley & Sons, 1971.

Kemeny, J. G., A. Schleifer, Jr., J. L. Snell, and G. L. Thompson. *Finite Mathematics with Business Applications*. Englewood Cliffs, N.J.: Prentice-Hall, 1972.

L'Esperance, W. L. *Modern Statistics for Business and Economics*. New York: The Macmillan Co., 1971.

Neter, J., and W. Wasserman. *Fundamental Statistics for Business and Economics*. Boston: Allyn & Bacon, 1966.

Parzen, E. *Modern Probability Theory and Its Applications*. New York: John Wiley & Sons, 1960.

Schlaifer, R. *Probability and Statistics for Business Decisions*. New York: McGraw-Hill Book Co., 1959.

Spurr, W. A., and C. P. Bonini. *Statistical Analysis for Business Decisions*. Homewood, Ill.: Richard D. Irwin, 1967.

Yamane, T. *Statistics: An Introductory Analysis*. New York: Harper & Row, 1967.

2.1. A pair of dice are rolled. Determine the collectively exhaustive set of outcomes. Using the classical definition, what is the probability of a total of seven? Verify this result by the use of the probability rules.

2.2. Because of the nature of the information, a marketing survey technique will produce a valid response only 80 percent of the time. Three people are interviewed on consecutive days. With a constructed probability tree, use the probability rules to calculate:

(1) the probability of three valid responses,
(2) the probability of one valid response,
(3) the probability of two or more invalid responses, and
(4) the probability of invalid, invalid, and valid responses, in that order.

2.3. During one week a company's personnel director interviews four men and two women for a job opening. The following week four men and four women are interviewed. With an assumed similar dispersion of performance capability for men and women applicants and no sexual bias in the selection, what is the probability that a woman will be selected? What is the probability that a woman who was interviewed the first week will be selected? If two people are selected, what is the probability that they will be of different sexes, and that they will have been interviewed in different weeks?

2.4.

Rental 1

```
4 R
4 W
2 B
```

Rental 2

```
1 R
1 W
8 B
```

At the Denver airport, two car rental companies have red, white, and blue winterized cars available for skiers (diagram). A group of skiers rents three cars from one of the companies. The company assigns cars without regard to color. Determine:

(1) the probability that the cars will be red, white, and blue;
(2) if the first two cars are red and white, the probability that the third will be blue; and

(3) if the cars come from the second company ($R2$), the probability that the third car will be blue.

2.5. Through personal promotion of a new industrial product, the company representative has a 60 percent chance of acquiring a new client. If a client purchases and uses the product once, there is a 90 percent chance of a repeat purchase. On an out-of-state business trip, the company representative will contact two prospective buyers.

1. What is the probability of two purchases from only one new customer?
2. What is the probability of two purchases in total?
3. List all possible total numbers of sales and calculate the associated probabilities.
4. Represent the information in question 3 by a distribution.

2.6. A man preparing for a trip has heard that the probability of a bomb being on the plane is .0001. Being highly concerned about bomb threats, he decides that the safest way to travel is to bring along his own bomb. Using newly acquired statistical models, he has formed the following "logic":

$P(\text{bomb}) = .0001$

$$P(2 \text{ bombs}) = P(\text{bomb})P(\text{bomb})$$
$$= (.0001)(.0001)$$
$$= .00000001.$$

With one chance in ten million he will feel safe.

Demonstrate mathematically what intuition suggests: He has not improved his plight—just increased his baggage on the flight.

2.7. King of spades
Queen of *hearts*
Jack of clubs
10 of *hearts*
four of *hearts*

This hand was drawn in a poker game among friends. Either a flush (*e.g.*, five hearts) or a straight (*e.g.*, AKQJ10 or KQJ109) will win. Should the King and Jack be discarded in the hope of drawing two hearts for a flush, or should the four be discarded in the hope of drawing an ace or nine for a straight?

After the foregoing decision has been made, six of the opponents' discards are thrown face up, revealing five hearts and no aces or nines. Will this additional information alter the decision?

2.8.

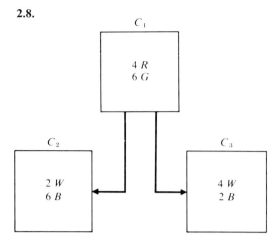

An item is selected from C_1. If it is red (R), a second item is drawn from C_2. If the first item is green (G), the second item is drawn from C_3. If the second item is white (W), what is the probability that the first item was red (R)?

2.9. There are three chests, each with two drawers. In each drawer there is either a $20 gold piece or a silver dollar. One chest contains two gold coins; one contains a gold and a silver coin; and one contains two silver coins.

One drawer of one chest is opened, disclosing a gold coin. What is the probability that this is the chest with two gold coins?

2.10. A tennis player is allowed two attempts to serve a ball into her opponent's service square. She always delivers a hard, flat, first serve and, if necessary, a slower-spin second serve. The probability of a successful delivery of the hard, flat serve is .50, and of the slower spin, .80. What is the probability that she will not double fault? If she changes her strategy to two slow-spin serves, what is the probability that she will not double fault?

2.11. A tennis player hits winners 40 percent of the time with a hard, flat serve and 20 percent of the time with a slower, angled-spin serve. The hard, flat serve is used 60 percent of the time. If a winner has just been hit, what is the probability that it was a hard, flat serve?

2.12. A student has a 20 percent chance of solving a certain problem. If he works a similar homework problem, his chance of a correct solution is increased to 90 percent. If he has worked 40 percent of the homework containing one related problem, what is the probability that he will miss this type of problem on a surprise quiz?

2.13. You feel tonight that there is a 60 percent chance of rain for tomorrow. More-over, the weatherman forecasts rain. The weatherman, however, is not always correct.

On rainy days, he forecasts rain 80 percent of the time. On fair days, he forecasts rain 10 percent of the time.

Adjust your initial personal probability assessment to take into account the added knowledge of the weatherman's prediction.

2.14. A production process has one of three possible states: (1) in control, (2) out of control with a type 1 problem, or (3) out of control with a type 2 problem. If the process is in control, an average of two defective items per 100 will be produced. If the process is out of control with a type 1 problem, 10 defectives per 100 will be produced. If it is out of control with a type 2 problem, the number of defective items will increase to 20 per 100.

The production manager, who has been watching the process for a number of hours, assigns subjective probabilities for the three possible conditions: $P(\text{control}) = .60$; $P(\text{out of control type 1}) = .30$; $P(\text{out of control type 2}) = .10$.

A sample of two items is taken and both are found to be defective. What are the production manager's *revised probabilities* for the three possible states of the process? Determine the adjustments using the conditional probability rule.

Construct a probability tree to represent the situation. Use the path probabilities on the probability tree to determine the same revised probabilities.

Construct a joint probability table. Determine the revised probabilities again from the joint probability table.

2.15. A marketing manager feels there is an 80 percent chance that a new product will be considered superior to its competitors. To confirm this feeling, a market research project is conducted. The research will have the following reliability. If the product really is superior, there is a 90 percent chance that the survey will find it superior. If the product is not really superior, there is a 40 percent chance that the survey will find it superior anyway.

Construct a probability tree and a joint probability table representing this situation.

The survey is conducted. It indicates that the product is superior. What is the manager's revised probability that the product really is superior?

3

Quantitative Decision Models

Having discovered a problem, the decision maker, consciously or subconsciously, progresses through a series of steps focused directly on *alternatives*. He or she gathers information to define and redefine alternatives. Once the alternatives are clearly identified, the decision maker refers to a value system to assign meaning or worth to the alternatives. The alternatives are then analyzed. The decision maker synthesizes the relevant information through the value system to sort out the best alternative.

All decisions contain common elements that have a similar procedural focus. Information, a value system, and structured logic are used to facilitate defining, clarifying, evaluating, and sorting alternatives. In this chapter, these essential ingredients are structured to form a general conceptual approach to problem solving. This general procedure will be used frequently throughout the text as a framework for model construction.

This chapter also contains several extensions of the general modeling procedure to be applied to simplified conditions in a decision environment of uncertainty. To facilitate a direct focus on the characteristics of modeling procedures, illustrative decision environments in early chapters are kept as simple as possible. In later chapters the decision environments will more closely resemble realistic situations.

A GENERAL MODEL FOR DECISION MAKING

The alternative focus of the decision process provides a natural structure for problem solving. In the most general form, *the model for decision making* consists of three steps:

1. List and define the alternatives.
2. Evaluate the alternatives.
3. Select the best alternative.

These are the fundamental requirements for any decision.

There are two major types of decision environments that require special refinement. For a decision environment containing uncertainty, the decision maker requires the means to define clearly the influence of uncertainty on the desirability of the alternatives. A second difficulty occurs when the decision environment contains an inexhaustible number of alternatives. In such a case, formal methods of structured logic are required to restrict the number of potentially optimal alternatives to an evaluable few. Together, stochastic models defining uncertainty and alternative restricting search procedures constitute much of the substantive part of the fields of management science and operations research.

BAYES' DECISION RULE

For a wide category of problems under conditions of uncertainty, *Bayes' decision rule* provides a systematic extension of the general model for decision making. It consists of the following steps:

1. List all feasible alternatives.

2. List the possible states of nature, future environments, or events.

3. Assign probabilities to the states of nature or events. (Assignments may be either objective or subjective.)

4. For each alternative determine the net payoff associated with the respective states of nature. (The payoff may be a monetary value or more generally a *measure of satisfaction*, usually expressed in utiles.)

5. Evaluate each alternative by computing an expected return. (The expected return is the *weighted sum of the payoffs multiplied by the probabilities*.)

6. Select the alternative with the highest expected return.

In relating these steps to the general model for decision making, the first four steps structure the influence of uncertainty in the definition of the alternatives. Step 5 provides a means for evaluating the alternatives. Step 6 is the same: select the *best* alternative.

An example will demonstrate how Bayes' decision rule systematically assembles relevant information to obtain a *best* alternative selection. A realtor has an opportunity to invest $1,000 for one year in land speculation. The return will depend on the local economic environment. There are three possibilities: rapid economic growth, normal economic growth, and minimal economic growth. In case of rapid economic growth (S_1), the investor will realize a profit of $400. For normal economic growth (S_2), his profit will be $200. For minimal economic growth (S_3), he will take a loss of $300. Having consulted available sources of information, he subjectively assesses the probabilities of the three economic environments as 20 percent, 50 percent, and 30 percent respectively. Restricting the problem to linear monetary considerations,[1] the investor's objective will be to maximize the expected monetary value (EMV).

The first step is to list and define the alternatives. In this case there are only two:

A_1: Enter into the investment.
A_2: Do not enter into the investment.

The second step is to evaluate each alternative in terms of the operative criterion: maximum expected monetary value (*max. EMV*). The problem can be re-formulated as follows:

A_1	A_2
$EMV_1 = ?$	$EMV_2 = ?$

The third step is to choose the best alternative—to choose the alternative with the largest EMV.

The second alternative (A_2) is easily evaluated. If the investment is not made, the expected monetary return will be zero: $EMV_2 = 0$. The first alternative (A_1) is not so intuitive and will require the more formalized approach specified by Bayes' decision rule.

States of Nature (S_i)	$p(S_i)$	A_1 ($\$_i$)	$\$_i p(S_i)$
S_1	.20	$400	$ 80
S_2	.50	200	100
S_3	.30	−300	−90
	1.00		$\sum_i \$_i p(S_i) = \$90$

TABLE 3.1

Calculating an Expected Monetary Value

---

[1] Linear monetary values infer proportionate worth for varying amounts of money. The extension to nonlinear monetary returns and nonmonetary elements of worth is covered in Chapters 5 and 6.

The states of nature (S_i), associated probabilities $(p(S_i))$, and payoffs $(\$_i)$ are easily assembled as in Table 3.1. A_1 has an expected monetary value of:

$$EMV_1 = \sum_i \$_i p(S_i)$$

$$= \$400(.20) + \$200(.50) + (\$-300)(.30)$$

$$= \$90.$$

Once the alternatives have been evaluated, the decision is straightforward:

$$\begin{array}{cc} \underline{A_1{}^*} & \underline{A_2} \\ EMV_1 = \$90 & EMV_2 = \$0 \end{array}.$$

With the highest EMV, A_1 is the preferred choice.

The Expected Monetary Value

The EMV is a special *expected value*. In general the expected value of a *random variable* X is expressed as:

$$E(X) = \sum_i X_i p(X_i)$$

$$= X_1 p(X_1) + X_2 p(X_2) + \cdots + X_n p(X_n).$$

If the random variable is a monetary quantity $(\$_i)$, then the expected value becomes an expected monetary value:

$$EMV = E(\$)$$

$$= \sum_i \$_i p(S_i)$$

$$= \$_1 p(\$_1) + \$_2 p(\$_2) + \cdots + \$_n p(\$_n).$$

The EMV is the *weighted sum of the monetary payoffs multiplied by the respective probabilities*. It represents the average return[2] or the expected return. In the previous example, the selected alternative had an expected return of $90. For a single investment, the investor will receive $400, $200, or $-300. A return of $90 is not a possibility. However, if this identical investment were made a large number of times, the average of all of the returns would approximate $90.

---

[2] To relate this concept to something familiar, the expected value is the average or mean of a distribution: $\mu_x = \sum_i X_i p(X_i)$.

For example, if the realtor were to make 100 such identical investments, S_1 with a return of $400 would be *most likely* to occur about 20 times. Similarly, S_2 with a return of $200, and S_3 with a loss of $300 would occur about 50 and 30 times, respectively. For the 100 investments, the *most likely* total return would be:

$400(20) + $200(50) − $300(30) = $9,000.

Therefore, on a per investment basis,

$$\text{average return} = \frac{\$9,000}{100}$$

$$= \$90.$$

Or stated more informedly:

$$EMV = \frac{\$400(20)}{100} + \frac{\$200(50)}{100} - \frac{\$300(30)}{100}$$

$$= \$400(.20) + \$200(.50) - \$300(.30)$$

$$= \$90.$$

These frequencies however, were only *estimates*. The return of $400 is only *most likely* to occur 20 times. In fact, it would probably appear with some other frequency. The probability of a substantial deviation from 20, however, becomes statistically remote.[3] In other words, as the number of similar investments increases, the probability that the actual result will differ from the expected result decreases significantly. If the investment is repeated a large number of times, the expected monetary value will be assumed to be a reasonably exact measure of the average return.

THE ECONOMIC WORTH OF AN OPPORTUNITY

If two simplifying assumptions are made regarding the decision environment, an expected monetary value can be used to evaluate the worth of an opportunity. The assumptions are:

(1) no relevant nonmonetary considerations, and
(2) a linear utility for money.

---

[3] It would be possible for $400 to occur each of the 100 times. Assuming independent trials, the probability of this exceptional result is $(.2)^{100}$ or $.789 \cdot 10^{-69}$—pragmatically nonexistent.

The first assumption implies that all relevant consequences in the decision environment can be adequately represented by a monetary measure of worth. The second assumption implies that monetary quantities are proportionate measures of worth. Regardless of present dollar endowments, each additional dollar provides the same additional increment of worth.[4] Both of these assumptions are considered fully in Chapter 6.

For this simplified decision environment, the decision maker is called an *EMV*'er. For an *EMV*'er, the expected monetary value will measure the worth of an opportunity. Consider the following game played by tossing a silver dollar: heads yields a return of $1; tails yields a loss of $1. The value of this game to an *EMV*'er is:

$$EMV = \frac{1}{2}(\$1) + \frac{1}{2}(\$1)$$

$$= \$0.$$

As intuition would suggest, the worth of this fair game is $0.

As a less obvious example, the silver dollar will be tossed twice: tails (T) pays nothing; heads (H) pays $5. What is the worth of this game to an *EMV*'er?

States of Nature (S_i)	$p(S_i)$	$\$_i$	$\$_i p(S_i)$
HH	¼	$10	$2.50
HT	¼	5	1.25
TH	¼	5	1.25
TT	¼	0	0
	1.0		$\sum_i \$_i p(S_i) = \$5.00$

TABLE 3.2
An *EMV* Evaluation

The desired statistic is the *EMV*. Bayes' decision rule provides a systematic procedure for assembling the relevant information. Table 3.2 summarizes the requisite information with the *EMV* statistic. In the long run and on the average, the expected return and worth of the game is $5.

The coin game may be further extended to require a payment for two tails. What payment will make this a fair game?

---

[4] This assumption is not always accurate. A multimillionaire would probably view a $100 gain or loss quite differently than would a college student.

States of Nature (S_i)	$p(S_i)$	$\$_i$	$\$_i p(S_i)$
HH	¼	$10	$10/4
HT	¼	5	5/4
TH	¼	5	5/4
TT	¼	$-X$	$-X/4$
			$EMV = \$5 - X/4$

TABLE 3.3

An Opportunity with a Payment

Bayes' decision rule provides this evaluation. For an EMV'er, the game is desirable as long as the EMV is positive. Substituting the variable X for the unknown payment, Table 3.3 provides an EMV of $\$5 - X/4$. For large values of X, the EMV will be negative. For small values of X, the EMV will be positive and the game will be favorable to the player. The maximum acceptable payment will occur at the point of indifference to play: where the EMV is zero. Therefore, setting the EMV equal to $0 and solving for X:

$$EMV = \$5 - \frac{X}{4}$$

$$\$0 = \$5 - \frac{X}{4}$$

and

$$X = \$20.$$

An EMV'er would be willing to pay up to $20 for the outcome two tails (Table 3.4). If more than $20 is required for this outcome, the EMV will be

States of Nature (S_i)	$p(S_i)$	$\$_i$
HH	¼	$10
HT	¼	5
TH	¼	5
TT	¼	$-20
		$EMV = \$0$

TABLE 3.4

A Fair Game

negative and the game undesirable. If less than \$20 is required, the *EMV* will be positive and the game desirable.

THE SENSITIVITY OF PROBABILITY ASSESSMENTS

In decision making under uncertainty, it is often difficult to make exact probability assessments. With only limited information the decision maker may be quite reluctant to rely heavily on subjective probability assessments. Additional information from sampling and other sources may not be readily available. There may be insufficient time for further inquiry. The cost of additional information may be excessive. In such a situation, the difficulty in assessing probabilities may be substantially reduced by determining the sensitivity of the choice to the probability assessments.

To illustrate, a decision is required regarding the purchase and resale of two groups of high-interest yield corporate bonds. The critical factor is the interest rate for similar bonds at the end of a four-month resale period. To simplify, the relevant states of nature are classified into a favorable interest rate (S_1) and an unfavorable interest rate (S_2). Because of recent economic uncertainties, the probabilities for the states of nature (S_1 and S_2), however, are unknown and difficult to determine.

States of Nature (S_i)	$p(S_i)$	Bond Group 1 (A_1)	Bond Group 2 (A_2)
S_1	p	\$10,000	\$7,000
S_2	$1 - p$	5,000	3,000
	1.0		

TABLE 3.5
An Alternative Insensitive to Probability

With the projected returns provided in Table 3.5, an analysis can still be performed. If the favorable interest rate (S_1) occurs, the first group of bonds will be preferred ($A_1{}^*$) to the second group (A_2):

	$A_1{}^*$	A_2
S_1	\$10,000	\$7,000

If an unfavorable interest rate (S_2) occurs, the first group of bonds is still preferred:

	A_1*	A_2
S_2	$5,000	$3,000

Regardless of the probabilities associated with the interest rates (S_1, S_2), a decision maker will always prefer to select the first group of bonds (A_1). The best alternative is insensitive to the probability assignments.

To demonstrate this concept further, a small subcontractor with limited equipment must choose between two projects. The estimated returns expressed in Table 3.6 are a function of contract bids and other factors. The contractor must decide promptly with limited probability information.

States of Nature (S_i)	$p(S_i)$	A_1	A_2
S_1	p	$500	$300
S_2	$1 - p$	100	300
	1.0		

TABLE 3.6

An Investment Alternative: Probabilities Unknown

Since the subcontractor is an *EMV*'er, the required statistic is the *EMV*. The *EMV*s cannot be determined, however, without probability assessments. The probabilities are required but unknown.

The unknown probabilities can be treated as variables. For the states S_1 and S_2, they are assigned respective values of p and $1 - p$. The *EMV* for each alternative can then be computed:

A_1: $EMV_1 = \$500(p) + \$100(1 - p)$

A_2: $EMV_2 = \$300(p) + \$300(1 - p)$.

For large values of p, A_1 is preferred to A_2. For small values of p, A_2 is preferred.

A value of p must exist to produce an indifference between the two alternatives. At this point:

$$EMV_1 = EMV_2$$

or

$$\$500(p) + \$100(1 - p) = \$300(p) + \$300(1 - p).$$

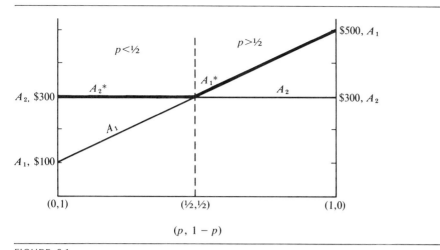

FIGURE 3.1
The Alternative Selections for Values of p

Solving for p,

$$p = \frac{1}{2}.$$

As Figure 3.1 verifies, a decision maker would be indifferent to a choice between A_1 and A_2 for $p = 1/2$:

$$A_1^*: EMV_1 = \$500 \left(\frac{1}{2}\right) + \$100 \left(\frac{1}{2}\right)$$

$$= \$300^*$$

$$A_2^*: EMV_2 = \$300 \left(\frac{1}{2}\right) + \$300 \left(\frac{1}{2}\right)$$

$$= \$300^*.$$

If $p > 1/2$, A_1 is preferred to A_2:

$$EMV_1 > EMV_2$$
$$A_1^* > A_2.$$

Concurrently, if $p < 1/2$, A_2 is the selection:

$$EMV_1 < EMV_2$$
$$A_1 < A_2^*$$

If p is 1/2, either alternative is equally acceptable:

$$EMV_1 = EMV_2$$
$$A_1^* = A_2^*.$$

The alternative selection has been reformulated in terms of a single probability consideration. If $p \geq 1/2$, select A_1; otherwise, select A_2. An exact probability assessment is not required. Instead, the probability need only be known within a wide specified range. An optimal decision can be made with very limited probability information.

THE CONDITIONAL PROFIT TABLE

In decision making under conditions of uncertainty, Bayes' decision rule can often be more efficiently extended by a conditional profit table. To illustrate, the manager of a tropical fish store must decide on the number of 55-gallon plexiglass aquariums to purchase from a supplier. Complete with hood and wrought iron stand, the aquariums can be purchased for $50 each, to be sale priced at $110. If *too many* aquariums are purchased, there will be associated costs for storage, handling, and tying up capital. These excessive costs are roughly estimated at $5 per unit.[5] Moreover, if the store carries *too few* aquariums, losses will accrue directly from lost sales of aquariums[6] and indirectly from lost sales of pumps, filters, fish, other related equipment, and general customer dissatisfaction. Excluding the direct lost profit from the sale, the cost of *too few* items is assessed at $40 per unit. Projected sales at the reduced price are:

Units demanded	Probabilities
0	.10
1	.30
2	.35
3	.20
4	.05
	1.00

---

[5] The estimate is assumed constant over all remaining items.
[6] No backorders will be taken at the sale price.

As with any problem, the first step is to define the alternatives clearly. A demand for more than four items is assumed immaterial. The alternatives are *restricted* to:

A_0	A_1	A_2	A_3	A_4
Stock 0	Stock 1	Stock 2	Stock 3	Stock 4.

Bayes' decision rule will facilitate the ordering of the information needed to evaluate alternatives. Following Bayes' procedure for each alternative, the required information and calculations are specified: list the potential demand; assign probabilities to demand; determine the net profit per level of demand; sum the product of the probabilities multiplied by the payoffs.

Now that demand and associated probabilities have been defined, the respective net profits must be determined. The net profit is determined by three factors: (1) profits from sales, (2) the *overage cost* for too many, and (3) the *underage cost* for too few. If zero units are stocked (A_0) and zero units are demanded, profits will total zero: $0 profits from sales, $0 *overage cost*, and $0 *underage cost*. If one unit is demanded, there will be a $40 *underage cost* for having one too few. Similarly, if two units are demanded, the underage cost will be $40 for each unit unavailable ($80). If three and four units are demanded, the losses increase to $120 and $160, respectively. The complete set of payoffs for A_0 is provided in Table 3.7. Summing the product of the payoffs by the probabilities, the *EMV* evaluating statistic becomes $-72.

State of Nature Demand (DD)	$p(DD)$	A_0
0	.10	$ 0
1	.30	-40
2	.35	-80
3	.20	-120
4	.05	-160
		EMV = $-72

TABLE 3.7
The *EMV* for A_0

The other alternatives can be evaluated similarly. A_1 will have the same states of nature and the same associated probabilities. The payoffs will vary with the quantity demanded. If the demand is zero, one item will be left in stock with an assessed *overage cost* of $5. If one unit is demanded, it will be sold for a profit of $60 or ($110 − $50). If two units are demanded, the one stocked will be sold for a profit of $60. The second customer will be turned away at an assumed loss of $40. The net profit will be $20. If three units are demanded:

	1 Stocked	Available Supply	
Customer 1	$ 60	1	sold
Customer 2	$−40	0	underage
Customer 3	$−40	0	underage
	$−20		

Similarly, if four units are demanded, an additional underage charge will reduce the payoff to $−60. Table 3.8 provides an EMV of $17.50 for A_1.

The evaluations can be made more efficiently. Since the states of nature and associated probabilities remain constant, all of the relevant information can be expressed in a single *conditional profit table* (Table 3.9).[7]

State of Nature Demand (DD)	$P(DD)$	A_1
0	2/20	$ −5
1	6/20	60
2	7/20	20
3	4/20	−20
4	1/20	−60
		$EMV = \$17.50$

TABLE 3.8

The EMV for A_1

States of Nature	$p(S_i)$	A_0	A_1	A_2	A_3	A_4
0	2/20	$ 0	$ −5			
1	6/20	−40	60			
2	7/20	−80	20			
3	4/20	−120	−20			
4	1/20	−160	−60			
	EMV_i	$ −72	$17.50			

TABLE 3.9

Conditional Profit Table

[7] So called because profits are dependent (or conditional) on the alternative selection and the demand.

Recognizing several relationships allows a systematic determination of each of the conditional profit values. There are three situations with defined payoffs: stock the proper quantity, stock too many, or stock too few. In this case, the conditional profits along the diagonal represent the proper quantity decisions. There is a profit of $60 per sale. Profits along the diagonal will start at zero and increase by increments of $60 (Table 3.10).

States of Nature	$p(S_i)$	A_0	A_1	A_2	A_3	A_4
0	2/20	$0				
1	6/20		$60			
2	7/20			$120		
3	4/20				$180	
4	1/20					$240

TABLE 3.10
Conditional Profit Table: The Diagonal Payoffs

Similarly, to *the right of the diagonal of best decisions, too many* units are ordered with an associated *overage cost* of $5 each. Therefore, directly to the right of each diagonal value, the payoffs will progressively decrease by increments of $5 (Table 3.11).

States of Nature	$p(S_i)$	A_0	A_1	A_2	A_3	A_4
0	2/20	$0	$-5	$-10	$-15	$-20
1	6/20		60	55	50	45
2	7/20			120	115	110
3	4/20				180	175
4	1/20					240

TABLE 3.11
Conditional Profit Table: Overage Payoffs

The payoffs to the *left of the diagonal* are as easily obtained. They are directly related to the constant underage cost. If zero units are stocked (A_0) and zero units are demanded, the proper quantity was purchased. The payoffs in the column below the proper quantity represent *too few* items with an associated underage cost. If zero units are stocked (A_0) and one unit is demanded, there will be a shortage of one unit with an underage cost of $40. If two units are demanded, there will be an underage cost of $80. The column payoffs to the left of the diagonal progressively decrease by the underage cost of $40 (Table 3.12).

The values to the left of the diagonal can also be derived by a row computation. If one unit is demanded, one unit should be stocked (A_1). If no units are stocked (A_0), there will be two costs: (1) $60 lost profit from the potential sale and (2) $40 underage cost from lost potential sales of related items. Compared with the proper number to stock, one unit too few will reduce profits by $100. Therefore, the row values to the left of the diagonal are progressively reduced by increments of $100 (Table 3.12).

States of Nature	$p(S_i)$	A_0	A_1	A_2	A_3	A_4
0	.10	$ 0				
1	.30	−40	$ 60			
2	.35	−80	20	$120		
3	.20	−120	−20	80	$180	
4	.05	−160	−60	40	140	$240

TABLE 3.12

Conditional Profit Table: Underage Payoffs

With the profit per sale, the overage cost, and the underage cost, a conditional profit table can be systematically constructed that contains all the information needed to select the best alternative. The complete set of summary *EMV* statistics is presented in Table 3.13. The best alternative is to purchase four 55-gallon plexiglass aquarium sets (A_4).

States of Nature	$p(S_i)$	A_0	A_1	A_2	A_3	A_4^*
0	.10	$ 0	$ −5	$−10	$−15	$−20
1	.30	−40	60	55	50	45
2	.35	−80	20	120	115	110
3	.20	−120	−20	80	180	175
4	.05	−160	−60	40	140	240
EMV:		$−72.00	$17.50	$75.50	$96.75	$97.00
maximum *EMV*:						$97.00

TABLE 3.13

Conditional Profit Table

THE CONDITIONAL OPPORTUNITY LOSS TABLE

With this problem, as with most others, a decision maker is not generally restricted to a single method for solution. This order quantity problem can be solved by applying Bayes' decision rule separately to each alternative or by condensing the information into a conditional profit table. It can also be expressed in terms of *opportunity losses* and solved with a *conditional opportunity loss table*.[8]

An opportunity loss is simply *the profits forgone by not selecting the best alternative*. For example, consider the following alternatives with associated profits:

A_1: $100

A_2: $-50

A_3: $0.

A_1 is obviously the best alternative. If it is selected, there will be no opportunity loss. If A_2 is selected, there will be an opportunity loss of $150: the $50 actual loss plus the $100 that could have been obtained by selecting A_1. Similarly, compared to the best alternative (A_1), A_3 has an opportunity loss of $100.

For the earlier order quantity problem, a conditional opportunity loss table can be constructed either from the initial cost and profit data or from the conditional profit table. Construction from the conditional profit table clarifies the direct relationship between the two analogous approaches.

The conditional profits in Table 3.13 can easily be converted into opportunity losses. An opportunity loss is the profit forgone by not making the best decision. In turn, a best decision presupposes the occurrence of a specific state of nature. For example, if zero units are demanded, there are five alternatives:

State of Nature	Conditional Profits				
	A_0	A_1	A_2	A_3	A_4
0	$0	$-5	$-10	$-15	$-20 .

The best of these is A_0 with $0 profits. The opportunity loss associated with A_0 is $0. If A_1 is selected, the cost of not making the best decision is $5. The

---

[8] Consistent with the concept of multiple solutions, this problem can also be solved by using a decision tree (Chapter 4), an inventory model (Chapter 15), linear programming (Chapters 8, 9, 10), or simulation (Chapter 17).

opportunity losses for the other alternatives are derived by a comparison with A_0:

State of Nature	Conditional Opportunity Losses				
	A_0	A_1	A_2	A_3	A_4
0	$0	$5	$10	$15	$20 .

If one unit is demanded, the conditional profits are:

State of Nature	Conditional Profits				
	A_0	A_1	A_2	A_3	A_4
1	$-40	$60	$55	$50	$45 .

The best alternative is A_1 with a profit of $60. The opportunity losses can again be derived by comparing the best return with each of the other alternatives:

State of Nature	Conditional Opportunity Losses				
	A_0	A_1	A_2	A_3	A_4
1	$100	$0	$5	$10	$15 .

The opportunity losses for the other rows are obtained in the same way. Table 3.14 contains the complete set of opportunity losses.

The conditional opportunity loss table could also be derived systematically from the original profit and loss information. The diagonal elements represent the best decision. If zero units are demanded, the best decision is to stock zero.

States of Nature	$p(S_i)$	A_0	A_1	A_2	A_3	A_4*
0	2/20	$ 0	$ 5	$ 10	$ 15	$20
1	6/20	100	0	5	10	15
2	7/20	200	100	0	5	10
3	4/20	300	200	100	0	5
4	1/20	400	300	200	100	0
	EOL:	$180	$90.5	$32.5	$11.25	$11.0
minimum	EOL:					$11.0*

TABLE 3.14
Conditional Opportunity Loss Table

If one unit is demanded, the best decision is to stock one. The conditional opportunity losses along the diagonal are all zero (Table 3.15).

The payoffs to the *right of the diagonal* represent *overage costs*. If zero units are demanded and one unit is stocked, there is an overage of one unit with an associated loss of $5. If two units are stocked, there is an overage of two units with a loss of $10. The opportunity losses to the right of the diagonal increase incrementally by the overage cost (Table 3.15).

The payoffs to the *left of the diagonal* represent *underage costs*. For example, if one unit is demanded and zero units are stocked, there is an underage of one unit with an associated opportunity loss of $100: $60 directly from the lost sale plus the $40 underage cost. Similarly, if two units are demanded and zero units are stocked, the opportunity loss is $100 for each unit demanded and not available—a total of $200. The opportunity loss to the left of the diagonal will increase by increments of $100 (Table 3.15).

Since the overage and underage costs are assumed constant, the complete conditional opportunity loss table can be constructed quite easily. The entire *diagonal of best decision* will have zero opportunity losses. To the right of the diagonal, the opportunity losses are incremented by the overage cost ($5). To the left of the diagonal, they are incremented by the total of the cost of a lost sale ($60) plus the underage cost ($40).

States of Nature	$p(S_i)$	A_0	A_1	A_2	A_3	A_4
0	2/20	$ 0	$ 5	$ 10	$ 15	$20
1	6/20	$100	0	5	10	15
2	7/20	200	100	0	5	10
3	4/20	300	200	100	0	5
4	1/20	400	300	200	100	0

TABLE 3.15

Conditional Opportunity Loss Table: Incremental Increases

Once the conditional opportunity loss table has been constructed, each alternative is evaluated by an appropriate criterion. In considering conditional profits, the criterion was the maximum expected monetary value: *max. EMV*. In considering conditional opportunity losses, the analogous criterion will be the minimum expected opportunity loss: *min. EOL*. The expected opportunity loss is an expected value, calculated as before by weighting the payoffs by the probabilities:

$$EOL = \sum_i OL_i p(OL_i).$$

The computed *EOL* values are summarized in Table 3.14. A_4 is the best choice with an *EOL* of $11.00. As might be expected, this decision is the same as that reached with the conditional profit table (Table 3.13).

THE EXPECTED VALUE OF PERFECT INFORMATION

The conditional profit table and the conditional opportunity loss table can provide more valuable information. They can be used to evaluate the cost of uncertainty.

In the previous order quantity problem (Table 13.3), the decision maker would select A_4 with an *EMV* of $97. Five percent of the time, four units will actually be demanded and A_4 will be the best choice. The remaining ninety-five percent of the time, the constant selection of A_4 will not be the best possible choice. However, if profits and probabilities are fully considered, A_4 still remains the best choice.

When demand is known, however, the decision can be improved. Assume that a perfect forecasting device has been developed to determine the exact unit demand. Under such conditions of *certainty*, the decision maker could always select the best alternative. If zero units were demanded, zero units would be stocked. If one unit was demanded, one unit would be stocked. At different times any of the five alternatives would be the best selection. Under certainty the conditional profits for the best alternatives appear along the diagonal of the conditional profit table (Table 3.16).

The probabilities for the various states of nature are still assumed to be valid. The forecasting device will indicate a demand for zero units 2/20 of the time; for one unit, 6/20 of the time, and so on.

Under certainty, therefore, the decision maker will select A_0 and receive $0 each time zero units are forecast. This will occur 2/20 of the time. Similarly,

States of Nature	$p(S_i)$	A_0	A_1	A_2	A_3	A_4
0	2/20	$0				
1	6/20		$60			
2	7/20			$120		
3	4/20				$180	
4	1/20					$240

TABLE 3.16

Conditional Profit Table: Conditions of Certainty

A_1, worth \$60, will be selected 6/20 of the time. With a perfect forecasting device, *under conditions of certainty*, the expected return will be:

$$EMV_c = \frac{2}{20}\,(\$0) + \frac{6}{20}\,(\$60) + \cdots + \frac{1}{20}\,(\$240)$$

$$= \$108.$$

Without the forecasting device, *under conditions of uncertainty*, the decision maker's consistent selection of A_4 will provide an expected return of \$97. The worth of the forecasting device, the cost of uncertainty, must be the difference between these two expected returns. The *expected value of perfect information (EVPI)* is therefore:

$$
\begin{aligned}
EMV_c &= \$108 \\
EMV_u{}^* &= 97 \\
\hline
EVPI &= \$11 \quad .
\end{aligned}
$$

The same conclusion can be obtained from the opportunity loss table. Under conditions of certainty, the best alternative is always selected. The expected opportunity loss will be zero: $EOL_c = \$0$. Under uncertainty, the best decision will be to select A_4 with an EOL_u of \$11. The difference between the expected return under certainty and the expected return under uncertainty must be the value of the information:

$$
\begin{aligned}
EOL_c &= \$\,0 \\
EOL_u{}^* &= 11 \\
\hline
EVPI &= \$11 \quad .
\end{aligned}
$$

Since the EOL_c is always zero and the $EVPI$ is the difference between the EOL_c and the $EOL_u{}^*$, the $EVPI$ must be the EOL for the best alternative under uncertainty ($EOL_u{}^*$).

The $EVPI$ often provides valuable information. It establishes the upper limit on the worth of information. With minimal computations it can be used to establish the maximum possible worth of a research project. If the research costs more than the $EVPI$, the project should be terminated on economic grounds. In this particular example, for a single application, a perfect forecasting device would be worth up to \$11. If it were obtainable for less than \$11, it would be an economically desirable consideration.

Since most forecasting models or market research projects produce less than perfect information, an important analogous consideration is the evaluation of imperfect or sample information. This concept will be developed in Chapter 4.

The Cost of Uncertainty and Certainty Equivalent

An additional set of relationships will facilitate a fuller understanding of the cost of uncertainty. The EMV_u plus the EOL_u for an alternative will equal the EMV_c:

$$EMV_u + EOL_u = EMV_c.$$

Table 3.17 provides the computations.

	A_0	A_1	A_2	A_3	A_4
EMV_u	$-72.00	$17.50	$75.50	$96.75	$97.00
EOL_u	$180.00	90.50	32.50	11.25	11.00
EMV_c	$108	$108	$108	$108	$108

TABLE 3.17

$EMV_u + EOL_u = EMV_c$

A closer analysis of A_4 will add clarity. If A_4 is selected, the EMV_u is $97. The expected loss for making less than the best decision is provided by the EOL_u. The constant selection of A_4 when, at times, better alternatives are available produces an EOL_u of $11 (Table 3.18). Consequently, if the return for

States of Nature	$p(S_i)$	A_4	
0	2/20	$20	
1	6/20	15	opportunity losses:
2	7/20	10	cost of nonoptimal
3	4/20	5	alternative selections
4	1/20	0	
		EOL_u = $11	expected cost for nonoptimal decisions

TABLE 3.18

EOL: The Expected Cost of Nonoptimality

A_4 is \$97 and the cost of nonoptimal selections is \$11, selecting the optimal alternative each time must be worth:

$$EMV_u + EOL_u = EMV_c$$
$$\$97 + \$11 = \$108.$$

The expected return under uncertainty plus the loss due to uncertainty will equal the expected return under certainty.

SUMMARY

Decision making is a process of defining, clarifying, evaluating, and sorting alternatives. Procedurally, the model for decision making prescribes the basics for problem solving: (1) list and define the alternatives; (2) evaluate the alternatives; and (3) select the best alternative.

In specialized decision environments, this general conceptual approach often requires modification. For decision environments containing extremely large numbers of alternatives, extended logic is required to restrict the number of alternatives to be evaluated. For decision environments containing uncertainty, additional steps are needed to define the influences of the uncertainty on the alternatives.

Bayes' decision rule facilitates a systematic definition of the alternatives under conditions of uncertainty. Moreover, in situations where the alternatives have the same uncertain influences, Bayes' decision rule can be extended to the more efficient conditional profit table and conditional opportunity loss table.

Bierman, H., Jr., C. P. Bonini, and W. H. Hausman. *Quantitative Analysis for Business Decisions*. Homewood, Ill.: Richard D. Irwin, 1973.

Chernoff, H., and L. E. Moses. *Elementary Decision Theory*. New York: John Wiley & Sons, 1959.

Dyckman, T. R., S. Smidt, and A. K. McAdams. *Managerial Decision Making Under Uncertainty*. New York: The Macmillan Co., 1969.

Halter, A. N., and G. W. Dean. *Decisions Under Uncertainty*. Cincinnati, Ohio: South-Western Publishing Co., 1971.

Paik, C. M. *Quantitative Methods for Managerial Decisions*. New York: McGraw-Hill Book Co., 1973.

Schlaifer, R. *Analysis of Decisions Under Uncertainty*. New York: McGraw-Hill Book Co., 1969.

Spurr, W. A., and C. P. Bonini. *Statistical Analysis for Business Decisions*. Homewood, Ill.: Richard D. Irwin, 1973.

Thierauf, R. J., and R. C. Klekamp. *Decision Making through Operations Research*. New York: John Wiley & Sons, 1975.

3.1. A speculative short-term investment opportunity offers potential returns of $10,000, $2,000, and $ −4,000. The respective probability assessments are .4, .4, and .2. What would this opportunity be worth to an *EMV'er*?

3.2. A blue chip stock paid a dividend of $2.80 per share in two of the last four disbursements. In the other two disbursements, the dividends were $2.10 and $.20. If these payments are considered representative, ceteris paribus, what is the expected level of dividends?

3.3. In the game of craps, one play is the *field bet*. A pair of dice is rolled. If a total of three, four, nine, 10, or 11 appears, the player wins the amount bet. If a total of two appears, the player wins double. A total of 12 pays triple the amount bet. If a total of five, six, seven, or eight appears, the player loses the amount bet.

What is the probability of winning? If $10 is placed on the field, what is the expected monetary value for the play?

3.4. A manager is contemplating making three sequentially related, two-state decisions (D_1, D_2, D_3). If he makes the right decision in each case, the return will be $80,000. If he makes a wrong decision in D_1, he will lose $1,000 and the other two options will be terminated. If he makes a wrong decision in D_2, he will lose $10,000 and the remaining option will be terminated. If he makes a wrong decision in D_3, he must make another two-state decision immediately. While a correct decision here produces no loss, a wrong decision will be costly.

If the manager must make equally likely guesses for each decision, what is the maximum tolerable loss? If the manager could obtain sufficient information to be 80 percent certain of making correct decisions, what would be the maximum loss?

3.5. A decision is required regarding the introduction of a new product. Depending on a competitor's reaction, the following table summarizes the estimated consequences of a strategy over the next three years:

Favorable:			Unfavorable:		
State of Nature (S_i)	$P(S_i)$	Present Worth	State of Nature (S_i)	$P(S_i)$	Present Worth
S_1	.2	$ 40,000	S_1	.2	$ −40,000
S_2	.6	240,000	S_2	.3	0
S_3	.2	400,000	S_3	.4	40,000
			S_4	.1	− 100,000

The probability of the favorable environment has been assessed at .8. What is the expected worth for this strategy?

3.6. A card game is played as follows: Two cards are dealt face up from a standard deck (52 cards). When it is his turn, the player can bet that the next card dealt will rank somewhere between the first two. The bet is restricted to the limit of the pot. If the player wins, the amount of the bet is taken from the pot. If the player loses, he adds the same amount to the pot and the play proceeds to the next player.

The pot presently contains $50. Two cards are dealt, they are a three and a Jack. It is your turn to bet. What will you do? How much would you expect to win or lose?

Being keenly observant, you have noticed that the last six cards dealt were a seven, Queen, ace, King, eight, and deuce. Does this information change your decision? If so, has this information any value? How much? Will these answers be appropriate for an *EMV'er*?

3.7. Your sweepstakes numbers have just arrived in the mail for the *Reader's Digest* $150,000 Sweepstakes. The Grand Prize is $24,000. In addition, there are two $10,000 prizes, four $5,000 prizes, six $1,000 prizes, eight $500 prizes, and 10,000 prizes of $10 each. According to the rules the odds of winning the respective prizes were published as follows: $10—one chance in 1,199; $500—one chance in 1,498,789; $1,000— one chance in 1,998,386; $5,000—one chance in 2,997,579; $10,000—one chance in 5,995,158; Grand Prize—one chance in 5,482,450.

To quote: "Don't let this chance for good fortune slip through your fingers . . . ." What is the expected monetary fortune from your sweepstake number?

3.8. An independent supplier is submitting a bid to supply a municipality with monthly shipments of materials over a two-year period. If the bid is submitted before the deadline, acceptance is guaranteed. The anticipated expected worth is $6,000. The bid with sample materials is ready for mailing. There are five days before the deadline and the municipality is only 450 miles away. The supplier must decide whether to send the bid and materials by air freight (first class) or by regular fourth-class mail. Either means will probably arrive on time, and the excessive weight makes air freight very costly. The teller estimates that the bid will arrive in about three days when sent fourth class. The cost and probability information are assessed as follows:

Means of Transit	Cost	Probability of Late Arrival
Air freight	$12.20	.01
Fourth class	1.40	.07

How should the bid be mailed? What is the expected net profit (anticipated profit less cost) for the best alternative?

3.9. A product purchased from a supplier produces a profit of $20. It has an *underage cost* of $4 and an *overage cost* of $2. The product has complete salvage value. It has been trial tested for 10 typical periods with the following results:

Demand	Frequency
4	1
5	2
6	3
7	3
8	1

Construct the conditional profit table to determine the proper number of products to purchase.

3.10. A product can be produced for $6 and sold for $10. Storage, handling, and other costs for *too many* items are estimated at $1. If the item is not available, customers will go elsewhere. Lost good will and other intangibles relating to future purchases for *too few* items are estimated at $2. An unsold item will retain 100 percent salvage value and can be sold in the next period. Projected demand is:

Demand	Probability
4	.20
5	.60
6	.20

Construct the conditional profit table. What is the proper number of products to produce? Construct the conditional opportunity loss table from the conditional profit table. What is the EMV_c? What is the $EVPI$?

3.11. A perishable product can be purchased in groups of 10 items for $4 each to be sold at $9 each. The sale will be a one-time event. If items are not sold, they will retain 50 percent of the purchase price as salvage value. The anticipated demand is:

Demand	Probability
20	.40
30	.40
40	.20

Construct a conditional profit table. What is the appropriate quantity of the product to purchase? What is the EMV_c?

3.12. A seasonal item can be purchased and sold at retail for a $40 profit. Storage, handling, and other overage costs average $2 per item. Lost future purchasing propensity and other underage related costs are assessed at $4 each. If the items are not sold during the coming peak demand period, they will be sold wholesale for $25 below the present retail price. While wholesale sales are guaranteed, retail sales have the following distribution:

Demand	Probability
4	.20
5	.40
6	.30
7	.10

How many items should be purchased? What is the expected value of perfect information?

3.13. On Saturday nights at a theater, a large box of fresh popcorn costs 30¢. With freshly melted butter, it costs 50¢. The total cost of producing a box of popcorn averages 10¢. The melted butter is sprayed on the regular popcorn at the time of the order. The cost of the added butter averages 8¢. Popcorn not sold must be thrown away. The demand estimates for this Saturday, expressed in probability terms, are:

Dry		Buttered	
Demand	Probability	Demand	Probability
100	.20	100	.10
200	.50	200	.30
300	.30	300	.40
		400	.20

The theater always has ample butter. How much popcorn should the theater produce? What is one evening's expected profit on popcorn?

3.14. A leather worker makes beautiful hand-tooled wallets. The materials for each wallet cost her $2. The items are sold in a nearby leather shop, and the shop owner charges $1 per wallet sold. By market-testing the wallets at two different prices, the leather worker obtained the following relative frequency estimates of daily demand:

Demand (at $5)	Probability	Demand (at $7)	Probability
3	.10	1	.10
4	.20	2	.20
5	.30	3	.40
6	.20	4	.20
7	.10		
8	.10		

Assuming that the demand estimates are acceptably accurate, which pricing policy should the leather worker use?

3.15. Twenty acres of a farmer's land is lowland marsh not suitable for crops. An oil company's geologist has conducted several tests to assess the probability of oil on this land. If oil is discovered, the 20 acres will have an estimated worth of $2 million. If oil is not discovered, the land will be worth $2,000 an acre. The oil company is willing to offer the farmer $600,000 for the property. What conclusion can be drawn regarding the geologist's assessment?

3.16. A large retail sporting goods store features tennis and camping equipment in the spring and summer and skiing equipment in the fall and winter. Spring is approaching with the store's annual ski close-out sale. A manufacturer's representative has just offered a good purchase price on some very fine skis. The store usually purchases these skis for $104 and sells them for $180. Because of an impending style change the supplier is ordering them in lot shipments of 100 pairs for $60 a pair. The store can buy up to four lot shipments.

The ski season is almost over. Before it ends, the store might sell as many as 400 of these skis at half the regular price. At this price the demand estimates are:

Demand	Probability
100	.20
200	.40
300	.30
400	.10

If they are not sold by the close of the season, the skis will have to be packed and stored in inventory to make way for camping and tennis equipment. The inventory related costs are assessed at $20 per pair of skis. In the fall, at the preseason sale, the remaining skis can be sale-priced at $110. The demand estimates are:

Demand	Probability
100	.80
200	.20

Any skis not sold can be cleared for $80.

How many skis should the store purchase? What is the *EMV*? What is the *EMV$_c$*? What is the *EVPI*?

4

The Decision Tree

Under conditions of uncertainty, Bayes' decision rule can be used to calculate an expected monetary value. For problems with numerous alternatives and similar states of nature, a more efficient approach is the conditional profit table or the opportunity loss table. Many problems, however, contain a *sequence* of dependent alternatives. In such a case, the states of nature are typically dissimilar. The conditional profit and opportunity loss tables cannot be used. Bayes' decision rule can still be applied. As the size of the problem increases, however, this basic model becomes excessively inefficient. For sequential decisions a decision tree will provide an improved expression of information and a more efficient analytical procedure.

THE STRUCTURE OF THE DECISION TREE

The decision tree simply and systematically structures the decision environment. It arranges the essential components of the decision environment into chronologically related *decision points* and *chance events*. Once the decision environment is structured, the associated payoff and probability information is inserted. Then, with the structurally defined relationships, the alternatives are evaluated and a best alternative is selected.

The following example demonstrates the construction and use of a decision tree. An investor has $25,000 and cannot borrow any additional capital. He is offered an investment opportunity (I_1) requiring $25,000, with an estimated return of either a profit of $10,000 or a loss of $10,000. The investment must be made tomorrow. The amount invested will be returned with the profit or loss in 25 days. There is a subjectively assessed probability of .60 for the profitable return. Moreover, one month hence, there is a second, similar opportunity (I_2).

It will require $20,000 with potential returns of either a $10,000 or a $4,000 profit, or a $2,000 loss. The respective probabilities for the returns are estimated at .40, .40, and .20. Again, the amount invested plus the return will be redeemable in 25 days. The investor wants to maximize his expected monetary return.

The problem can be organized in terms of the alternatives. The investor can select investment 1 (I_1), investment 2 (I_2), both investments (I_1, I_2) or no investments (NI_1, NI_2).

A_1	A_2	A_3	A_4
I_1, NI_2	NI_1, I_2	I_1, I_2	NI_1, NI_2

The criterion used to evaluate the alternatives is the EMV. Therefore, the decision-making process is directed at obtaining the respective EMV values:

A_1	A_2	A_3	A_4
EMV_1	EMV_2	EMV_3	EMV_4

The alternative with the highest EMV will be selected.

event	$p(e_i)$	payoff
profit	.6	$ 10,000
loss	.4	$-10,000
		$EMV_1 = $ $2,000

TABLE 4.1
Alternative 1: I_1, no I_2

event	$p(e_i)$	payoff
profit$_1$	.4	$10,000
profit$_2$	.4	4,000
loss$_1$	.2	-2,000
		$EMV_2 = $ $5,200

TABLE 4.2
Alternative 2: no I_1, I_2

event	$p(e_i)$	payoff
profit, profit$_1$	.24	$20,000
profit, profit$_2$	.24	14,000
profit, loss$_1$	.12	8,000
loss	.40	−10,000
		$EMV_3 = \$5,120$

TABLE 4.3
Alternative 3: I_1, I_2

It is possible to evaluate each alternative separately by Bayes' decision rule (Tables 4.1, 4.2, and 4.3). A decision tree, however, is conceptually and computationally more efficient. The construction of a decision tree begins by representing the decisions and associated events chronologically. The first decision is whether or not to enter into investment 1. This decision is represented by a *decision fork* with associated *decision branches*:

Decision   Decision
Fork   Branches

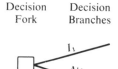

If investment 1 is selected, there is an associated *chance fork* representing the subsequent uncertain outcomes of the decision:

Chance   Chance
Fork   Branches

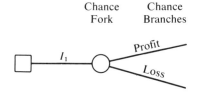

Similarly, associated with the decision branch of NI_1, there is a *chance fork* with a single *chance branch*:

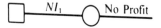

The termini of the chance branches form new decision forks. If I_1 is selected and a profit results, a choice exists between I_2 and NI_2. If I_1 is selected and a loss results, there is no choice except NI_2. The $10,000 loss would leave only $15,000 of the required $20,000. On the other hand, if I_1 is not selected, I_2 is a guaranteed opportunity (Figure 4.1).

The Decision Tree

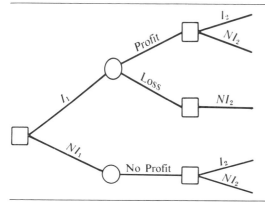

FIGURE 4.1
New Decision Forks

The termini of the decision branches form new chance forks representing the events associated with each decision. If I_2 is selected, three chance returns are possible. If NI_2 is selected, there will be no profits. Through time, the decision branches and associated chance branches systematically form a complete tree of alternatives. They map the structure of the decision environment. Figure 4.2 illustrates the *complete set of decision forks and related chance events*—the chronologically related structural components of the decision.

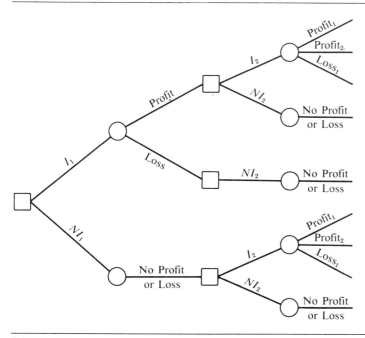

FIGURE 4.2
Sequential Structure of the Decision Environment

The Structure of the Decision Tree

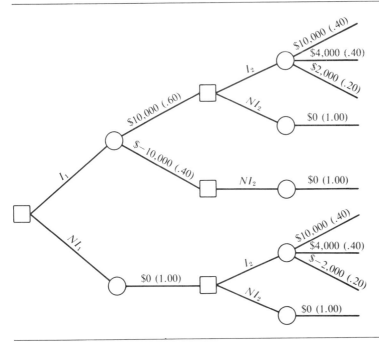

FIGURE 4.3
The Decision Tree

At the chance forks, the *relevant payoff and probability information* is added to the decision tree. Figure 4.3 illustrates the *complete decision tree*. It contains all the information essential to an alternative selection.

AVERAGING OUT AND FOLDING BACK

Once a problem has been properly structured, the relevant relationships clearly defined, and the required information gathered, the next step in the decision-making process is to analyze and evaluate the alternatives. For a decision tree, this is accomplished by a process of *backward induction* commonly referred to as *averaging out and folding back*. The last decision is made first. Incrementally, the process of decision making progresses backward from decision fork to decision fork until the first decision has been made. A selection is made between the *decision branch* alternatives at each *decision fork*. The decision branches that are not selected are blocked (//) and excluded from further consideration. The final remaining path of alternatives, the remaining *nonblocked branches of the tree*, represent the *best decision*.

The Decision Tree

In Figure 4.4 this process is applied to the present problem. The last *decision fork* contains two alternative branches: I_2 or NI_2. Evaluating the associated chance events provides:

$$I_2: EMV = \$10,000(.4) + \$4,000(.4) - \$2,000(.2)$$
$$= \$5,200$$

$$NI_2: EMV = \$0(1.00)$$
$$= \$0.$$

Obviously the I_2 decision branch is preferred. Since the NI_2 branch will never be selected, it is blocked (//) from further consideration. The expected return from the selected branch is placed above the decision fork square for further comparisons.

The analysis now proceeds to the preceding decision fork. The decision is to select either I_1 or NI_1. The branches are evaluated in terms of associated chance events and the remaining decision branch selections.

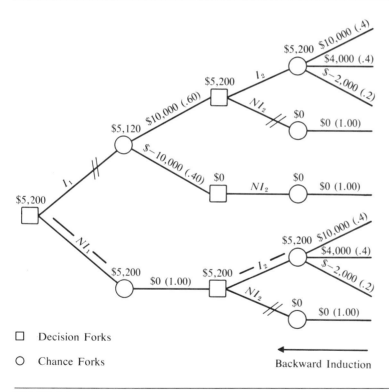

☐   Decision Forks

◯   Chance Forks

Backward Induction

FIGURE 4.4

Averaging Out and Folding Back

If I_1 is selected, there are two possible chance branches. The top branch contains a .60 chance of returning $10,000 directly and guaranteeing the decision fork at the terminus of the chance branch. The alternative at this decision fork has already been selected: I_2 with an EMV of $5,200. Therefore, there is a .60 chance of a return of $10,000 plus a guarantee of I_2 with an expected return of $5,200. The bottom branch contains a .40 chance of a loss of $10,000 and an expected return of zero from the subsequent remaining decision branch. The expected return from the I_1 branch is therefore:

$$EMV = .60(\$10,000 + \$5,200) + .40(\$-10,000 + \$0)$$
$$= \$5,120.$$

The NI_1 branch will result in no direct return plus a guarantee of the following decision fork (I_2) with an EMV of $5,200. The EMV for the NI_1 branch is:

$$EMV = 1.00(0 + 5,200)$$
$$= \$5,200.$$

Considering all possible influences, the NI_1 branch is preferred. The I_1 branch is therefore blocked. With no preceding decision forks, the remaining unblocked decision branches represent the best set of alternatives. I_1 should not be selected in order to guarantee sufficient funds for I_2.

THE DECISION TREE FOR DECISION MAKING

A second example will clarify the application, flexibility, and generality of the decision tree. The top management of an organization must decide on the size of a new plant in order to develop a new product line. The new facility must satisfy the market demand for the next eight years. The decision has been reduced to the choice between a large plant and a small plant. The market demand over the period has been classified as either high, moderate, or low.

With the specified decision environment, this information is ready to be structured with a decision tree. The decision fork will contain two branches: the large plant (Lp) and the small plant (Sp). Each of these branches has similar chance forks representing the potential levels of demand: high (H_D), moderate (M_D), or low (L_D). The decision tree becomes:

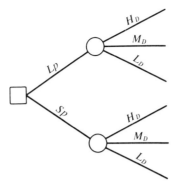

It provides a network of the alternatives and associated events.

The next step is to evaluate the alternatives with an *EMV* criterion:

A_1: *Lp* $EMV_L =$

A_2: *Sp* $EMV_S =$

Before making the *EMV* calculations, the decision maker must obtain the probabilities and payoffs for the chance branches. Marketing estimates provide the probabilities:

Level of Demand	Probabilities
High	.50
Moderate	.30
Low	.20

Engineering estimates provide an estimated present value cost of $2 million for the large plant and of $.8 million for the small plant.[1] The present value of discounted cash flows at 12 percent for the eight-year period (excluding the plant cost) are expressed as a function of demand. They are:

Return: Present Value ($ millions)		
Demand	Large Plant	Small Plant
High	$4.2	$2.0
Moderate	2.8	2.0
Low	1.4	1.4

---

[1] The cost estimates include such considerations as direct costs, financing cost, and the discounted salvage value.

Considering construction costs, the estimated potential returns from the investments are:

Net Return (profit minus facility cost) ($ millions)

Demand	Large Plant	Small Plant
High	$2.2	$1.2
Moderate	.8	1.2
Low	− .6	.6

The probability and payoff information are added to the decision tree at the chance branches:

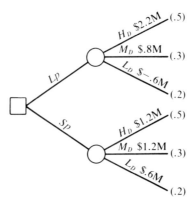

Averaging out and folding back provides *EMV* evaluations at the chance forks (Table 4.4, Figure 4.5). As indicated in Figure 4.5, the best alternative is the large plant, with an estimated present value of $1.22 million.

Demand	$p(e_i)$	A_1: Lp	A_2: Sp
H_D	.5	$2.2M	$1.2M
M_D	.3	.8M	1.2M
L_D	.2	− .6M	.6M
		$EMV_L = 1.22M*$	$EMV_S = 1.08M$

TABLE 4.4

The *EMV* Comparisons

The Decision Tree

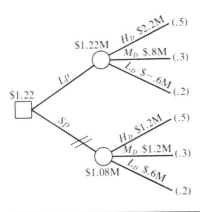

FIGURE 4.5
Selecting the Best Alternative

The Decision to Obtain Sample Information

In the foregoing example, given no additional information, the decision is to construct a large plant. If a high demand does actually occur, this is the correct choice. However, if demand is only moderate, a small plant with an expected return of $1.2 million will be preferable to a large plant with an expected return of $.8 million. And if demand is low, the small plant ($.6 million) will again be preferable to the large plant ($−.6 million). Therefore, unless demand is high, the large plant should not be constructed. Knowledge of the actual demand might improve the decision (Table 4.5).

Demand	Proper Construction Decision	Expected Return
H_D	Lp	$2.2M
M_D	Sp	1.2M
L_D	Sp	.6M

TABLE 4.5
The Correct Plant Decision

A market survey could be conducted to improve the assessment of demand and thereby improve the organization's chance of making a proper decision. The marketing department estimates that a *sufficiently reliable* survey will cost approximately $100,000. Is the *additional information* worth the cost?

The Expected Value of Perfect Information

To answer this question, the maximum potential worth of the survey is computed. If the survey costs exceed the maximum potential benefit, a more complex analysis can be avoided.

The survey will provide information that will reduce the uncertainty of demand. The statistic measuring the cost of uncertainty is *the expected value of perfect information (EVPI)*.

As was previously indicated, the *EVPI* is derived by subtracting the *expected return with the information* from the *expected return without the information*:

Expected Monetary Value Under Certainty (EMV_c)

Expected Monetary Value Under Uncertainty (EMV_u)

Expected Value of Perfect Information ($EVPI$)

The expected return with a perfect survey minus the expected return without any survey must be the worth of a perfect survey.

If the *actual* demand were known in advance, the organization could be guaranteed the right decision. If a high demand were known (H_D), a large plant would be constructed. Similarly, if a moderate (M_D) or low demand (L_D) were known, the small plant would be the decision (Table 4.5). Under certainty, the *EMV* is:

Demand	Probability	Decision and $ Return
H_D	.50	Lp ($2.2M)
M_D	.30	Sp ($1.2M)
L_D	.20	Sp ($ .6M)
		EMV_c = $1.58M

Under certainty, the correct alternative selections will yield an EMV_c of $1.58 million.

Under uncertainty, the decision will be the single alternative selection with the highest *EMV*. From the earlier analysis, the decision will be to construct the large plant with an EMV_u of $1.22 million.

With complete information, with a perfect prediction of demand, the *EMV* will be $1.58 million. With incomplete information, under uncertain demand conditions, the expected return is $1.22 million. The information, the perfect predictor, must be worth the difference:

$$
\begin{aligned}
EMV_c &= \$1.58M \\
-EMV_u &= \ \ 1.22M \\
\hline
EVPI &= \$ \ .36M
\end{aligned}
$$

Perfect information concerning demand has a maximum potential worth of $360,000. The survey providing additional information costs $100,000. If the survey will provide *enough* additional information, it will be worth the cost. A closer investigation appears warranted.

Structuring the New Decision Environment

The survey will provide *improved*, not *perfect*, information. The reliability of the survey must be incorporated into the analysis. A decision tree will facilitate the structuring of the expanded decision environment.

The survey will indicate one of three levels of demand: high demand (S_{HD}), moderate demand (S_{MD}), and low demand (S_{LD}). These are represented as a new chance fork on the original decision tree:

Given the survey prediction, the same decision fork for plant size and chance fork for demands will occur. Figure 4.6 illustrates the new survey branches on the expanded decision tree.

Following the structuring, the respective alternatives at the decision forks are analyzed. This will require payoff and probability information for the calculation of comparative *EMV* values.

The payoffs create no difficulty. They are the same as those provided earlier. They are added to the decision tree in Figure 4.7.

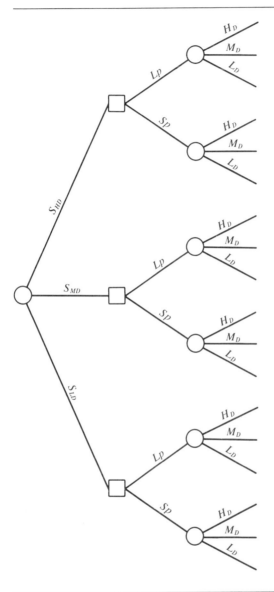

FIGURE 4.6
The Decision Tree with Survey Branches

Probability Calculations at Chance Forks

Two types of chance fork probabilities require evaluation. The first are *the probabilities of the survey results:* $P(S_{HD})$, $P(S_{MD})$, $P(S_{LD})$. The second are *the probabilities of the actual demand conditions given the survey results:*

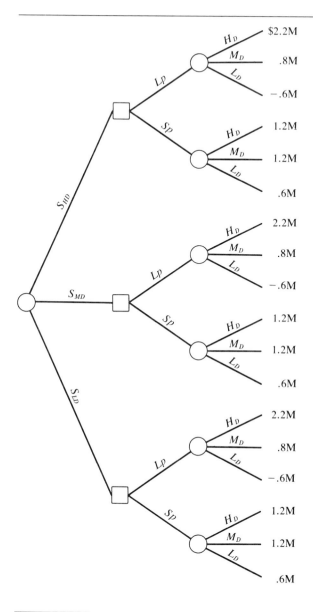

FIGURE 4.7
The Decision Tree with Payoffs

$P(H_D \mid S_{HD})$, $P(M_D \mid S_{HD})$, $P(L_D \mid S_{HD})$, . . . , $P(L_D \mid S_{LD})$. Both of these types of probabilities require careful consideration.

Since the survey will not produce perfectly accurate predictions, the assessment of the probability of survey results contains added complications.

The reliability and potential bias of the survey must be built into these assessments.

From past experience and unique expectations, the research group must provide *estimates of survey reliability*. In this case, the following assessments have been provided. If demand is truly high, the conditional probability that the survey will correctly predict a high demand is .80. Similarly, the probability that the survey will *incorrectly* predict a moderate and low demand are .15 and .05, respectively:

Survey Prediction (S)	Actual High Demand (H_D)
High (S_{HD})	$P(S_{HD} \mid H_D) = .80$
Moderate (S_{MD})	$P(S_{MD} \mid H_D) = .15$
Low (S_{LD})	$P(S_{LD} \mid H_D) = .05$
	1.00

The reliability of the survey results for the other demand conditions is summarized in Table 4.6.

Survey Result (S)	Actual Demand High (H_D)	Moderate (M_D)	Low (L_D)
S_{HD}	.80	.20	.10
S_{MD}	.15	.70	.20
S_{LD}	.05	.10	.70

TABLE 4.6
Conditional Probabilities: $P(S_D/D)$

With this information it is possible to determine the *probabilities of the survey results*: $P(S_{HD})$, $P(S_{MD})$, and $P(S_{LD})$. Each of these can be calculated as the probability of a *compound event*. Using the five-step procedure outlined in Chapter 2, the probability that the survey will predict a *high demand* is systematically derived. There are three ways of getting a survey prediction of high demand: (1) actual high demand and a correct high prediction, (2) moderate demand and an incorrect high prediction, and (3) low demand and an incorrect high prediction. With this in mind, the first three steps are:

(1) $P(S_{HD}) = P(H_D \cap S_{HD}$ OR

(2) $P(S_{HD}) = P(H_D \cap S_{HD}$ OR $M_D \cap S_{HD}$ OR $L_D \cap S_{HD})$

(3) $P(S_{HD}) = P(H_D \cap S_{HD}) + P(M_D \cap S_{HD}) + P(L_D \cap S_{HD})$
$= P(H_D)P(S_{HD} \mid H_D) + P(M_D)P(S_{HD} \mid M_D) + P(L_D)P(S_{HD} \mid L_D).$

Using the originally assessed prior probabilities of H_D, M_D, and L_D (Table 4.4) and the conditional probabilities (Table 4.6), the remaining two steps are:

(4) $P(S_{HD}) = (.5)(.8) + (.3)(.2) + (.2)(.1)$

(5) $P(S_{HD}) = .40 + .06 + .02$
$= .48.$

The probability that the survey will predict a high demand is .48.

The probability of the other two chance events is obtained similarly. The probability that the survey will predict a moderate demand is:

$P(S_{MD}) = P(H_D \cap S_{MD} \text{ OR } M_D \cap S_{MD} \text{ OR } L_D \cap S_{MD})$
$= P(H_D \cap S_{MD}) + P(M_D \cap S_{MD}) + P(L_D \cap S_{MD})$
$= .075 + .210 + .040$
$= .325.$

Similar calculations provide $P(S_{LD})$.

Table 4.7 summarizes the complete set of probability information. It will serve as a valuable reference to a decision maker seeking probability information.

| | | Actual Demand (D) | | | Marginal Prob: |
		H_D	M_D	L_D	$P(S_D)$
Survey Prediction (S_D)	S_{HD}	$P(S_{HD} \cap H_D) =$ .40	$P(S_{HD} \cap M_D) =$ .06	$P(S_{HD} \cap L_D) =$ .02	$P(S_{HD}) = .480$
	S_{MD}	$P(S_{MD} \cap H_D) =$ .075	$P(S_{MD} \cap M_D) =$ .21	$P(S_{MD} \cap L_D) =$ .04	$P(S_{MD}) = .325$
	S_{LD}	$P(S_{LD} \cap H_D) =$ .025	$P(S_{LD} \cap M_D) =$ .03	$P(S_{LD} \cap L_D) =$ .14	$P(S_{LD}) = .195$
		$P(H_D) = .5$	$P(M_D) = .3$	$P(L_D) = .2$	1.00

TABLE 4.7
Joint Probability Table: $P(D \cap S_D) = P(D)P(S_D/D)$

The probabilities of the survey results are introduced at the chance fork:

These assessments take into account both the *initial prior probabilities for demand conditions* and the *accuracy and reliability of the survey*.

The information needed for averaging out and folding back is almost complete. The probabilities at the last chance forks are still required. The uppermost of these is:

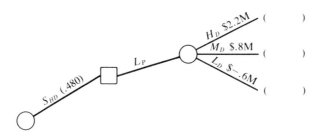

The probabilities of H_D, M_D and L_D require computation.

The probability of H_D was initially assessed as .50. On this branch, the survey has predicted a high demand (S_{HD}). The initial *prior probability* should be adjusted for the survey. If the survey provided perfect predictions, the probability of H_D would be adjusted to 1—the survey result would infer the actual demand. The survey however, will not provide a perfect prediction. There will be some potential inaccuracy. If the survey predicts a high demand (S_{HD}), the occurrence of H_D is not guaranteed—the $P(H_D) < 1$. The probability of H_D at the chance fork will be the *prior probability of H_D adjusted for the survey conclusion*—the conditional probability, $P(H_D \mid S_{HD})$:

Prior Probability + Information → Conditional Probability
(adjusted prior probability)

$P(H_D)$ + survey conclusion (S_{HD}) = $P(H_D \mid S_{HD})$.

The calculus of probability provides an exact measure of the conditional probability:

$$P(H_D \mid S_{HD}) = \frac{P(H_D \cap S_{HD})}{P(S_{HD})}.$$

In this expression the numerator is a *joint probability* and the denominator is a *marginal probability*. Since the joint probability table (Table 4.7) contains all joint and marginal probabilities, it will furnish the information required for the computation:

$$P(H_D \mid S_{HD}) = \frac{P(H_D \cap S_{HD})}{P(S_{HD})}$$

$$= \frac{.400}{.480}$$

$$= .833.$$

With the aid of the joint probability table, the conditional probabilities for the other two branches are similarly derived.

$$P(M_D \mid S_{HD}) = \frac{P(M_D \cap S_{HD})}{P(S_{HD})}$$

$$= \frac{.060}{.480}$$

$$= .125$$

and

$$P(L_D \mid S_{HD}) = \frac{P(L_D \cap S_{HD})}{P(S_{HD})}$$

$$= \frac{.020}{.480}$$

$$= .042.$$

The probabilities at this uppermost chance fork are now complete (Figure 4.8). The probabilities at the other chance forks are computed.[2] Figure 4.9 represents the complete decision tree with all survey information.

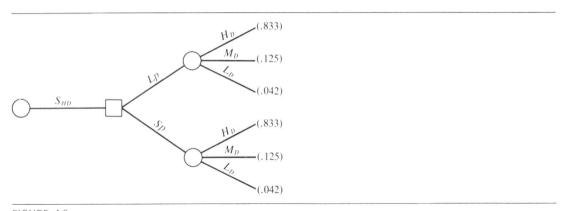

FIGURE 4.8

The Decision Tree with Conditional Probabilities

[2] A note on the conditional probability calculations for this collectively exhaustive set of events:

$$P(H_D \mid S_{MD}) = \frac{P(H_D \cap S_{MD})}{P(S_{MD})}$$

$$= \frac{\boxed{P(H_D \cap S_{MD})}}{\boxed{P(H_D \cap S_{MD})} + P(M_D \cap S_{MD}) + P(L_D \cap S_{MD})}$$

$$P(M_D \mid S_{MD}) = \frac{\boxed{P(M_D \cap S_{MD})}}{P(H_D \cap S_{MD}) + \boxed{P(M_D \cap S_{MD})} + P(L_D \cap S_{MD})}$$

$$P(L_D \mid S_{MD}) = \frac{\boxed{P(L_D \cap S_{MD})}}{P(H_D \cap S_{MD}) + P(M_D \cap S_{MD}) + \boxed{P(L_D \cap S_{MD})}}$$

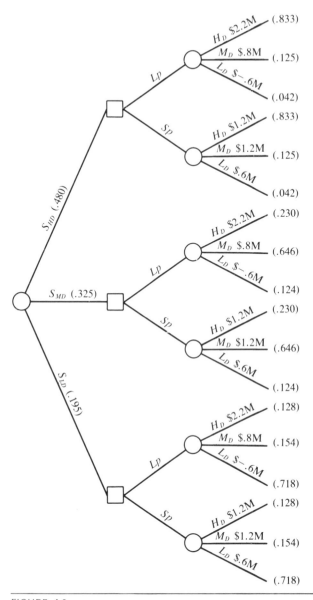

FIGURE 4.9

The Decision Tree with Information

Averaging Out and Folding Back

With a decision tree complete with information, the decision forks are analyzed by averaging out and folding back. The *EMV*s for the last decision are calculated first (Figure 4.10). The decision branch with the highest *EMV* is selected. The other branches are blocked (Figure 4.11).

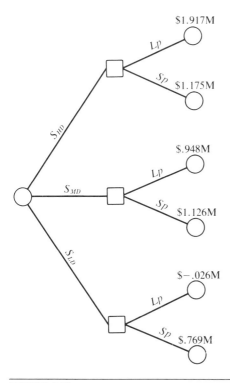

FIGURE 4.10
The Last Decision First

If the survey predicts a high demand (S_{HD}), the decision will be to construct a large plant with an expected return of $1.917 million. If the survey predicts a moderate or low demand (S_{MD} or S_{LD}), the decision will be to construct a small plant with an expected return of $1.126 million or $.769 million.

The expected return at the chance fork of survey results can now be evaluated. Table 4.8 provides an EMV of $1.436 million. If the survey is conducted, excluding survey costs, there will be an expected return of $1.436 million.

The first decision—whether to conduct the survey—can now be made. The entire decision tree is illustrated in Figure 4.12. If no survey is conducted, the large plant with an EMV of $1.22 million will be built. If the survey is conducted, the survey will determine the plant decision. If a high demand is predicted (S_{HD}), the large plant will be built. If a moderate or low demand is predicted (S_{MD} or S_{LD}), the small plant will be built. With the survey information, these decisions provide an EMV of $1.436 million. Since the survey can be conducted for $100,000, the net expected return for the survey option is $1.336 million. This exceeds the net expected return for the no-survey option ($1.22 million). The survey should be conducted.

The Decision Tree for Decision Making

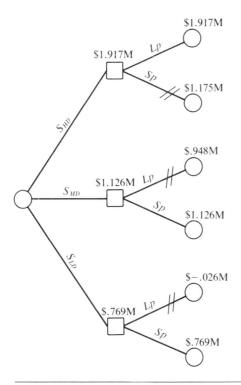

FIGURE 4.11
Selecting the Best Decision Branch

Events	$p(e_i)$	$\$_i(M)$
S_{HD}	.480	1.917
S_{MD}	.325	1.126
S_{LD}	.195	.769
		$EMV = \$1.436M$

TABLE 4.8
Survey Chance Fork

The Decision Tree

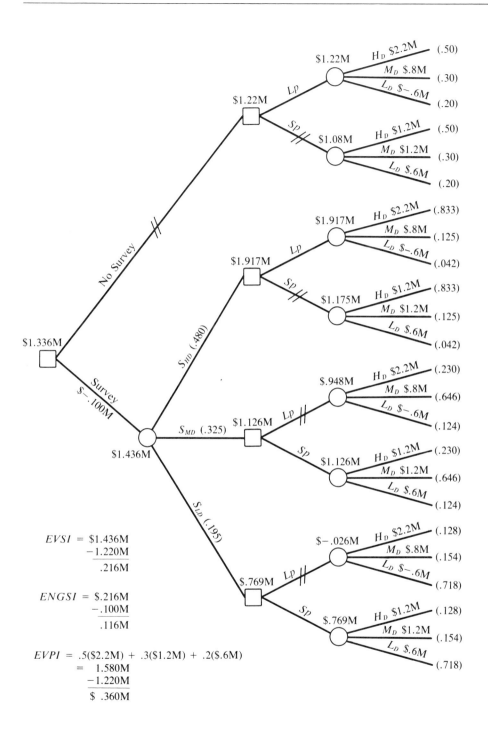

FIGURE 4.12
The Decision Tree Analysis

The Expected Value of Sample Information

In the foregoing analysis, the worth of the survey *to improve the alternative selection* can be expressed by a commonly used statistic: *the expected value of sample information (EVSI)*. Conceptually, the *EVSI* can be derived by the logic used to derive the *EVPI*. The expected return with the information is compared to the expected return without the information. The difference is the expected value of the information. If no survey is conducted, the best decision will produce an *EMV* of $1.22 million. If the survey is conducted to obtain sample information, the best set of alternatives will produce an *EMV* of $1.436 million. The sample information creating the difference must be worth:

Return with Sampling $1.436M

− Return Without Sampling   1.220M

Value of Sample Information (*EVSI*) = $ .216M

Another related statistic used to measure the desirability of sampling is *the expected net gain from sample information (ENGSI)*. By including the cost of the sample, it measures the net benefit:

ENGSI = *EVSI* − cost of sample information.

Quantitatively, it is:

ENGSI = $216,000 − $100,000
         = $116,000.

In this case the decision to sample improves the best alternative by $116,000. As long as the *ENGSI* is positive, obtaining sample information will be an improved choice.

PREPOSTERIOR ANALYSIS

Preposterior analysis is a process of investigating the consequences of a decision prior to making the decision. The previous market survey is an example. The consequences of the survey were investigated prior to conducting the survey. Before making a decision about the survey, the best set of alternatives for assumed survey results was determined and evaluated. The economic worth of the survey information was also measured.

To clarify the use of the decision tree in preposterior analysis, consider an acceptance sampling problem. An ongoing production process produces a large number of units of a product. The process is either in control or out of control. If it is in control, 98 percent of the machined products will meet quality standards, and 2 percent will be defectives. If the process is out of control, past records indicate that the expected level of *good* items will be reduced to 80 percent.

There are two potential difficulties. First, if the process is out of control and left unadjusted, contracted reliability standards will not be maintained. The resulting costs of customer complaints, 100 percent inspection of certain groups of output, and other associated costs are estimated at $400. Second, if the process is in control and is shut down unnecessarily, past records reveal that the down time spent looking for a nonexistent cause will average $120.

The production process is reset for large production lots every four hours. From past records, the process was set properly and remained in control 90 percent of the time. In the remaining 10 percent of the time, it was set improperly or it went out of control shortly after the production run had begun. The production manager would like to develop a proper decision rule for this process. One consideration is to obtain sample information. Specifically, the manager wants to evaluate the possibility of sampling two items shortly after the process has begun a new run. Table 4.9 summarizes the relevant information.

Production State	Relative Frequency	Probability of Defective | State
Control (C)	.90	$P(d|C)$ = .02
Out of Control (OC)	.10	$P(d|OC)$ = .20

Costs:		
Out of Control Process Run	Shut Down Control Process	Sample (n=2)
$400	$120	$8

TABLE 4.9

The Production Process

The first step in evaluating this option is to construct a decision tree. The first decision is to sample (S) or not to sample (NS). If no sample is taken, the second decision will be to continue the process (C_T) or to stop the process (S_T). Associated with each of these decision branches is a chance fork with two chance branches: in control (C) and out of control (OC).

If the sample pf two items is taken, at the sample chance fork there will be three chance events: no defectives ($d = 0$), one defective ($d = 1$), or two defectives ($d = 2$). Associated with each of these chance events will be a decision fork with continue (C_T) and stop (S_T) branches. Each of these decision branches in turn contains a chance fork with two chance branches: in control (C) and out of control (OC). Figure 4.13 indicates the structure of the decision tree.

The next step is to include the cost and probability information for the averaging out and folding back. To provide an alternative approach and to

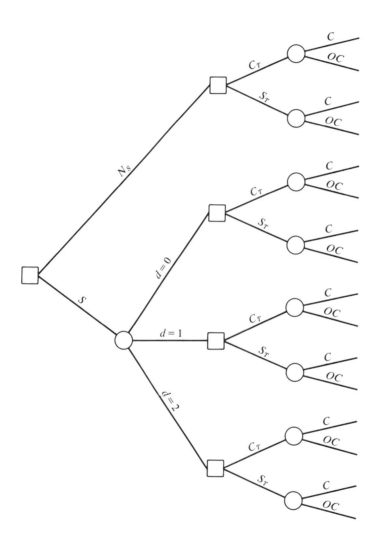

FIGURE 4.13
The Structure of the Decision Environment

State of Nature	Action Selected	
	Continue (C_T)	Stop (S_T)
Control (C)	$ 0	$120
Out of Control (OC)	400	0

TABLE 4.10

Opportunity Loss Table

facilitate computations, the payoffs will be expressed as opportunity losses (Table 4.10).

The required probability information is most easily expressed in a joint probability table (Table 4.11). In this table the marginal probabilities correspond to the sample results. The conditional probabilities at the terminus chance branches of the tree are derived by a single division. For example:

$$P(C \mid 0d) = \frac{P(C \cap 0d)}{P(0d)}.$$

Reading the numerator and denominator from the joint probability table:

$$P(C \mid 0d) = \frac{.8643}{.9283}$$

$$= .9311.$$

The other conditional probabilities are derived similarly.

The payoff and probability information is now added to the decision tree. Complete with averaging out and folding back, the final tree is represented in Figure 4.14. The best decision is to sample. If no defectives are discovered, the

State of Nature	Sample Result # defectives			
	d = 0	d = 1	d = 2	Marginal Prob.
Control (C)	.8643	.0353	.0004	$P(C)$ = .90
Out of Control (OC)	.0640	.0320	.0040	$P(OC)$ = .10
Marginal Prob.	.9283	.0673	.0044	1.00

TABLE 4.11

Joint Probability Table

process should be continued, with an expected opportunity loss of $27.56. If one or two defectives are discovered, the process should be stopped, with expected opportunity losses of $62.94 and $10.91 respectively. The probabilities for each of these three decisions are indicated on the sample chance branches. The expected opportunity loss from sampling is:

$$EOL = .9283(\$27.56) + .0673(\$62.94) + .0044(\$10.91)$$
$$= \$29.87.$$

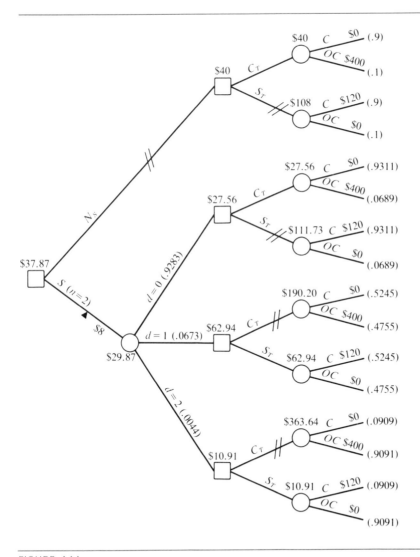

FIGURE 4.14
The Decision to Sample

The sample of two items will cost $8. The total expected opportunity loss will be $37.87. The decision not to sample and to let the process continue has an *EOL* of $40. The decision to sample is preferable.

Sampling Statistics

Three important statistics are associated with the decision to sample: the *EVPI*, the *EVSI*, and the *ENGSI*. All three statistics are easily computed from the information presented in Figure 4.14.

The *EVPI* can be read directly from the top decision fork of the decision tree. With perfect information—if the true state of the process was always known—the correct decision would always be made. If the process was in control, it would be allowed to continue. If the process was out of control, it would be stopped:

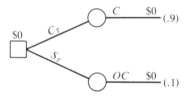

Under *certainty*, the expected opportunity loss would be $0.

If a decision must be made under *uncertainty*, however, the process will be continued with an *EOL$_u$* of $40:

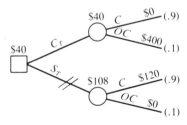

The *EVPI* will be the difference between the expected return under certainty and the expected return under uncertainty:

$$
\begin{aligned}
EOL_u &= \$40 \\
-EOL_c &= 0 \\
\hline
EVPI &= \$40 \quad .
\end{aligned}
$$

The maximum value of the additional information is $40. Since the problem has been expressed in terms of opportunity losses, the *EVPI* is the decision fork value on the no-sample (*NS*) branch.

The *EVSI* is also readily obtainable from the decision tree. Without sample information the best decision is to continue the process with an EOL_u of $40. With sample information the decision is to continue if there are no defectives; otherwise, to stop. With the sample information, the EOL_s is reduced to $29.87. The *EVSI* must be:

$$\begin{array}{rl} EOL_u = & \$40.00 \\ -EOL_s = & \$29.87 \\ \hline EVSI = & \$10.13 \end{array}$$

The expected value of sample information is $10.13. It cost $8 to take the sample. The *ENGSI* is:

$$\begin{aligned} ENGSI &= EVSI - \text{cost of sample} \\ &= \$10.13 - \$8 \\ &= \$\ 2.13. \end{aligned}$$

An Optimal Sampling Plan

Since a sample of two items has improved the decision rule, a larger sample might improve the decision even further. The maximum potential gained from sampling is the *EVPI* of $40. The sample of two items has accounted for only part of this potential: $10.13 to be exact. A potential exists for a larger sample to improve the decision.

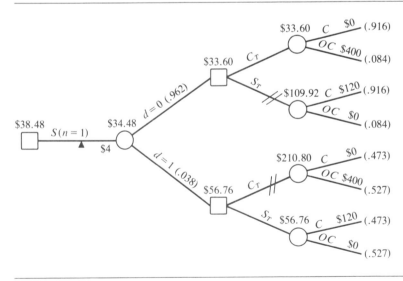

FIGURE 4.15
Sampling Plan ($n = 1$)

In determining the optimal sample size, two basic opposing costs must be considered. As the sample size increases, the additional information reduces the uncertainty and improves the decision. As the sample size increases, however, so does the sampling cost. Preposterior analysis will evaluate the net economic effect of different sample sizes.

For a sample (n) of only one, Figure 4.15 indicates the complete analysis. The decision rule is to stop the process for a defective with an EOL_{s1} of $38.48. If n is increased to three, the decision rule is to stop the process for any defectives with an EOL_{s3} of $38.80 (Figure 4.16). Comparing the three sampling plans, Table 4.12 indicates that a sample of two items is preferred.

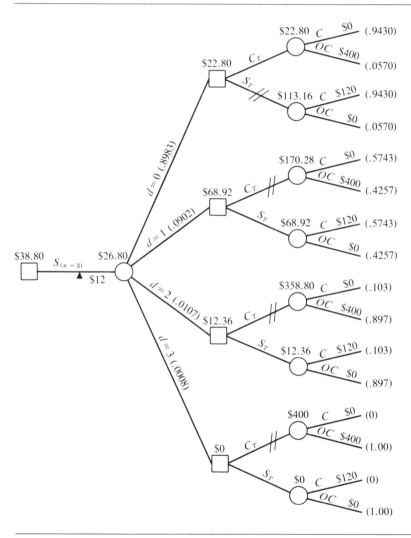

FIGURE 4.16

Sampling Plan (n = 3)

Sample Size	EOL_s at chance fork	Sample Cost	Net EOL_s
$n = 1$	$34.48	4	$38.48
$n = 2$	29.87	8	37.87*
$n = 3$	26.80	12	38.80

TABLE 4.12
Evaluation of the Sampling Plans

As the sample size increases, the EOL_s at the chance fork will be reduced less and less. Since the cost of sampling remains constant, any sample larger than two items will decrease the cost of uncertainty at the chance fork by less than the cost of the information. Samples of more than two items are not economically justified.

THE ECONOMIC WORTH OF AN IMPROVED ALTERNATIVE

In calculating the *EVPI* or the *EVSI*, a comparison is made between the expectation with additional information and the expectation without additional information. If the information improves the decision, the information is imputed a worth of the difference in improved expectation. This same logic can be extended beyond the evaluation of additional information to include any resource that improves the decision. This more general paradigm is the expected value of a resource providing an improved alternative (*EVR*).

Reconsider the investment decision expressed in Figure 4.4. The investor has $25,000 in available funds. Investment 1 (I_1) requires $25,000. At the end of the month, these funds are returned with a gain of $10,000 or a loss of $10,000. Investment 2 ($I_2$) requires $20,000. It will occur shortly after the return from I_1. Note that if I_1 is selected and $10,000 lost, there will only be $15,000 of remaining capital. Investment 2 will not be possible (Figure 4.4). The lack of capital will restrict this alternative. If removing this restriction will improve the final decision, the means of removing it will have an expected economic worth: the *expected value of a resource* (*EVR*).

If the investor can borrow $5,000, the alternatives will be improved (Figure 4.17). If the $20,000 capital is available, the decision will be changed from NI_1 and I_2 (Figure 4.4) to I_1 and I_2 (Figure 4.17). The expected worth of the option

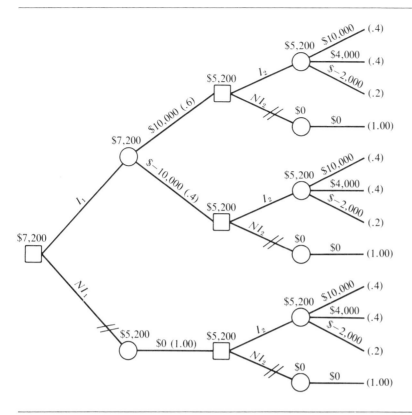

FIGURE 4.17
Borrowing Permissible

to borrow $5,000—the expected value of the improved alternative—must be the difference in expectations (Figure 4.17):

$$
\begin{aligned}
EMV_{I_1, I_2} &= \$7,200 \\
-EMV_{NI_1, I_2} &= \$5,200 \\
\hline
EVR &= \$2,000 \quad .
\end{aligned}
$$

Whenever money, information, or any other resource can be used to improve the alternatives, the expected worth of that resource can be evaluated:

$$
EVR = EMV_{\text{posterior}} - EMV_{\text{prior}}.
$$

If the resource can be made available for less than the EVR, the decision can be improved.

SUMMARY

To analyze different decision environments efficiently, the decision maker needs specialized tools. For a decision environment containing a sequence of related decisions, the decision tree is a most effective modeling device. Expressed in terms of decision points with associated chance events, the decision tree chronologically structures all relevant relationships in the decision environment. With the inclusion of associated payoff and probability information, the fully defined decision environment can be analyzed by averaging out and folding back.

A decision tree may also facilitate the evaluation of experimentation or other activities designed to improve the decision. Important summary statistics are the *EVPI*, the *EVSI*, the *ENGSI*, and the *EVR*. They are used to determine the economic feasibility of obtaining additional information, the optimal quantity of additional information, or the value of any resource improving the decision.

BIBLIOGRAPHY

Gupta, S. K., and J. M. Cozzolino. *Fundamentals of Operations Research for Management*. San Francisco: Holden-Day, 1974.

Hamburg, M. *Statistical Analysis for Decision Making*. New York: Harcourt, Brace, Jovanovich, 1970.

Magee, J. F. "Decision Trees For Decision Making," *Harvard Business Review*, July–August, 1964, pp. 126–138.

————. "How to Use Decision Trees in Capital Investment," *Harvard Business Review*, September–October, 1964, pp. 79–96.

Paik, C. M. *Quantitative Methods for Managerial Decisions*. New York: McGraw-Hill Book Co., 1973.

Pratt, J., H. Raiffa, and R. Schlaifer. *Introduction to Statistical Decision Theory*. New York: McGraw-Hill Book Co., 1965.

Raiffa, H. *Decision Analysis: Introductory Lectures on Choices Under Uncertainty*. Reading, Mass.: Addison-Wesley Publishing Co., 1968.

Schlaifer, R. *Analysis of Decisions Under Uncertainty*. New York: McGraw-Hill Book Co., 1969.

————. *Probability and Statistics for Business Decisions*. New York: McGraw-Hill Book Co., 1959.

Spurr, W. A., and C. P. Bonini. *Statistical Analysis for Business Decisions*. Homewood, Ill.: Richard D. Irwin, 1973.

Trueman, R. E. *An Introduction to Quantitative Methods for Decision Making*. New York: Holt, Rinehart & Winston, 1974.

4.1. A game is played with a coin and a die. The coin is tossed first. If a tail appears, the player loses $10 and the game is over. If a head appears, the player wins $10 and has the option of (a) receiving an additional $100, or (b) rolling a die. If the die is rolled, the payoffs are (a) $1,000 for rolling a six and (b) a loss of $360 for rolling a one.

Construct a decision tree to indicate the best decision and the value of the game.

4.2. A company is considering two strategies for selling a new industrial product. One alternative is to have a sales representative demonstrate the product and provide the potential client with a free sample. The sample will cost the company $120. The other alternative is to demonstrate the product and attempt to sell it for the normal $100 profit. The probability of a sale is assessed as .40. If the product is used, there is an 80 percent chance of acquiring a client with the present value of repeat purchases estimated at $2,000. If it is not used, no future sales are assumed.

Construct a decision tree to find the appropriate sales strategy. At what probability of a sale will the two strategies be monetarily equivalent?

4.3. You have been selected as a lucky winner in a contest. You have the option of receiving a $50 bill or of selecting a bill at random from container 1 or container 2. If you draw a bill from one of the containers, the bill is yours and the game is over. If you draw a piece of paper, you are offered another choice: $100 or a draw from container 3.

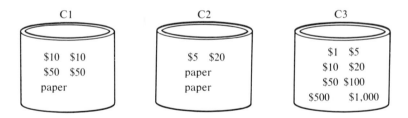

Indicate the best decision with a clearly labeled decision tree.

4.4. An investor has $80,000. Two known investment opportunities will occur at the beginning of each of the next two months:

Time	Investment	Cost	Payoff	Probability
1st month	1	$80,000	$ − 40,000	.60
			20,000	.40
2nd month	2	$100,000	20,000	.20
			40,000	.30
			60,000	.40
			− 20,000	.10

The initial investment will be refunded along with the payoff at the end of each month. *No money can be borrowed.*

Using a decision tree to represent the decision environment, find the best decision and the expected return.

If $20,000 could be borrowed, what is the maximum an *EMV*'er might rationally pay for this loan?

4.5. An investor is contemplating the purchase of a block of 100 shares of a common stock. The purchase will be made either today at the close of trading or tomorrow. The present near-closing price is $54 a share. Tomorrow the price is expected to be either $56 or $51 depending on evolving economic climates.

Express the investor's problem in a decision tree.

If the investor is unwilling to assign an exact probability to tomorrow's prices, over what range of probabilities for the drop in price should he wait to buy tomorrow?

4.6. A proposed advertising campaign is nearing the final decision stages. Sufficient benefit must be substantiated before the project will receive the go-ahead. The probability of sufficient benefit is .70, and of insufficient benefit, .30. Precampaign testing has been conducted. The reliability of the results is:

	Actual State	
Pretesting Result	Sufficient Benefit	Insufficient Benefit
Favorable	.80	.35
Unfavorable	.20	.65

If the pretest results are favorable, adjust the probabilities for the advertising campaign.

4.7. An investor has $60,000 and the following investment opportunities:

Investment	Cost	Entry	Exit	Payoff	Probability
1	$25,000	Today	10 days	$ 10,000	.50
				− 12,000	.50
2	71,000	11 days	12 days	60,000	.60
				40,000	.30
				20,000	.10

The investment, at the indicated cost, must be made on the entry date to be returned with a payoff on the exit date. Only one potential source for additional funds is available. A lender offers the investor the following loan contract to be agreed upon today: If the profitable return occurs for investment 1, $1,000 will be loaned for the one-day duration of investment 2. Payment is required immediately following the loan period.

What is the maximum the investor would pay for a 50 percent chance to borrow $1,000 for one day? What kind of loan contract should the investor seek?

4.8. Over the next six-month period, four investment opportunities will become available. In three days from now, investments 1, 3, and 4 have entry dates sequentially spaced at two-month intervals. Each investment will have a duration of two months minus four days. Investment 2 will begin in 15 days and last for one month and six days. In all cases, the capital must remain invested until the end of the period. The cash requirements, return over investment, and probabilities are:

Investment	Cash Requirements	Return	Probability
1	$100,000	$ 20,000	.80
		− 10,000	.20
2	100,000	40,000	.70
		− 30,000	.30
3	80,000	24,000	.60
		16,000	.30
		− 20,000	.10
4	140,000	60,000	.50
		40,000	.30
		20,000	.10
		− 10,000	.10

Only $100,000 is available for investment. No funds can be borrowed.

1. What set of investments should be selected? What is the expected monetary return?
2. If some presently held assets could be sold immediately for $20,000 at an anticipated loss of $15,000, should the same investments be selected?
3. Each investment can be entered into only once. If $200,000 were available, which set of investments should be selected? What would be the expected monetary gain?

4.9. An oil wildcatter must decide whether or not to drill at a new site. The hole will be either dry, wet, or a gusher. The subjectively based net returns and probabilities are:

State of Hole	Return	Probability
Dry	$ − 100,000	.60
Wet	180,000	.30
Gusher	800,000	.10

1. Construct a decision tree to find the appropriate course of action and the expected monetary return.

2. Construct a decision tree under conditions of certainty. What is the EMV_c? What is the $EVPI$?

4.10. Refer to the situation described in Problem 4.9. The wildcatter has another option. For $20,000 seismic sounding of the geological structure can be conducted. The reliability of the test is:

Seismic Indication of Geological Structure	Actual State of the Hole Dry	Wet	Gusher
Poor	.70	.20	.10
Good	.25	.60	.50
Excellent	.05	.20	.40

For example, if the hole is actually dry, the probability that the seismic indication will be poor is .70: $P(\text{poor} \mid \text{dry}) = .70$.

1. Construct a new decision tree containing the information from seismic testing.
2. Develop a joint probability table for seismic testing and the state of the hole.
3. Include all probabilities and returns on the decision tree. Average out and fold back to find the best decision and expected return.
4. Find the $EVSI$ and $ENGSI$ relating to the seismic tests.

4.11. An analysis of the expected profitability is required before adding a new product to a product line. If the product is successful in the market, the product will have a net discounted cash flow with a present value of $600,000. If the product is unsuccessful, the corresponding net present value will be a loss of $300,000. Considering present and anticipated competition, the marketing product development group assess the odds of success at .70.

Market research can be conducted to test consumer reaction. Two types of survey can be conducted. Survey type 1 will cost $50,000. The more reliable survey type 2 costs an additional $30,000. The following survey reliability estimates are available:

Survey Type 1 Result	Actual Market Reaction Successful	Unsuccessful
Favorable Survey	.80	.30
Unfavorable Survey	.20	.70

Survey Type 2 Result	Actual Market Reaction Successful	Unsuccessful
Favorable Survey	.95	.15
Unfavorable Survey	.05	.85

1. Without considering the research projects, what is the best decision and expected return?
2. What is the EMV_c and $EVPI$?
3. Construct a decision tree that includes the option to conduct either of the research projects. Include all relevant information on the decision tree, and average out and fold back.
4. What is the $ENGSI$?

5

Decision Criteria Under Uncertainty Without Probability Information

Decision making is an information-utilizing, goal oriented process of identifying, clarifying, and sorting alternatives. An essential element of this process is a value system with which to measure the worth of alternatives. Formally, the value system is expressed by a decision criterion. The decision criterion provides a quantifiable measure of the degree to which an alternative attains an objective. It evaluates and sorts alternatives. An inquiry into the decision process would not be complete without an analysis and comparison of common decision criteria.

CLASSIFYING THE DECISION ENVIRONMENT

The appropriateness of a decision criterion is related to the particular structure of the decision environment. Therefore, before decision criteria are analyzed, the decision environment will be broadly classified into several specialized categories. Table 5.1 represents the *basic structure* of the important informational components of the decision environment. At the top of the table, the A_j's represent the alternative courses of action. At the far left, the S_i's indicate the states of nature that influence the desirability of the alternatives. The $P(S_i)$'s are the assigned probabilities for the states of nature. In the body of the table, the u_{ij}'s represent the conditional return associated with the state of nature (i) and alternative (j). This basic structure can be related to the conditional profit and opportunity loss tables in Chapter 3.

States of Nature (S_i)	$P(S_i)$	Alternatives (A_j)				
		A_1	A_2	A_3	$\ldots$	A_n
S_1	$P(S_1)$	u_{11}	u_{12}	u_{13}	$\ldots$	u_{1n}
S_2	$P(S_2)$	u_{21}	u_{22}	u_{23}	$\ldots$	u_{2n}
.	.	.	.	.	.	.
.	.	.	.	.	.	.
.	.	.	.	.	.	.
S_m	$P(S_m)$	u_{m1}	u_{m2}	u_{m3}	$\ldots$	u_{mn}

TABLE 5.1

The General Structure of the Decision Environment

Historically, taxonomical subdivisions of the decision environment have been based on the availability of information. With this focus, the most general classification includes all informational components. Restrictions on the availability of information constitute important subclassifications.

Departing from tradition,[1] the most general classification is defined in this text as *decision making under uncertainty*. This general category contains two natural subdivisions: probability information is either *known* or *unknown* (Table 5.2). These will be referred to respectively as: (1) *decision making under uncertainty with probability information*, and (2) *decision making under uncertainty without probability information*. Although the terms are less descriptive, decision theorists have commonly called the former *decision making under risk* and the latter *decision making under uncertainty*.[2]

These two major subcategories may be subdivided further. Decision making under uncertainty with probability information contains a special case when the probability assignment is made to a single state of nature (S_k). This special case is referred to as *decision making under certainty*. The assumption of certainty—perfect determination of the state of nature—typically represents a simplification of the decision environment.[3] While very few real-world environments explicitly meet the requirement of certainty, the potential loss in accuracy

[1] The traditional decision theory classifications are certainty, risk (probabilities), and uncertainty (no probabilities). To bridge the gap between "objectivist" and "subjectivist" (or "Bayesian") definitions of probability, D. W. Miller and M. K. Starr have added a new category part way between risk and uncertainty: decision-making under partial information (*Executive Decisions and Operations Research* (Englewood Cliffs, N.J.: Prentice-Hall, 1969)).

[2] Since decision-making under uncertainty is increasingly used in the literature for both subcategories, the term uncertainty in the subcategories (risk and uncertainty) may be misleading.

[3] To facilitate modeling, the size of the abstraction of the real world is made less complex. While this makes modeling easier, the abstraction considered is less inclusive.

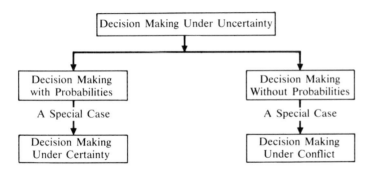

TABLE 5.2

Classification of the Decision Environment

from this simplification is usually more than outweighed by the considerable ease in modeling.

Decision making under uncertainty without probability information also contains an important subdivision. The environmental states (S_i) may be either: (1) not influenced by the decision or (2) influenced by the decision. To distinguish clearly between these two possibilities, environmental states influenced by decisions are referred to as *decision making under conflict*. This category includes those decision environments where one or more opponents may select a reciprocating or counter strategy.

In terms of *the decision environment classification*, this chapter will consider the application of decision criteria to an environment of *uncertainty without probability information*. Chapter 6 will extend considerations to decision making under *uncertainty with probability information*. Emphasis will then be directed to the other two subclasses. Chapter 7 treats *decision making under conflict*. Chapters 8 through 13 consider *decision making under certainty* almost exclusively.

States of Nature	$P(S_i)$	A_1	A_2	A_3	$\cdots$	A_n
S_k	$P(S_k) = 1.00$	u_{k1}	u_{k2}	u_{k3}	$\cdots$	u_{kn}

TABLE 5.3

Decision Making Under Certainty

DECISION CRITERIA WITHOUT PROBABILITY INFORMATION

Decision theorists have suggested several criteria for a decision environment under uncertainty without probability information.[4] Without probabilities of the states of nature, the criteria are primarily philosophical or psychological. The decision maker may be very optimistic and attempt the best payoff, ignoring potential losses. On the other hand, he or she may be pessimistic and cautiously seek a high level of security. He or she may select an intermediate position of optimism-pessimism, or some more *rational* approach to cope with an environment of absolute uncertainty.

In decision making under uncertainty without probability information, the specific criteria to be considered are: (1) maximax, (2) minimax-maximin, (3) minimax regret, (4) the criterion of optimism, and (5) the criterion of rationality. Although the criteria vary substantially in logical supportability, the breadth of approach indicates the inherent difficulty of decision making under uncertainty without probability information.

To provide a common basis for comparison, the decision criterion will be applied to a single decision environment. A small investor would like to purchase one of three stocks listed on the New York Stock Exchange. The stock must be sold within one month. The desirability of the stock will depend on the economic environment at the time of the sale. The probabilities of the economic states of nature a month hence are unknown. Table 5.4 summarizes the relevant information.

States of Nature	Alternative Blocks of Stocks		
(Economic Outlook)	A_1	A_2	A_3
Favorable	$600	$250	$100
Normal	50	200	100
Unfavorable	−200	−100	100

TABLE 5.4
The Decision Environment

The Maximax Criterion

Maximax is a criterion for a very optimistic decision maker. As the name suggests, the maximum payoff is determined for each alternative. Of these maxima, the alternative with the maximum return is selected: the maximum of

---

[4] The classification is often referred to as decision making under ignorance.

the maxima. *The criterion specifies the selection of the alternative with the best possible return.*

Maximax is easily applied. For the stock market investment problem, Table 5.5 provides the alternative selection. The maximum per alternative is listed and the maximum of these selected. A_1 is the selection with the highest potential return—$600.

States of Nature (Economic Outlook)	Alternatives A_1*	A_2	A_3
Favorable	$600	$250	$100
Normal	50	200	100
Unfavorable	−200	−100	100
Maxima	$600	$250	$100
Maximax	$600		

TABLE 5.5

Maximax: A_1

Although always attempting the best return has appeal, this approach has several apparent weaknesses. Maximax *ignores most of the available information.* All payoffs except the highest payoff per alternative are ignored. Besides containing the best return, A_1 also contains the worst. Furthermore, whether the worst return is $−200 or $−200,000, the alternative selection will not be affected. Maximax appears overoptimistic—or possibly overdesperate.

The maximax criterion is deficient in another important quality. For a given state of nature, a constant improvement of each alternative should not affect the alternative selection: the criterion should maintain *row linearity.*[5] For example, in Table 5.6, the maximax selection is A_1. An assumed windfall gain of $100 for S_2 improves both alternatives by $100. Both alternatives have the same improvement and the same chance of obtaining the improvement.

A logically consistent criterion should therefore lead to the same alternative selection both before and after the adjustment. The maximax selection, however, changes to A_2. The criterion does not possess *row linearity*—it is logically inconsistent.

---

[5] An excellent analysis of the logical consistency of criteria is provided by A. N. Halter and G. W. Dean in *Decisions Under Uncertainty with Research Applications* (Cincinnati, Ohio: South-Western Publishing Co., 1971).

States of Nature	Alternatives A_1*	A_2	Windfall Gain of $100 for S_2 States of Nature	A_1	A_2*
S_1	$100	$10	S_1	$100	$ 10
S_2	0	50	S_2	100	150
Maxima	$100	$50	Maxima	$100	$150
Maximax	$100*		Maximax		$150*

TABLE 5.6

Maximax: No Row Linearity

The Minimax-Maximin Criterion

The minimax criterion recommended by Abraham Wald is at the opposite extreme of maximax. It is a criterion for a decision maker with a pessimistic view of the states of nature. It is based on the assumption that the worst state of nature will occur. Minimax provides for the selection of *the minimum of the maximum losses*. The maximum loss is listed for each alternative and the minimum of these is selected. The criterion guarantees the best of the worst losses. It offers the decision maker a guaranteed security level.

If the payoff table is expressed in terms of gains instead of losses, an analogous criterion is to select the maximin gain: the maximum of the minimum guaranteed gains. Whether the returns are profits or losses, minimax and maximin both specify the selection of the alternative with the *best of the worst* returns.

Tables 5.7 and 5.8 illustrate the application of these two criteria. For minimax loss (Table 5.7) the maximum loss is determined per alternative. If

States of Nature (Economic Outlook)	Alternatives A_1	A_2	A_3*
Favorable	$600	$250	$100
Normal	50	200	100
Unfavorable	−200	−100	100
Maximum Loss	$−200	$−100	$100
Minimax			$100*

TABLE 5.7

Minimax Losses: A_3

no losses are present, as in A_3, the worst return is used. The alternative with the best of the worst returns is selected. Similarly, for maximin gains (Table 5.8), the minimum guaranteed gain is indicated per alternative. If losses as well as gains are present, as in A_1, the worst return (-200) is used. Of the guaranteed returns, the alternative with the largest guarantee is selected.

States of Nature (Economic Outlook)		Alternatives	
	A_1	A_2	A_3*
Favorable	$ 600	$ 250	$100
Normal	50	200	100
Unfavorable	−200	−100	100
Minimum Guaranteed Gain	$−200	$−100	$100
Maximin			$100*

TABLE 5.8
Maximin Gains: A_3

The minimax and maximin criteria might be more generally expressed as a single criterion: *minimax-maximin*. Minimax-maximin provides the same conclusion as the separate criteria: it specifies selecting the alternative with the best of the worst returns. Table 5.9 provides the application of the minimax-maximin criterion.

The minimax-maximin criterion is very conservative. It considers only the worst return for each alternative. All other information is ignored. While providing the highest security, it ignores the potential for higher returns.

States of Nature (Economic Outlook)	A_1	A_2	A_3
Favorable	$600	$250	$100
Normal	50	200	100
Unfavorable	−200	−100	100
Worst	$−200	$−100	$100
Best of Worst, Minimax-Maximin			$100*

TABLE 5.9
Minimax-Maximin: A_3

Decision Criteria Under Uncertainty Without Probability Information

Minimax-maximin has another drawback—it does not possess *row linearity*. As indicated in Table 5.10, if $100 is subtracted from each alternative for S_2, the alternative selection is changed from A_1 to A_2. The criterion is inherently inconsistent for linear row changes.

States of Nature		A_1*	A_2		States of Nature		A_1	A_2*
							$\Delta S_2 \downarrow \$100$	
S_1		$ 0	$–70		S_1		$ 0	$–70
S_2		–50	20		S_2		–150	–80
	Worst	$–50	$–70			Worst	$–150	$–80
	Best of Worst	$–50*				Best of Worst		$–80*

TABLE 5.10

Minimax-Maximin: Lacking Row Linearity

The Minimax Regret Criterion

L. J. Savage once argued that after making a decision and experiencing the consequences, a decision maker may regret not having selected the best alternative. He recommended a criterion to minimize the regret: *minimax regret*. The criterion converts the conditional payoffs into a regret table and then applies the minimax principle.

A regret is a feeling of loss associated with the difference between what was done and what could have been done—the difference between the decision made and the best decision. For an assumed state of nature, there is a best alternative with zero regret. All less desirable alternatives produce regret. Actually, the concept of a regret and a regret table are already familiar. They are the previously discussed *opportunity loss* and *opportunity loss table*. Minimax regret applies minimax to an opportunity loss table.

The stock option problem can easily be converted to a regret table. If the favorable economic environment occurs, the best decision will be to select A_1 with a return of $600. If A_1 is actually selected, there will be no regret. If A_2 is selected, however, the return will be only $250. Since the return could have been $600, there will be regret for the $350 difference. The complete matrix of regrets is presented in Table 5.11.

Applying the minimax criterion to the regret table, the alternative with the best of the worst *opportunity losses* is selected. The worst regret associated with A_1 is $300; with A_2, $350; and with A_3, $500. With a regret of $300, A_1 has the minimum of these maximum regrets.

Minimax regret has many of the same drawbacks as minimax-maximin. One additional drawback is the *loss* of information regarding the differences

States of Nature (Economic Outlook)	A_1	A_2	A_3
Favorable	$600	$250	$100
Normal	50	200	100
Unfavorable	−200	−100	100

Regret Table

States of Nature	A_1*	A_2	A_3
Favorable	$ 0	$350	$500
Normal	150	0	100
Unfavorable	300	200	0
Maximum Regret	$300	$350	$500
Minimax Regret	$300*		

TABLE 5.11

Minimax Regret: A_1

between the rows. For example, if $1,000 is added to each alternative for the *unfavorable* state of nature, the regret table and alternative selection are not altered (Table 5.12). While this quality maintains *row linearity*, it does not maintain the *independence of irrelevant alternatives*. That is, disregarding an alternative which would not have been selected should not logically affect the other alternative selections.

In the stock option problem, an undesirable and infeasible fourth alternative is introduced. The new consideration and associative regret table are provided in Table 5.13. In this problem, the new alternative (A_4) is not selected.

States of Nature (Economic Outlook)	A_1	A_2	A_3	States of Nature (Economic Outlook)	A_1*	A_2	A_3
Favorable	$600	$250	$100	Favorable	$ 0	$350	$500
Normal	50	200	100	Normal	150	0	100
Unfavorable	800	900	1,100	Unfavorable	300	200	0
				Maximum	$300	$350	$500
				Mimimax	$300*		

TABLE 5.12

Minimax Regret: Disregards Differences Between Rows

Decision Criteria Under Uncertainty Without Probability Information

States of Nature (Economic Outlook)	A_1	A_2	A_3	A_4
Favorable	$600	$250	$100	$600
Normal	50	200	100	450
Unfavorable	−200	−100	100	−700

Regret Table				
States of Nature	A_1	$A_2{}^*$	A_3	A_4
Favorable	$ 0	$350	$500	$ 0
Normal	400	250	350	0
Unfavorable	300	200	0	800
Maximum	$400	$350	$500	$800
Minimax Regret		350*		

TABLE 5.13

Minimax Regret: With Irrelevant Alternative

Since it is not selected, removing it from consideration should not affect the selection of the best alternative. However, *with this irrelevant alternative*, the alternative choice is A_2 (Table 5.13). *Without the irrelevant alternative*, the alternative choice is A_1 (Table 5.11). The irrelevant alternative has changed the decision—a logically questionable conclusion.

The Criterion of Optimism

The minimax-maximin and minimax regret assume a pessimistic view of the state of nature. The worst is assumed to happen and the highest security level is sought. L. Hurwicz argued that a decision maker who feels somewhat optimistic about the state of nature should be able to express these feelings rationally without moving to the extreme of maximax. His suggestion is to make a compromise between the extremes of optimism and pessimism. A weighted average of the best and worst returns is calculated for each alternative. The alternative with the highest weighted value is selected. A weight of α is assigned between zero and one for the best return and $1 - \alpha$ for the worst return.

If the decision maker assigns a *coefficient of optimism* (α) of .6, the alternatives will have the relative desirabilities expressed in Table 5.12. A_1 has the highest index of optimism-pessimism.

Like the earlier criteria, the criterion of optimism is not without fault.

	A_1*	A_2	A_3
Best Return ($\alpha = .60$)	$600 (.60)	$250 (.60)	$100 (.60)
Worst Return ($1 - \alpha = .40$)	−200 (.40)	−100 (.40)	100 (.40)
Optimism-Pessimism Index	$280	$110	$100
Maximum Optimism-Pessimism Index	$280*		

TABLE 5.14

Criterion of Optimism: A_1

A coefficient of optimism of one leads to a maximax decision. A coefficient of zero produces minimax-maximin. Like maximax and minimax-maximin, the criterion of optimism does not possess *row linearity*. As indicated in Table 5.15, there are other noteworthy criticisms. A_1 has a return of zero if S_1 occurs and a return of 100 for all other states of nature. On the other hand, A_2 has a return of 100 for S_1 and a return of zero for all other states of nature. Regardless of the coefficient of optimism, the optimism-pessimism index is the same for both alternatives—the alternatives appear equally desirable. If the

States of Nature	A_1*	A_2*
S_1	0	100
S_2	100	0
S_3	100	0
.	.	.
.	.	.
.	.	.
S_n	100	0
Optimism-Pessimism Index	$100\alpha + 0(1 - \alpha)$	$100\alpha + 0(1 - \alpha)$
Maximum Optimism-Pessimism Index	$100\alpha + 0(1 - \alpha)$*	$100\alpha + 0(1 - \alpha)$*

TABLE 5.15

Criterion of Optimism: Equal Optimism-Pessimism Indexes

decision maker is completely ignorant of the true state of nature, however, A_1 is logically superior to A_2. As the number of states of nature increases, A_1 provides an approximate guarantee of 100, while A_2 provides a guarantee of zero.

Another criticism is that the criterion cannot combine equal alternatives randomly without altering the choice—it lacks *convexity*. Table 5.16 demonstrates this difficulty. Regardless of the α chosen, A_1 and A_2 are equally desirable. Therefore, a third equally acceptable alternative (A_3) should consist of a toss of a fair coin between these equally desirable choices. A_3 specifically, represents A_1 chosen half of the time and A_2 chosen the other half. The return for A_3 should equal the average of A_1 and A_2.

States of Nature	A_1*	A_2*	Randomization A_3
S_1	1	0	½
S_2	0	1	½
S_3	0	0	0
Optimism-Pessimism Index	1α	1α	½α
Maximum Optimism-Pessimism Index	1α*	1α*	

TABLE 5.16
Criterion of Optimism: Lacking Convexity

However, when the criterion is applied to the three alternatives for all α's other than zero, A_1 and A_2 are always preferable to A_3. The criterion is inconsistent.

The Criterion of Rationality

The criterion of rationality, attributed to Laplace, is based on the *principle of insufficient reasoning*: if there is no reason to believe that one state of nature is more likely than another, they should be assumed equally likely. The criterion of rationality prescribes the assignment of equal probability weights to the states of nature, the calculation of an expected value for each alternative, and the selection of the alternative with the maximum expected value.

The application of this criterion to the stock option problem is straightforward (Table 5.17). The three states of nature are assigned equal probabilities of one-third. The EMVs are calculated. A_1, with the maximum expected value, is selected.

States of Nature (Economic Outlook)	$P(S_i)$	A_1*	A_2	A_3
Favorable	⅓	$600	$250	$100
Normal	⅓	50	200	100
Unfavorable	⅓	−200	−100	100
$E(A_j)$		$150	$116⅔	$100
Maximum $E(A_j)$		$150*		

TABLE 5.17

Criterion of Rationality: A_1

States of Nature	$P(S_i)$	A_1*	A_2	Windfall Gain of $100 for S_2 States of Nature	$P(S_i)$	A_1*	A_2
S_1	½	$100	$10	S_1	½	$100	$ 10
S_2	½	0	50	S_2	½	100	150
$E(A_j)$		$ 50	$30	$E(A_j)$		$100	$ 80
Maximum $E(A_j)$		$ 50*		Maximum $E(A_j)$		$100*	

TABLE 5.18

Criterion of Rationality: Maintains Row Linearity

States of Nature	$P(S_i)$	A_1*	A_2	A_3	A_4	Removal of Irrelevant Alternative A_4 States of Nature	$P(S_i)$	A_1*	A_2	A_3
Favorable	⅓	$600	$250	$100	$600	Favorable	⅓	$600	$250	$100
Normal	⅓	50	200	100	450	Normal	⅓	50	200	100
Unfavorable	⅓	−200	−100	100	−700	Unfavorable	⅓	−200	−100	100
$E(A_j)$		$150	$116⅔	$100	$116⅔	$E(A_j)$		$150	$116⅔	$100
Maximum $E(A_j)$		$150*				Maximum $E(A_j)$		$150*		

TABLE 5.19

Criterion of Rationality: Unaffected by Removal of Irrelevant Alternatives

States of Nature	$P(S_i)$	$A_1{}^*$	$A_2{}^*$	Randomization $A_3{}^*$
S_1	$\frac{1}{3}$	1	0	$\frac{1}{2}$
S_2	$\frac{1}{3}$	0	1	$\frac{1}{2}$
S_3	$\frac{1}{3}$	0	0	0
$E(A_j)$		$\frac{1}{3}$	$\frac{1}{3}$	$\frac{1}{3}$
Maximum $E(A_j)$		$\frac{1}{3}{}^*$	$\frac{1}{3}{}^*$	$\frac{1}{3}{}^*$

TABLE 5.20

Criterion of Rationality: Maintains Convexity

In considering the objections to this criterion, it is interesting to note that it maintains the properties the others violate: row linearity, independence of irrelevant alternatives, and convexity. Using the previous examples of violations, Tables 5.18, 5.19, and 5.20 demonstrate that the criterion of rationality maintains these qualities. In each case, the criterion was consistent in producing the same alternative selection before and after the adjustment of the problem.

Unfortunately, the difficulty of *row duplication* still remains. In the stock option problem, the decision maker may discover that there are three distinct, unfavorable economic environments that would produce poor returns. Replacing the one unfavorable state of nature with three separate unfavorable states, the problem might be restated in terms of the five categories (Table 5.21). Equal probability weights of one-fifth are now assigned to each state of nature. The alternative selection is changed from A_1 to A_3.

Viewed another way, the new problem with row duplication (Table 5.21) can be collapsed into two distinct expressions with different alternative selections (Table 5.22). Obviously, one of these must be incorrect—the criterion contains a potentially serious fault.

States of Nature	$P(S_i)$	A_1	A_2	$A_3{}^*$
Favorable	$\frac{1}{5}$	$600	$250	$100
Normal	$\frac{1}{5}$	50	200	100
Unfavorable 1	$\frac{1}{5}$	−250	−100	100
Unfavorable 2	$\frac{1}{5}$	−250	−100	100
Unfavorable 3	$\frac{1}{5}$	−250	−100	100
$E(A_j)$		$−20	$ 30	$100
Maximum $E(A_j)$				$100*

TABLE 5.21

Criterion of Rationality: Row Duplication

Decision Criteria Without Probability Information

| Collapsed Form No. 1 | | | | |
States of Nature	$P(S_i)$	A_1	A_2	$A_3{}^*$
Favorable	$^1/_5$	600	250	100
Normal	$^1/_5$	50	200	100
Unfavorable	$^3/_5$	-250	-100	100
	$E(A_j)$	-20	30	100
Maximum	$E(A_j)$			100^*
Collapsed Form No. 2				
States of Nature	$P(S_i)$	$A_1{}^*$	A_2	A_3
Favorable	$^1/_3$	600	250	100
Normal	$^1/_3$	50	200	100
Unfavorable	$^1/_3$	-250	-100	100
	$E(A_j)$	150	$116^2/_3$	100
Maximum	$E(A_j)$	150^*		

TABLE 5.22

Criterion of Rationality: Row Duplication in Collapsed Form

THE APPROPRIATE CRITERION UNDER IGNORANCE

In decision making under uncertainty without probability information, a number of criteria suggest the means for selecting an appropriate alternative. None is without serious fault. *They all ignore information relevant to a logically consistent alternative selection.* Probability information is ignored by the very definition of an assumed state of ignorance. Most of the criteria ignore most of the payoff information. The resultant deficiency has produced the associated *reductio ad absurdum propositions:* the lack of row linearity, the dependence of irrelevant alternatives, nonconvexity, and row duplication. The misuse of information has led to a misinformed decision. The criteria are logically inconsistent and unacceptable.

In decision making under uncertainty without probability information, there is no appropriate criterion without highly questionable special assumptions. Therefore, whenever possible, a decision maker should attempt to avoid a decision environment of complete ignorance.

SUMMARY

In analyzing the appropriateness of decision criteria, the type of decision environment is a critical consideration. Most generally, the decision environment can be structured as decision making under uncertainty. Depending on the availability of probability information, there are four major classifications: (1) decision making with probability information, (2) decision making under certainty, (3) decision making without probability information, and (4) decision making under conflict. In this chapter the analysis is restricted to decision making without probability information. Subsequent chapters consider the other three classifications.

For decision making without probability information, the decision theory literature contains several common criteria: maximax, minimax-maximin, minimax regret, the criterion of optimism, and the criterion of rationality. Each of these is based primarily on the philosophical or psychological attitudes of the decision maker.

Maximax is a very optimistic criterion. Assuming the most favorable state of nature, the decision maker selects the maximum of the maximum returns per alternative. Regardless of other realities, maximax attempts to obtain the highest return.

At the other end of the spectrum, minimax-maximin is very pessimistic. The worst possible state of nature is assumed for each alternative. The decision maker selects the best of the worst possibilities—the highest guaranteed security level. The prime underlying assumption is the inevitability of the worst state of nature. Nature is assumed to be an intelligent, willful adversary.

Minimax regret is similar in concept to minimax-maximin. In essence, minimax regret applies minimax-maximin to a conditional opportunity loss table instead of a conditional profit table. More information about alternative column comparability is considered. However, at the same time, information about row comparability is lost.

The criterion of optimism attempts a compromise between maximax and minimax-maximin—between extreme optimism and extreme pessimism. The maximax and minimax for each alternative are subjectively weighted by a *coefficient of optimism*. The result is a special, weighted average of the best and worst outcomes per alternative.

Another attempt to cope with a decision environment without probability information is the criterion of rationality. Without any probability information, in absolute ignorance, this criterion assigns equal probabilities to the states of nature. The criterion focuses on the number of states of nature and whether each should actually be assigned equal probability weight.

In a decision environment without probability information a number of criteria suggest the means for selecting an appropriate alternative. Upon analysis, none is without potential serious fault. None of the criteria considers all of the relevant information in the decision environment. In most cases, most of the payoff information is ignored. By the definition of a state of ignorance, probability information is not considered. The resulting deficiencies create such severe logical inconsistencies as to render each criterion unacceptable. In an environment of uncertainty without probability information—an environment of ignorance—there is no logically consistent or logically supportable criterion. A decision maker must avoid a decision environment of complete ignorance.

BIBLIOGRAPHY

Bierman, H., Jr., C. P. Bonini, and W. H. Hausman. *Quantitative Analysis for Business Decisions*. Homewood, Ill.: Richard D. Irwin, 1973.

Chernoff, H., and L. Moses. *Elementary Decision Theory*. New York: John Wiley & Sons, 1959.

Easton, A. *Complex Managerial Decisions Involving Multiple Objectives*. New York: John Wiley & Sons, 1973.

Halter, A. N., and G. W. Dean. *Decisions Under Uncertainty with Research Applications*. Cincinnati, Ohio: South-Western Publishing Co., 1971.

Luce, R. D., and H. Raiffa. *Games and Decisions*. New York: John Wiley & Sons, 1958.

Miller, D. W., and M. K. Starr. *Executive Decisions and Operations Research*. Englewood Cliffs, N.J.: Prentice-Hall, 1969.

Plane, D. R., and G. A. Kochenberger. *Operations Research for Managerial Decisions*. Homewood, Ill.: Richard D. Irwin, 1972.

Savage, L. J. "The Theory of Statistical Decision," *Journal of the American Statistical Association* 46 (1951): pp. 55–67.

Thierauf, R. J., and R. C. Klekamp. *Decision Making Through Operations Research*. New York: John Wiley & Sons, 1975.

Tummala, V. M. R. *Decision Analysis with Business Applications*. New York: Intext Educational Publishers, 1973.

Decision Criteria Under Uncertainty Without Probability Information

5.1. An investor has heard from a friend that a significant pharmacological break-through is anticipated by a small medical research organization. Funds can either be left in present investments or transferred to the purchase of over-the-counter stock in the medical research organization. The anticipated short-run returns are:

	Stock	Present Investments
Major breakthrough	$12,000	$200
Minor breakthrough	2,000	200
No breakthrough	− 500	200

What decision would be made under:

1. minimax-maximin?
2. minimax regret?

Do the decisions differ? Why or why not?

5.2. A student taking an examination is confronted with a decision to answer or not to answer one of the questions. The hesitancy is due to the grading system: right minus wrong. The question is worth 20 points. The student feels confident but not certain about the answer.

What will the student do if she applies the philosophies of:

(1) maximax,
(2) minimax-maximin,
(3) minimax regret,
(4) criterion of optimism ($\alpha = .90$), and
(5) criterion of rationality?

Which criterion appears to be the most appropriate? Provide the underlying reasoning.

5.3. In a tight basketball game against a rival university, State has just put the ball into play at the opponent's end of the court. State is behind by one point, with three seconds remaining in the game. The star guard has the ball at half-court. Which criteria would compel the guard to shoot?

5.4. A person runs into an old friend who tells him about a "golden opportunity"—to invest in a gold mine. In the late 1800s, the mine was claimed and prospected by the friend's great-grandfather. Upon his death in 1894, the mine was closed down. Only with the recent increase in gold prices had the mine been reopened. And what do you know—gold! Now for just $4,000, a 10 percent ownership can be purchased. Excluding ownership cost, the anticipated returns are listed below.

States of Nature	10% Ownership in Mine
Major Mother Lode Claim	$50,000
Small Workable Vein	8,000
Unproductive Vein	−1,000

What decision would the person make using these criteria:

(1) maximax,
(2) minimax-maximin,
(3) minimax regret,
(4) criterion of optimism ($\alpha = .10$), and
(5) criterion of rationality?

Using the same states of nature, would a trip to the mine possibly change the decision provided by any of these criteria?

5.5. The owner of a new condominium has an option to purchase a fire insurance policy providing complete coverage for $200. If there is a fire, the estimated loss without the policy is $50,000.

Construct a payoff matrix and indicate the decision made, using:

(1) maximax,
(2) minimax-maximin, and
(3) criterion of rationality.

If the decision environment is common knowledge, what major difficulty is encountered in applying the criterion of rationality?

5.6. A wildcatter is considering drilling for oil. If the hole is dry, the cost will be $10,000. If it is wet, a net profit of $40,000 is expected. If it is very wet, the net profit is expected to reach $200,000. Without seismic testing the chances of success cannot be easily determined. What decision would be made with:

(1) minimax-maximin,
(2) maximax,
(3) minimax regret, and
(4) criterion of rationality?

What would be the long-run effect of continually applying the minimax-maximin criterion for all potential holes? Would the effect differ for minimax regret? What would happen in the long run to a maximax wildcatter?

What coefficient of optimism is required to start drilling?

If seismic tests are conducted with favorable results, would there be any change in the criterion of rationality? Can a more "rational" approach be recommended?

What results would be required from seismic testing before a person using minimax-maximin principles would drill?

5.7. A small organization is considering adding an important new product to the present product line. The introduction will require the purchase of new machinery and the expansion of plant facilities. Five levels of demand are anticipated. The projection of net profits is provided below:

	High-capacity Machines Substantial Expansion	Low-capacity Machines Small Expansion	Do Not Add Product No Expansion
Very High Demand	$ 50,000	$ 12,000	$0
High Demand	20,000	12,000	0
Moderate Demand	− 5,000	4,000	0
Low Demand	− 12,000	− 2,000	0
Very Low Demand	− 20,000	− 10,000	0

What would be the specific decision of someone who employs minimax-maximin? What general conclusion can be drawn about that person?

What decision would be produced by using the criterion of optimism ($\alpha = .40$)? In this situation, which demand levels will probably be the least likely to occur?

5.8. The owners of a small "mom-and-pop" grocery store are considering introducing fresh, homemade lemon and berry pies. The pies would be displayed in a glass case near the cash register. The daily demand is not anticipated to exceed four pies. The pies would be priced at $4. The cost is estimated at $2 per pie. The probability of demand for this new sales item is unknown.

If the store owners sell only fresh pies daily, how many pies should be baked using a minimax criterion?

If the owners can guarantee the sale of as many as three leftover pies to three neighbors down the street for $2 each, what decision should be made under minimax?

If fresh and leftover sales do not absorb all of the pies, the "owners-pie makers" have decided to eat one of the pies themselves. The pie would still be assumed to be worth the production cost. Would the minimax decision change in this situation?

5.9. A staunch "objectivist" believes that probabilities must relate strictly to long-run, relative frequencies of events. He has just walked to the corner of a moderately busy intersection. Considering the possibility of being hit by a passing car, he must decide whether or not to attempt crossing the street. With the symbol U representing a unit of satisfaction, the objectivist considers the situation in terms of this payoff matrix:

	Action	
States of Nature	Wait	Walk
Safe	− 4 U	4 U
Car	0 U	− 200 U

If he uses minimax-maximin, minimax regret, or the criterion of rationality, what will be his fate?

What can be concluded about the worth he ascribes to the outcomes in the payoff matrix?

What will the objectivist eventually have to do to get across the street?

5.10. A short vacation is being considered for the forthcoming three-day weekend. The options are: (1) to go north to the mountains for fishing and camping; (2) to go south to play tennis; or (3) to stay at home. The weather appears to be the critical factor. Measured in units of satisfaction (U), the anticipated levels of desirability are:

Weather	North for Fishing–Camping	South for Tennis	Activities at Home
Sun	4 U	-1 U	1 U
Rain	-2 U	3 U	1 U

Make the choice according to:

(1) maximax,
(2) minimax-maximin, and
(3) criterion of rationality.

The weather in the northern mountains, the southern area, and at home is usually quite different. Four days before the trip the latest weather forecasts were for a growing chance of rain in the north and a good possibility of clearing skies with sunny weather in the south. Does the realization of different weather patterns for each proposed vacation area affect any of the earlier alternative selections?

Does the weather forecast affect the decisions?

Since an "objectivist" is not classically able to assign accurate probabilities to the states of nature, does the weather really have any affect at all on the decisions?

6

Decision Criteria Under Uncertainty With Probability Information

A value system is essential to decision making. In the decision process, this value system is expressed as a criterion to assign relative worth to outcomes and to sort alternatives. In Chapter 5 several common criteria were evaluated for a decision environment of uncertainty without probability information. None was without serious fault. The chapter drew an important conclusion: *In a decision environment of uncertainty without probability information, there is no acceptable criterion.*

Lacking an appropriate criterion to guide logically consistent alternative selections, a decision maker must avoid a decision environment of uncertainty without probability information. This chapter provides a means for resolving this difficulty. It indicates a model for converting a decision environment without probability information into one with probability information. It then continues the search for an appropriate criterion in a decision environment of uncertainty with probability information.

QUANTIFYING PROBABILITY INFORMATION BY THE STANDARD LOTTERY

A probability is a summarization of information relating to the likelihood of an event—a composite of information about an environmental state. Except in the rarest situations (in which case someone else should probably make the decision), the decision maker will have some information about the decision environment. Theoretically, then, the decision maker can use this information to assess probabilities subjectively.[1] Past experience, experimentation, judgment, intuition, and wisdom regarding the decision environment can be quantitatively expressed in the form of a *subjective probability assessment*.

Fortunately, subjective probabilities can be quantified by the *standard lottery*. The decision maker is offered two options to win a reward (R). Option 1 is to receive R if the state of nature to be evaluated occurs. Option 2 is to receive R if a specific item is drawn randomly from a *known population*. If the content of the known population is specified in option 2, the decision maker can choose between the two options. The contents of the known population in option 2 can then be continually adjusted until the decision maker feels indifferent to the choice between the options.

At the point of indifference, the expected gains from option 1 and option 2 are equal:

$$EV_1 = EV_2.$$

Both options provide the same perceived worth. Since the probability of winning with the known population in option 2 is known, a single equation with a single unknown can be structured. The unknown probability of the state of nature in option 1 can be solved. With the unknown probability of the state of nature $(P(S))$, the known population probability $(P(f^*))$, and the reward (R), the single equation:

$$EV_1 = EV_2$$

becomes:

$$Rp(S) + 0(1 - p(S)) = Rp(f^*) + 0(1 - p(f^*))$$
$$p(S) = p(f^*).$$

The probability for the two options must be the same. The probability of the state of nature in option 1 must equal the probability of the favorable outcome from the known population (Table 6.1).

The stock option problem used in Chapter 5 demonstrates how easy it is to quantify a subjective probability assessment. To review, a small investor is considering the purchase of one of three stocks on the New York Stock Exchange (Table 6.2). Since the stock must be sold within one month, the desirability of the purchase is assumed to depend on the economic environment at the time of the sale. The probabilities of the economic states a month hence are unknown.

The standard lottery will be used to quantify the subjective evaluation of the normal economic outlook (S_2). The decision maker will be given an oppor-

---

[1] Such subjective assessments will at least concur with the decision maker's beliefs. If they are used properly the resulting decision will be consistent with the decision maker's understanding of the decision environment.

Option 1	Option 2
Decision Environment	Known Population

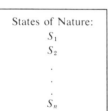

States of Nature:
$$S_1$$
$$S_2$$
.
.
.
$$S_n$$

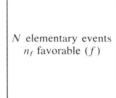

N elementary events
n_f favorable (f)

Return R if S_1 occurs

Return R if favorable
item is drawn

Expected Return:

$$R_p(S_1) + 0(1 - p(S_1))$$

Expected Return:

$$R_p(f) + 0(1 - p(f))$$

n_f in known population adjusted to f^* at the point of indifference:

Option 1 = Option 2

$$R_p(S_1) + 0(1 - p(S_1)) = R_p(f^*) + 0(1 - p(f^*))$$

$$p(S_1) = p(f^*)$$

TABLE 6.1

The Standard Lottery

tunity to win $100 by selecting one of the two options. Option 1 will consist of waiting one month to determine which of the three economic conditions actually occurs. If the normal economic outlook prevails, the decision maker will receive the $100. Option 2 consists of drawing one tennis ball at random from a basket of 100 tennis balls. Fifty of the balls are bright yellow and 50 are white. If a yellow ball is drawn, the decision maker will receive the reward one month hence.

States of Nature (Economic Outlook)	Alternative Stocks		
	A_1	A_2	A_3
Favorable: S_1	$600	$250	$100
Normal: S_2	50	200	100
Unfavorable: S_3	-200	-100	100

TABLE 6.2

The Decision Environment of the Stock Purchase

If the decision maker selects option 2, he must intuitively feel that it is more likely than option 1. He must feel that the probability of drawing a yellow ball is greater than the probability of normal economic conditions. The probability of randomly drawing a yellow ball is a known value of one-half. The probability of normal economic conditions therefore, must be less than one-half.

The contents of the basket are adjusted more favorable to option 1. The number of yellow balls is reduced to 30 of the 100. The two options are then offered again. If the decision maker prefers option 1, the inference is that he believes the probability of winning with option 1 to be greater than with option 2. The probability of normal economic conditions is greater than the probability of drawing a yellow ball—greater than .30.

The contents of the basket (known population) are adjusted until the decision maker feels indifferent to the choice between the two options. At this point, the two options are equal—the probability of winning is the same for both. Therefore, if this point of indifference is reached with, say, 42 yellow balls in the known population, the probability of winning with option 2 will be .42. And since the decision maker feels exactly the same about the two options, the probability for the other option must be identical. The subjective probability assessment for the normal economic outlook must be .42.

The other two economic conditions can be similarly evaluated. For a chance at a reward, the decision maker will be given the option of (1) gambling that the state of nature to be evaluated will occur, or (2) gambling that a draw from a known population will be favorable. The contents of the known population are adjusted systematically until the point of indifference is reached. The probability of the event to be evaluated will be equal to the known probability of the favorable draw from the population.

DECISION CRITERIA UNDER UNCERTAINTY WITH PROBABILITY INFORMATION

Using the structured logic afforded by the standard lottery, the decision maker can avoid a decision environment of ignorance. He or she can use available information to quantify subjectively based probability assessments for the states of nature. The decision maker can thus transform *the decision environment to one of decision making under uncertainty with probability information.*

In such a decision environment there are two common criteria: (1) *maximum likelihood* and (2) *maximum expected monetary value*. The appropriateness of each is considered below.

The Maximum Likelihood Criterion

The maximum likelihood criterion is frequently applied in everyday usage. The premise for a decision maker's use of this criterion is straightforward.

The state of nature with the maximum likelihood of occurrence is assumed to occur. Given this assumption, the best alternative has the highest return *associated with that state of nature.*

Table 6.3 illustrates the ease with which this criterion may be applied. Since S_2 has the highest probability, it will be assumed to occur. If S_2 does occur, the choice will be between A_1, with a return of \$100, and A_2, with a return of \$40. Obviously, A_1 is the better selection.

State of Nature	$p(S_i)$	A_1*	A_2
S_1	.10	\$ 10	\$20
→ S_2	.90	100	40
Maximum Likelihood S_2		\$100	\$40
Maximum Return		\$100*	

TABLE 6.3
Maximum Likelihood

This criterion has appeal for certain problems. If the most likely event does occur, the best decision will be guaranteed. For a one-of-a-kind decision with a very large probability for one state of nature, a decision maker might be willing to gamble with high odds of success. This method of choice will lead to the best decision more frequently than any other.

There is a more sobering reality, however. A decision maker who gambles on the most likely state of nature ignores much potentially valuable information. None of the other states of nature and their associated payoffs are considered. If there are more than two states of nature, more than half of the information will be ignored.

Table 6.4 illustrates the potential drawback of considering only the state of nature with the highest probability. S_2 with a probability of .50, is assumed certain, while S_3, with a probability of .49, is assumed nonexistent. The large negative payoffs associated with A_1 for states other than S_2 are ignored entirely. The returns associated with S_1 and S_3 have no effect on the alternative selection.

The criterion also has the drawback of row duplication. Table 6.5 illustrates a problem leading to the selection of A_1. If the decision maker were to reclassify S_2 more accurately into three new subclassifications (Table 6.5(b)), the alternative selection would shift to A_2. The method of selection appears capricious.

A criterion is deficient to the extent that it fails to consider relevant information. To the extent that it ignores much essential information, the maximum likelihood criterion is correspondingly deficient. This criterion cannot be recommended for decision making under uncertainty with probability information.

State of Nature	$p(S_i)$	$A_1{}^*$	A_2
S_1	.01	$-10,000	$100
→S_2	.50	101	100
S_3	.49	-100,000	100
Maximum Likelihood S_2		$101	$100
Maximum Return		$101*	

TABLE 6.4

Maximum Likelihood: Nonuse of Potentially Critical Information

State of Nature	$p(S_i)$	$A_1{}^*$	A_2
S_1	.40	$ 20	$60
→S_2	.60	100	40
Maximum Likelihood S_2		$100	$40
Maximum Return		$100*	

State of Nature	$p(S_i)$	A_1	$A_2{}^*$
→S_1	.40	$ 20	$60
S_2	.20	90	30
S_3	.20	100	40
S_4	.20	110	50
Maximum Likelihood S_1		$ 20	$60
Maximum Return			$60*

TABLE 6.5

Maximum Likelihood: Row Duplication

An Expected Monetary Value Criterion

Bayes' decision rule is another criterion that can be applied to a decision environment of uncertainty with probability information. The criterion specifies the selection of the alternative with the maximum expected value. The application of this criterion to the stock problem with an assumed subjective probability distribution is presented in Table 6.6.

If a decision maker selects one alternative for a large number of identical decision environments, the calculated EMV for this alternative will tend to equal the average of the actual returns. The larger the number of identical

State of Nature	$p(S_i)$	A_1	A_2*	A_3
Favorable	.24	$600	$250	$100
Normal	.42	50	200	100
Unfavorable	.34	−200	−100	100
EMV		$ 97	$110	$100
Maximum EMV			$110*	

TABLE 6.6
The Maximum Expected Monetary Value

decision environments, the more exact the EMV measure of anticipated average return.[2] Therefore, for a repetitive decision environment, the decision maker can use the EMV confidently to determine what to expect for each alternative. He or she will only logically select the alternative with the highest return—the alternative with the maximum EMV.

For a one-time decision, the supporting claims are not as tangible. The criterion satisfies the earlier requirement of inclusion of all probability and payoff information. It desirably maintains the properties of *independence*, *row linearity*, *convexity*, and *row duplication*. Under conditions of uncertainty, the maximum *EMV* appears to be an appropriate criterion. It appears to be the one that should be used.

MAXIMUM EXPECTED MONETARY VALUE: A LIMITATION

The *EMV* criterion is still something less than ideal. If it were ideal, the resulting alternative selection should be acceptable to the decision maker. The alternative selection should be consistent with the decision maker's feelings and judgment. In many situations, however, the typical decision maker will be unwilling to accept any *EMV* criterion selection. The criterion demonstrates an inconsistency in application.

St. Petersburg's paradox is an excellent illustration of the crux of the inconsistency. A decision maker has the opportunity to play a game in which a fair coin is tossed until a tail appears. The payoff is 2^n¢, n being equal to the

---

[2] This concept was more fully developed in Chapter 3 when the EMV was initially introduced.

total number of tosses. The potential payoffs, therefore, would be (T = tails, H = heads):

T	2¢
HT	4¢
HHT	8¢
$HHHT$	16¢
$\vdots$	$\vdots$

Before proceeding, stop for a moment and think this game over carefully. Now, how much would you *really* pay to play once?

The typical student is willing to pay about four cents. The worth of the opportunity can be computed. If an *EMV* criterion is acceptable, the opportunity will be worth the *EMV* value. Table 6.7 provides the calculation. The *EMV* is infinite.

State of Nature	$p(S_i)$	$\$_i$
H	1/2	2¢
HT	1/4	4¢
HHT	1/8	8¢
$HHHT$	1/16	16¢
.	.	.
.	.	.
.	.	.
H_nT_1	$1/2^{n+1}$	2^{n+1}¢
.	.	.
.	.	.
.	.	.

Expected Worth:
$$EMV = 1/2(2¢) + 1/4(4¢) + 1/8(8¢) + 1/16(16¢) + \ldots + 1/2^{n+1}(2^{n+1}) + \ldots$$
$$EMV = \$\infty$$

TABLE 6.7
The St. Petersburg's Paradox

To avoid semantic confusion, it would not be objectionable to substitute $1,000 trillion for infinity. The expected return—the return on the average—will therefore be $1,000 trillion. That is, if the game were played a very large number of times, the player would average $1,000 trillion *per play*. Are you willing to adjust your earlier estimate? Now how much would you pay for the chance to play once?

Even after being shown these calculations, and being offered a second chance to bid on this truly "golden" opportunity, most students still will not increase their offer much above four cents. Only after a little persuasion will a few students begin to think in terms of a dollar. The paradox: the intuitive worth to the student is four cents; the worth to an *EMV*'er is the mathematical expectation of $1,000 trillion. The appreciable difference between these two evaluations represents the inability of an *EMV* criterion to produce a decision consistent with a decision maker's personal feelings and judgment—consistent with the decision maker's true value system.

A second simple decision environment more clearly demonstrates the potential discrepancy between the selection of a typical decision maker and that of an *EMV*'er. A game is played one time by tossing a fair coin. The three alternatives are expressed in Table 6.8.

State of Nature		$p(S_i)$	$A_1{}^*$	$A_2{}^*$	A_3
Heads		.50	$100	$-30	$0
Tails		.50	-80	50	0
	EMV		$ 10	$ 10	$0
	Maximum	EMV	$ 10*	$ 10*	

TABLE 6.8
Expected Monetary Value: An Unacceptable Result

When a number of students were offered this choice, the majority selected alternative 3. In essence they decided to not play. On the other hand, the *EMV* evaluation indicates that A_1 and A_2 are far better choices. Of the few students who did not select A_3, most preferred A_2 over A_1. The *EMV* evaluation indicates that they are equally desirable. Moreover, of the students who preferred A_1 over A_2, *none* was willing to pay $10 for the opportunity to play. With *EMV*s of $10, both A_1 and A_2 should be worth $10 to an *EMV*'er. Although they fully agreed with the appropriateness of an *EMV* criterion, *none* of the students was willing to accept the decision dictates of the criterion.

The game was then altered rather "insignificantly." The monetary payoffs were reduced proportionately from dollars to cents (Table 6.9). When these same students were again asked to make an alternative selection, most of them were willing to accept A_1 and A_2. In fact, several students were willing to pay the *EMV* value of the preferred alternative for the opportunity to play. The "insignificant" alteration has significantly influenced the decision maker. For the *new* decision environment, an *EMV* criterion appears very appropriate indeed.

State of Nature	$p(S_i)$	$A_1{}^*$	$A_2{}^*$	A_3
Heads	.50	100¢	−30¢	0¢
Tails	.50	−80	50	0
	EMV	10¢	10¢	0¢
Maximum	EMV	10¢*	10¢*	

TABLE 6.9

Expected Monetary Value: An Acceptable Conclusion

For the typical student, different quantities of money do not represent proportionate measures of worth. A student views a decision involving tens or hundreds of dollars differently than he views a similar decision involving tens or hundreds of thousands of dollars. And for the often impoverished student, a decision involving dollars is different from a decision involving cents.[3]

The worth associated with money by a decision maker is often *nonlinear*—different quantities of money will often represent disproportionate worth. Therefore, if an alternative selection is to be consistent with a decision maker's value system, monetary quantities are not appropriate.

States of Nature	$p(S_i)$	$\$_i$
S_1	$p(S_1)$	$\$_1$
S_2	$p(S_2)$	$\$_2$
.	.	.
.	.	.
.	.	.
S_n	$p(S_n)$	$\$_n$
	1.00	

TABLE 6.10

Monetary Payoffs May Not Appropriately Measure Worth

---

[3] At some level, every decision maker succumbs to the *law of diminishing marginal utility: Additional units of an item tend to increase the total level of satisfaction, but less proportionately than previous quantities.*

THE STANDARD GAMBLE PROCEDURE

There is a procedure for converting inappropriate nonlinear monetary measures of worth into appropriate linear measures of worth. It is the *standard gamble procedure* developed by John von Neumann and Osker Morganstern. By utilizing information from the decision maker's value system, it structures a set of logic to transform nonlinear monetary values into linear measures of worth. It converts unacceptable monetary values into acceptable quantifications (Table 6.11).

All States of Nature, All Probability Information		Value (V_i): Adjusted for Monetary ($\$_i$) Information	
States of Nature	$p(S_i)$	$\$_i$	V_i
S_1	$p(S_1)$	$\$_1$	V_1
S_2	$p(S_2)$	$\$_2$	V_2
.	.	.	.
.	.	.	.
.	.	.	.
S_n	$p(S_n)$	$\$_n$	V_n

TABLE 6.11
Informational Components Consistent with the Decision Maker's Value System

The standard gamble is similar to *the standard lottery*. Two monetary values are selected to provide a standard for making relative comparisons. To measure the worth of a third monetary value relative to the two standard values, all three monetary values are expressed by a set of relationships. By selecting between two known options containing these three monetary values, the decision maker can express his or her personal feelings of relative desirability. A set of structured logic containing the decision maker's personal preference will be formed. This expression will represent a *single equation* containing a *single unknown*. With some algebra, the single equation can be solved for the unknown. The unknown worth of a monetary value can be transformed into an exact measure of relative worth.

More specifically, a decision maker is given a choice between two options: (1) option A, with a guaranteed monetary return, and (2) option B, with a probability p of one monetary return and a probability $1 - p$ of a second monetary return. The monetary return for option A is a value between the two values in option B. Therefore, as the probability in option B is changed, the decision maker will vary in preference between the two options. The value of the probability is adjusted until the decision maker is *indifferent* to the choice

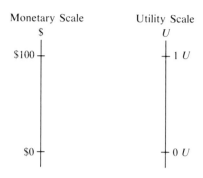

Monetary Scale
$

$100

$0

Utility Scale
U

1 U

0 U

FIGURE 6.1

A Standard for Relative Comparison

between the two options. For this specific probability, the two options are preferred equally. For the decision maker, the expected returns for the two options can be mathematically equated. This will form a single equation with a single unknown. The single equation can be solved for the unknown relative measure of worth.

This procedure is applied to the decision environment specified in Table 6.8. There are five possible monetary returns: $100, $50, $0, $-30, and $-80. The objective is to convert each of these *nonproportinate levels of worth* into a *common proportionate measure of relative worth*—to convert each monetary measure of worth into a corresponding common utility measure of worth.

The first step is to define an initial scale to provide a basic standard for relative comparison. In Figure 6.1, the values of $100 and $0 were *arbitrarily selected* and assigned levels of satisfaction of one utile and zero utiles respectively. The only essential requirement of this assignment is that the values must be logically consistent: $100 is valued more highly than $0; therefore, $100 must be assigned a higher level of satisfaction than $0. The values of one and zero were selected to facilitate conceptual compaiisons and computations.

The second step is to transform $50 to the utility scale by forming the two options. Keep in mind that the objective is to *form a single equation with the utility of $50 as the single unknown*. The two options will contain three monetary values; therefore, two of these must be known. The two standard values—$100 and $0—serve this purpose. With option A containing the middle value of worth, the two options are:

Option *A*   Option *B*
‾‾‾‾‾‾   ‾‾‾‾‾‾

$50 100p$ + $0(1 − p).

Option A provides a *guarantee* of $50. Option B provides a *probability p* of getting $100 and a *probability* 1 − p of getting $0.

If the probability of getting the $100 is very large, option B will be preferable to the guaranteed $50 of option A. Similarly, if p is very small, the $50 of option A will be preferable to a small chance of $100 and a large chance of $0 option B. For a specific decision maker at a given time, there will exist a value for p that makes the options equivalent. This *point of indifference* will equate the two options and form the *single equation*.

The equivalence between the two options is obtained by varying the value of p in option B. For example, a value of p equal to .80 might first be inserted into option B:

Option *A*   or   Option *B*
_____   _____

   $50   .80($100) + .20($0).

The decision maker then is asked to select one of the options. If option B is selected, the expected utility perceived from option B must be greater than that from option A:

$E(U_A) < E(U_B)$.

Since an equality is required for an exact measure of the relative worth of the $50, the value of p is adjusted more favorable to option A. For $p = .30$, the decision maker is again given a choice:

Option *A*   or   Option *B*
_____   _____

   $50   .30($100) + .70($0).

If option A is preferred:

$U_A > U_B$.

At this point, the value of p to equate the two options must be between .80 and .30. The decision maker is again offered the options with a new value of p within this range. The questioning continues by adjusting p within a smaller and smaller range until the point of indifference is reached.

At the point of indifference (say, $p = .65$), the decision maker perceives the expected satisfactions for option A to be equal to those for option B:

$E(U_A) = E(U_B)$.

While they are not equivalent monetarily:

Option *A*   Option *B*
_____   _____

   $50 $\neq$ .65($100) + .35($0)
   $50 $\neq$ $65
  EMV_A $\neq$ EMV_B,

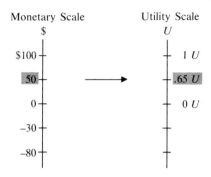

Monetary Scale
$

Utility Scale
U

$100 — — 1 U

50 — — .65 U

0 — — 0 U

−30 —

−80 —

FIGURE 6.2
Transforming Dollars to a Linear Utility Scale

The options are equivalent in terms of the decision maker's expected level of satisfaction. The *difference between monetary value and personal value is the exact discrepancy that is being clarified and built into the analysis.*

Again, from the standpoint of an expected utility, the options are identical:

$E(U_A) = E(U_B)$.

In terms of personal worth:

$U_{\$50} = .65\, U_{\$100} + .35\, U_{\$0}$.

An *equation* has been formed containing one unknown and two known utility values. By referring to the basic standard to convert monetary values into utility equivalents, the utility value of the unknown can be solved:

$U_{\$50} = .65(1\ U) + .35(0\ U)$
$\therefore\ U_{\$50} = .65\ U.$

Fifty dollars has a *relative worth* of .65 utiles (Figure 6.2).

The other monetary values are derived in the same way. To determine the utile worth of $−80$, option A and option B are again constructed to generate a single equation with the $U_{\$-80}$ as the solvable unknown. Two monetary values with known utility worth are required. They can be any two of the known values: $100, $0, or $50. To simplify computations, $100 and $0 will be used again. With the middle value as the guaranteed return,[4] the alternatives are:

Option *A*

Option *B*

$0

$100p + ($−80)(1 − p)$.

---

[4] If option A does not contain the middle value, no value of p will equate the options.

The choice is between a guaranteed $0 and a chance p of winning $100, plus a chance $1 - p$ of losing $80.

The value of p is now systematically adjusted until the decision maker feels indifferent to the choice between the two alternatives. If the value of p equating the two options is .70:

$$E(U_A) = E(U_B)$$
$$U_{\$0} = .70\, U_{\$100} + .30\, U_{\$-80}.$$

Taking the utility of $0 and $100 from the utility scale,

$$0\, U = .70(1\, U) + .30\, U_{\$-80}.$$

Solving for $U_{\$-80}$,

$$U_{\$-80} = -2.33\, U.$$

The utility of a loss of $80 is equivalent to -2.33 utiles.

The utility for $\$-30$ is determined in the same way to complete the transformation of the nonlinear monetary values into linear utility equivalences (Figure 6.3). With the complete utility scale, the previous problem can be

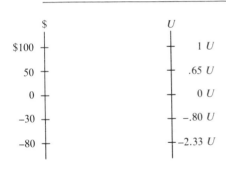

FIGURE 6.3
The Complete Utility Scale of Proportionate Worth

properly evaluated. In place of each monetary value, the corresponding utility worth is substituted. The evaluating statistic is also changed from maximum *EMV* to the utility counterpart: *maximum expected utility value—maximum EUV*.

Table 6.12 provides the decision that is consistent with the decision maker's feelings and judgment. The *proper* decision is to select A_3. The standard gamble makes possible the conversion of monetary returns that do not represent relative worth into quantitative expressions of relative worth. It transforms

State of Nature	$p(S_i)$	A_1		A_2		A_3*	
Heads	½	$~~100~~	1 U$	$~~-30~~	-.80 U$	$0	0 U$
Tails	½	$~~-80~~	-2.33 U$	$~~-50~~	.65 U$	$0	0 U$
		EUV	$-.665 U$		$-.025 U$		$0 U$
	Maximum	EUV					$0 U$*

TABLE 6.12
The Expected Utility Value

unacceptable quantitative payoffs into acceptable quantitative payoffs. The standard gamble enables a decision maker to adjust the often unacceptable EMV criterion into an acceptable EUV criterion.

BAYES' DECISION RULE: AN EXPECTED UTILITY VALUE CRITERION

Even with an appropriate consideration of the nonlinearity of monetary returns, using the procedure described above, the adjusted expected value criterion does not allow for the consideration of all potentially relevant information. Many, if not most, decisions contain *significant nonmonetary considerations*. These considerations must be built into an acceptable analysis.

For example, consider an *atypical* student's solution to a *typical* problem. An undergraduate must decide late Friday night either to work or to study over the weekend. He has a midterm examination in a quantitative methods course on Monday morning. Since the student wants to enter graduate school eventually, he needs a course grade of B or better. On the other hand, the student's financial position is bleak. A loan under the National Defense Education Act barely covers his tuition, room, board, and basic essentials. He considers additional finances a must for a proper life style. For his own peace of mind, rather than make an entirely subjective decision, the student seeks quantitative support for decision that will provide a maximum expected gain.

Being a good student in quantitative methods, he begins the analysis by clearly defining the alternatives. There are only two truly relevant actions to consider: to work or to study. Since his flexible work schedule is restricted to full days, the alternatives for the weekend are: A_1, work two days (W_2, S_0); A_2, work one day, study one day (W_1, S_1); or A_3, study two days (W_0, S_2).

Having listed the alternatives, he then begins to evaluate them. With a fixed take-home salary of $42 a day, the monetary returns for the alternatives are:

(W_2, S_0) A_1	(W_1, S_1) A_2	(W_0, S_2) A_3
$84	$42	$0

The reward from studying, however, is not so easily quantified. The grade depends not only on the present preparation, *but* also on the difficulty of the examination. To complicate matters, the instructor prepares new problems for each examination. The return from studying is uncertain.

After considerable thought, the student reasons that this must be *decision making under uncertainty without probability information*. The decision environment is separated into three possible states. The examination will be either hard, moderately hard, or easy. From classroom experience, conversations with classmates and former students, and reference to several old examinations, he has gathered enough information to be reasonably confident in assigning subjective probabilities to the environmental states. In terms of his own personal definition of hard, moderately hard, and easy, he assigns to these states respective values of .4, .5, and .1. He is pretty sure that the examination is not going to be easy.

Using his own personal definition of the environmental states, the student assesses the payoffs from studying. Considering his present preparedness, if he chooses to work both days (A_1) and the examination is hard, the *subjectively assessed* grade will be an F. However, if the examination is only moderately hard, the subjectively assessed grade will be a C. And if the exam is easy, the grade will be a B. Assessments for the other alternatives are summarized in Table 6.13.

Expressed only in terms of monetary returns, the alternative selection is the $84 associated with A_1. Expressed only in terms of returns from study,

Environmental States (S_i): The Midterm Examination	Subjective Probabilities $p(S_i)$	Work 2, Study 0 A_1	Work 1, Study 1 A_2	Work 0, Study 2 A_3
Hard	.4	F	C	B
Moderately Hard	.5	C	B	A
Easy	.1	B	A	A

TABLE 6.13

The Decision Environment for Studying

however, the alternative selection is the high grade associated with A_3. The objective is to combine both work and study into a single consideration. The monetary and scholastic returns can be combined into a total return in a single conditional profit table. For example, if A_1 is selected and a hard exam is given, the return will be $84 for the two days work and an F grade on the exam. The decision environment reflecting work and study is expressed in Table 6.14.

Environmental States (S_i)	$p(S_i)$	A_1	A_2	A_3
Hard	.4	$84 + F	$42 + C	$0 + B
Moderately Hard	.5	$84 + C	$42 + B	$0 + A
Easy	.1	$84 + B	$42 + A	$0 + A

TABLE 6.14

The Decision Environment for Work and Study

The remaining task is the evaluation of each alternative. The criterion is to maximize the expected level of satisfaction. The remaining difficulty is to develop a meaningful combination of dollars and grades—to resolve the proverbial problem of "adding apples and oranges."

Both dollars and grades can be transformed into a utility measure of satisfaction. Expressed in this common measure of worth, the dollars and grades can be added. The standard gamble procedure provides the means to acquire the decision maker's personal feelings of perceived relative worth. It provides the means to transform dollars and grades into utiles.

Each of the monetary and nonmonetary returns must be transformed to the utility scale of proportionate worth. To provide the required reference for relative worth, the $84 is assigned one utile and $0 is assigned zero utiles (Figure 6.4). The standard gamble will provide the relative worth of $42. The student has two hypothetical options: option A, with a guaranteed return of $42, or option B, with a probability p of $84 and a probability $1 - p$ of $0. The value of p is adjusted systematically until the options are equally desirable. This will produce a single equation with a single solvable unknown. The personal point of indifference and solution is provided in Table 6.15.

Next, the grades are transformed into utiles. Starting with the A, the student first determines its relative location on the monetary scale. This is accomplished by a simple comparison. A guaranteed A without study is compared with a guaranteed $84. If the A is preferred, it will be placed above the $84. If the $84 is preferred, the A will be placed below the $84. A similar comparison is made between the A and $42. If the A is preferred to the $42, it will be located between $84 and $42.

Decision Criteria Under Uncertainty With Probability Information

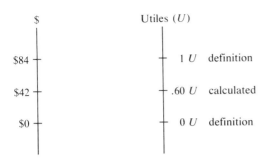

FIGURE 6.4
Transforming Dollars into Utiles

For this particular student, the A is preferred to the $84. Consequently, it is located above the $84 on the *monetary and nonmonetary scale* (Figure 6.5). The standard gamble procedure is employed as before. In this case, one of the options will contain the nonmonetary return. Using the already defined $84 and $0 to determine the worth of the A,[5] the two options will be:

Option A	Option B
$84	$Ap + \$0(1 - p)$.

Option A	Option B
$42	$\$84p + \$0(1 - p)$

Point of indifference at $p = .60$:

$$\text{Option A} = \text{Option B}$$
$$E(U_A) = E(U_B)$$
$$U_{\$42} = .60U_{\$84} + .40U_{\$0}$$

Expressed in utiles:

$$U_{\$42} = .60(1\ U) + .40(0\ U)$$
$$U_{\$42} = .60\ U$$

TABLE 6.15
The Relative Worth of $42

———

[5] Besides $84 and $0, the student could have used $84 and $42 or $42 and $0.

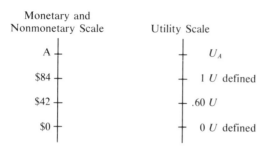

Monetary and
Nonmonetary Scale Utility Scale

A ┼ ┼ U_A

$84 ┼ ┼ 1 U defined

$42 ┼ ┼ .60 U

$0 ┼ ┼ 0 U defined

FIGURE 6.5

Monetary and Nonmonetary Transformations

Option A will consist of a guaranteed $84 with *no work or effort*. Option B will provide a probability p of an A grade *with no effort* and a probability $1 - p$ of $0.

For the student, the point of indifference is $p = .70$. For this likelihood, option A and option B are equivalent: the expected satisfactions from both are equal. This will produce the equality between the options, the single equation and solution for the unknown:

Option A = Option B
$\quad E(U_A) \quad = \quad E(U_B)$.

Specifically,

$$U_{\$84} = .70\ U_A + .30\ U_{\$0}.$$

In terms of utiles,

$$1\ U = .70\ U_A + .30(0\ U).$$

Solving:

$$U_A = 1.43\ U.$$

Each of the other grades is evaluated by a separate standard gamble. The complete scale of transformed monetary and nonmonetary returns is provided in Figure 6.6. Dollars and grades have been assigned proportionate measures of common worth.

Given a hard examination, the total utility of A_1 can be measured. The return associated with A_1 and a hard examination is $84 and an F grade. The levels of satisfaction are 1 U and -5.4 U respectively, or a total of -4.4 U. For A_1 and a moderately hard examination the returns are $84 and a C. The associated net

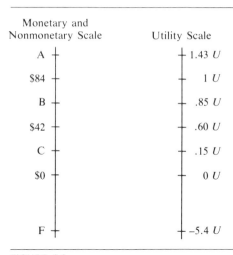

Monetary and Nonmonetary Scale	Utility Scale
A	1.43 U
$84	1 U
B	.85 U
$42	.60 U
C	.15 U
$0	0 U
F	−5.4 U

FIGURE 6.6

Returns Expressed as Relative Measures of Worth

satisfaction is 1.15 U. Using the utility scale in Figure 6.6, the decision environment of monetary and grade returns can be expressed as appropriate relative measures of worth (Table 6.16).

Once the payoffs are *standardized*, the alternatives can be evaluated by the expected utility value (EUV). As Table 6.16 illustrates, the best alternative for the student is A_3—take two days off work and study for the examination. Alternative 2, to work one day and study one day, is similarly desirable.[6] The student definitely would not be "rational" to work both days.

Environmental States (S_i)	$p(S_i)$	A_1	A_2	A_3*
Hard	.4	−4.4 U	.75 U	.85 U
Moderately Hard	.5	1.15 U	1.45 U	1.43 U
Easy	.1	1.85 U	2.03 U	1.43 U
	EUV	−1.400 U	1.045 U	1.069 U
Maximum	EUV			1.069 U*

TABLE 6.16

The Decision Environment with Standardized Payoffs

[6] Other considerations might be built into the analysis: the desirability of work compared to that of study, the relationship of the examination material to forthcoming material—all aspects of the decision environment might be more fully explored.

Nonmonetary considerations play an important role in a wide category of decisions. A person contemplating a new job will consider much more than salary. Many factors influencing the person's life style will significantly influence the decision: the new location, weather conditions, disruption of family, lost association with friends, the sale of a home, immediate and long-range promotional opportunities, and so forth. In an organizational setting, the evaluation of a manager's perception of the relative worth of both monetary and nonmonetary organizational returns might provide valuable insight into the rationale behind a manager's decisions. It should clarify why certain decisions have been made and what kind of decisions will probably be forthcoming. It will help explain why the production, marketing, and finance departments' executives rationally propose varied solutions; or what a manager's relative tradeoffs are between such corporate objectives as growth, profits, and personnel benefits. With a standardization of monetary and nonmonetary things of worth, a decision maker can begin to more fully understand another decision maker's value system—more fully understand the rationale of another decision maker's choice.

APPLYING AN EXPECTED UTILITY VALUE CRITERION

An appropriate decision criterion must consider the relevant information in a decision environment. If nonlinear monetary considerations or nonmonetary considerations are important, the criterion must consider them. This can be accomplished by extending the *EMV* criterion to the more general *EUV* criterion. Two common decision environments are considered below to demonstrate the potentially different decisions produced by these criteria.

The Rationality of Insurance

The rationality of purchasing insurance has frequently been questioned. The argument against insurance goes something like this. The buyer of insurance is gambling a small premium against a very, very small probability of avoiding a very large loss. Since the insurance company must keep records, support salesmen, and produce a profit, all of these costs must be included in the insurance premium. As a result, the mathematical odds must be favorable to the insurance company and, therefore, unfavorable to the buyer.

The owner of a home fire insurance policy might counter with the following reasoning. I insure my house because I hardly miss the yearly premium. If it should burn down without coverage, I would sustain a terrible loss. When I insure, I can guarantee my standard of living, and my income remains approximately the same. If I don't insure, I will be risking too large a loss.

Both arguments have appeal. Both appear to possess some truth. Considering the number of fire, life, accident, automobile, death, income protection, malpractice, and other insurable interest policies sold daily, can either the insurance companies or all of these people be wrong? For the sake of inquiry, a student is offered a hypothetically simplified insurance policy. For a premium of only $20, the policy will provide 100 percent protection against the total loss of the student's $2,000 automobile. The actuarial likelihood of making a claim on the policy is .0064.

For the insurance company, there is an expected gain of £7.20 (Table 6.17). If the number of similar policies is very large, the *law of large numbers* virtually guarantees that only a certain proportion of claims will be filed. The probability that the average return per policy will deviate substantially from the *EMV* value becomes statistically remote. In essence, if a large number of policies are sold, the insurance company is guaranteed a gain of $7.20.

Events	$p(e_i)$	Insurance Policy
Claim	.0064	$-1,980.00
No Claim	.9936	20.00
	$EMV =$	$7.20

TABLE 6.17
The Insurance Company's Expected Gain

If the insurance company stands to gain $7.20 per policy, then the purchaser must stand to lose the same sum. Table 6.18 verifies the expected monetary loss. Viewed from a monetary standpoint, the policy is not preferable—the first argument appears supportable.

Events	$p(e_i)$	Insurance A_1	No Insurance A_2*
Claim	.0064	$-20	$-2,000
No Claim	.9936	-20	0
	EMV	$-20	$-12.80
Maximum	EMV		$-12.80*

TABLE 6.18
The *EMV*'er: No Insurance

The argument against insurance is correct for an *EMV*'er—the purchase will result in an expected monetary loss. However, most people are not *EMV*'ers. Monetary losses will not represent linearly consistent measures of lost value. Most people will assign small premium payments and large losses a disproportionate worth. The *EUV*'er may view insurance quite differently.

In order to reconsider insurance from an *EUV* perspective, the purchaser's utility function for money is required. The shape of the utility function typically follows the traditional principle of *diminishing marginal utility*. As more and more money is accumulated, each additional amount provides a less than proportionate increase in satisfaction. For positive monetary gains, the slope of the utility function decreases with increasing quantities of money, eventually approaching an upper limit. For monetary losses, the disutility increases more than proportionately with increasing monetary loss, flattening as the amount of loss becomes very large. A typical utility function will take the shape expressed in Figure 6.7.

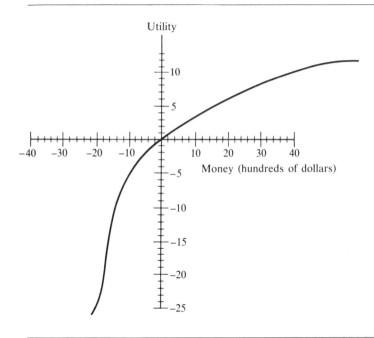

FIGURE 6.7
A Characteristic Utility Scale

Substituting a monetary scale for the student into Figure 6.7, the monetary values in the insurance decision can be transformed into utility values. Table 6.19 presents the alternative selection expressed in terms of perceived worth. The decision is to purchase insurance. From the decision maker's point of view, the policy is truly a rational choice.

Decision Criteria Under Uncertainty With Probability Information

Events	$p(e_i)$	Insurance $A_1{}^*$	No Insurance A_2
Claim	.0064	$-.110\ U$	$-26\ U$
No Claim	.9936	$-.110\ U$	$0\ U$
	EUV	$-.110\ U$	$-.1664\ U$
Maximum	EUV	$-.110\ U^*$	

TABLE 6.19

The EUV'er: Purchase Insurance

Considering most people's disproportionate worth for money and their aversion to large losses, a rational decision maker can benefit from insurance. Since an insurance company will sell a large number of similar policies, the EMV will accurately measure their expected gains. As long as salesmen, paperwork, interest on capital, and other costs can be covered, the insurance company will profit from selling the policy. Both parties have the prospect of a gain. The purchase of insurance will lead to mutual benefit, mutual satisfaction. No wonder insurance companies have been around for so long.

The Rationality of a Portfolio

Another interesting application of an EUV criterion is demonstrated in the following investment decision. Table 6.20 summarizes the possibilities. If the investor applies an EMV criterion, A_1 with an EMV of $10,000 is the better choice. A_2 with an EMV of $-2,500 appears unacceptable.

States of Nature	$p(S_i)$	Investment 1 $A_1{}^*$	Investment 2 A_2
S_1	.5	$30,000	$-15,000
S_2	.5	-10,000	10,000
	EMV	$10,000	$ -2,500
Maximum	EMV	$10,000*	

TABLE 6.20

An Investor's Decision: Monetary Consideration

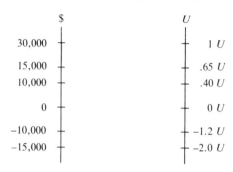

The Investor's Utility for Money

$	U
30,000	1 U
15,000	.65 U
10,000	.40 U
0	0 U
−10,000	−1.2 U
−15,000	−2.0 U

FIGURE 6.8

The Investor's Utility for Money

If the investor reconsiders the choice from a utility perspective (Figure 6.8), neither investment is acceptable (Table 6.21). It should be emphasized that A_2 *appears* undesirable from both a monetary and a utility perspective.

The tentative conclusions to the investment decision are (1) to select A_1 in terms of EMV and (2) to select neither alternative in terms of EUV. However, there is another possibility. Applying EUV, the investor might decide to select both A_1 and A_2. Selecting both separately undesirable alternatives produces a net expected gain. As indicated in Table 6.22, this new alternative provides an EUV of $+.325\ U$. While A_2 was undesirable from both a monetary and a utility standpoint, it provides a perfect hedge against losses.

From a monetary point of view, the combined alternative is desirable. It will always be less desirable, however, than the best of the separate alternatives. A combined alternative can never improve the alternative choice.

From a utility point of view, however, the conclusion is altered. Neither alternative is desirable separately. Combined, they provide a new, improved choice. A combined alternative can improve the best of the separate alternatives. In terms of an investor's value system, a hedge against losses is rational—a portfolio can provide an improved choice.

States of Nature	$p(S_i)$	Investment 1 A_1	Investment 2 A_2
S_1	.5	1.0 U	−2.0 U
S_2	.5	−1.2 U	.4 U
	EUV	−.10 U	−.80 U

TABLE 6.21

An Investor's Decision: Utility Consideration

States of Nature	$p(S_i)$	Monetary Consideration A_1^*	A_2	$A_1 + A_2$
S_1	.5	$30,000	$-15,000	$15,000
S_2	.5	-10,000	10,000	0
	EMV	$10,000	$ -2,500	$ 7,500
Maximum	EMV	$10,000*		

States of Nature	$p(S_i)$	Utility Consideration A_1	A_2	$A_1 + A_2^*$
S_1	.5	1.0 U	-2.0 U	.65 U
S_2	.5	-1.2 U	.4 U	0 U
	EUV	-.1 U	-.8 U	+.325 U
Maximum	EUV			.325 U*

TABLE 6.22

The Investor's Hedge Against Loss: A Portfolio Selection

SUMMARY

Using the standard lottery to structure subjective feelings into measured probabilities, a decision environment of uncertainty without probability information can be transformed into one with probability information. If the decision maker will fully express an understanding of the decision environment, a decision environment without an acceptable criterion can be converted into a decision environment with an acceptable criterion.

With probability information available, an *EMV* criterion becomes a candidate for consideration. While it maintains the properties of logical consistency, this criterion is based on two limiting assumptions. First, monetary quantities represent proportionate measures of worth. Second, the decision does not involve any important nonmonetary considerations. Most decision environments, however, do not adhere strictly to these assumptions. In such cases, an *EMV* criterion will not consider potentially critical information. It will not be an appropriate criterion.

The standard gamble procedure resolves this difficulty. Using the decision maker's personal value structure, it allows the transformation of nonlinear monetary and nonmonetary consequences into a common linear utility measure of worth. With these measures of worth, the *EMV* criterion is converted into an *EUV* criterion. Fully considering the relevant informational components of a decision environment, an *EUV* criterion will provide logically consistent and acceptable alternative selections. It is an appropriate criterion.

BIBLIOGRAPHY

Bierman, H., Jr., C. P. Bonini, and W. H. Hausman. *Quantitative Analysis for Business Decisions.* Homewood, Ill.: Richard D. Irwin, 1973.

Easton, A. *Complex Managerial Decisions Involving Multiple Objectives.* New York: John Wiley & Sons, 1973.

Friedman, M., and L. J. Savage. "The Utility Analysis of Choices Involving Risk." *Journal of Political Economy*, August 1948, pp. 279–304.

Gupta, S. K., and J. M. Cozzolino. *Fundamentals of Operations Research for Management.* San Francisco: Holden-Day, 1974.

Halter, A. N., and G. W. Dean. *Decisions Under Uncertainty with Research Application.* Cincinnati: South-Western Publishing Co., 1971.

Horowitz, I. *An Introduction to Quantitative Business Analysis.* New York: McGraw-Hill Book Co., 1965.

Mosteller, F., and P. Nogee. "An Empirical Measurement of Utility." *Journal of Political Economy*, October 1971, pp. 371–404.

Paik, C. M. *Quantitative Methods for Managerial Decisions.* New York: McGraw-Hill Book Co., 1973.

Raiffa, H. *Decision Analysis: Introductory Lectures on Choices Under Uncertainty.* Reading, Mass.: Addison-Wesley Publishing Co., 1968.

Schlaifer, R. *Analysis of Decisions Under Uncertainty.* New York: McGraw-Hill Book Co., 1969.

————. *Probability and Statistics for Business Decisions.* New York: McGraw-Hill Book Co., 1959.

Siegel, S. "Level of Aspiration and Decision Making." *Psychological Review* 64 (1957): pp. 253–262.

Swalm, R. O. "Utility Theory—Insights into Risk Taking." *Harvard Business Review*, November-December 1966, pp. 123–136.

von Neumann, J., and O. Morgenstern. *Theory of Games and Economic Behavior.* Princeton: Princeton University Press, 1944.

6.1. How appropriate is an *EMV* criterion for a large gambling casino? What conclusion can be drawn regarding the value of *EMV* to the gamblers?

6.2. To what extent should the night crew foreman in charge of production rely on an *EMV* criterion?

6.3. In making personal loan decisions, should a bank's loan officer use an *EMV* criterion? Should the borrower?

6.4. Consider the following alternatives:

States of Nature	$p(S_i)$	Actions A_1	A_2	A_3
S_1	.2	$ 0	$1,000	$ 0
S_2	.5	1,000	0	− 100
S_2	.3	− 500	0	1,000

1. Which alternative would a large organization select?
2. Which alternative would you select? Construct your own utility scale and determine the quantitative verifiability of your selection. (In the case of a loss, payment must be made within four days.)

6.5. Confronted with the indicated alternatives, at what value of p will an *EMV*'er be indifferent?

States of Nature	$p(S_i)$	A_1	A_2
S_1	p	$ 20,000	$200
S_2	$1 - p$	− 2,000	200

6.6. To prevent students from getting too far behind, an economics instructor periodically gives surprise quizzes. One of the students in the class is deciding whether or not to prepare for a possible quiz. Although she doesn't mind studying the material, she has other commitments and to prepare tonight will produce 2 utiles of lost satisfaction. If she is not prepared and there is no quiz, the gains and losses are insignificant. If she is not prepared and there is a quiz, the anticipated loss will be around 10 utiles. If she is prepared and there is a quiz, the anticipated gain will be 4 utiles of satisfaction.

The student assesses the chances of a quiz at one in six. If she uses a maximum likelihood criterion, what will she do? Since the probability of no quiz exceeds that of a quiz at any given meeting, how well will the student who uses maximum likelihood do on the quizzes?

6.7. The owner of a small business has been offered the opportunity to form a partnership and expand activities. The present worth of his business is approximately $400,000. If the partnership works out as expected, his share of the new organization is estimated to exceed $900,000. If the expansion is not successful, however, the present business will be completely lost. All indicators strongly predict success. In fact, very conservative probability assessments indicate an 80 percent chance of a successful expansion.

If the owner decides not to expand, what conclusion would you draw regarding his utility for money? How much would an *EMV*'er pay for this opportunity? If the owner were an *EMV*'er, what monetary worth would he have to assign to his small business to support the decision not to expand?

6.8. A person has a utility of four for $400 and a utility of one for $0. If this person feels indifferent to the choice between a guaranteed $400 and the chance to toss a fair coin with heads paying $1,000 and tails nothing, what is the inferred utility assignment for $1,000?

6.9. A person has a choice between two alternatives: a guaranteed $100 or a chance at $10,000 with the possibility of a loss of $-1,000. If the person has a utility index of 2 *U* for the $100 and of 10 *U* for $10,000, and an indifference probability of .24 for the $10,000 option, what is the utility measure for $-1,000?

6.10. A new home owner has an option to purchase a fire insurance policy providing complete coverage for $250. If there is a fire, the estimated loss without the policy is $70,000. The actuarial estimate of a fire loss is .0006. The utility for the $250 payment is $-.1$. The $70,000 loss has a utility index of -200. Is the insurance policy an attractive alternative for the home owner?

6.11.

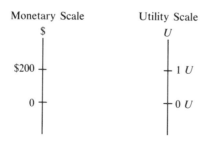

Quantitatively express your personal level of satisfaction for a seven-day, all-expense-paid ski vacation for two to Aspen, Colorado. The vacation can be taken any time within the next two years. Air fare, lodging, lift tickets, and four days of lessons are included in the package. If you don't like skiing, there is the lodge, swimming in a heated pool, and evenings on the town.

6.12. For certain small investments, three financial analysts have indicated the utility functions used in alternative selections:

Analyst 1: $U = 4 + 1(\$)$
Analyst 2: $U = 2 + .5(\$)$
Analyst 3: $U = 1 + .1(\$)$ $\$ = $ Monetary Value.

For monetary decisions, which analyst's utility function will an EMV'er prefer?

6.13. To refute the proverbial maxim, "you cannot add apples and oranges," your quantitative analysis professor has submitted the following alternative selection:

States of Nature	$p(S_i)$	A_1	A_2
S_1	.3	4 oranges	$1
S_2	.5	2 apples	2 oranges
S_3	.2	50¢ & 1 apple	1 apple

Quantitatively demonstrate a rational choice, using an EUV criterion with your own value system.

6.14. The manager of a food packing plant is considering the expansion of production facilities to a new area. He has the following information:

States of Nature	$p(S_1)$	Expanded Facilities A_1	Present Facilities A_2
S_1	.60	$ 8,000,000	$1,000,000
S_2	.40	− 6,000,000	1,000,000

What kinds of considerations might result in the selection of A_2? What might the manager want to do before making the final decision?

6.15. A potential criminal is completing plans to burglarize a wealthy household while the owners are away on a four-day vacation. He estimates the black-market value of the take, mostly jewelry, at $25,000. He assesses his chance of being caught at .10.

Viewed solely from a *monetary* perspective, what loss must be associated with getting caught to prevent the crime?

The would-be robber is willing to spend a year in jail for $20,000 in tax-free income. If an increase in the sentence requires a proportional increase in income, what is the minimum sentence required to deter him?

If the potential criminal (who has no prior record) assesses his maximum jail sentence at two years (with good behavior), what will be his inevitable decision (solely from a monetary perspective)? What is the minimum haul necessary to make the robbery a rational choice?

What must society do to dissuade this potential criminal—to make the robbery a less desirable alternative?

6.16. A new park with picnic and tennis facilities has been proposed at a city council meeting. To justify the expenditure, outline an approach the city planners might use to quantify the perceived worth of the park to local taxpayers.

6.17. On a beautiful Sunday morning near the end of finals, a student is confronted with a conflict of interest. He has just been invited to have a great time with a friend at a nearby lake. But on Monday morning he has a final examination in quantitative analysis.

Before deciding, he requested the friend's indulgence while he analyzed the situation. To the friend's utter amazement, the student performed the following analysis. The final was assumed to be either easy, average, or hard. If it was easy, he expected an A, whether he studied or not. If it was average, he expected an A with study and probably a B with no study. If the test was hard, however, he expected only a B with study and with no study a D.

To provide a measure of worth, a B was assigned one utile. An A was worth twice as much as B. Moreover, the student felt indifferent to the choice between (1) a B with certainty or (2) a 90 percent chance of an A and a 10 percent chance of a D.

From limited acquired knowledge, the student subjectively assessed the probabilities for a hard, average, and easy examination at .20, .40, and .40, respectively. He estimated the projected satisfaction from the trip at about .8 utiles.

The student's objective was to maximize expected satisfaction. What was his decision? If his friend could provide an additional .2 utiles of persuasion, would this alter his decision?

7

Decision Making in a Competitive Environment: Game Theory

In many situations, an inherent conflict of interest exists between parties competing for a common return. Examples of decision making under conflict include: athletic competition, collective bargaining, contract bidding, political campaigning, military deployment strategy, pricing strategy, and bartering in the process of exchange. When a competitor's actions can materially influence a decision, the competitor's behavior must be included as part of the decision environment, game theory provides a decision maker with formal models to incorporate this aspect into the decision environment—to facilitate decision making under conflict.

ASSUMPTIONS AND CLASSIFICATION OF A COMPETITIVE ENVIRONMENT

A decision environment of conflict is typically complex and multidimensional. Instead of depending on a probabilistically measured *constant state of nature*, the desirability of alternatives depends on the *adaptive behavior of competing opponents*. A proper decision, therefore, will depend on many factors affecting adaptive competitive behavior. These include the number of competitors, the degree of conflicting interests, the basic psychological character of the players, the force one opponent can impose on another, the timing of the selected course of action, the level of direct communication, the possibility and desirability of coalitions and countercoalitions, the availability of information, and the rationality of play.

To simplify, only a clearly specified part of the complex real-world environment will be *abstracted* for model development. The underlying assumptions, the rules of the game, are as follows: 1. The players act rationally and intelligently. 2. The players attempt to maximize gains and minimize losses. 3. All relevant information is known to each player. 4. The players make individual decisions without direct communication. and 5. The players simultaneously select their respective courses of action.

If any of these assumptions is not maintained, the decision maker's desired course of action may be materially altered. If the opponent does not play intelligently or rationally, lacks relevant information, does not attempt to maximize gains and minimize losses, or allows the selected course of action to be known in advance, it is usually possible to find a better strategy.

Classification of a Competitive Environment

The theory of rational behavior in an environment of competitive conflict—game theory—is usually classified according to the number of competitors and the level of competition. This taxonomy provides four categories:

(1) Two-person games
   (a) Zero-sum
   (b) Nonzero-sum

(2) N-person games
   (a) Zero-sum
   (b) Nonzero-sum

The categories tend to be self-explanatory. The *two-person game* represents a *competitive situation consisting of two opponents.* The *n-person game consists of n players* where *n typically infers a value larger than two.* The term *zero-sum* is less obvious. It means that the *sum of the returns to the players is zero.* If, for example, there are two players, one player's gain will be the other player's loss. In a *nonzero-sum game, the returns to the respective players* are *not* in direct opposition. For example, an organization's advertising campaign might increase not only the organization's sales but also those of competitors within the industry. Similarly, competing organizations might each develop a retail outlet in one sales area, resulting in a net deficit for both.

A TWO-PERSON ZERO-SUM GAME WITH A PURE STRATEGY

The following example illustrates the basic properties of a two-person zero-sum game. In a regional sales area, two companies compete for the same consumer market. Both companies are considering the possibility of adding a new product to the present product line. Both companies are required to choose between two strategies: 1. Introduce the new product. 2. Don't introduce the new product. For practical purposes the regional duopolistic market is fixed in size. New sales obtained by one company result in proportional lost sales for the other company. One company's gains are the other's losses: a zero-sum situation.

The respective returns for the players' strategy selections are represented by a *joint conditional profit matrix* (Table 7.1). If company A introduces the new product and company B does not, the joint strategy $S_{A_1}S_{B_2}$ will produce a 7 percent increase in market share for company A and a 7 percent loss for company B. Similarly, for the joint play $S_{A_2}S_{B_1}$, company A will lose 5 percent of the market to company B. Table 7.1 provides the other anticipated market share effects, expressed in terms of gains for company A and losses for company B.

| | | Company B | |
		S_{B1}: New Product	S_{B2}: No New Product
Company A	S_{A1}: New Product	2	7
	S_{A2}: No New Product	−5	0

TABLE 7.1
A Two-Person Zero-Sum Game

In game theory problems two important questions must be answered: 1. What strategy or strategies should a rational intelligent, informed player select? 2. What is the associated value of the game? Before providing a mathematical solution these questions will be answered logically.

Starting the analysis from company A's perspective (Table 7.2), company A might focus on company B's potential selection. If company B introduced the new product (S_{B_1}), company A would prefer to introduce a similar new product (S_{A_1}). In other words, company A would prefer a gain of 2 percent (S_{A_1}) to a loss of 5 percent (S_{A_2}). Similarly, if company B does not introduce the product (S_{B_2}), company A would prefer S_{A_1}, with a 7 percent gain, to S_{A_2}, with a 0 percent gain. In fact, regardless of company B's strategy selection, company A will always have a preferable outcome by selecting S_{A_1} instead of S_{A_2}. The only rational, intelligent, informed strategy selection for company A must be S_{A_1}—to introduce the new product expanding the product line.

Being a rational, intelligent, informed player too, company B realizes that company A will choose S_{A_1}. Therefore, assuming that company A will introduce the product (S_{A_1}), company B has a choice between S_{B_1}, with a loss of 2 percent, and S_{B_2}, with a loss of 7 percent. Company B will prefer to introduce a similar new product (S_{B_1}) and lose only 2 percent of the market share.

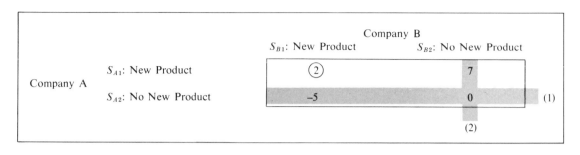

		Company B	
		S_{B1}: New Product	S_{B2}: No New Product
Company A	S_{A1}: New Product	②	7
	S_{A2}: No New Product	−5	0 (1)
			(2)

TABLE 7.2

$S_{A_1}S_{B_1}$: The Logical Choice

The logical resolution of the competitive situation is for both companies to introduce a new product, with company A receiving a 2 percent increase in market share:

Company A S_{A_1}: Introduce New Product
Company B S_{B_1}: Introduce New Product
Value of the game (V_A): 2 percent of market share to company A

Before proceeding, some game theory terminology may be useful. If a strategy is *as good as or better than another for all of the opponent's plays*, it is termed a *dominating strategy*. In Table 7.2, if company B selects S_{B_1}, company A will prefer S_{A_1}. If company B selects S_{B_2}, company A will still prefer S_{A_1}. For all of company B's plays, S_{A_1} is preferable to S_{A_2}: S_{A_1} dominates S_{A_2}. Moreover, since the *dominated* strategy will never be selected, it can be removed from further analysis.

If a player has a *single strategy that dominates all the others*, it is called *pure strategy*. In the final solution of the new product problem, company A selected the dominant *pure strategy* S_{A_1} and company B the *pure strategy* S_{B_1}.

An Appropriate Criterion for a Competitive Environment

In order to select a proper alternative, an appropriate criterion is required to evaluate and sort alternative stratagems. A decision environment against an opponent is substantially different from the earlier decision environments against *nature*. In an environment against *nature*, the decision maker was confronted with *uncertain states of nature*. The uncertainty could be quantified by objective or subjective probability statements. In the present competitive environment, the decision maker is confronted with a *thinking opponent with opposing interests*. The probabilities associated with an opponent's play may not be known or knowable. Furthermore, without probability assessments, the previously recommended criteria against *nature* (*EUV* or *EMV*) are no longer operative.

In an environment of conflict, a different decision criterion is required. Of the criteria previously considered, the *minimax-maximin* (Chapter 5) appears most suitable. In a decision environment against *nature*, minimax-maximin was demonstrably conservative. It provided the highest guaranteed level of security. Against a rational, intelligent, informed opponent, a guaranteed level of security has much more appeal. If the opponent selects the most rational, intelligent, informed plays, the *best* conceivable counterstrategy cannot provide more than the highest guaranteed gain—cannot be better than minimax-maximin.

The Minimax-Maximin Solution

The minimax-maximin criterion provides a very systematic means for resolving the problem summarized in Table 7.1. To review briefly: *Minimax selects the alternative with the minimum of the maximum losses*—the best of the worst losses. It is the appropriate criterion for the *loser* of the game. *Maximin selects the maximum of the minimum guaranteed gains*—the best of the worst guaranteed gains. It is the appropriate criterion for the *winner*. In fact, if the payoff matrix contains both gains and losses for each player, either criterion will yield the same result. Minimax and maximin both select the best of the worst outcomes.

In the previous problem, minimax and maximin can be applied in the margin of the payoff matrix (Table 7.3). For each player, the worst outcome per alternative is listed and the best of the worst options is selected.

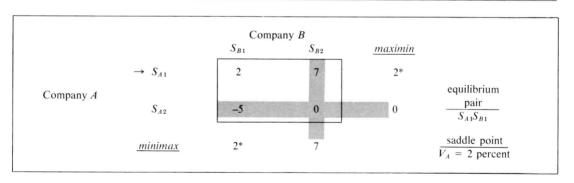

TABLE 7.3

The Minimax-Maximin Solution

For example, if company A plays S_{A_1}, the worst outcome will be a gain of 2 percent of the market. If company A plays S_{A_2}, the worst outcome will be a gain of 0 percent. The best of the worst, the maximin, is S_{A_1} with a *guaranteed* gain of 2 percent.

If the maximum of the row minima is equal to the minimum of the column maxima (maximin = minimax), the optimal pure strategy selection for both players and the value of the game are specified:

A	B	V_A
S_{A_1}	S_{B_1}	2 percent

Such a *pure strategy* solution is often referred to as an *equilibrium pair*. Neither player can move from this *equilibrium* without risking a worsened position. Moreover, since the point of intersection of the players' pure strategies is the row minimum and column maximum, this point is commonly called a *saddle point*. It will be equal to the value of the game (2 percent).

A TWO-PERSON ZERO-SUM GAME WITH A MIXED STRATEGY

A new decision environment involves two companies' selection of sales promotion strategies. Each company has three strategies in a fixed, regional, duopolistic market. The effectiveness of the strategy is measured by the company's increase in the market share. One company's gains, however, are the other's losses: the returns are zero-sum. In terms of the gain in market share to company A, Table 7.4 provides the summary of information for the game.

The first step in the analysis is to determine the minimax and maximin. If the two are equal, the pure strategy solution and value of the game will be specified by the *saddle point* for the *equilibrium pair*. As Table 7.4 illustrates, minimax is not equal to the maximin. There is no saddle point or equilibrium pair. There is no best *pure strategy* solution for either player.

With no pure strategy solution, both players will prefer to alter the strategy selection or play a *mixed strategy*. The causal reasoning is readily demonstrated.

		Company B			
		S_{B1}	S_{B2}	S_{B3}	*maximin*
	S_{A1}	7	−6	8	−6*
Company A	S_{A2}	−7	8	−7	−7
	S_{A3}	5	−8	4	−8
	minimax	7*	8	8	

TABLE 7.4
Sales Promotion Strategies

Decision Making in a Competitive Environment: Game Theory

If company A always selects S_{A_1}, company B will select S_{B_2}, providing a 6 percent loss for company A. If company A always selects S_{A_2}, company B will select either S_{B_1} or S_{B_3}, and company A will lose 7 percent. Similarly, if company A selects a pure strategy of S_{A_3}, company B will select S_{B_2}, producing a loss of 8 percent to company A. On the other hand, if company B plays any pure strategy, it will suffer a similar loss. A pure strategy is not desirable for either player.

Once both players realize the necessity of a mixed strategy, the next logical step is to remove any *dominated* strategies. Again, one strategy dominates another when it is as good as or better than the other for all of the opponent's strategy selections. Table 7.5 provides the comparison of S_{A_1} with S_{A_2} for all of company B's alternatives. If company B plays S_{B_1}, company A will prefer S_{A_1}, with a gain of 7 percent, to S_{A_2}, with a loss of 7 percent. If company B plays S_{B_2}, company A will prefer S_{A_2}, with a gain of 8 percent. If company B plays S_{B_3}, company A will again prefer S_{A_1} (a gain of 8 percent) to S_{A_2} (a loss of 7 percent). S_{A_1} and S_{A_2} are each preferred part of the time. Neither strategy will be preferred in all cases. Because the removal of either strategy entails a potential disadvantage, there is no dominance.

	$S_{B1}\downarrow$	$S_{B2}\downarrow$	$S_{B3}\downarrow$
S_{A1}	7*	−6	8*
S_{A2}	−7	8*	−7

TABLE 7.5
S_{A_1} Does Not Dominate S_{A_2}

Table 7.6 provides a similar comparison of S_{A_1} and S_{A_3}. If S_{B_1} is selected, company A will prefer S_{A_1}. If S_{B_2} or S_{B_3} is selected, S_{A_1} will again be preferred. For all of the opponent's plays, S_{A_1} is preferred over S_{A_3}. There is no situation favorable to S_{A_3}. S_{A_1} dominates S_{A_3}—S_{A_3} should be removed from the analysis.

	$S_{B1}\downarrow$	$S_{B2}\downarrow$	$S_{B3}\downarrow$
S_{A1}	7*	−6*	8*
S_{A3}	5	−8	4

TABLE 7.6
S_{A_1} Dominates S_{A_3}

Company B will undertake a similar search for dominance. Being intelligent, rational, and informed, company B will realize that, for the previous reasons, company A will never play S_{A_3}. In terms of company A's remaining plays (S_{A_1} and S_{A_2}), S_{B_1} will be compared with S_{B_2}, S_{B_1} with S_{B_3}, and S_{B_2} with S_{B_3}. As Table 7.7 indicates, S_{B_1} is as good as or better than S_{B_3} for all of company A's selections. S_{B_1} dominates S_{B_3}, and therefore S_{B_3} will be removed from further analysis.

	S_{B1}	S_{B3}
S_{A1}	7*	8
S_{A2}	−7*	−7*

TABLE 7.7

S_{B_1} Dominates S_{B_3}

After company B has removed S_{B_3}, company A's strategy selections must be checked again for dominance. S_{A_1} and S_{A_2} are compared; neither dominates. This is only to be expected. Since no pure strategy exists for either player, at least two strategy selections for each player must remain.

A Mixed Strategy Solution for Company A: A Graphic Solution

With the removal of dominated strategies, the game is reduced to the alternatives in Table 7.8. Company A will play S_{A_1} some proportion of the time (p) and

		Company B			
		S_{B1}	S_{B2}	S_{B3}	
	S_{A1}	7	−6	8	p
Company A	S_{A2}	−7	8	−7	$1 - p$
	S_{A3}	5	−8	4	(1) S_{A3} dominated by S_{A1}

(2)

S_{B3} dominated by S_{B1}

TABLE 7.8

The Reduced Problem

S_{A_2} the remaining proportion of the time $(1 - p)$. The objective will be to define the best p producing the highest guaranteed value of the game (V_A).

As with other problems, a solution can be reached by following the general model for decision making:

1. List all alternatives.
2. Restrict the number of alternatives.
3. Evaluate those remaining.
4. Select the *best*.

In constructing the alternative space (Figure 7.1), company A's mixed strategy selections can be represented by a continuum on the horizontal axis. At one extreme, company A will always play S_{A_1} and never S_{A_2} represented by $A(1, 0)$. At the other, it will always play S_{A_2} and never S_{A_1} $A(0, 1)$. The remainder of the continuum is divided proportionately between the use of S_{A_1} and S_{A_2}.

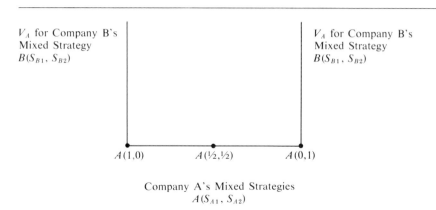

FIGURE 7.1

The Alternative Space

Company A's mixed strategy alternatives are now ready for evaluation. The desirability of each alternative depends on company B's alternative selection. The value of the game (V_A) for each of company A's alternatives in terms of company B's play can be represented on the vertical axis.

Company A's alternative $A(1, 0)$ can be evaluated by referring to the reduced problem (Table 7.8). If company B always plays S_{B_1} and never S_{B_2} $B(1, 0)$, company A will receive a 7 percent increase in market share. If company B selects $B(0, 1)$, company A will receive 6 percent. Company B might also select $B(1/2, 1/2)$. In this case, for a given play, company A will receive either 7 percent or -6 percent, depending on company B's specific play. Since company

B will play S_{B_1} and S_{B_2} half of the time each, the expected payoff to company A will be:

$$V_A = 7 \cdot P(S_{B_1}) - 6 \cdot P(S_{B_2})$$

$$B(\tfrac{1}{2}, \tfrac{1}{2})$$

$$V_A = 7 \cdot \frac{1}{2} - 6 \cdot \frac{1}{2}$$

$$V_A = \frac{1}{2}.$$

For select alternatives for company B, the expected payoffs to company A for strategy $A(1, 0)$ are represented in Figure 7.2. Note that, regardless of B's alternative, A's expected payoff cannot be more than 7 percent or less than -6 percent. These values are the extremes associated with B's respective selection of $B(1, 0)$ or $B(0, 1)$. If any combination of S_{B_1} and S_{B_2} is chosen as a mixed strategy, the expected payoff to A will have to fall within these boundaries.

A similar set of evaluations can be performed for the other extreme alternative $A(0, 1)$. For the select alternatives for company B, the expected

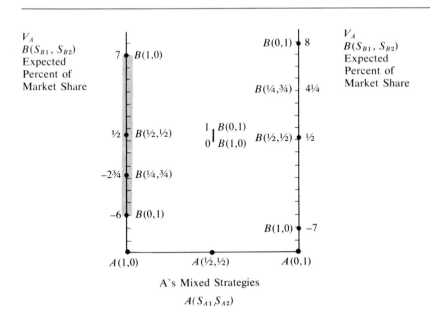

FIGURE 7.2
Evaluating Select Joint Alternatives

Decision Making in a Competitive Environment: Game Theory

payoffs to company A will be:

$B(S_{B_1}, S_{B_2})$	V_A for $A(0, 1)$
$B(1, 0)$	-7
$B(0, 1)$	8
$B(1/2, 1/2)$	$1/2$
$B(1/4, 3/4)$	$4\ 1/4.$

These values are included in Figure 7.2.

Note that the extreme alternatives for company B of $B(1, 0)$ and $B(0, 1)$ establish the *boundary* for the expected payoffs to company A. If company B selects $B(1, 0)$ and company A selects a mixed strategy of $A(p, 1 - p)$, the expected payoff becomes:

$$V_A = 7p - 7(1 - p).$$
$$B(1, 0)$$

For varying selections of p, the payoff will vary likewise. A more acceptable expression will be:

$$V_{A_i} = 7p_i - 7(1 - p_i).$$
$$B(1, 0)$$

This is a linear equation representable by a straight line through the previously derived three points associated with $B(1, 0)$.

Similarly, $B(0, 1)$ will represent a boundary of expected payoff values for varying mixed strategies for company A:

$$V_{A_j} = -6p_j + 8(1 - p_j).$$
$$B(0, 1)$$

This equation can also be represented graphically for all of company A's possibilities.

Figure 7.3 provides the linear *boundary equations* representing the bounded region of expected returns for all of company A's mixed strategy selections. The shaded area represents the alternative space for company A as a function of the joint mixed strategy selections by both companies. If company A selects a mixed strategy of $A(1, 0)$, for example, the expected payoff will be in the range of -6 percent to 7 percent. If company A selects $A(0, 1)$, the range is -7 percent to 8 percent. If company A selects $A(1/2, 1/2)$, the bounded expected payoffs are narrowed to 0 percent and 1 percent.

The *boundary equations* provide company A with a measure of the desirability of each alternative mixed strategy in terms of all of company B's possibilities. The remaining task is to select the *best* alternative.

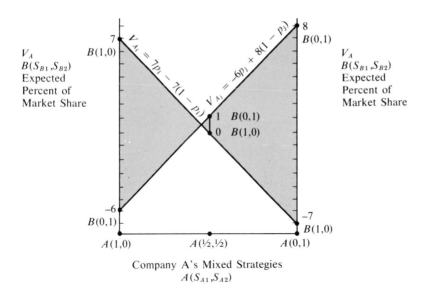

FIGURE 7.3

The Bounded Region of Expected Returns

The minimax-maximin criterion will be used to define *best*. Refer to Figure 7.4, which depicts company A's alternative space. The objective is to find the alternative that provides the *highest guaranteed return regardless of the opponent's selection*. If company A selects $A(1, 0)$, the guarantee will be the worst expected payoff of -6 percent. If company A selects $A(3/4, 1/4)$, the return will be between 3.5 percent and -2.5 percent, depending on company B's play. The highest guarantee will be along the lower boundary at -2.5 percent of market share. If company A selects the mixed strategy $A(1/2, 1/2)$, the return will be in the range from 0 percent to 1 percent. The highest guaranteed payoff will be the lowest value of 0 percent. If company A selects $A(0, 1)$, the highest guarantee regardless of company B's play will be on the lowest boundary at -7 percent of market share.

For a given alternative for company A, all of the guarantees are located on the lower of the two boundary equations. The lower boundary equations, therefore, define the *guaranteed returns* for company A's mixed strategy selections. They define a *new reduced alternative space*. The optimal mixed strategy selection will be restricted to the guaranteed returns along the lower of these two lines.

Compare the guaranteed returns along the lower boundary equations (Figure 7.4). The highest guarantee is located at the intersection of the two boundary equations. Regardless of the opponent's ingenuity, this mixed strategy provides the maximum guaranteed return—the maximin optimal strategy selection.

Decision Making in a Competitive Environment: Game Theory

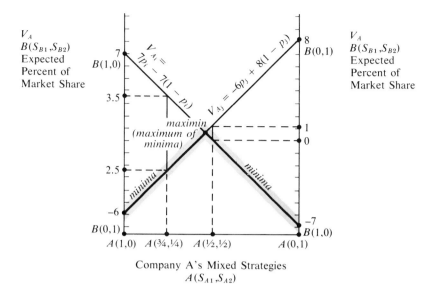

FIGURE 7.4

The Maximin Solution

The specific solution can be obtained by simultaneously solving the two boundary equations for p and V_A:

$$V_{A_i} = 7p_i - 7(1 - p_i)$$
$$V_{A_j} = -6p_j + 8(1 - p_j).$$

At the point of intersection, both equations have the same value for p and V_A. The i and j subscripts can be dropped. The equations can be set equal and solved for p:

$$V_{A_i} = V_{A_j}$$
$$7p - 7(1 - p) = -6p + 8(1 - p)$$
$$p = \frac{15}{28}.$$

The value of the game (V_A) can be derived by substitution into either equation:

$$V_A = -6p + 8(1 - p)$$
$$V_A = -6\frac{15}{28} + 8\left(1 - \frac{15}{28}\right)$$
$$V_A = \frac{1}{2} \text{ percent of market share.}$$

A Two-Person Zero-Sum Game with a Mixed Strategy

The optimal mixed strategy for company A is:

$$S_{A_1}: \quad p = \frac{15}{28}$$
$$V_A = \frac{1}{2}.$$
$$S_{A_2}: 1 - p = \frac{13}{28}$$

If company A plays this *best* mixed strategy, no matter how well the opponent plays, there will be a guaranteed expected return of 1/2 percent. Moreover, no matter how poorly company B plays, company A will still have an expected gain of 1/2 percent. Regardless of company B's alternative selection, the maximin mixed strategy will guarantee company A an expected return of exactly 1/2 percent increase in market share.

Company A is Guaranteed V_A Regardless of Company B's Play

A closer examination will clarify company A's guaranteed return. Refer to Figure 7.4. For company A's minimax solution, the boundary equations intersect with a common payoff. One boundary equation represents the expected return for all of company A's mixed strategies associated with $B(1, 0)$. The other boundary equation represents the return for those associated with $B(0, 1)$. At $A(15/28, 13/28)$, they both have $V_A = 1/2$. If the expected return to company A is the same regardless of company B's play, then any mixed strategy for company B must provide the same V_A of 1/2.

Two additional alternatives for company B, $B(1/4, 3/4)$ and $B(1/2, 1/2)$, will help to clarify this point. Figure 7.2 provides the expected return for $A(1, 0)$ associated with each of these alternatives. If corresponding expected returns are derived for $A(0, 1)$, the four values make it possible to construct two additional linear equations. For the arbitrarily selected strategies $B(1/4, 3/4)$ and $B(1/2, 1/2)$, Figure 7.5 gives the two new equations that represent the expected return to company A over the continuum of its mixed strategies.

The critical fact is the *intersection of all four equations at* $A(15/28, 13/28)$. With this mixed strategy for company A, all four of company B's mixed strategies yield an expected return of 1/2 percent. Moreover, to generalize, any equations representing one of company B's mixed strategies will produce the same intersection with the same value of the game. Company A is *guaranteed* 1/2 percent no matter how wise or whimsical, how flawless or foolhardy, the stratagem of company B.

A Graphic Solution for Company B

Given the reasoning underlying a mixed strategy selection, what is the optimal mixed strategy for company B? Starting with the reduced payoff matrix in Table 7.9, the objective is to determine the best proportional use of S_{B_1} and

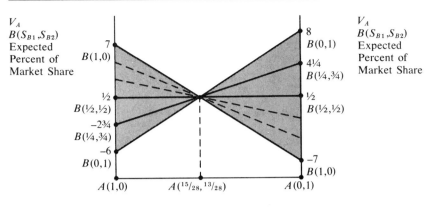

FIGURE 7.5
A Guaranteed Return

S_{B_2}—the best values of p' and $1 - p'$. The solution can be obtained systematically as follows:

1. On the horizontal axis, list all alternative mixed strategies for company B: $B(S_{B_1}, S_{B_2})$.

2. On the vertical axis, indicate the expected payoff to company A associated with the joint mixed strategy selections.

3. Use the four extreme joint mixed strategy selections to develop the two boundary equations.

4. Solve the point of intersection of the two boundary equations for the optimal solution.

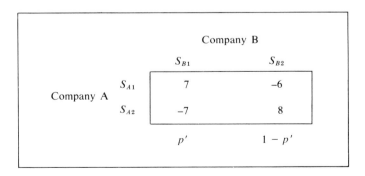

TABLE 7.9
A Mixed Strategy for Company B

Company B's alternative space is constructed parallel to that for company A. The only difference is that company B's mixed strategies will be on the horizontal axis, while company A's mixed strategies will be on the vertical axis. To maintain consistency with the payoff matrix stated in terms of returns to company A, the evaluation of the alternative space will be conducted in terms of V_A.

The two boundary equations are derived from the extreme joint strategy selections. First, company B's extreme of $B(1, 0)$ is evaluated with both of company A's extremes, $A(1, 0)$ and $A(0, 1)$:

	V_A
$B(1, 0), A(1, 0)$	7
$B(1, 0), A(0, 1)$	-7.

Next, company B's other extreme of $B(0, 1)$ is evaluated with both of company A's extremes:

	V_A
$B(0, 1), A(1, 0)$	-6
$B(0, 1), A(0, 1)$	8.

Figure 7.6 graphically represents these four extreme evaluations. The two boundary equations can be separately formed by joining the two points associated with $A(1, 0)$ and those associated with $A(0, 1)$.

The boundary equations indicate the range of payoffs for each of company B's mixed strategy selections. Having clearly defined its alternative space, company B now seeks the lowest guaranteed loss in market share: the minimax solution. If company B selects $B(1, 0)$, the best guarantee will be a loss of 7 percent (Figure 7.6). If Company B selects $B(3/4, 1/4)$, the best guarantee will be a loss of 3 3/4 percent. If it selects $B(0, 1)$, the best guarantee will be a loss of 8 percent. For all other mixed strategies, *the guaranteed returns fall on upper of the two boundary equations*. The lowest guaranteed loss will be the minimum of the maxima—the minimax at the intersection of the two boundary equations.

The optimal mixed strategy and the value of the game can be read directly from the graph or solved for mathematically. The boundary equations are:

$$V_{A_i} = 7p_i' - 6(1 - p_i')$$
$A(1, 0)$

$$V_{A_j} = -7p_j' + 8(1 - p_j').$$
$A(0, 1)$

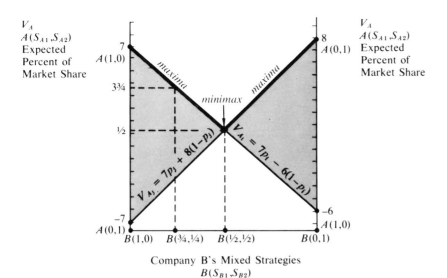

V_A
$A(S_{A1}, S_{A2})$
Expected
Percent of
Market Share

V_A
$A(S_{A1}, S_{A2})$
Expected
Percent of
Market Share

Company B's Mixed Strategies
$B(S_{B1}, S_{B2})$

FIGURE 7.6

Setting the equations equal and solving for p':

$$V_{A_i} = V_{A_j}$$

$$7p' - 6(1 - p') = -7p' + 8(1 - p')$$

$$p' = \frac{1}{2}.$$

Substituting p' to obtain V_A:

$$V_A = 7p' - 6(1 - p')$$

$$V_A = 7 \cdot \frac{1}{2} - 6 \cdot \frac{1}{2}$$

$$V_A = \frac{1}{2}.$$

The minimax mixed strategy for company B is $B(1/2, 1/2)$. By using this strategy, company B will lose no more and no less than 1/2 percent of market share, regardless of company A's alternative selection.

THE *NXM* TWO-PERSON ZERO-SUM GAME

In a two-person zero-sum game, the players quite frequently have more than two nondominated strategies. A $2X3$ game provides the conceptual foundation for the more general *nxm* case.[1]

Two contractors compete locally for county and industrial contracts. The contracts are awarded to whomever submits the lowest sealed bid. With communication and price fixing illegal, each company considers three contract bidding strategies: (1) bid low, (2) bid for a normal return, and (3) bid high. The net economic consequences of the joint strategy selections are provided in the payoff matrix of Table 7.10. They are represented as utility for contractor A. Both contractors are knowledgeable about the joint returns. For practical purposes, the game can be assumed to be zero-sum.

		Contractor B			
		Low Bid	Normal Bid	High Bid	
		S_{B1}	S_{B2}	S_{B3}	minimax
	Low Bid $\quad S_{A1}$	1½	¾	½	½*
Contractor A	Normal Bid $\quad S_{A2}$	−1	1	2½	−1
	High Bid $\quad S_{A3}$	−1	−1	2	−1
	maximin	1½	1*	2½	

TABLE 7.10
Competitive Bidding

The analysis will provide a solution of the game for contractor A. More specifically, the analysis will determine the optimal mixed strategy for contractor A—the best proportional use of the three respective bidding strategies.

The first step is to derive the minimax and maximin to determine whether a pure strategy is best. Since the minimax and maximin are not equal (Table 7.10), there is no equilibrium pair pure strategy solution. Contractor A can do better with a mixed strategy.

---

[1] More sophisticated, larger problems require the more powerful models of linear programming (Chapter 8, 9, 10, 11) and simulation (Chapters 17, 18).

Before analyzing mixed strategies, any dominated strategies are removed. According to Table 7.10, S_{A_2} is as good as or better than S_{A_3} for each of contractor B's selections. S_{A_2} dominates S_{A_3}—S_{A_3} is removed from the analysis (Table 7.11). Further checking of the reduced problem for both players (Table 7.11) reveals no other dominated strategies. The next step, therefore, is to determine the best proportional use (p) for S_{A_1} and $(1 - p)$ for S_{A_2}.

		Contractor B			
		S_{B1}	S_{B2}	S_{B3}	
	S_{A1}	1½	¾	½	p
Contractor A	S_{A2}	−1	1	2½	$1 - p$

TABLE 7.11
The Reduced Bidding Problem

As before, the alternative space of contractor A's mixed strategies can be represented graphically. The pure strategy selections for contractor B will form the boundaries defining the range of payoffs for contractor A's options (Figure 7.7). The operative criterion (minimax-maximin) will define the highest guaranteed gain—the optimal mixed strategy selection.

The three *boundary equations* in Figure 7.7 define the bounded region of expected payoffs for contractor A. All guaranteed returns will be on the lowest of the three boundary equations. The highest guaranteed gain, therefore, will be located at the highest point on the lowest of the boundary equations—the intersection of the boundary equations formed by $B(1, 0)$ and $B(0, 1, 0)$.

The optimal mixed strategy and associated value of the game can be read directly from the graph or more precisely solved mathematically. The two intersecting boundary equations are:

$$V_{A_i} = 1\frac{1}{2} p_i - 1(1 - p_i)$$

$$V_{A_j} = \frac{3}{4} p_i - 1(1 - p_i).$$

Solving for the decision variables:

$$p = \frac{8}{11}$$

$$V_A = \frac{9}{11} \text{ utiles.}$$

$$1 - p = \frac{3}{11}$$

The NXM Two-Person Zero-Sum Game 191

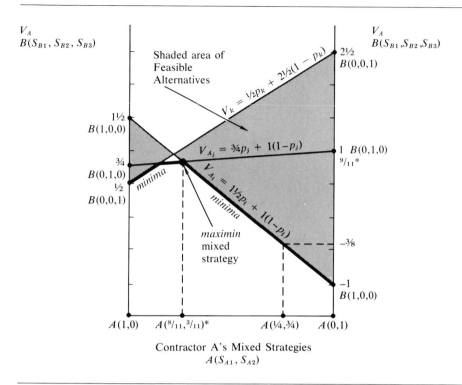

FIGURE 7.7

The Optimal Mixed Strategy

The optimal mixed strategy for contractor A is $A(8/11, 3/11)$ with an expected value of 9/11 utiles.

THE ADVANTAGE OF A GAME AGAINST *NATURE*

A decision against *nature* and a decision against a rational intelligent, informed opponent are distinctly different. These two important types of decision environments are compared below.

Consider the two-person zero-sum game outlined in Table 7.12. Player A's opponent is first assumed to be player B: a rational, intelligent, informed player seeking to minimize losses. Next, player A's opponent is assumed to be *nature*, with a fixed strategy of play. The two decision environments are then compared in terms of the expected payoff to player A.

In the first situation, player A will select a minimax-maximin criterion. Since player A will receive gains in all cases, maximin will be appropriate.

	Player B \ Nature		
	$S_{B1} \backslash S_{N1}$	$S_{B2} \backslash S_{N2}$	
Player A S_{A1}	7	5	p
S_{A2}	4	8	$1 - p$

TABLE 7.12

The Decision Environment

Moreover, since there are no dominating strategies, player A will prefer a mixed strategy: S_{A_1}, p of the time; S_{A_2}, $1 - p$ of the time.

The optimal value for p can be derived by solving the two boundary equations (Figure 7.8) at the point of intersection:

$$V_A = 7p + 4(1 - p) \qquad p = \frac{2}{3}; \qquad 1 - p = \frac{1}{3}.$$

$$V_A = 5p + 8(1 - p)$$

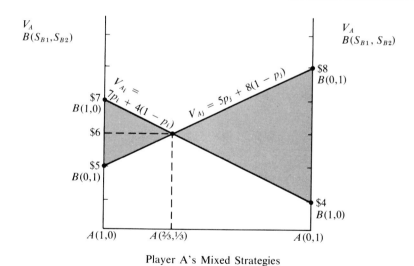

Player A's Mixed Strategies
$A(S_{A1}, S_{A2})$

FIGURE 7.8

The Best Mixed Strategy Against an Opponent

The Advantage of a Game Against Nature

The value of the game will be:

$$V_A = 7p + 4(1 - p)$$

$$V_A = 7 \cdot \frac{2}{3} + 4 \cdot \frac{1}{3}$$

$$V_A = \$6.$$

Playing against a rational, intelligent, informed opponent, player A can select $A(2/3, 1/3)$ and be guaranteed \$6 regardless of the opponent's play.

Now reconsider the situation with *nature* in place of player B. *Nature* will play some *fixed mixed strategy*. For example, *nature's* strategy might be $N(3/4, 1/4)$. Player A's best alternative against such a *known fixed play* is clearly apparent in Figure 7.9. The best alternative will be $A(1, 0)$, with an expected return of \$6.5. Any other alternative will lead to a lower expected return. Moreover, since *nature* is not capable of adjusting the mixed strategy, there is no reason not to play S_{A_1} every time.

The same conclusion can be reached using Bayes' decision rule (Chapter 3). This approach is applied in Table 7.13, the optimal solution again being $A(1, 0)$, with a V_A of \$6.5.

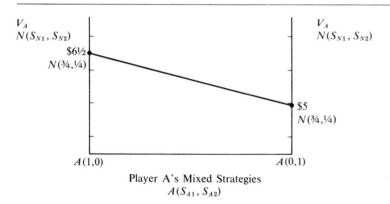

FIGURE 7.9

The Best Pure Strategy Against *Nature*

States of Nature (S_i)	$p(S_i)$	S_{A_1}	S_{A_2}
S_{N_1}	3/4	7	4
S_{N_2}	1/4	5	8
	EMV	$6\frac{1}{2}$*	\$5

TABLE 7.13

The Alternative Selection Against *Nature*

An assumption requiring examination is *nature's* selection of the strategy $N(3/4, 1/4)$. Therefore, another possible strategy selection for *nature* will be considered: $N(1/5, 4/5)$. In this case, player A's best strategy will be $A(0, 1)$, with an expected gain of $7 1/5 (Figure 7.10). Against *nature*, as distinct from a rational, intelligent, informed opponent, player A does best using a pure strategy selection.

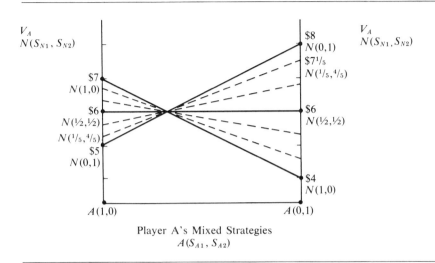

Player A's Mixed Strategies
$A(S_{A1}, S_{A2})$

FIGURE 7.10

Selecting an Improved Pure Strategy Against Nature

Except in one unlikely case, player A can always do better against *nature* than against an opponent. If by chance *nature* were to play *the minimax solution* $N(1/2, 1/2)$, player A's gains would be restricted to $6 regardless of player A's strategy selection (Figure 7.10).

If *nature's* mixed strategy is anything other than $N(1/2, 1/2)$, however, player A can do better than against an opponent. If *nature* plays a mixed strategy with the proportion of S_{N_1} exceeding 1/2, player A should play $A(1, 0)$ and obtain more than $6. If the proportion of S_{N_1} is less than 1/2, player A should play $A(0, 1)$ for an improved solution:

$N(S_{N_1}, S_{N_2})$	$A(S_{A_1}, S_{A_2})$	V_A
$N[(1/2)\uparrow, (1/2)\downarrow]$	$A(1, 0)$	$V_A > \$6$
$N(1/2, 1/2)$	$A(p_i, 1 - p_i)$ for all i	$V_A = \$6$
$N[(1/2)\downarrow, (1/2)\uparrow]$	$A(0, 1)$	$V_A > \$6.$

Unless *nature's* strategy corresponds coincidentally with the minimax selection, player A can obtain an expected payoff exceeding $6 by selecting the proper *pure strategy*.

If a player has the choice of playing a two-person zero-sum game against *nature* or against a rational, intelligent, informed opponent, it will be to his advantage to play *nature*. Using available information to assess *nature's* strategy probabilistically, a player can do better than minimax-maximin.

OUTGUESSING AN OPPONENT

A decision maker's ability to do better than select a minimax-maximin strategy against *nature*, has been demonstrated. Next, the possibility of a better strategy than minimax-maximin against a rational, intelligent, informed opponent will be explored. Refer to the two-person zero-sum game in Table 7.14. Each player has a chance to gain $8 or to lose $6. The players have identical opportunities.

		Player B		minimax-maximin	
		S_{B1}	S_{B2}		
Player A	S_{A1}	8	−6	p	½
	S_{A2}	−8	6	$1 − p$	½
		p'	$1 − p'$		
	minimax-maximin	³/₇	⁴/₋		
		$V_A = \$0$			

TABLE 7.14

A Game with Equal Opportunities

Player A's options will be analyzed first. If player B plays the minimax-maximin solution of $B(3/7, 4/7)$, it doesn't matter what player A does: the expected payoff will be $0, regardless. If player B does not play $B(3/7, 4/7)$, player A will have two *alternatives*:

1. Select the minimax-maximin solution of $A(1/2, 1/2)$ with an expected gain of $0 regardless of player B's play.

2. Select some other strategy.

Decision Making in a Competitive Environment: Game Theory

Considering all of player A's alternatives as illustrated in Figures 7.11 and 7.12, player A can do better when player B does not play $B(3/7, 4/7)$. If player B plays $B(1/7, 6/7)$, or any other mixed strategy with a proportional use of S_{B_1} below $3/7$, player A can do better by increasing the proportional use of S_{A_2} above $1/2$. Similarly, if player B plays S_{B_1} proportionally above $3/7$, player A can do better by playing S_{A_1} proportionally above $1/2$:

$B(S_{B_1}, S_{B_2})$	$A(S_{A_1}, S_{A_2})$	V_A
$B[(3/7)\downarrow, (4/7)\uparrow]$	$A[(1/2)\downarrow, (1/2)\uparrow]$	$V_A > \$0$
$B[(3/7)\uparrow, (4/7)\downarrow]$	$A[(1/2)\uparrow, (1/2)\downarrow]$	$V_A > \$0.$

If player B plays a strategy other than the minimax-maximin strategy of $B(3/7, 4/7)$, player A can improve his position. If the game is played continuously over a long enough period of time, player A can estimate player B's mixed strategy from *sample information*. Knowing player B's mixed strategy, player A can vary from $A(1/2, 1/2)$ to take advantage of player B's variation from $B(3/7, 4/7)$.

If it is advantageous for player A to move from the *equilibrium* mixed strategy of $A(1/2, 1/2)$, the maximum potential gain will be derived from a *pure strategy selection* (see Figures 7.11 and 7.12). However, a pure strategy requires considerable caution. A pure strategy by player A will be noticed,

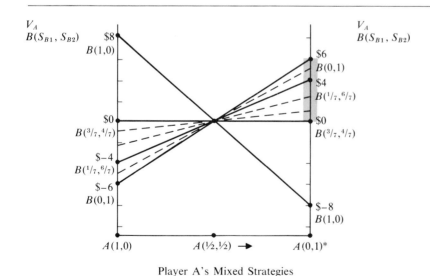

FIGURE 7.11
Player A's Alternative Space: S_{A_2} Preferred

Outguessing an Opponent

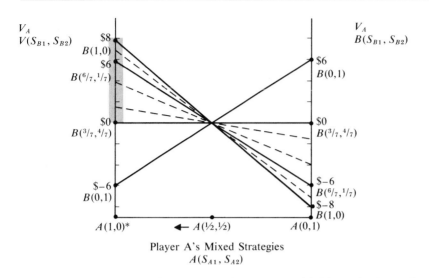

FIGURE 7.12

Player A's Alternative Space: S_{A_1} Preferred

without question, by player B. Player B will undoubtedly take appropriate counter measures. Therefore, any move from player A's equilibrium of $A(1/2, 1/2)$ must be made carefully—although most *excess* gains do require some risk.

In essence, if player B moves from a minimax-maximin equilibrium mixed strategy, player A has the potential to improve his own position. To do this, however, player A must move from *his* equilibrium mixed strategy. The further player A moves from equilibrium, the more he stands to gain. Yet he must keep in mind that player B is in a similar position. The further player A moves from equilibrium to take advantage of player B, the greater player B's potential to take advantage of player A. If player A tries for *excess gains*, he had better be careful. It might be wise, assuming player B isn't rational, intelligent, or informed. It might be wise, assuming player A can *outplay* or *outguess* player B. If player B is a truly rational, intelligent, informed opponent, however, player A probably won't be able to average any more than the minimax-maximin expected gain.

THE NONZERO-SUM GAME

In many competitive environments, one player's gain is not the other players loss. For a utilities company, a wage increase followed by a service rate increase may benefit both labor and management. In an industry with few competitors,

Decision Making in a Competitive Environment: Game Theory

a price leader's raise in prices may signal followership with benefits to the entire industry. On the other hand, price wars and other forms of excessive competition may reduce profits for all competitors.

In addition, the players may have nonlinear utilities for money. While the monetary gains to one player may be the monetary losses to the other player, the real gains to one player will not be the real losses to the other player. Nonmonetary gains that are of significant importance to one player may be nonexistent or unimportant to the other player. For these and other reasons, most competitive environments tend to be nonzero-sum.

The characteristics of a nonzero-sum game are best illustrated by several examples. The first of these is the well-known *prisoner's dilemma*. Two organizations are considering constructing a new retail outlet in a certain expanding sales area. Each has two choices: build or don't build. The payoff matrix in Table 7.15 represents their respective returns. Organization A's payoffs are on the bottom; organization B's are on the top. For the joint play $S_{A_1}S_{B_2}$, for example, organization A will receive 20 units of satisfaction (utiles) and organization B will lose 40 units.

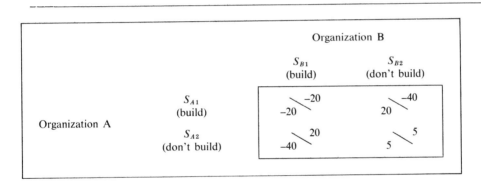

TABLE 7.15
A Nonzero-Sum Game

Organization A will have the specific payoffs expressed in Table 7.16. Checking for dominance, organization A finds S_{A_1} preferable to S_{A_2} regardless of organization B's selection. S_{A_1} dominates strategy S_{A_2}—strategy S_{A_2} is therefore removed from the analysis.

Organization B considers its options (Table 7.17) and draws a similar conclusion. Comparing S_{B_1} with S_{B_2} for all of the opponent's plays, B will always prefer S_{B_1} over S_{B_2}. On *logical* grounds, organization B will never play S_{B_2}—strategy S_{B_2} is therefore removed from the analysis.

The *rational* decision will be for organization A to select S_{A_1} and organization B to select S_{B_1}. Both organizations will build retail outlets in the growing new sales area for a loss of 20 utiles each. If they were not quite so "rational", they might have decided not to build (S_{A_2}, S_{B_2}) and gain 5 utiles each.

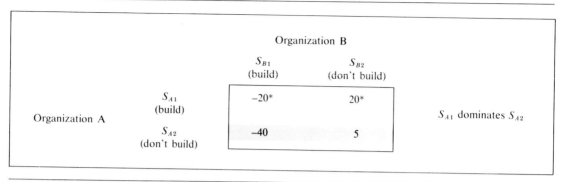

	Organization B		
	S_{B1} (build)	S_{B2} (don't build)	
Organization A	S_{A1} (build)	−20*	20*	S_{A1} dominates S_{A2}
	S_{A2} (don't build)	−40	5	

TABLE 7.16

Organization A's Perspective

The preceding logic does not necessarily lead to a satisfactory resolution of the nonzero-sum game. Both organizations could have done better by *irrationally* selecting $S_{A_2}S_{B_2}$. Attempting a strategy other than the *rational* solution $(S_{A_1}S_{B_1})$, however, does pose a difficulty. Organization A may attempt to avoid losing 20 utiles by selecting S_{A_2} and gambling that organization B will do likewise. However, if organization B selects S_{B_1} instead of S_{B_2}, organization A will lose 40 utiles. Furthermore, organization B will be highly motivated by the associated 20 utiles to select S_{B_1}. If organization A attempts to avoid the loss, it may have to pay a high price. Moreover, knowing that organization A may make such an attempt, organization B may be very satisfied to remain at S_{B_1}.

But remember, organization B is exactly in the same position as organization A. They are confronted with a dilemma. Both may have to suffer a large loss when gains are available.

Nonzero-sum games do not lend themselves to easily derived satisfactory solutions. If the players were allowed to violate the rules by communicating directly, an entirely different solution might emerge. Moreover, if it were

	Organization B		
	S_{B1} (build)	S_{B2} (don't build)	
Organization A	S_{A1} (build)	−20*	−40	S_{B1} dominates S_{B2}
	S_{A2} (don't build)	20*	5	

TABLE 7.17

Organization B's Perspective

necessary to make a series of similar decisions regarding the construction of outlets in many locations, the players' indirect communication in the market might tend to produce an improved solution.

Another example illustrates the potential irresolute quality of an *optimal* solution. Consider the payoff matrix expressed in Table 7.18. The payoffs are symmetrical: player A and player B are in the same position with similar opportunities.

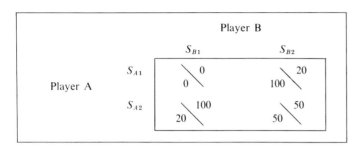

TABLE 7.18
Symmetrical Payoffs

With no dominating strategies, both players appear to have a mixed strategy selection. Assuming that they play each morning for a period of several months, several scenarios depict potential competitive behavior. Concerned with the prospect of obtaining 100 utiles, player A may continually select S_{A_1}. This would leave player B with the following choice:

	S_{B_1}	S_{B_2}
S_{A_1}	0	20.

He will be *forced* to select S_{B_2} and obtain 20 utiles rather than 0. Player A will be very satisfied with this solution and will continue to play S_{A_1}. In this case, the daily result may be:

	Play	Payoff
Player A	S_{A_1}	100
Player B	S_{B_2}	20 .

Player B appears trapped.

It will not be long, however, before player B realizes that he has the same opportunities as player A. In an attempt to improve his returns, player B may start playing S_{B_1}. If he does, one of several things may happen. First, if neither player is willing to yield his chance to gain 100 utiles, they may both continue to play $S_{A_1}S_{B_1}$ indefinitely:

	Play	Payoff
Player A	S_{A_1}	0
Player B	S_{B_1}	0 .

Second, after sustaining enough punishing zeros, player B may eventually give in by reverting to the earlier play of S_{B_2}:

	Play	Payoff
Player A	S_{A_1}	100
Player B	S_{B_2}	20 .

Third, player A may weaken first and play S_{A_2}:

	Play	Payoff
Player A	S_{A_2}	20
Player B	S_{B_1}	100 .

Any of these joint plays is possible depending on the strength and determination of the respective opponents.

There are several other interesting possibilities. After both have remained long enough at $S_{A_1}S_{B_1}$ with a payoff of zero, the players may begin to seek a compromise. Both players may switch to strategy 2:

	Play	Payoff
Player A	S_{A_2}	50
Player B	S_{B_2}	50 .

They may make this switch simultaneously after only a few disheartening zeros. One player may also attempt to communicate this course of action to the other. For example, player A may continually switch from S_{A_1} to S_{A_2} until B eventually changes to S_{B_2}.

Also, contemplating a struggle in which both seek 100s and obtain 0s, one player may attempt a *cooperative solution* that will provide the highest total joint return. One possibility is the previously mentioned $S_{A_2}S_{B_2}$ solution, with payoffs of 50 utiles for each. A better option would be for the players to alternate between $S_{A_1}S_{B_2}$ and $S_{A_2}S_{B_1}$:

	Play	Payoff	Average Payoff
Player A	S_{A_1}, S_{A_2}	20, 100	60
Player B	S_{B_2}, S_{B_1}	100, 20	60.

Repeatedly alternating between strategy 1 and strategy 2 will provide each player with an average gain of 60 utiles.

If one player were in a more powerful position, the players might agree to any of a number of return-dividing schemes. One possible sequential play favoring player A might be:

	Play	Payoff	Average Payoff
Player A	S_{A_1}, S_{A_1}, S_{A_1}, S_{A_2}, S_{A_2}	100, 100, 100, 20, 20	68
Player B	S_{B_2}, S_{B_2}, S_{B_2}, S_{B_1}, S_{B_1}	20, 20, 20, 100, 100	52

Nonzero-sum games are inherently complex. Because the initial assumptions are oversimplified for the complexities of the decision environment, they typically lack a guaranteed stable solution. In this simple case, six potential solutions were developed (Table 7.19). None of these is guaranteed. The solution

Play (S_A, S_B)	V_A, V_B
S_{A1}, S_{B2}	100,20
S_{A2}, S_{B1}	20,100
S_{A1}, S_{B1}	0,0
S_{A2}, S_{B2}	50,50
alternating	average
$\begin{cases} S_{A1}, S_{B2} \\ S_{A2}, S_{B1} \end{cases}$	60,60
$\begin{cases} S_{A1}, S_{A1}, S_{A1}, S_{A2}, S_{A2} \\ S_{B2}, S_{B2}, S_{B2}, S_{B1}, S_{B1} \end{cases}$	68,52

TABLE 7.19
Several Possible Solutions

will depend heavily on the psychology and the power of the particular opponents. Without special assumptions to incorporate these aspects into the analysis, a satisfactory solution to nonzero-sum games may be far from obvious.

THE N-PERSON GAME

Competitive environments frequently contain more than two opponents. They are n-person games. As the number of opponents increases, the potential form of competitive behavior increases substantially. Groups of opponents may form coalitions against one another. Moreover, if there are many opponents, counter coalitions and counter-counter coalitions may appear. The alternative forms of competitive behavior become exhausting—a full analysis becomes exceedingly complex.

Form of competition	*AB*	*ABC*	*ABCD*	
	A-B	*A-B-C*	*A-B-C-D*	
		AB-C	*ABC-D*	*AB-C-D*
		AC-B	*ABD-C*	*AC-B-D*
		BC-A	*ACD-B*	*AD-B-C*
			BCD-A	*BC-A-D*
				BD-A-C
			AB-CD	*CD-A-B*
			AC-BD	
			AD-BC	

TABLE 7.20
Possible Competing Groups

As indicated in Table 7.20, the two-person game has only 1 dimension of competition. If a third opponent is introduced, the dimension of competition increases to 4. All three opponents can compete separately against each other, or groups of two can form a coalition against a third. With a fourth player the dimension of competition increases to 14. There is the possibility not only of coalitions, but of counter coalitions. Finally, in a five-player game, there are 51 separate possible forms of competition (Table 7.21). This has not allowed for the possibility that an individual may belong to more than one group or may move from one group to another.

As the number of players increases, other complications are also introduced. The assumption that each group will act as a rational, intelligent, informed unit becomes questionable. Moreover, to complicate an already

A-B-C-D-E	ABCD-E	ACDE-B	
	ABCE-D	BCDE-A	
AB-C-D-E	ABDE-C		
AC-B-D-E			
AD-B-C-E	A-BC-DE	ABC-D-E	ABC-DE
AE-B-C-D	A-BD-CE	ABD-C-E	ABD-CE
BC-A-D-E	A-BE-CD	ABE-C-D	ABE-CD
BD-A-C-E	B-AC-DE	ACD-B-E	ACD-BE
BE-A-C-D	B-AD-CE	ACE-B-D	ACE-BD
CD-A-B-E	B-AE-CD	ADE-B-C	ADE-BC
CE-A-B-D	C-AB-DE	BCD-A-E	BCD-AE
DE-A-B-C	C-AD-BE	BCE-A-D	BCE-AD
	C-AE-BD	BDE-A-C	BDE-AC
	D-AB-CE	CDE-A-B	CDE-AB
	D-AC-BE		
	D-AE-BC		
	E-AB-CD		
	E-AC-BD		
	E-AD-BC		

TABLE 7.21

Fifty-One Potential Competing Units with Five Players

complex situation, n-person games tend to be nonzero-sum. The potential permutative behavior of play can become as perplexingly complex as the intricate, interwoven fabric of real-world competitive behavior.

SUMMARY

Game theory provides a means for analyzing a decision environment containing conflict. Under simplified conditions, it provides a framework for analyzing rational, intelligent, informed behavior in a competitive environment.

The simplest case is the two-person zero-sum game. The minimax and maximin are calculated for each player. If the two are equal, they will define the best pure strategy for each player and also specify the value of the game,

If the minimax and maximin are not equal, the players will prefer to select mixed strategies. After the removal of dominated strategies, a player's alternative space of mixed strategies can be plotted and restricted by boundary equations. The optimal mixed strategy will be located at the intersection of the boundary equations.

Unfortunately, most competitive environments do not correspond to the simple structure of the two-person zero-sum model. They tend to violate one or more of the underlying assumptions. They tend to be n-person and non-zero-sum. Most competitive environments are highly complex. They do not readily lend themselves to simple model development.

BIBLIOGRAPHY

Bierman, H., Jr., C. P. Bonini, and W. H. Hausman. *Quantitative Analysis for Business Decisions*. Homewood, Ill.: Richard D. Irwin, 1973.

Burger, E. *Introduction to the Theory of Games*. Englewood Cliffs, N.J.: Prentice-Hall, 1963.

Davis, M. D. *Game Theory: A Nontechnical Introduction*. New York: Basic Books, 1970.

Dorfman, R., P. A. Samuelson, and R. M. Solow. *Linear Programming and Economic Analysis*. New York: McGraw-Hill Book Co., 1958.

Friedman, L. "Game Theory Models in the Allocation of Advertising Expenditures." *Operations Research*, September–October 1958, pp. 699–709.

Glickman, A. M. *An Introduction to Linear Programming and the Theory of Games*. New York: John Wiley & Sons, 1963.

Kemeny, J. G., A. Schleifer, Jr., J. L. Snell, and G. L. Thompson. *Finite Mathematics with Business Applications*. Englewood Cliffs, N.J.: Prentice-Hall, 1972.

Loomba, N. P., and E. Turban. *Applied Programming for Management*. New York: Holt, Rinehart & Winston, 1974.

Luce, R. D., and H. Raiffa. *Games and Decisions*. New York: John Wiley & Sons, 1957.

May, F. B. *Introduction to Games of Strategy*. Boston, Mass.: Allyn & Bacon, 1970.

McKensey, J. C. C. *Introduction to the Theory of Games*. New York: McGraw-Hill Book Co., 1952.

Morgenstern, O. "The Theory of Games." *Scientific American*. Volume 180, No. 5, 1949, pp. 22–25.

Owen, G. *Game Theory*. Philadelphia: W. B. Saunders Co., 1968.

Shubik, M. *Strategy and Market Structure*. New York: John Wiley & Sons, 1959.

Shubik, M., ed. *Game Theory and Related Approaches to Social Behavior*. New York: John Wiley & Sons, 1964.

Thierauf, R. J., and R. C. Klekamp. *Decision Making Through Operations Research*. New York: John Wiley & Sons, 1975.

Vajda, S. *An Introduction to Linear Programming and the Theory of Games*. New York: John Wiley & Sons, 1960.

von Neumann, J., and O. Morgenstern. *Theory of Games and Economic Behavior*. Princeton: Princeton University Press, 1947.

Williams, J. D. *The Complete Strategyst*. New York: McGraw-Hill Book Co., 1954.

7.1. Two local companies each have two alternative strategies for distributing a new product. The following diagram expresses the relative percent market share advantage to company A:

		Company B	
		S_{B1}	S_{B2}
Company A	S_{A1}	10	−6
	S_{A2}	−2	−8

Determine the optimal minimax-maximin solution for each company and the value of the game.

7.2.

		Player B		
		S_{B1}	S_{B2}	S_{B3}
	S_{A1}	10	4	6
Player A	S_{A2}	8	4	4
	S_{A3}	−6	2	8

Locate and remove all dominated strategies. From the remaining payoff matrix, what conclusions can you draw about appropriate strategies and the value of the game?

7.3. The two top collegiate milers are contemplating prerace competitive strategies. The matrix represents anticipated yard advantage to miler A:

		Miler B		
		S_{B1}	S_{B2}	S_{B3}
Miler A	S_{A1}	12	8	10
	S_{A2}	10	8	8

Graph the alternative space for miler A. From the graph, determine the optimal strategy for miler A and the expected outcome. What is the graphic characteristic of dominance? From the graph, what is miler B's best option?

7.4. Neighboring new car dealers select new advertising strategies each week. The relative market share effects are approximated roughly by:

		Dealer B	
		S_{B1}	S_{B2}
Dealer A	S_{A1}	10	-8
	S_{A2}	-4	6

Over a long period, if dealer A repeatedly selects the pure strategy S_{A_1}, what will dealer B do? If dealer A repeatedly selects the pure strategy S_{A_2}, what will dealer B do? If dealer B repeatedly selects the pure strategy S_{B_1}, what behavior can be expected from dealer A? What conduct would you recommend to each dealer for rational play?

7.5.

		Player B	
		S_{B1}	S_{B2}
Player A	S_{A1}	4	-4
	S_{A2}	-2	0

Player A has decided to play a mixed strategy of $A(1/5, 4/5)$. For each of the following mixed strategies for player B, determine the expected value of the game for player A: $B(1, 0)$, $B(1/2, 1/2)$, $B(3/4, 1/4)$, and $B(4/5, 1/5)$.

What conclusion can you draw regarding player A's mixed strategy? Against player A's mixed strategy, what is the best strategy for player B? What is the worst strategy for player B?

7.6. Two nations negotiate on the tonnage price of wheat. The joint strategies with relative percentage selling prices (seller's perspective) are as follows:

		Buyer		
		S_{B1}	S_{B2}	S_{B3}
	S_{A1}	12	10	-10
Seller	S_{A2}	-10	0	-25
	S_{A3}	15	-20	8

Determine the graphic minimax-maximin solution for the seller. Determine the minimax-maximin solution for buyer B.

7.7. Two competing hardware stores are planning to construct new retail outlets in one of two nearby towns. Of the total population of both towns, 40 percent is in town 1 and 60 percent is in town 2. Assuming that price, service, and selection of merchandise are comparable, customers will purchase from the nearest store. If the competitors both locate in the same town, they will divide the sales from both towns evenly between them.

With payoffs representing percent of total sales for both towns, develop the 2 × 2 zero-sum payoff matrix for the two competitors. Find the associated optimal strategy selection for each and the value of the game.

7.8.

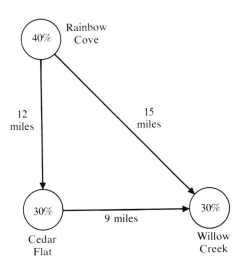

Two competing retail sporting goods companies are each considering opening a bait and tackle shop on Trout Lake. French's Bait & Tackle Shop and The Fisherman would have comparable pricing and product lines. For practical purposes, a town's complete patronage will go to the shop in that town. If both shops locate in the same town, sales will be evenly divided between them. If a town does not have a shop, travel to a town with a shop will be inversely proportional to the square of the distance.

The diagram provides the percentage of potential customers per town and the distance between towns. The location of each shop will be based on the maximum anticipated sales. Construct a payoff matrix to indicate where French's Bait & Tackle Shop should be located. What percentage of sales can be guaranteed? With this chosen location, could French's ever do better than the guaranteed percentage?

7.9. The management of a company and the union representing a large segment of the work force are preparing for the annual wage negotiations. The union can select one of four strategy options. Management has three potential strategies. The dollar hourly wage increases both parties anticipate from joint strategies are provided below:

		Union			
		S_{B1}	S_{B2}	S_{B3}	S_{B4}
	S_{A1}	−.40	−.25	−.20	−.50
Management	S_{A2}	−.20	0	−.10	−.25
	S_{A3}	−.10	−.10	−.05	−.30

What strategies and hourly wage increase can be expected?

7.10. The campaign headquarters of two candidates for public office are planning the weekly emphasis of their respective campaigns. The payoff matrix of relative advantages is represented as follows:

			Democratic Incumbent	
			Domestic Issues S_{B1}	Foreign Issues S_{B2}
Republican Candidate	Domestic Issues	S_{A1}	4	−7
	Foreign Issues	S_{A2}	−5	8

What is the optimal strategy for each candidate? Who will win the game?

7.11. Two guilty suspects have been arrested for a crime. During separate questioning, each suspect is given the opportunity to confess in exchange for a reduced sentence. Moreover, if a suspect confesses and his associate still pleads innocent, a full confession with accompanying state's evidence will return a suspended sentence for that suspect. If neither confesses, a good lawyer can assure them both the minimum prison term. The following payoff matrix depicts the situation:

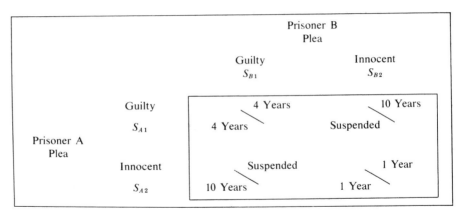

What will be the outcome of the questioning?

7.12. Two companies compete with advertising. The companies have the following utility measures of expected desirability:

		Company B	
		Advertise S_{B1}	Don't Advertise S_{B2}
Company A	Advertise S_{A1}	-20 / -20	2 / -25
	Don't Advertise S_{A2}	-30 / 30	10 / 8

What is the anticipated strategy selection? What type of dilemma does the joint selection pose?

7.13. Two grocery stores in the same marketing area compete by advertising weekly specials in the local newspaper. Depending on their respective assortments of items and prices, one store can gain sales at the other's expense. In terms of the percentage increase in sales to store A, the following diagram represents the payoff matrix for the two stores' respective advertising strategies:

		Advertising Strategies Store B			
		S_{B1}	S_{B2}	S_{B3}	S_{B4}
Advertising Strategies Store A	S_{A1}	-14	10	-5	8
	S_{A2}	7	-5	0	-12
	S_{A3}	12	-4	2	-4
	S_{A4}	8	-6	0	-12

Determine the optimal strategy for store **A** and the expected increase in sales from advertising.

7.14. Two competing gas stations are on opposite corners of a busy intersection. There are no other stations nearby. Sales volume is primarily a function of relative gas prices between the two stations' posted prices. The stations set prices each morning for the entire day. Each day three pricing strategies are considered: lower yesterday's price, maintain yesterday's price, raise yesterday's price. The change in daily sales volume expressed in relative joint dollar returns is provided below:

		Station B Pricing Strategy		
		Lower S_{B1}	Maintain S_{B2}	Raise S_{B3}
Station A Pricing Strategy	Lower S_{A1}	-10 \ -10	-12 \ 4	-20 \ 20
	Maintain S_{A2}	4 \ -12	0 \ 0	-4 \ 15
	Raise S_{A3}	20 \ -20	15 \ -4	10 \ 10

What strategy will the two stations prefer? For how long?

If the two station owners play golf together each weekend, would you adjust your answers to the two previous questions?

If one station bought the other station, what pricing behavior might you expect?

MATHEMATICAL PROGRAMMING

PART TWO

8

An Introduction to Linear Programming

Man has always been concerned with a proper allocation of scarce resources. This problem virtually invades all human endeavors. Fortunately, linear programming has been developed as a formal means for optimally solving this problem.

In 1947, George Dantzig and his associates in the U.S. Department of the Air Force formally presented a systematic procedure for solving a linear programming problem. Since then, the development and application of linear programming have grown enormously. One recent text on linear programming contains a 17-page bibliography of books and articles on this important quantitative tool. In 1970, an IBM report on computer usage estimated that 25 percent of all scientific computations on computers were devoted to linear programming and closely related techniques.[1]

Linear programming is an extraordinarily general and powerful quantitative model. Its applications are extensive. They include the allocation of workers, machines, money, or materials for the most productive use. Linear programming is used in blending crude oils for gasoline; portfolio selection; multiperiod production scheduling; the location of a new plant; water resource distribution; and planning the development of underdeveloped countries—to mention only a few examples. Many large organizations, such as General Mills, have linear programming models to interrelate and allocate the major resources for the entire organization.

---

[1] F. S. Hiller and G. J. Lieberman, *Introduction to Operations Research* (San Francisco: Holden-Day, 1974), p. 15.

FORMULATING A PROBLEM

The allocation of resources in a simple product mix problem will demonstrate the formulation of a decision environment as a linear programming problem. Two students have been hired part-time to aid in production. Worker 1 is available for twelve hours per week; worker 2, for eight hours. There are two possible products: product 1 worth $20, and product 2, worth $25. Worker 1 can produce one unit of product 1 in four hours and one unit of product 2 in three hours. Worker 2 can produce one unit of product 1 in two hours and one unit of product 2 in four hours. Any unfinished products can be completed the following week.

The general model for decision making provides a logical approach to the problem:

1. List and define the alternative space.

2. Restrict the alternatives.

3. Evaluate the remaining alternatives.

4. Select the best alternative.

The relevant information is summarized in Table 8.1.

Resource Constraints

Since the workers can produce *independently* of each other, the first consideration is the best utilization of worker 1. The alternative space of production

Resources	Availability
Worker 1 (W_1)	12 hours/week
Worker 2 (W_2)	8 hours/week

Utilization of Resources	
Worker 1	4 hours → Product 1
	3 hours → Product 2
Worker 2	2 hours → Product 1
	4 hours → Product 2

Product Value	
Product 1	$20
Product 2	$25

TABLE 8.1
Relevant Information

possibilities for worker 1 can be defined directly in terms of the availability of the resource. Specifically, the resource, worker 1, cannot be utilized more than the time available:

utilization of the resource $\leq$ availability of the resource.

This fundamental establishes an upper boundary on production: a restriction on the allowable number of units of product 1, product 2, or combination of both products.

If worker 1 produces product 1 only, the restriction on the *number of units of product 1* (X_1) can be specified. With four hours required per unit and twelve hours of available time, the acceptable values of X_1 are defined by:

(hours per unit)(no. of units)
$$4X_1 \qquad \leq 12$$
$$\text{time utilized} \qquad \text{time available.}$$

The number of units of product 1 (X_1) cannot exceed three.

Similarly, if worker 1 produces units of product 2 only:

$$3X_2 \leq 12$$
$$\text{time utilized} \qquad \text{time available.}$$

The number of units of product 2 (X_2) cannot exceed four.

If worker 1 produces both products, the *resource constraint* becomes:

time for   time for
product 1   product 2
$$4X_1 \quad + \quad 3X_2 \quad \leq 12$$
total time utilized   time available.

The time utilized on product 1 plus the time utilized on product 2 cannot exceed the total time the resource is available. *The values of X_1 and X_2 are thus restricted by the availability of the resource.*

For example, the production of two units of product 1 and one unit of product 2 (2, 1) is a feasible alternative:

$$4(2) + 3(1) \leq 12.$$

At four hours each, the two units of product 1 require a total of eight hours. The one unit of product 2 requires three hours. The total of eleven hours required does not exceed the twelve-hour limit.

The alternative (2, 2), however, is infeasible:

$$4(2) + 3(2) \nleq 12.$$

The 14 hours required exceed the 12-hour limit.

Nonnegative Constraints

To more completely specify the alternative space, an additional restriction of the decision variables is formalized by *nonnegative constraints*:

$$X_1 \geq 0$$
$$X_2 \geq 0.$$

The values of X_1 and X_2 cannot be negative. A negative production output is simply an impossibility.

Evaluating Alternatives: The Objective Function

The *alternative space of all possible values for the decision variables* (X_1, X_2) *is defined by the resource constraint and the nonnegative constraints:*

$$4X_1 + 3X_2 \leq 12 \quad \text{resource constraint}$$
$$X_1 \geq 0; X_2 \geq 0 \quad \text{nonnegative constraints.}$$

All feasible values of X_1 and X_2 must satisfy these requirements.

With the alternative space defined, the alternatives require evaluation. With product 1 worth \$20 and product 2 worth \$25, profits can be expressed by an *objective function*:

Profit = \$20 (number of units of product 1) + \$25 (number of units of product 2).

With f the value of the objective function and the decision variables:

$$f = \$20X_1 + \$25X_2.$$

For example, if worker 1 produces two units of product 1 and one unit of product 2, profit will be:

$$f = \$20(2) + \$25(1)$$
$$f = \$65.$$

All other alternatives can be evaluated in the same way.

The Formulated Problem

The objective function and constraint equations provide a formal statement of the problem:

Find (X_1, X_2): $f_{max} = 20X_1 + 25X_2$ (objective function)

subject to
the restrictions: $4X_1 + 3X_2 \leq 12$ (resource constraint)
$X_1 \geq 0; X_2 \geq 0$ (nonnegative constraints).

The *constraint equations define the domain of alternatives. The objective function provides the means to evaluate alternatives.* The problem is to find the values for the *decision variables* (X_1, X_2) that maximize the objective function subject to the constraints.

A GRAPHIC SOLUTION

To provide a better conceptualization of the alternatives, the alternative space can be expressed graphically. The resource constraint and nonnegative constraints are plotted. The bounded region of feasible alternatives occupies the shaded area in Figure 8.1.

The nonnegative constraints restrict X_1 and X_2 to the positive quadrant. The resource constraint further restrict X_1 and X_2 to the requirements:

$4X_1 + 3X_2 \leq 12.$

At the extreme boundary,

$4X_1 + 3X_2 = 12.$

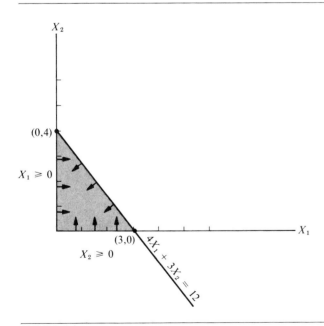

FIGURE 8.1

The Bounded Region of Feasible Alternatives

This is a linear equation with easily determined intercepts. On the X_1 axis (for X_2 equal to zero), X_1 will be 3:

$$4X_1 + 3(0) = 12$$
$$X_1 = 3.$$

Similarly, setting X_1 equal to zero, the X_2 intercept becomes:

$$4(0) + 3X_2 = 12$$
$$X_2 = 4.$$

The inequality ($\leq$) in the resource constraint infers that the resource can be utilized for any number of hours less-than-or-equal-to 12. Different levels of utilization, therefore, produce a family of parallel linear equations. The (X_1, X_2) values on this family of parallel lines represents the *area of feasible alternatives* (Figure 8.2).

Although still infinite in number, the feasible alternatives are restricted to the specified bounded region. Before the alternative can be evaluated, additional logic is required to restrict the alternative space to a measurable few alternatives.

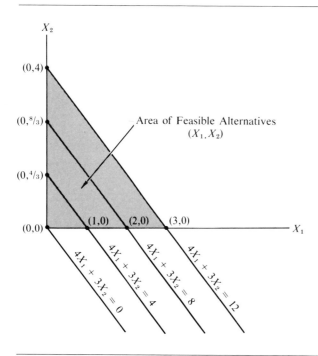

FIGURE 8.2

The Inequality Constraint

An Introduction to Linear Programming

If the solution (0, 0) is considered, improved solutions can be obtained by moving along the X_1 (horizontal) axis. With a move to (1, 0), there is one additional unit of product 1, increasing profits. Movements along the X_1 axis require no sacrifice and only increase profits. They should be made horizontally as far as possible to the extreme of (3, 0). Movements along the X_2 (vertical) axis are likewise profitable. A movement of one unit will increase profits by $25: nothing given up, profits gained. It would be only rational to move vertically to the extreme of (0, 4).

The same logic can be applied to any arbitrarily selected feasible alternative. Starting from point A in Figure 8.3, for example, better alternatives are found by moving horizontally, vertically, or anywhere between the lines formed by these movements. Such movements simply increase the number of profitable units of X_1, X_2, or both. They should therefore be extended as far as possible—extended to the boundary of the resource constraint. The best feasible alternative must be on this *boundary equation*.

On the boundary equation, similar reasoning further restricts the search for the optimal solution. By substituting one product for the other, it will be economically advantageous to move either up or down the boundary equation. For example, a movement up the boundary equation from (3, 0) can be evaluated (Table 8.2). Adding one unit of X_2 will require a reduction of 3/4

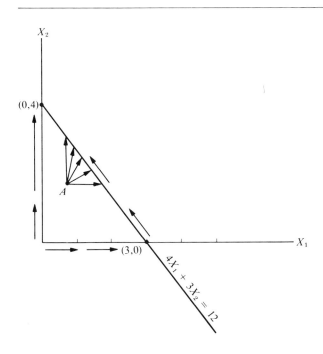

FIGURE 8.3
Restricting Alternatives to the Boundary Equation

X_2 for X_1		X_1 for X_2	
$\Delta X_2\uparrow$	$\Delta X_1\downarrow$	$\Delta X_1\uparrow$	$\Delta X_2\downarrow$
1	$-\tfrac{3}{4}$	1	$-\tfrac{4}{3}$
$\Delta f\uparrow = (-\tfrac{3}{4})(\$20) + (1)(\$25)$		$\Delta f\downarrow = (1)(\$20) - (\tfrac{4}{3})(\$25)$	
$= \$10$		$= -\$13\tfrac{1}{3}$	

TABLE 8.2

Substitution Along the Boundary Equation

units of X_1. The economic effect of moving from $(3, 0)$ to $(2\,1/4, 1)$ is $-3/4(\$20) + 1(\$25)$, or $10. The substitution of units of X_2 for units of X_1 is desirable. Starting at $(3, 0)$, movements along the boundary equation should be made as far as possible to the extreme $(0, 4)$.

Starting at the extreme of $(0, 4)$ on the boundary equation, moving down the equation to add one unit of X_1 will require giving up $4/3$ units of X_2. As Figure 8.3 illustrates, gaining three units of X_1 entails losing four units of X_2— one unit of X_1 is obtained by a loss of $4/3$ units of X_2. The increase in X_1 contributes $20, while the decrease in X_2 costs $33\ 1/3$. The total economic effect of the movement from $(0, 4)$ to $(1, 2\,2/3)$ is a net loss of $13\ 1/3$. It is not desirable to move down the equation (Table 8.2).

An extremely important conclusion can be formalized. Any feasible alternative inside the boundary equation will have a better alternative on the boundary equation. On the boundary equation, better alternatives are found by moving as far as possible in one direction.[2] The best alternatives must be at an extreme point on the boundary of feasible alternatives. *The optimal solution must be a corner point value.*

The search for the optimal solution can be restricted to extreme corner points on the boundary of feasible alternatives. The corner points can be evaluated and the best selected (Table 8.3). Worker 1 should produce four units of product 2 for a profit of $100.

A Corner Point Solution for Worker 2

With the alternatives restricted to corner points, the best allocation of worker 2 is readily determined. Refer back to Table 8.1. The allocation of worker 2 can

---

[2] The only time the optimal solution may be other than a corner point is when the substitution and price ratios indicate no advantage to move in either direction along the boundary equation. In such a case, all points along the line will be optimal, including the corner points. This will occur when the corner points for the boundary equation produce the same profit. More specifically, it will occur when the slope of the objective function is the same as the slope of the boundary equation.

Alternatives (X_1, X_2)	$f = \$20X_1 + \$25X_2$
$A_1 (3,0)$	$f(3,0) = \$60$
$A_2 (0,4)$	$f(0,4) = \$100*$

TABLE 8.3

The Alternative Space of Feasible Corner Points

be formulated as:

Find the best X_1, X_2: $f_{max} = 20X_1 + 25X_2$
subject to: $\qquad\qquad 2X_1 + 4X_2 \leq 8$
$\qquad\qquad\qquad X_1 \geq 0; X_2 \geq 0.$

Figure 8.4 provides the area of feasible alternatives.

With the optimal solution at a corner point on the bounded region, the corner points can be evaluated and the best selected (Table 8.4).[3] Worker 2 should produce four units of product 1 for a profit of $80.

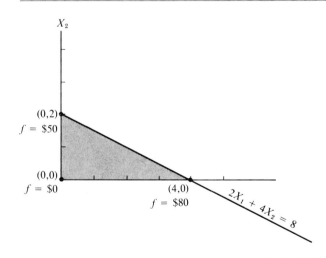

FIGURE 8.4

Alternative Space (X_1, X_2) for Worker 2

<hr>

[3] If both products were unprofitable, the corner point $(0, 0)$ would be optimal. Therefore, a more general consideration would include the origin $(0, 0)$.

Alternatives (X_1, X_2)	$f(X_1, X_2) = \$20X_1 + \$25X_2$
A_0 (0,0)	$f(0,0) = \$0$
A_1 (4,0)	$f(4,0) = \$80^*$
A_2 (0,2)	$f(0,2) = \$50$

TABLE 8.4

Alternative Space for Worker 2

Since each worker can produce *independently* of the other, the problem of allocating both workers consists of two separate subproblems. The final allocation of the workers is:

Worker 1 produce four units of product 2 (0, 4) for $100
Worker 2 produce four units of product 1 (4, 0) for $80.

The best possible allocation will yield a profit of $180.

INTERDEPENDENT RESOURCES: JOINT CONSTRAINTS

A more common allocation problem involves the joint use of several resources. For example, two workers have been hired to aid in the production of two products. Worker 1 is available for a maximum of 20 hours; worker 2 for 18 hours. Each product must go through two separate stages: (1) construction and (2) painting and packaging. Because each has special talents, worker 1 will construct the products and worker 2 will paint and package them. Worker 1 can construct product 1 in four hours and product 2 in five hours. Worker 2 requires six hours to paint and package product 1 and three hours for product 2. When complete, product 1 is worth $100 and product 2, $80. Unfinished products can be completed the following week, and there is sufficient demand to absorb production supply. Table 8.5 summarizes relevant information. The *decision variables* X_1 and X_2 will be used to represent the number of units of product 1 and product 2 respectively.

In forming the boundary for feasible alternatives, the alternatives are again restricted by the availability of resources. The 20 hours of available time

Resources	Availability (weeks)
Worker 1	20 hours
Worker 2	18 hours
Utilization of Resources	
Worker 1	4 hours → Product 1
(construction)	5 hours → Product 2
Worker 2	6 hours → Product 1
(paint and package)	3 hours → Product 2
Product Value	
Product 1 $100	
Product 2 $80	

TABLE 8.5
Relevant Information

for worker 1 will limit construction possibilities. Formally, the restrictions imposed by worker 1 are:

time for   time for   worker 1

product 1   product 2

$$4X_1 \quad + \quad 5X_2 \quad \leq \quad 20 \quad \text{construction constraint}$$

total time utilized   time available.

The painting and packaging limitations imposed by worker 2 are:

time for   time for   worker 2

product 1   product 2

$$6X_1 \quad + \quad 3X_2 \quad \leq \quad 18 \quad \text{painting and packaging constraint}$$

total time utilized   time available.

The alternative production levels are evaluated by an *objective function*:

Profit = $100 (number of units of product 1) + $80 (number of units of product 2),

or more efficiently,

$$f_{\max} = \$100X_1 + \$80X_2.$$

The criterion for alternative selection is profit maximization.

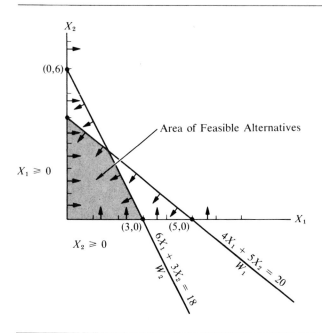

FIGURE 8.5
The Alternative Space (X_1, X_2)

Including nonnegative constraints prohibiting negative production, the formulated problem is stated as:

Find (X_1, X_2): $f_{max} = 100X_1 + 80X_2$ objective function

subject to: $4X_1 + 5X_2 \leq 20$ worker 1 construction constraint
$6X_1 + 3X_2 \leq 18$ worker 2 painting and packaging constraint

$X_1 \geq 0; X_2 \geq 0$ nonnegative constraints.

The alternative space of feasible (X_1, X_2) output levels is represented by the shaded area in Figure 8.5. Worker 1 restricts X_1 and X_2 values to the left of $4X_1 + 5X_2 = 20$, and worker 2 to the left of $6X_1 + 3X_2 = 18$. The nonnegative constraints restrict the alternative space to the positive quadrant. Feasible alternatives must maintain all constraints.

The Optimal Solution: A Corner Point

Before evaluating the corner points, all nonjointly constrained alternatives will be shown to be impossible. Anywhere along the line $4X_1 + 5X_2 = 20$, worker

1 is working to capacity (Figure 8.5). At (0, 4) or (5, 0), all 20 hours of available time are fully utilized:

$$4X_1 + 5X_2 = 20,$$

at (0, 4)

$$4(0) + 5(4) = 20,$$

and at (5, 0)

$$4(5) + 5(0) = 20.$$

The alternative (5, 0) is a possibility for worker 1.

Along the other boundary equation $6X_1 + 3X_2 = 18$, worker 2 is likewise utilized to full capacity (18 hours). Beyond this boundary, worker 2 cannot produce within the time restriction. To produce at (5, 0), for example, would require 30 hours:

$$6(5) + 3(0) = 30.$$

Since only 18 hours are available, this level of production would require 12 hours of overtime. In terms of worker 2, the solution (5, 0) is infeasible.

As another consideration, both workers could separately produce product 1 to capacity. Worker 1 could produce at (5, 0) and worker 2 at (3, 0) (Figure 8.5). At the end of each week, five units of product 1 will be constructed and three units painted and packaged. There will be three completed products and two unfinished products in inventory. After five weeks there will be ten unfinished items in inventory. Moreover, since the unfinished items require the special talents of worker 2, who is already working to capacity, they can never be completed. There will be an inventory problem.

Any alternative not satisfying all of the constraints will be undesirable. It will either require more resources than are available or create an inventory problem. All *desirable* feasible alternatives are within both constraints inside the shaded area in Figure 8.5.

A Corner Point Solution

The optimal solution is a corner point on the bounded region of feasible alternatives. It can therefore be identified by: (1) defining each feasible corner point; (2) evaluating them; and (3) selecting the best one.

Except for the corner point at the intersection of the boundary equations, each feasible corner point has been defined. At the intersection, both equations have the same (X_1, X_2) coordinates. In essence, there are two equations with two unknowns:

$$4X_1 + 5X_2 = 20$$
$$6X_1 + 3X_2 = 18.$$

The equations can be solved simultaneously for the unknowns.

Elementary row operations is a common procedure for solving systems of equations for unknowns. *The procedure consist of performing valid additions, subtractions, multiplications, and divisions on the set of equations.* These operations are performed to *transform the equations into a solution format for the variables.*

Row operations will be performed on the constraint equations to express equation I in a solution format for X_1:

$$4X_1 + 5X_2 = 20 \qquad \text{equation I}$$
$$6X_1 + 3X_2 = 18 \qquad \text{equation II.}$$

The procedure will remove X_2 by a multiplication and a subtraction. A division will then transform the equation into the proper solution for X_1.

First, equation I and equation II are expressed in a new form by multiplying the first equation by three and the second by five:

$$3 \cdot \text{I} = \text{I}' \qquad 12X_1 + 15X_2 = 60$$
$$5 \cdot \text{II} = \text{II}' \qquad 30X_1 + 15X_2 = 90.$$

Equation II' is then subtracted from equation I' to form a new equation I":

$$\text{I}' - \text{II}' = \text{I}'' \qquad -18X_1 + 0X_2 = -30.$$

Equation I" is now divided by -18:

$$\text{I}''/-18 = \text{I}''' \qquad 1X_1 + 0X_2 = 1\ 2/3.$$

At the point of intersection, X_1 is equal to 1 2/3.

At this position, the value of X_1 is usually substituted into either initial equation to solve for X_2. To clarify the use of row operations to adjust a set of equations into a solution form for a variable, row operations are used to solve for X_2:

I	$4X_1 + 5X_2 =$	20
II	$6X_1 + 3X_2 =$	18
$6 \cdot \text{I} = \text{I}'$	$24X_1 + 30X_2 =$	120
$4 \cdot \text{II} = \text{II}'$	$24X_1 + 12X_2 =$	72
$\text{II}' - \text{I}' = \text{II}''$	$0X_1 - 18X_2 =$	-48
$\text{II}''/-18 = \text{II}'''$	$0X_1 + 1X_2 =$	$48/18.$

An Introduction to Linear Programming

Alternative (X_1, X_2)	$f = 100X_1 + 80X_2$
A_1 (0,0)	$f(0,0) = \$0$
A_2 (3,0)	$f(3,0) = \$300$
A_3 (0,4)	$f(0,4) = \$320$
A_4 (1⅔,2⅔)	$f(1⅔,2⅔) = \$380^*$

TABLE 8.6

The Alternative Space (Corner Points)

Equation II has been transformed into a solution form for variable X_2:

$$0X_1 + 1X_2 = 2\ 2/3.$$

The boundary equations in a solution form for the variables is:

$$1X_1 + 0X_2 = 1\ 2/3$$

$$0X_1 + 1X_2 = 2\ 2/3.$$

In a proper solution format, the coefficient is always one for the solution variable and zero for the other variable.

With all corner points defined, the next step is to evaluate each, using the objective function, and to select the best. Table 8.6 and Figure 8.6 contain the

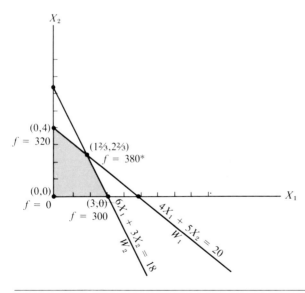

FIGURE 8.6

The Complete Graphic Solution

optimal solution. Each week worker 1 should use all 20 hours to construct 1 2/3 units of product 1 and 2 2/3 units of product 2. Worker 2 should use all 18 hours to paint and package these constructed products.

A MINIMIZATION PROBLEM

Besides maximizing profits, many problems are concerned with minimizing costs. In fact, every maximization problem can be represented in terms of opportunity losses (Chapter 3) and expressed analogously as a minimization problem (Chapter 10). The following example will demonstrate the corner point solution to a minimization problem.

A farmer wants to provide a herd of Herefords with a minimum-cost nutritious diet. He is considering two feed grains: feed 1, costing 15 cents a pound, and feed 2 costing 22 cents. Cows require three essential nutrients: nutrient 1, nutrient 2, and nutrient 3. The respective minimum daily nutrient requirements per cow are 20 units, 14 units, and 16 units. One pound of feed 1 provides 4 units of nutrient 1 and 1 unit each of the others. One pound of feed 2 provides 2 units of nutrients 1 and 2 plus 4 units of nutrient 3 (Table 7.8). The problem is to determine the most economical blend of feed grains to satisfy each cow's daily nutritional requirements.

The first step is to formulate the problem. A formulated linear programming problem will contain *decision variables* evaluated by a linear *objective function* and subject to restrictions specified by *structural* and *nonnegative constraints*.

The decision variables are the sought information: the number of pounds of feed 1 (X_1) and the number of pounds of feed 2 (X_2) needed to provide the most economic blend satisfying the nutritional requirements. The objective function measure of the economic desirability of the decision variables will be:

$$f_{min} = 15X_1 + 22X_2 \qquad \text{objective function.}$$

Ingredients	Feed 1	Feed 2	Minimum daily Requirements
Nutrient 1	4	2	20
Nutrient 2	1	2	14
Nutrient 3	1	4	16

TABLE 8.7

Feed Contents and Requirements

An Introduction to Linear Programming

The total cost will be 15 cents times the number of pounds of feed 1 (X_1) plus 22 cents times the number of pounds of feed 2 (X_2).

The decision variables cannot acquire any arbitrarily selected values. They are subject to the restrictions imposed by the nutritional requirements. The amount of nutrient 1 obtained from feed 1 and feed 2 must be at least 20 units:

$$\text{nutrient 1 from feed 1} + \text{nutrient 1 from feed 2} \geq \overset{\text{total nutrient 1 required}}{20 \text{ units.}}$$

Since every pound of feed 1 provides 4 units of nutrient 1, and every pound of feed 2 provides 2 units:

$$4X_1 + 2X_2 \geq 20 \qquad \text{nutrient 1 constraint.}$$

For example, five pounds of feed 1 and four pounds of feed 2 would provide 28 units of nutrient 1, satisfying the requirement:

$$4(5) + 2(4) > 20$$
$$20 + 8 > 20.$$

In the same way, the values of the decision variables (X_1, X_2) must be sufficient to satisfy the requirements of nutrient 2 and nutrient 3. Expressed as linear structural constraints:

$$1X_1 + 2X_2 \geq 14 \qquad \text{nutrient 2 constraint}$$
$$1X_1 + 4X_2 \geq 16 \qquad \text{nutrient 3 constraint.}$$

Also, the values for X_1 and X_2 cannot be negative:

$$X_1 \geq 0$$
$$X_2 \geq 0 \qquad \text{nonnegative constraints.}$$

The formulated problem becomes:

Find (X_1, X_2): $f_{\min} = 15X_1 + 22X_2$ objective function
subject to: $4X_1 + 2X_2 \geq 20$ nutrient 1 constraint
            $1X_1 + 2X_2 \geq 14$ nutrient 2 constraint
            $1X_1 + 4X_2 \geq 16$ nutrient 3 constraint
            $X_1 \geq 0; X_2 \geq 0$ nonnegative constraints.

The objective is to find the best values of X_1 and X_2 to make the objective function as small as possible, subject to the restrictions imposed by the structural and nonnegative constraints.

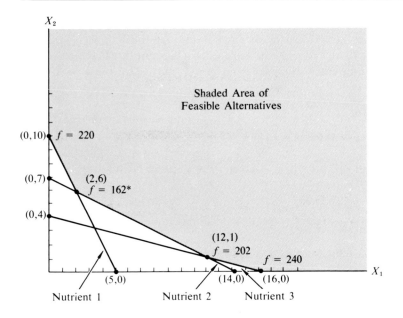

FIGURE 8.7

The Feed Mix Problem

Once the problem has been formuiated, the search procedure used earlier can be employed: 1. Plot the area of feasible alternatives. 2. Define the feasible corner points. 3. Evaluate the feasible corner points. 4. Select the best feasible corner point. In Figure 8.7 the constraint equations are plotted to define the area of feasible alternatives.

The corner points at the intersection of the nutrient constraints are found by solving the intersecting equations simultaneously for the common co-ordinates. For example, the coordinates of the nutrient 1 and nutrient 2 constraints can be *transformed* by *row operations* into the proper *solution format* for the variables:

I $4X_1 + 2X_2 = 20$ nutrient 1
II $1X_1 + 2X_2 = 14$ nutrient 2.

To solve for X_1, the effect of X_2 is removed by subtracting equation II from equation I:

I − II = I′ $3X_1 + 0X_2 = 6.$

This new form of equation I is divided by three:

I′/3 = I″ $1X_1 + 0X_2 = 2.$

X_1 has a value of two.

An Introduction to Linear Programming

In the same way, row operations can be applied to transform equation II into a solution form for X_2:

I	$4X_1 + 2X_2 = 20$
II	$1X_1 + 2X_2 = 14$
$4 \cdot II = II'$	$4X_1 + 8X_2 = 56$
$II' - I = II''$	$0X_1 + 6X_2 = 36$
$II''/6 = II'''$	$0X_1 + 1X_1 = 6.$

X_2 has a value of six.

The constraint equations properly transformed into a solution format for the variables are:

$$1X_1 + 0X_2 = 2 \quad \text{equation I}$$
$$0X_1 + 1X_2 = 6 \quad \text{equation II.}$$

The coordinate of intersection is (2, 6).

Each of the corner points is defined in Figure 8.7. They can be evaluated by substitution into the objective function (Table 8.8). The optimal corner point, the least costly values of (X_1, X_2) satisfying the constraints, is:

$$X_1 = 2$$
$$X_2 = 6 \qquad f(2, 6) = \$162.$$

By providing each cow with two pounds of feed 1 and six pounds of feed 2 daily, the farmer is guaranteed the satisfaction of the nutritional requirements at the lowest possible cost.

Alternative (X_1, X_2)	$f = 15X_1 + 22X_2$
A_1 (0,10)	$f(0,10) = \$220$
A_2 (2,6)	$f(2,6) = \$162*$
A_3 (12,1)	$f(12,1) = \$202$
A_4 (16,0)	$f(16,0) = \$240$

TABLE 8.8
Feasible Corner Points

STRUCTURING LINEAR PROGRAMMING PROBLEMS

The term *linear programming* is derived from two essential components of the model. First, the *structured logic* necessary to define and evaluate alternatives can be expressed in terms of *linear equations*. Second, the *search for the optimal* solution is a clearly defined sequence of steps—a *programmed procedure*. *Linear programming*, then, can be viewed as *a systematic linear search procedure*.

Once a decision environment has been structured into a linear programming format, even with thousands of constraints, an optimal solution can be efficiently obtained (*e.g.*, with the computer supported simplex procedure, Chapter 9). To accomplish this, however, a decision environment must first be structured into a linear programming format—into a proper *set of structured linear equations*. Three examples will further demonstrate the structuring of a decision environment as a formulated linear programming problem.

Formulating a Product-Mix Problem

In the first decision environment, a company is experiencing a slowdown of normal activities. During the next month, the planning, milling, and assembly departments are expected to have idle capacities of 60, 100, and 80 hours. respectively. Three specialty items can be produced with these facilities: product 1, product 2, and product 3. Product 1 requires 2 hours of planning, 3 hours of milling, and 6 hours of assembly. Product 2 requires 2 hours of planning, 4 hours of milling, and 5 hours of assembly. Product 3 requires 4 hours of planning and 2 hours each of milling and assembly. The company has already accepted orders for two units of product 1 and four units of product 3. Product 1 provides a per unit profit contribution of $150. Products 2 and 3, are worth $160 and $200, respectively. The objective is to allocate the available resources maximize profits.

A properly formulated linear programming problem will contain an *objective function*, *structural constraints*, and *nonnegative constraints*. The objective function is of the form:

$$f_{max} = C_1X_1 + C_2X_2 + \cdots + C_nX_n.$$
(or $_{min}$)

It will contain each *decision variable* (X_j) and the per unit contribution (C_j) to the objective for the associated decision variable activity. The objective will be either maximization or minimization.

The objective function is readily formed. The objective is the maximization of profits. The decision variables are the product outputs producing profits: X_1 = the number of units of product 1; X_2 = the number of units of product 2; and X_3 = the number of units of product 3. The per unit profit contributions are provided: C_1 = $150; C_2 = $160; and C_3 = $200. The objective function is:

$$f_{max} = 150X_1 + 160X_2 + 200X_3.$$

The values of the decision variables are *restricted* by the availability of the resources required to produce the products. There are three resources with specified levels of availability: the planning, milling, and assembly departments with 60, 100, and 80 hours, respectively. Since the availability of the resources cannot be exceeded:

$$a_{11}X_1 + a_{12}X_2 + a_{13}X_3 \le 60 \qquad \text{planning constraint}$$
$$a_{21}X_1 + a_{22}X_2 + a_{23}X_3 \le 100 \qquad \text{milling constraint}$$
$$a_{31}X_1 + a_{32}X_2 + a_{33}X_3 \le 80 \qquad \text{assembly constraint.}$$

In the planning constraint, the 60 hours of available time can be utilized for the three products:

time utilized product 1		time utilized product 2		time utilized product 3		time available
$a_{11}X_1$	$+$	$a_{12}X_2$	$+$	$a_{13}X_3$	$\le$	60
$\begin{pmatrix}\text{utilization per} \\ \text{unit product 1}\end{pmatrix}\begin{pmatrix}\text{no. of units} \\ \text{product 1}\end{pmatrix}$						

The a_{ij} are the *technical coefficients of production*[4] or the utilization of the resource per unit of product output. Since output 1 requires 2 hours of the planning resource, $a_{11} = 2$. Similarly, the utilization rates of the resource to produce product 2 and product 3 are 2 hours and 4 hours respectively: $a_{12} = 2$, $a_{13} = 4$. The planning constraint is:

$$2X_1 + 2X_2 + 4X_3 \le 60 \qquad \text{planning constraint.}$$

With the resource utilization rates from the initial statement of the decision environment, the complete set of resource constraints are:

$$2X_1 + 2X_2 + 4X_3 \le 60 \qquad \text{planning constraint}$$
$$3X_1 + 4X_2 + 2X_3 \le 100 \qquad \text{milling constraint}$$
$$6X_1 + 5X_2 + 2X_3 \le 80 \qquad \text{assembly constraint.}$$

The problem contains two other specified restrictions on the values of the decision variables. Orders have been already taken for two units of product 1 and four units of product 3. To maintain these orders, the resulting constraints are:

$$1X_1 \ge 2$$
$$1X_3 \ge 4.$$

---

[4] In the expression a_{ij}, the i denotes the resource and the j the activity (product).

With nonnegative constraints, the formulated problem becomes:

Find (X_1, X_2, X_3): $f_{max} = 150X_1 + 160X_2 + 200X_3$
subject to:
$$2X_1 + 2X_2 + 4X_3 \leq 60$$
$$3X_1 + 4X_2 + 2X_3 \leq 100$$
$$6X_1 + 5X_2 + 2X_3 \leq 80$$
$$1X_1 \qquad\qquad \geq 2$$
$$1X_3 \geq 4$$
$$X_1 \geq 0; X_2 \geq 0; X_3 \geq 0.$$

The formulated problem is now ready for a linear programming solution.

Formulating an Investment Decision

In the second decision environment, a loan company has $4,000,000 available for four types of loans. Table 8.9 lists the loan categories and the annual returns. The company's liquidity policy is not to allow business, personal, and automobile loans to exceed 30 percent of total loans. Moreover, at least half of all mortgages must be first mortgages. The company would like to maximize the loan returns within liquidity policy restrictions.

The *decision variables* will be the number of dollars made available for each loan category:

X_1 = funds for business loans
X_2 = funds for personal loans
X_3 = funds for automobile loans
X_4 = funds for first mortgage loans
X_5 = funds for second mortgage loans.

The objective function will contain each decision variable and the associated contribution to the objective:

$$f_{max} = .14X_1 + .16X_2 + .11X_3 + .09X_4 + .12X_5.$$

Loan Category	Annual Return
Business Loans	14%
Personal Loans	16%
Automobile Loans	11%
First Mortgage Loans	9%
Second Mortgage Loans	12%

TABLE 8.9
Loan Information

An Introduction to Linear Programming

The decision variables are restricted by the total funds available for all loans:

$$1X_1 + 1X_2 + 1X_3 + 1X_4 + 1X_5 \leq 4,000,000.$$

The decision variables are further restricted by the liquidity policy. The total of business, personal, and automobile loans must be less than 30 percent of the total loanable funds:

$$1X_1 + 1X_2 + 1X_3 \leq 120,000.$$

Also, at least half of all mortgages must be first mortgages:

$$X_4 \geq .50(X_4 + X_5)$$

or

$$.50X_4 - .50X_5 \geq 0.$$

Adding nonnegative constraints, the formulated problem becomes:

$$
\begin{aligned}
f_{max} &= .14X_1 + .16X_2 + .11X_3 + .09X_4 + .12X_5 \\
&\quad 1X_1 + 1X_2 + 1X_3 + 1X_4 + 1X_5 \leq 4,000,000 \\
&\quad 1X_1 + 1X_2 + 1X_3 \qquad\qquad\qquad \leq \quad 120,000 \\
&\quad\qquad\qquad\qquad\quad .50X_4 - .50X_5 \geq 0
\end{aligned}
$$

$$X_1 \geq 0; X_2 \geq 0; X_3 \geq 0; X_4 \geq 0; X_5 \geq 0.$$

Linear programming algorithms will provide a maximum annual return while maintaining liquidity policy.

Formulating an Advertising Media Selection Decision

In the third decision environment, a consulting firm wishes to allocate a company's $56,000 advertising budget optimally between two select media: an industrial trade magazine and the *Wall Street Journal*. One unit of advertising will cost $8,000 in the magazine and $4,000 in the *Journal*. The target market has been separated into two groups based on demographic and economic factors. The magazine will reach 4,000 people in group 1 and 5,000 people in group 2. The *Journal* will reach 10,000 people in group 1 and 3,000 in group 2. Exposure to group 2 is three times as effective as exposure to group 1. A commitment has already been made to use at least two units of each medium. The objective is to maximize total effective exposure.

The decision variables relate to the units of the media selected: $X_1 =$ the number of units of the industrial trade magazine; $X_2 =$ the number of units of the *Wall Street Journal*. The objective function will be:

$$f = C_1X_1 + C_2X_2.$$

In this case, the objective is the maximization of exposure. A unit of the industrial trade magazine will reach 4,000 in group 1 and 5,000 in group 2. Since group 2 is three times as important, the *coefficient of exposure effectiveness* will be:

$$C_1 = 1(4,000) + 3(5,000)$$
$$= 19,000.$$

Similarly, the coefficient of exposure effectiveness of one unit of the *Wall Street Journal* is:

$$C_2 = 1(10,000) + 3(3,000)$$
$$= 13,000.$$

The objective function measuring relative exposure effectiveness is:

$$f_{max} = 19,000X_1 + 13,000X_2.$$

The constraints are more easily derived. With the per unit magazine cost of \$8,000, the per unit *Journal* cost of \$4,000, and a total budget of \$56,000, the budgetary restriction is:

$$8,000X_1 + 4,000X_2 \le 56,000.$$

With two units of each medium committed:

$$1X_1 \ge 2$$
$$1X_2 \ge 2.$$

The formulated linear programming problem is:

$$f_{max} = 19,000X_1 + 13,000X_2$$
$$8,000X_1 + 4,000X_2 \le 56,000$$
$$1X_1 \qquad\qquad \ge 2$$
$$\qquad\quad 1X_2 \ge 2$$
$$X_1 \ge 0; X_2 \ge 0.$$

With the decision environment formulated as a linear programming problem a linear programming algorithm will provide the optimal solution—the discovery of the media that will maximize effective exposure within budgetary and commitment restraints.

SUMMARY

The allocation of resources is an exceedingly general problem area. Once this type of decision environment has been formulated into a proper linear structure, a linear programming algorithm will provide an optimal solution.

The decision environment of an allocation of resources problem can be formulated in terms of five basic elements: decision variables; the availability of resources; resource utilization rates; objective contribution rates; and the objective. The decision variables define the alternative ways the resources can be used to accomplish the objective. The availability of the resources and the resource utilization rates define the restrictions of the values of the decision variables—the restrictions of the alternative available courses of action. The contribution rates relate the decision variables to the accomplishment of the objective. In a linear programming formulation, all of the relevant information of a decision environment is related in terms of formally structured linear relationships.

A formulated linear programming problem contains two major components: linear constraints and an objective function. The linear constraints define feasible alternative values for the decision variables. The objective function provides a means to evaluate alternatives. With these two components, a linear programming model provides a systematic method for obtaining the optimal values for the decision variables. An alternative space is defined for feasible values of the decision variables. The search for the best alternative is retricted to corner points on the boundary of this defined domain of feasible alternatives. The corner points are evaluated by the objective function. The corner point best satisfying the objective is the optimal solution.

The graphic procedure presented in this chapter for solving a linear programming problem is easily applied and easily understood. However, it has a severe limitation. It is restricted to problems that can be graphed. The size of the problem cannot exceed three dimensions. Most problems are much larger. Many problems contain hundreds or thousands of dimensions. A more powerful model is needed—the mathematically based simplex method (Chapter 9).

BIBLIOGRAPHY

Bierman, H., Jr., C. P. Bonini, and W. H. Hausman. *Quantitative Analysis for Business Decisions.* Homewood, Ill.: Richard D. Irwin, 1973.

Boulding, K. E., and W. A. Spivey. *Linear Programming and the Theory of the Firm.* New York: Macmillan Co., 1960.

Charnes, A., and W. W. Cooper. *Management Models and Industrial Applications of Linear Programming,* 2 Vols. New York: John Wiley & Sons, 1961.

Childress, R. L. *Mathematics for Managerial Decisions.* Englewood Cliffs, N.J.: Prentice-Hall, 1974.

Dantzig, G. B. *Linear Programming and Extensions.* Princeton: Princeton University Press, 1963.

Dorfman, R., P. A. Samuelson, and R. M. Solow. *Linear Programming and Economic Analysis.* New York: McGraw-Hill Book Co., 1958.

Gass, S. I. *Linear Programming: Methods and Applications.* New York: McGraw-Hill Book Co., 1969.

Gaver, D. P., and G. L. Thompson. *Programming and Probability Models in Operations Research.* Belmont, Calif.: Wadsworth Publishing Co., 1973.

Hadley, G. *Linear Programming.* Reading, Mass.: Addison-Wesley Publishing Co., 1962.

Hillier, F. S., and G. J. Lieberman. *Introduction to Operations Research.* San Francisco: Holden-Day, 1967.

Kim, C. *Introduction to Linear Programming.* New York: Holt, Rinehart and Winston, 1971.

Levin, R. I., and C. A. Kirkpatrick. *Quantitative Approaches to Management.* New York: McGraw-Hill Book Co., 1975.

Levin, R. I., and R. P. Lamone. *Linear Programming for Management Decisions.* Homewood, Ill.: Richard D. Irwin, 1969.

Loomba, N. P. *Linear Programming, An Introductory Analysis.* New York: McGraw-Hill Book Co., 1964.

Loomba, N. P., and E. Turban. *Applied Programming for Management.* New York: Holt, Rinehart and Winston, 1974.

Riley, V., and S. I. Gass. *Bibliography on Linear Programming and Related Techniques.* Baltimore: Johns Hopkins Press, 1958.

Spivey, W. A., and R. M. Thrall. *Linear Optimization.* New York: Holt, Rinehart and Winston, 1970.

Stockton, R. S. *Introduction to Linear Programming.* Homewood, Ill.: Richard D. Irwin, 1971.

Strum, J. E. *Introduction to Linear Programming.* San Francisco: Holden-Day, 1972.

Thierauf, R. J., and R. C. Klekamp. *Decision Making Through Operations Research.* New York: John Wiley & Sons, 1975.

Wagner, H. M. *Principles of Operations Research with Applications to Managerial Decisions.* Englewood Cliffs, N.J.: Prentice-Hall, 1969.

8.1. Two resources can be allocated daily for two activities. The associated linear programming formulation is:

$f_{max} = 4X_1 + 5X_2$
subject to: $2X_1 + 1X_2 \leq 8$
$\qquad\qquad 1X_1 + 2X_2 \leq 4$
$\qquad\qquad X_1 \geq 0; X_2 \geq 0.$

Graphically determine the optimal value for the decision variables in this problem.

8.2. Two workers are utilized to produce two products. The formulation of the weekly allocation is as follows:

$f_{max} = 40X_1 + 10X_2$
subject to: $5X_1 + 4X_2 \leq 40$ worker 1
$\qquad\qquad 4X_1 + 6X_2 \leq 48$ worker 2
$\qquad\qquad X_1 \geq 0; X_2 \geq 0.$

Plot the bounded region of feasible alternatives. Locate and evaluate each feasible corner point. Find the optimal corner point solution.

8.3. A blending of ingredients has been formulated as a linear programming problem:
$f_{min} = 20X_1 + 28X_2$

subject to: $1X_1 + 1\,1/2\,X_2 \geq 12$
$\qquad\qquad 2X_1 + 1\,1/2\,X_2 \geq 16$
$\qquad\qquad X_1 \geq 0; X_2 \geq 0.$

Plot the constraint equations. Shade in the area of feasible alternatives. Determine the optimal corner point.

8.4. $f_{max} = 100X_1 + 2X_2$
$\qquad$ subject to: $3X_1 + 2X_2 \leq 12$
$\qquad\qquad\qquad 2X_1 + 4X_2 \leq 16$
$\qquad\qquad\qquad X_1 \geq 0; X_2 \geq 0.$

Determine the optimal solution graphically by the corner point method.

8.5. Two products have the indicated profit contributions and constraints:

$f_{max} = 12X_1 + 16X_2$
subject to: $4X_1 + 3X_2 \leq 24$
$\qquad\qquad 2X_1 + 4X_2 \leq 20$
$\qquad\qquad X_1 \qquad\quad \geq 4$
$\qquad\qquad X_1 \geq 0; X_2 \geq 0.$

Plot the three constraints. Shade in the area of feasible alternatives. Select the best alternative.

8.6. Two resources can be used as follows:

$f_{max} = 60X_1 + 65X_2$
subject to: $3X_1 + 4X_2 \leq 48 \qquad$ resource 1
$\qquad\qquad 4X_1 + 5X_2 \leq 40 \qquad$ resource 2
$\qquad\qquad X_1 \geq 0; X_2 \geq 0.$

Determine the optimal allocation of the two resources by the corner point method. What is the total utilization of resource 1 and resource 2? Will these conclusions apply for any objective function?

8.7. $f_{max} = 400X_1 + 2X_2$
subject to: $1\,1/2\,X_1 + 2X_2 = 24$
$\qquad\qquad 4X_1 + 1X_2 = 16$
$\qquad\qquad X_1 \geq 0; X_2 \geq 0.$

Plot the two constraint *equations*. Shade in the area of feasible alternatives. Determine the optimal solution.

8.8. $f_{max} = 4X_1 + 5X_2$
subject to: $1X_1 + 2X_2 \leq 20$
$\qquad\qquad 2X_1 + 1X_2 \leq 24$
$\qquad\qquad X_1 \geq 0; X_2 \geq 0.$

Plot and shade the area of feasible alternatives. Determine the best corner point. Then perform the same steps on the following:

$f_{min} = -4X_1 - 5X_2$
subject to: $1X_1 + 2X_2 \leq 20$
$\qquad\qquad 2X_1 + 1X_2 \leq 24$
$\qquad\qquad X_1 \geq 0; X_2 \geq 0.$

What important inference can you draw?

8.9. $f_{max} = 20X_1 + 22X_2$
subject to: $8X_1 + 6X_2 \leq 48$
$\qquad\qquad 6X_1 + 8X_2 \leq 48$
$\qquad\qquad 7X_1 + 7X_2 = 44$
$\qquad\qquad X_1 \geq 0; X_2 \geq 0.$

Plot the constraints. Lightly shade the area of feasible alternatives produced by the first two constraints. Darkly shade all feasible alternatives subject to all three constraints. Locate the optimal corner point.

8.10. Three resources can be utilized as follows:

$f_{max} = \$40X_1 + \$60X_2$
subject to: $4X_1 + 1X_2 \leq 20$ resource 1
$2X_1 + 2X_2 \leq 16$ resource 2
$1X_1 + 4X_2 \leq 20$ resource 3
$X_1 \geq 0; X_2 \geq 0.$

Plot the area of feasible alternatives, evaluate the corner points, and find the profit associated with the optimal solution.

8.11. Determine the optimal graphic solution to the following minimization problem:

$f_{min} = 10X_1 + 8X_2$
subject to: $6X_1 + 4X_2 \geq 36$
$5X_1 + 8X_2 \geq 40$
$X_2 \geq 2$
$X_1 \geq 0; X_2 \geq 0.$

Plot the objective function through the optimal corner point. Label the coordinates for the associated X_1 and X_2 intercepts.

8.12. $f_{max} = 10X_1 + 8X_2$
subject to: $5X_1 + 2X_2 \leq 20$
$2X_1 + 6X_2 \leq 24$
$X_1 \geq 0; X_2 \geq 0.$

Plot the objective function through the coordination (1, 0), (2, 0), and the optimal corner point. What conclusion can you draw?

8.13. Two resources can be used independently to manufacture two products. The restriction on output for the first resource (R_1) is represented by:

$4X_1 + 3X_2 \leq 24$ R_1.

The restriction for the second resource (R_2) is:

$4X_1 + 6X_2 \leq 36$ R_2.

The profitability of the two products is represented by:

$f = 60X_1 + 80X_2.$

What is the potential profitability obtainable from the first resource? How much can be obtained from both resources?

8.14. Solve the following set of equations simultaneously by row operations. Label each row operation as the equations are transformed into a solution for the variables. State the equation in the final solution format for the two variables:

$$4X_1 + 6X_2 = 12$$
$$8X_1 + 4X_2 = 16.$$

8.15. Plot the two resource constraints:

$$2X_1 + 4X_2 \leq 16 \qquad R_1$$
$$5X_1 + 2X_2 \leq 20 \qquad R_2.$$

The objective function is:

$$f_{max} = \$40X_1 + \$36X_2.$$

Locate the point where the second constraint intersects the X_1 axis. Move upward from this intercept to the point that includes exactly one unit of X_2. What is the total economic effect of the addition of the unit of X_2? What can you conclude about feasible solutions on the boundary of the second resource constraint?

8.16. A company can use two workers to manufacture product 1 and product 2 during a business slowdown. Worker 1 will be available for 20 hours and worker 2 for 24 hours. Product 1 will require 5 hours of labor from worker 1 and 3 hours of specialized skill from worker 2. Product 2 will require 4 hours from worker 1 and 6 hours from worker 2. The finished products will contribute a net profit of $60 for product 1 and $50 for product 2. At least two units of product 2 must be manufactured to satisfy a contract requirement.

    Formulate the decision environment into the proper linear programming structure. Solve the formulated problem graphically.

8.17. Over the next scheduling period, a production manager can allocate resources to the manufacture of three products: product 1, product 2, and product 3. Each product must pass through four processes: production, assembly, painting, and shipping. Each unit of product 1 requires four hours of production, two hours of assembly, half an hour of painting, and half an hour of shipping. Product 2 requires two hours of production, one hour of assembly, one hour of painting, and half an hour of shipping. Product 3 requires one hour, three hours, 1 1/2 hours, and one hour respectively.

    The time available in each work area is: production, 640 hours; assembly, 420 hours; painting, 200 hours; and shipping, 140 hours. Production levels are always planned to cover minimum sales requirements. Minimum sales projections for the three products are 80 for product 1, 40 for product 2, and 50 for product 3. Moreover, a shortage of materials will restrict the combined output of products 2 and 3 to no more than 120. Product 1 contributes $140 to profits. Products 2 and 3 contribute $75 and $195 respectively.

    Formulate as a linear programming problem with the objective of determining the optimal product mix to maximize profit contribution. (Formulate only; do not solve the problem.)

8.18. A Nebraska farmer has 200 acres of land to be allocated in the spring to wheat, corn, or soybeans. The three crops have projected profits per acre of $120, $90, and $70, respectively. The per acre labor requirements to plant, prepare, and harvest the crops are 36 hours for wheat, 20 hours for corn, and 28 hours for soybeans. The farmer and his sons will provide a labor force of 6,200 hours over the spring crop growing season.

Formulate the allocation of the farmer's acreage and labor to maximize profits from the spring planting.

8.19. An investor would like to allocate $200,000 of available funds in a portfolio selection from four major categories: bonds, blue chip stocks, speculative stocks, and cash. The projected annual returns and subjective risk factor assessments of these categories are summarized in the table below. The investor would like to maintain at least $10,000 in cash and maintain an average risk factor of not over 2.8. He does not want speculator stocks to exceed 30 percent of the funds. Formulate as a linear programming problem with the allocation objective of maximizing annual return with liquidity and risk preference restrictions.

Investment Category	Annual Return	Risk Factor
Bonds	10%	1
Blue Chip Stocks	14%	3
Speculative Stocks	20%	6
Cash	0	0

8.20. Given the following production requirements, formulate as a linear programming problem:

	Machine 1	Machine 2	Labor
Product A	2	2	4
Product B	1	2	2
Product C	2	4	5

Availability of Resources:

Machine 1	240 hours
Machine 2	260 hours
Labor	420 hours

Minimum Sales Requirement:

Product B	25 units
Product C	42 units

Maximum Production from Raw Materials Shortages:

Product C	54 units

Value of Output:

Product A	$80
Product B	$65
Product C	$75

8.21. A decision environment has acquired the following linear programming structure:

$$f_{max} = 120X_1 + 150X_2$$
$$\text{subject to: } 4X_1 + 1X_2 \le 40$$
$$2X_1 + 5X_2 \le 40$$
$$1X_1 + 3X_2 \le 32$$
$$X_1 \ge 0; X_2 \ge 0.$$

Create a hypothetical decision environment from which this formulation could have been derived.

8.22. Confronted with multiperiod scheduling compounded by seasonal product demand, a production manager would like to find the optimal balance between the cost of overtime and inventory carrying costs. The company is contracted to supply 7,000 units of a product over a three-month period: 1,000 units in May, 2,000 in June, and 4,000 in July. The present facilities allow the production of only 2,000 units per month on a regular time basis. If required, a maximum of an additional 1,000 units per month can be produced in overtime. The regular time cost per unit is $4. Overtime per unit cost is $5.50. Items can be stored in inventory at a monthly cost of $1.20 per unit.

Formulate as a linear programming problem, minimizing total production costs to meet contract requirements. Express the decision variables by X_{ijk}. The subscript i will represent the month produced, j the type shift, and k the month delivered. For example, X_{112} will represent units produced in May by the regular shift to be shipped for delivery in June.

8.23. On Friday afternoon a student has just completed final examinations in marketing and management. He has three remaining finals scheduled for next week: quantitative business analysis (QBA), accounting, and finance. Between now and the last final, he will have a maximum of 32 hours available for study. The QBA final is worth 40 percent of the course grade. The accounting and finance finals are worth 25 and 30 percent of the respective course grades. With no study, the student assumes a score of 60 on the QBA final. With 10 hours of study, he assumes a score of 80. With 20 hours of study, he assumes a perfect score (100). Furthermore, he believes that there is a linear relationship between time spent studying and score improvement. That is, every study hour spent on QBA will return two points on the exam. Having made similar assessments for the other two subjects, he assumes the accounting score at 65 with no study, with a return of 2.4 points per study hour, and the finance score at 75, with a return of 1.8 points per study hour. A score of less than 80 on any final is not acceptable.

While the other two are three-unit courses, accounting is a special five-unit course. The University assigns grades by the *score* in the classes. With the objective of maximizing grade point average, formulate the utilization of the student's study time as a linear programming problem.

9

Linear Programming: The Simplex Method

The simplex method is a mathematical procedure for solving linear programming problems. It extends the severely limited graphical procedure presented in Chapter 8. Instead of being restricted to *three dimensions* by graphically representing the alternative space, the simplex method is extended to *any number of dimensions* by mathematically representing the alternative space. Accompanied by the computational facility of a large computer, the simplex method can solve linear programming problems containing hundreds or thousands of dimensions.

The simplex procedure is similar to the graphical procedure for solving linear programming problems. In terms of a mathematical representation instead of a graphical representation, the simplex procedure defines feasible alternatives; restricts potential optimal feasible alternatives to a finite number; and evaluates these alternatives to isolate the best one. Regarding the definition of feasible alternatives, the characteristics of linear constraints will always restrict the domain of feasible alternatives to a convex polyhedron (Figures 9.1, 9.2, and 9.3). Regarding the restriction of potential optimal feasible alternatives, the optimal solution must be a corner point on this convex polyhedron. In essence, the simplex procedure will define and evaluate corner points on the surface of a convex polyhedron of feasible alternatives to isolate the best alternative.

Procedurally, the simplex method starts at a corner point on the surface of the convex polyhedron of feasible alternatives. Each adjacent corner point on this polyhedron is then economically evaluated. If there are economically improved adjacent corner points, a move is made to one of these improved corner points. The evaluations and movements are repeated. If there are no

Mathematical Representation   Graphical Representation

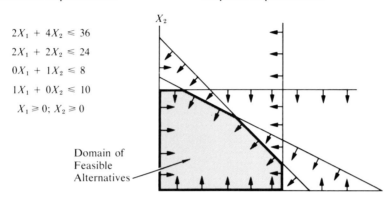

$$2X_1 + 4X_2 \leq 36$$
$$2X_1 + 2X_2 \leq 24$$
$$0X_1 + 1X_2 \leq 8$$
$$1X_1 + 0X_2 \leq 10$$
$$X_1 \geq 0; X_2 \geq 0$$

Domain of
Feasible
Alternatives

FIGURE 9.1

A Convex Polygon: A Convex Polyhedron with Two Dimensions

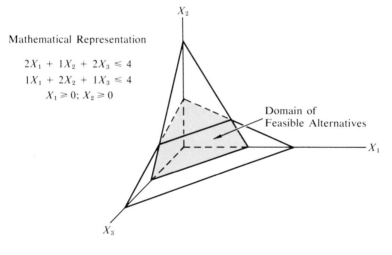

Graphical Representation

Mathematical Representation

$$2X_1 + 1X_2 + 2X_3 \leq 4$$
$$1X_1 + 2X_2 + 1X_3 \leq 4$$
$$X_1 \geq 0; X_2 \geq 0$$

Domain of
Feasible Alternatives

FIGURE 9.2

A Convex Polyhedron with Three Dimensions

remaining economically improved adjacent feasible corner points,[1] the optimal solution has been reached.

---

[1] If there are no better adjacent corner points, it can be shown that no better feasible corner points can exist. This does not exclude the possibility of more than one best corner point.

Mathematical Representation	Graphical Representation

$$2X_1 + 1X_2 + 2\tfrac{1}{2}X_3 + 1\tfrac{1}{2}X_4 \leq 162$$

$$1\tfrac{1}{2}X_1 + 2X_2 + \tfrac{1}{2}X_3 + 2X_4 \leq 148$$

$$\tfrac{1}{2}X_1 + 1\tfrac{1}{2}X_2 + 3X_3 + 2\tfrac{1}{2}X_4 \leq 124$$

$$4\tfrac{1}{2}X_1 + 2X_2 + 1X_3 + \tfrac{1}{2}X_4 \leq 272$$

$$X_1 \geq 0;\ X_2 \geq 0;\ X_3 \geq 0;\ X_4 \geq 0.$$

No Graphical Representation Possible

FIGURE 9.3

A Convex Polyhedron with Four Dimensions

In Figure 9.4, the process would start at corner point A. The two adjacent corner points B and G are then evaluated. If B represents an economic improvement,[2] a move is made to this corner point. Corner point C is then evaluated. Continuing this process, movements are made from $A \rightarrow B \rightarrow C \rightarrow D \rightarrow E$. A move from E to F will be found uneconomical. With no economically improved adjacent feasible corner points, E is the optimal solution.

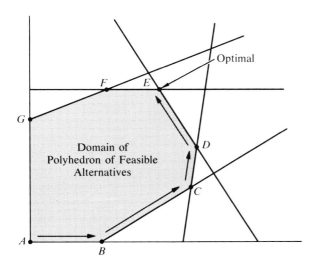

FIGURE 9.4

From Corner Point to Improved Adjacent Corner Point

___

[2] If E were optimal, G would also be an improved corner point. The optimal solution could have been reached by $A \rightarrow G \rightarrow F \rightarrow E$.

In this context, the simplex procedure will require the following internal operations:

(1) a method for starting at a corner point on the convex polyhedron of feasible alternatives;

(2) a method for evaluating adjacent feasible corner points;

(3) a method for avoiding infeasible corner points; and

(4) a method for moving from one feasible corner point to an improved feasible corner point.

Once fully developed and integrated, these essential operations will define the step-by-step functioning of the simplex method.

THE ADDITION OF SLACK VARIABLES

To compare the simplex method with the already familiar graphical solution, an example given in Chapter 8 will be reintroduced. The problem concerns the allocation of two workers to produce two products (Table 8.1):

Find X_1, X_2: $f_{max} = 100X_1 + 80X_2$ objective function
subject to: $4X_1 + 5X_2 \leq 20$ W_1 construction constraint
            $6X_1 + 3X_2 \leq 18$ W_2 painting and packaging constraint
            $X_1 \geq 0; X_2 \geq 0$ nonnegative constraints.

In the graphical analysis, the optimal solution had to be a corner point value. The simplex method's search for an optimal solution, therefore, can be *restricted only to feasible corner points*. The mathematical definition of corner points, however, produces a complication. The two resource constraints are *inequalities* that represent two families of parallel lines (Figure 9.5). The infinite intersecting lines provides an infinite number of *mathematically defined corner points*. Defining an infinite alternative space, inequalities prohibit a means for obtaining an optimal solution.

Fortunately, this difficulty can be readily resolved. A *slack variable* (S_j) can be introduced to maintain the conceptual properties of the inequality ($\leq$) while mathematically forming an *equality*. With slack variables S_1 and S_2 for the respective workers:

Time for product 1	+	Time for product 2	+	Slack time (idle time)	=	Total time available	
$4X_1$	+	$5X_2$	+	$1S_1$	=	20	W_1
$6X_1$	+	$3X_2$		$+ 1S_2$	=	10	W_2

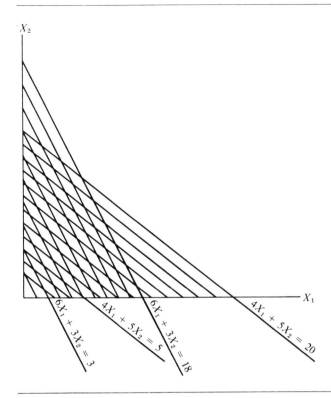

FIGURE 9.5

An Infinite Number of Intersections—An Infinite Number of
Corner Points

The slack variables "take up the slack" between the time utilized and the total
time available. They make it possible for a resource to be used less-than-or-
equal-to total time available. And at the same time, they form an equality. As
will be demonstrated shortly, they confine the alternative space to a finite
number of corner points.

The Alternative Space with Slack Variables

Reexpressed with slack variables, the boundary of feasible alternatives is
defined by the constraints:

$$4X_1 + 5X_2 + S_1 \qquad = 20 \qquad W_1$$
$$6X_1 + 3X_2 \qquad + S_2 = 18 \qquad W_2$$
$$X_1 \geq 0; X_2 \geq 0.$$

The alternative space will contain four variables: X_1, X_2, S_1, S_2.

The Addition of Slack Variables

The resource constraints provide the required information to define corner points. At the origin, X_1 and X_2 are both zero. The values for S_1 and S_2 are:

$4X_1 + 5X_2 + 1S_1 = 20 \qquad W_1$
$4(0) + 5(0) + 1S_1 = 20$

$S_1 = 20.$

$6X_1 + 3X_2 + 1S_2 = 18 \qquad W_2$
$6(0) + 3(0) + 1S_2 = 18$

$S_2 = 18.$

At the intersection of the worker 2 constraint on the X_1 axis, X_1 is three and X_2 is zero. Substituting these values into the constraints:

$4X_1 + 5X_2 + 1S_1 = 20 \qquad W_1$
$4(3) + 5(0) + 1S_1 = 20$

$S_1 = 8.$

$6X_1 + 3X_2 + 1S_2 = 18 \qquad W_2$
$6(3) + 3(0) + 1S_2 = 18$

$S_2 = 0.$

The corner point is (3, 0, 8, 0). All other corner points can be determined in the same way (Table 9.1 and Figure 9.6).

In order to evaluate the corner points, the slack variables are introduced into the objective function. With slack or idle time contributing nothing to profits, the appropriate *contribution coefficient* (C_j) will be zero. The new objective function is:

$f_{max} = 100X_1 + 80X_2 + 0S_1 + 0S_2.$

Alternative (X_1, X_2, S_1, S_2)

A_1: (0,0,20,8)
A_2: (3,0,8,0)
A_3: (5,0,0,–12)*
A_4: (0,4,0,6)
A_5: (0,6,–10,0)*
A_6: (1⅔,2⅔,0,0)

*infeasible

TABLE 9.1

The Alternative Space of Corner Points

Linear Programming: The Simplex Method

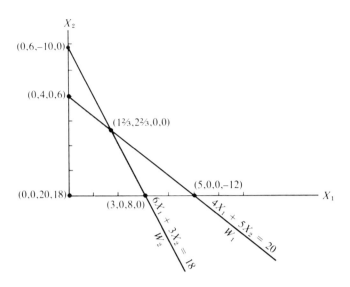

FIGURE 9.6
Alternative Space (X_1, X_2, S_1, S_2)

In Table 9.1 and Figure 9.6, a new difficulty becomes apparent. The corner points $(5, 0, 0, -12)$ and $(0, 6, -10, 0)$ are infeasible. At $(5, 0, 0, -12)$, for example, the associated output is five units of product 1, zero units of product 2, zero hours of idle time for worker 1, and -12 hours of idle time for worker 2. Note, the required idle time for worker 2 is -12. This is equivalent to 12 hours of overtime—which exceeds this resource's availability. This corner point is *infeasible* and must be excluded from consideration.

To formally prevent infeasible corner points from negative valued slack variables, *nonnegative constraints* are introduced:

$$S_1 \geq 0; S_2 \geq 0.$$

Infeasible overutilization of the resources will no longer be possible.

To allow a mathematical definition and evaluation of all feasible alternatives, the problem statement becomes:

Find (X_1, X_2, S_1, S_2): $f_{max} = 100X_1 + 80X_2 + 0S_1 + 0S_2$
subject to:
$$4X_1 + 5X_2 + 1S_1 \qquad = 20 \quad W_1$$
$$6X_1 + 3X_2 \qquad + 1S_2 = 18 \quad W_2$$

$$X_1 \geq 0; X_2 \geq 0; S_1 \geq 0; S_2 \geq 0.$$

AN INITIAL FEASIBLE SOLUTION

The simplex procedure starts at a corner point on the surface of a convex polyhedron of feasible alternatives. This starting solution must be a *corner point* and it must be *feasible*.

The alternative space has been defined in terms of four variables (X_1, X_2, S_1, S_2). The corner points are determined from the two resource constraints:

$$4X_1 + 5X_2 + 1S_1 + 0S_2 = 20 \qquad W_1$$
$$6X_1 + 3X_2 + 0S_1 + 1S_2 = 18 \qquad W_2.$$

With two equations, the maximum number of solvable variables is two. This poses a potential difficulty.

Since each corner point has been previously defined from the constraint equations (Figure 9.6), this difficulty must be surmountable. As illustrated in Figure 9.7, each of the alternatives is defined in terms of the four variables (X_1, X_2, S_1, S_2). For any particular point, $X_1 = 1$ and $X_2 = 1$ for example, the other two variables can be solved from the constraint equations:

$$4(1) + 5(1) + 1S_1 + 0S_2 = 20 \qquad W_1$$
$$6(1) + 3(1) + 0S_1 + 1S_2 = 18 \qquad W_2.$$

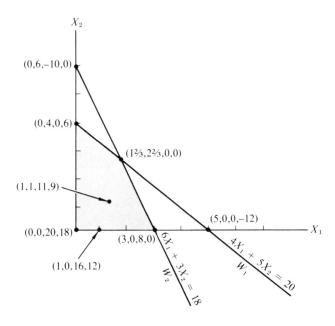

FIGURE 9.7

The Alternative Space (X_1, X_2, S_1, S_2)

Linear Programming: The Simplex Method

At $(X_1 = 1, X_2 = 1)$, $S_1 = 11$ and $S_2 = 9$. The coordinate is $(1, 1, 11, 9)$. If two variables are specified, the other two variables are solvable from the two constraints.

A close inspection of the alternative space leads to an important discovery. Each and every corner point contains two variables with specified values of zero. At the origin, X_1 and X_2 are both zero. Where the second constraint intersects the X_1 axis, X_1 and S_2 are both zero. At the intersection of the two resource constraints, S_1 and S_2 are zero. At corner points, with two variables specified at zero, the two resource constraints can be used to solve for the remaining two variables.[3]

With corner points defined by two variables having values other than zero, the next requirement of a starting solution is *feasibility*. A set of variables defining the corner point must be on the surface of the convex polyhedron of feasible alternatives. In this case there are six possibilities:

X_1, X_2 X_2, S_1

X_1, S_1 X_2, S_2

X_1, S_2 $S_1, S_2.$

By setting the other two variables equal to zero, the coordinates for any of these sets of variables can be solved from the constraint equations. An *arbitrary selection, however, cannot* be made. The set of variables selected may be *infeasible*. This will be denoted by a negative solution value for one of the variables (Figure 9.7). An infeasible corner point must be discarded—a new set of variables must be selected.

The danger of an arbitrarily selected infeasible corner point increases with the size of the problem. In the present problem, there are 6 corner points: 4 feasible and 2 infeasible. The probability of arbitrarily selecting an infeasible corner point is 2/6. With three constraints (Figure 9.8(a)), there will be 5 feasible and 5 infeasible corner points. The probability of an infeasible selection increases to 5/10. With five constraints (Figure 9.8(b)), there are 21 corner points—14 infeasible. The probability of an initial infeasible selection is now 14/21. Moreover, if the first selection is found infeasible and discarded, the probability of a second infeasible selection is still 14/20.

With N_V representing the number of variables and N_C the number of constraints, the total number of corner points can be determined by:

$$\binom{N_V + N_C}{N_C} = \frac{(N_V + N_C)!}{N_V!\, N_C!}.$$

---

[3] For a problem containing n constraints, the corner points will be definable by n nonzero valued variable, solvable from the n constraints.

(a)

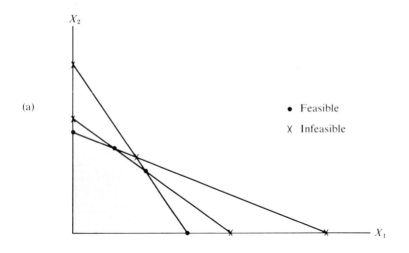

• Feasible

X Infeasible

(b)

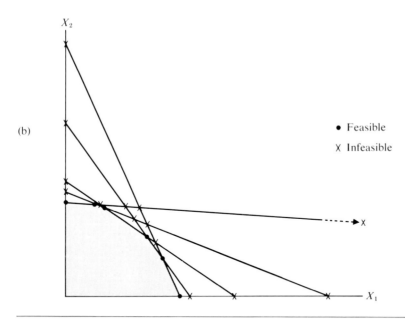

• Feasible

X Infeasible

FIGURE 9.8
Infeasible Corner Points

For a problem allocating 10 resources to 10 possible activities, there will be 184,756 corner points.[4] If there are 14 resources and 14 activities, there will be

---

[4] Without added variables:

$$\binom{10 + 10}{10} = \frac{20!}{10! \, 10!} = 184,756.$$

40,116,600 corner points. For 20 resources and 20 activities, there will be 137,846,528,820 corner points. For large problems, the number of corner points becomes virtually infinite. Since *almost all* of the corner points will be *infeasible*, the selection *cannot be arbitrary. The initial starting solution must be a guaranteed feasible corner point.*

Fortunately, for any convex polyhedron formed by less-than-or-equal-to ($\leq$) resource constraints, the slack variables (S_j) guarantee feasibility. In the present problem, S_1 and S_2 provide an initial feasible starting solution.

THE SIMPLEX TABLEAU

The information essential to a solution can be presented in a tableau instead of raw equations. Information is required for the *four basic operations*: (1) the definition of corner point solutions (the resource constraints); (2) the economic evaluation of these corner points (the objective function); (3) the economic evaluation of adjacent corner points (the objective function and resource constraints); and (4) the movement to improved feasible corner points (the resource constraints and nonnegative constraints). The essential information will be the *objective function, resource constraints*, and *nonnegative constraints*.

With the assumption of nonnegativity understood, a tableau can be designed to house the informational requirements:

$$f = 100X_1 + 80X_2 + 0S_1 + 0S_2 \qquad \text{objective function}$$

Solution Variables   Quantity

$$20 = 4X_1 + 5X_2 + 1S_1 + 0S_2 \ W_1 \qquad \text{resource constraints}$$
$$18 = 6X_1 + 3X_2 + 0S_1 + 1S_2 \ W_2$$

In a more efficient coefficient format:

Solution Variable	Quantity	100 X_1	80 X_2	0 S_1	0 S_2	
	20	4	5	1	0	W_1
	18	6	3	0	1	W_2

In the *matrix of coefficients*, plus signs are inferred, and negative signs are included when required.

The First Simplex Tableau

To gurantee an initial feasible solution, the starting corner point will contain the slack variables (S_1, S_2). The body of the tableau will represent the constraint equations expressed in a *solution format* for the variables in the solution. The resource constraints are:

$$4X_1 + 5X_2 + 1S_1 + 0S_2 = 20 \quad W_1$$
$$6X_1 + 3X_2 + 0S_1 + 1S_2 = 18 \quad W_2.$$

As was previously indicated, since variables not in the solution have values of zero:

$$4(0) + 5(0) + \boxed{1S_1 + 0S_2 = 20 \quad W_1}$$
$$6(0) + 3(0) + \boxed{0S_1 + 1S_2 = 18 \quad W_2}$$

In terms of the tableau, the initial feasible solution for variables S_1 and S_2 is:

C_j	Sol. Var.	Quantity	100 X_1	80 X_2	0 S_1	0 S_2	
0	S_1	20			1	0	eq.I
0	S_2	18			0	1	eq. II
	Z_j	0					

The total contribution to the objective (the value of the objective function) is represented by the first element (Z_0) in a Z_j row. The column calculation is:

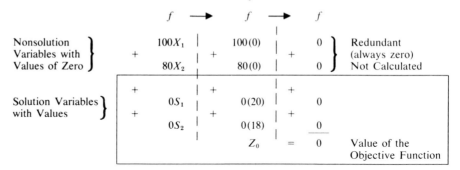

$$
\begin{aligned}
&f \longrightarrow \quad f \longrightarrow \quad f \\
\left.\begin{array}{l}\text{Nonsolution}\\ \text{Variables with}\\ \text{Values of Zero}\end{array}\right\} &+ \begin{array}{c}100X_1\\ 80X_2\end{array} + \begin{array}{c}100(0)\\ 80(0)\end{array} + \begin{array}{c}0\\ 0\end{array} \left.\right\}\begin{array}{l}\text{Redundant}\\ \text{(always zero)}\\ \text{Not Calculated}\end{array}
\end{aligned}
$$

The column to the far left represents the per unit contribution (C_j) for the variables in the solution. When these values are multiplied by the values of the solution variables, the summed product is the objective function evaluation of the corner point solution:

C_j	Sol. Var.	Quantity	
0	S_1	20	0(20)
0	S_2	18	+ 0(18)
		Z_0 =	0

Linear Programming: The Simplex Method

From the tableau, the corner point solution and evaluation are:

$S_1 = 20$
$S_2 = 18$ solution variables (basis variables)

$X_1 = 0$
$X_2 = 0$ nonsolution variables (nonbasis variables)

$f = \$0$ the value of the objective function (Z_0).

Although economically unappealing, this solution provides a guaranteed feasible corner point on the surface of the convex polyhedron of feasible alternatives.

EVALUATING ADJACENT CORNER POINTS

The next step is the evaluation of adjacent corner points (Figure 9.9). The present solution is $S_1 = 20$, $S_2 = 18$, $X_1 = 0$, and $X_2 = 0$. There are two

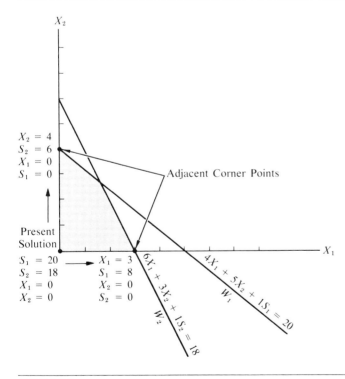

FIGURE 9.9
Adjacent Corner Points

adjacent corner points on the respective axes. The question is: Should a movement be made from the present corner point in either of these two directions? Should units of X_1 or X_2 be entered into the solution?

The net economic effect of a movement along the X_1 axis will be evaluated. The present corner point solution allocates all available resources to S_1 and S_2. If units of product 1 are to be produced, part of the *present* solution must be sacrificed. The production of units of product 1 will not only generate an economic gain but also result in a loss of the present level of idle time.

The net economic effect of adding a unit of product 1 to the present solution is provided in Table 9.2. In the present solution, worker 1 is idle for 20 hours and worker 2 is idle for 18 hours. If one unit of product 1 is to be produced, 4 hours of worker 1's idle time must be reallocated to the production of product 1:

$$4X_1 + 5X_2 + 1S_1 = 20 \qquad \text{worker 1}$$
$$4(0) + 5(0) + 1S_1 = 20 \qquad \text{present solution}$$

$$S_1 = 20.$$

$$4(1) + 5(0) + 1S_1 = 20 \qquad \text{solution with one unit of product 1}$$

$$S_1 = 16.$$

To allow production of a unit of product 1, S_1 must be decreased by four units:

$$\Delta S_1 \!\downarrow = 4.$$

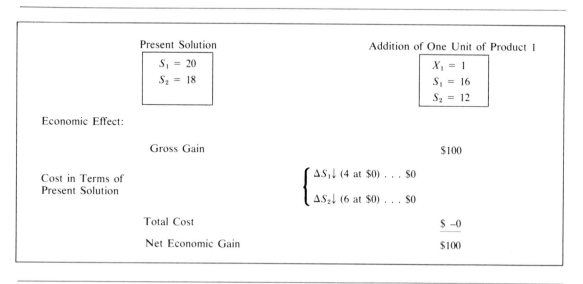

	Present Solution		Addition of One Unit of Product 1
	$S_1 = 20$		$X_1 = 1$
	$S_2 = 18$		$S_1 = 16$
			$S_2 = 12$
Economic Effect:			
	Gross Gain		$100
Cost in Terms of Present Solution		$\{$ $\Delta S_1\!\downarrow$ (4 at $0) . . . $0	
		$\Delta S_2\!\downarrow$ (6 at $0) . . . $0	
	Total Cost		$ –0
	Net Economic Gain		$100

TABLE 9.2

The Economic Effect of Adding X_1 to the Solution

Similarly, worker 2 must utilize 6 hours of idle time to complete a unit of product 1:

$$6X_1 + 3X_2 + 1S_2 = 18 \qquad \text{worker 2}$$
$$6(0) + 3(0) + 1S_2 = 18 \qquad \text{present solution}$$

$$S_2 = 18$$

$$6(1) + 3(0) + 1S_2 = 18 \qquad \text{solution with one unit of product 1}$$

$$S_2 = 12.$$

Consequently,

$$\Delta S_2\!\downarrow = 6.$$

Economically, if one unit of product 1 is produced, there is a gross increase in profits of $100. There is also a sacrifice (or cost) in terms of the present solution: four units of S_1 and six units of S_2. With S_1 and S_2 both at a value of zero, the total economic loss is zero. The net economic effect of adding a unit of product 1 is a net gain of $100. Product 1 is advantageous; variable X_1 will improve the solution.

A similar set of computations measures the net economic effect of adding variable X_2 to the solution. One unit of product 2 will produce a gain of $80. In terms of the present solution, there will be a loss of five units of S_1 (worth zero) and three units of S_2 (worth zero) for a total cost of $0. The net economic effect of adding a unit of product 2 to the present solution will be a net gain of $80. Product 2 is likewise advantageous; variable X_2 will improve the solution.

This same evaluation can be obtained directly from the simplex tableau. The tableau in a solution format for S_1 and S_2 is:

C_j			100	80	0	0
	Sol. Var.	Quantity	X_1	X_2	S_1	S_2
0	S_1	20			1	0
0	S_2	18			0	1
	Z_j	0				

Entering the rest of the constraint equations:

C_j			100	80	0	0
	Sol. Var	Quantity	X_1	X_2	S_1	S_2
0	S_1	20	4	5	1	0
0	S_2	18	6	3	0	1
	Z_j	0				

If one unit of X_1 is added to the present solution, *the gross gain* of $100 is in the row above the X_1 variable (C_1). *The cost in terms of the present solution* is easily obtained. If one unit of X_1 is entered, four units of S_1 and six units of S_2 must be given up. These values are the *technical coefficients of substitution* between the variable to be entered and the variables in the solution. They are located in the *column beneath the variable to be entered.* Moreover, the worth of the variables to be depleted is in the column to the left of the solution variables. Therefore, from the tableau, if one unit of X_1 is entered into the solution, there will be a loss of four units of S_1 at a value of zero and six units of S_2 at a value of zero. In terms of the present solution, the total cost of adding one unit of X_1 is zero.

Adding this information directly to the tableau, the *loss in terms of the present solution* for adding a variable at the head of the column can be represented by a Z_j row. The net economic effect can be determined by subtracting the loss in terms of the present solution $(Z_1 = 0)$ from the gain $(C_1 = 100)$. The *net economic effect* of adding a variable can be represented by a *net economic evaluation row* $(C_j - Z_j)$:

If one unit of X_1 is entered into the next solution, the value of the objective function will be increased by $100.

The economic effect of entering any variable not in the present solution can be evaluated in the same way. If one unit of X_2 is entered, the gross gain is $80 (C_2). There will also be a loss of five units of S_1 and three units of S_2, both at a value of zero. The total loss in terms of the present solution will be indicated by Z_2 equal to zero. The net economic effect on the objective function is $C_2 - Z_2 = 80$. Note, the net economic evaluation for the variables already in the solution (S_1, S_2) will always be zero. If one unit of S_1 is entered into the solution, one unit of S_1 will be given up. The new solution will be the same as the present solution with no economic effect.

The complete first simplex tableau with the evaluation of nonsolution variables is:

C_j	Solution Variables	Quantity	100 X_1	80 X_2	0 S_1	0 S_2
0	S_1	20	4	5	1	0
0	S_2	18	6	3	0	1
	Z_j	0	0	0	0	0
	$C_j - Z_j$		100	80	0	0

Either X_1 or X_2 can be entered advantageously into the next solution. Both are improved adjacent corner points.

Selecting One of Several New Variables

The simplex procedure introduces only one new variable at a time. The new variable is an adjacent *feasible* corner point. If more than one variable is introduced, the simplex method will not guarantee feasibility. Moreover, in large problems, the entry of more than one variable will inevitably be infeasible—off the surface of the convex polyhedron of feasible alternatives.[5]

In the present case, both X_1 and X_2 represent economically advantageous adjacent corner points. The introduction of either variable will eventually lead to the same optimal solution. However, in some cases, one variable may be more efficient to introduce.

Figure 9.10 provides an illustration. The initial corner point is at the

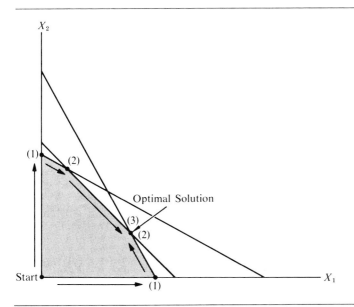

FIGURE 9.10
Selecting an Entry Variable

[5] This is the same difficulty as an arbitrary selection of initial starting variables.

origin. X_1 and X_2 both contribute positively to profits and, therefore, could advantageously be added to the next solution. If X_1 is added, the second adjacent corner point will be the optimal solution. However, if X_2 is added, three adjacent corner points are required before reaching the same optimal solution. X_1 is the preferable first addition. If X_2 is added first, approximately 50 percent more computations will be required.

While there is often a significant advantage in adding one variable rather than another, the proper selection cannot be easily made. In Figure 9.10, the optimal solution was assumed known in two dimensions. In an unsolved problem, the optimal solution will be unknown and usually in n dimensions. Determining the variable that leads most rapidly to the optimal solution is typically as difficult as determining the solution to the problem.

A very simple criterion is adequate for selecting the new variable. Enter the new variable with the greatest per unit improvement in the objective function—the variable with the *most favorable net economic evaluator* $(C_j - Z_j)$. Without additional information,[6] this selection of a variable *will tend to* lead to the optimal corner point more rapidly.

ENTERING A NEW VARIABLE

The variable with the most favorable economic evaluator will be entered into the next solution. Referring to the $C_j - Z_j$ row in the first tableau:

C_j	Solution Variables	Quantity	100 X_1	80 X_2	0 S_1	0 S_2	
0	S_1	20	4	5	1	0	eq. I
0	S_2	18	6	3	0	1	eq. II
	Z_j	0	0	0	0	0	
	$C_j - Z_j$		100	80	0	0	

X_1 should be entered into the solution.

In entering a new variable, there are two logical approaches. One is to determine *the maximum number of units that can be entered.* The other is to

---

[6] The variable contributing most in total (value · quantity) to the objective function would be even more desirable. However, this would require both the per unit worth and the solution value for the variable. In turn, this requires the mathematical solution for the corner points (which is computationally as demanding as developing the next tableau). Moreover, this variable is not guaranteed to lead to the optimal solution any more rapidly.

determine *the minimum number that must be entered.* Either approach will lead to the same conclusion: the maximum number allowable always equals the minimum number required.

Since every unit of X_1 entered increases profits by $100, as many units of X_1 as possible are desired. As expected, however, the resource constraints will restrict entry. Each resource constraint will impose a specific restriction.

As previously indicated, for every unit of X_1 entered into the solution, 4 units of S_1 and 6 units of S_2 must be given up. In terms of the first resource constraint (equation I), the value of S_1 is 20. Therefore, without forcing S_1 to an infeasible negative value, the maximum X_1 enterable will be:

$$S_1: \frac{20}{4} = 5.$$

Every unit of X_1 entered requires 4 units of S_1. With 20 units of S_1 available, the maximum allowable units of X_1 is 5.

The second constraint (equation II) also restricts the value of X_1. Every unit of X_1 entered requires 6 units of S_2. With 18 units of S_2 available, the maximum value for X_1 will be:

$$S_2: \frac{18}{6} = 3.$$

Since the alternatives are subject to both constraints, the maximum number of units of X_1 will be the smaller of these *substitution quantities*:

$$S_1: \frac{20}{4} = 5$$

$$S_2: \frac{18}{6} = 3^*.$$

The maximum number of units of X_1 enterable into the next solution will be three.

This concept is clearly demonstrated in Figure 9.11. The present solution is at the origin. As many units of X_1 as possible are to be entered into the solution. In a move along the X_1 axis, X_1 is restricted by both constraints. According to the first constraint, X_1 cannot exceed five. According to the second constraint, X_1 cannot exceed three. Consistent with both constraints, X_1 cannot exceed three.

The number of units of X_1 to be entered can also be considered in terms of the minimum required. As was mentioned before, corner points are defined by two nonzero variables. Presently, they are S_1 and S_2. To move to a new corner point, the entry of a new variable will require the removal of one of the

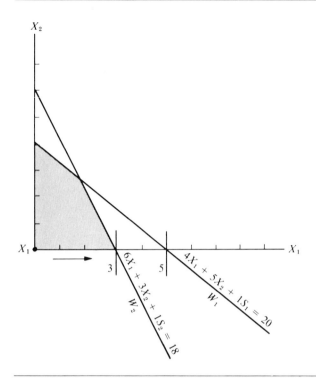

FIGURE 9.11

The Maximum Entry Quantity

present solution variables. The value of X_1 must be large enough to force one of the present solution variables from the solution.

The *substitution quantities* provide this information:

$$S_1: \frac{20}{4} = 5$$

$$S_2: \frac{18}{6} = 3^*.$$

If 1 unit of X_1 is entered, 4 units of S_1 and 6 units of S_2 must be given up. There are 20 units of S_1 and 18 units of S_2 in the present solution. Consequently, if 5 units of X_1 are entered, all 20 units of S_1 will be removed: S_1 will be forced from the solution. Similarly, if 3 units of X_1 are entered, 18 units of S_2 will be removed. The value of S_2 will be reduced to zero—removed from the solution.

Removing either solution variable is not sufficient. The new variable must not violate any of the constraints. If 5 units of X_1 are entered into the solution, 20 units of S_1 and 30 units of S_2 will be forced from the solution:

$$X_1 \downarrow (5)$$
$$\Delta S_1 \downarrow 20 \leftarrow 4(5)$$
$$\Delta S_2 \downarrow 30 \leftarrow 6(5).$$

Starting with a value of 20, S_1 will be reduced to 0 or removed from the solution. With a present value of only 18, S_2 will take on a value of -12: a violation of nonnegative constraint. Entering 5 units of X_1 will not provide a feasible corner point (Table 9.3).

Present Solution	New Solution After Entering Five Units of X_1
$X_1 = 0$	$X_1 = 5^*$
$X_2 = 0$	$X_2 = 0$
$S_1 = 20^*$	$S_1 = 0$
$S_2 = 18^*$	$S_2 = -12^*$
* Variable in solution	

TABLE 9.3

Entering Too Much X_1: Violation of the Nonnegative Constraint

Three units of X_1 however, can be entered into the solution. If 3 units of X_1 are entered, 12 of the 20 units of S_1 and 18 of the 18 units of S_2 will be forced from the solution (Table 9.4). After 3 units of X_1 are entered, only 8 units of S_1 and 0 units of S_2 will remain. With a new value of zero, the variable S_2 will be removed from the solution. The nonnegative constraints will be maintained.

Present Solution	New Solution After Entering Three Units of X_1
$X_1 = 0$	$X_1 = 3^*$
$X_2 = 0$	$X_2 = 0$
$S_1 = 20^*$	$S_1 = 8^*$
$S_2 = 18^*$	$S_2 = 0$
* Variable in solution	

TABLE 9.4

Entering X_1 and Removing S_2

Present Solution	New Solution After Entering 1 Unit of X_1
$X_1 = 0$	$X_1 = 1^*$
$X_2 = 0$	$X_2 = 0$
$S_1 = 20^*$	$S_1 = 16^*$
$S_2 = 18^*$	$S_2 = 12^*$
*Variable in solution	

TABLE 9.5

Entering Too Few X_1: Too Many Variables

If less than three units of X_1 are entered, no variable will be forced from the solution (Table 9.5). The new solution will contain more variables than constraint equations. It will not be a corner point solution.

Exactly three units of X_1 must be entered into the next solution. The maximum amount of the new variable allowable is the minimum amount required. The amount to enter will be equal to the minimum substitution quantity. The solution variable associated with the minimum substitution quantity will be removed from the solution.

The variable associated with a *negative substitution quantity* cannot be removed. The value of the substitution quantity for the removal variable will be the solution value for the entry variable. If a variable with a negative substitution quantity is selected for removal, the solution value for the new entry variable will violate the nonnegative constraint. Therefore, the variable to be removed will always have *the minimum positive substitution quantity.*

The substitution quantities have an important special function. In entering a new variable, the removal of the variable associated with the minimum positive substitution quantity will always provide a new *feasible* corner point. The minimum positive substitution quantity does not allow negative valued variables into the solution. It *maintains the nonnegative constraints.* It guarantees that the search for the optional solution will stay on the surface of the convex polyhedron of feasible alternatives.

THE SECOND TABLEAU: A NEW CORNER POINT SOLUTION

In the process of entering a new variable into the solution, the new tableau will acquire a specified form. The required amount of the new variable will force one of the variables from the solution. In this case, three units of X_1 are entered, forcing S_2 from the solution at a value of zero. Moreover, the entry of three units of X_1 will also require an adjustment of the other solution variable.

For every unit of X_1 entered, four units of S_1 must be given up. Since S_1 is initially 20 and three units of X_1 are entered, S_1 will acquire a new adjusted value of 8 (Table 9.4). In the new tableau, X_1 will have a value of 3 and S_1 will have a value of 8.

The second tableau, representing the new corner point, will be:

C_j			100	80	0	0	
	Sol. Var.	Quantity	X_1	X_2	S_1	S_2	
0	S_1	8	0		1		W_1
100	X_1	3	1		0		W_2
	Z_j	300	100		0		
	$C_j - Z_j$		0		0		

The body of the tableau still provides the two constraint equations in a solution format. However, instead of solving for (S_1, S_2), they are expressed in an adjusted solution form for (S_1, X_1). Since nonsolution variables (X_2, S_2) have values of zero, the constraint equations must be:

$$8 = 0X_1 + 1S_1 \qquad W_1$$
$$3 = 1X_1 + 0S_1 \qquad W_2.$$

The first equation is in a solution form for S_1; the second equation for X_1.

The new corner point has been defined and evaluated. The solution is:

$$\begin{aligned} S_1 &= 8 \\ X_1 &= 3 \end{aligned} \qquad \text{solution variables}$$

$$\begin{aligned} S_2 &= 0 \\ X_2 &= 0 \end{aligned} \qquad \text{nonsolution variables}$$

$$f = \$300 \qquad \text{value of the objective function.}$$

The next logical step is to determine whether there is an improved adjacent corner point—whether a new variable should be introduced into the solution.

Transforming Constraint Equations for Net Economic Evaluators

The desirability of entering a new variable is provided in the *net economic evaluator row* $(C_j - Z_j)$. In order to obtain these values, the Z_j's must be determined. In order to obtain the Z_j's, the unknown coefficients in the constraint equations must be determined.

In Table 9.6, the net economic evaluators $(C_2 - Z_2)$ and $(C_4 - Z_4)$ are required to evaluate the desirability of entering variables X_2 and S_2. In order to obtain $(C_2 - Z_2)$, Z_2 is required. In turn, to obtain Z_2, the two column

C_j			100	80	0	0	
	Sol. Var.	Quantity	X_1	X_2	S_1	S_2	
0	S_1	8	0	a_{12}	1	a_{14}	eq. I
100	X_1	3	1	a_{22}	0	a_{24}	eq. II
	Z_j	300	100	Z_2	0	Z_4	
	$C_j - Z_j$		0	$C_2 - Z_2$	0	$C_4 - Z_4$	

TABLE 9.6

Information Needed to Evaluate Adjacent Corner Points

values labeled a_{12} and a_{22} are required. Similarly, $C_4 - Z_4$ can be derived only via a_{14} and a_{24}. In order to measure the desirability of a new variable, the complete constraint equations must be developed.

The second equation associated with the new entry variable is:

$$3 = 1X_1 + 0S_1 \quad \text{equation II.}$$

Or in terms of all of the variables:

$$3 = 1X_1 + a_{22}X_2 + 0S_1 + a_{24}S_2.$$

The values of a_{22} and a_{24} are presently unknown.

Before X_1 was entered into the solution, equation II was in a solution form for variable S_2:

$$18 = 0S_1 + 1S_2 \quad \text{equation II (first tableau).}$$

Or with all variables:

$$18 = 6X_1 + 3X_2 + 0S_1 + 1S_2.$$

When X_1 was entered into the solution, this equation was transformed from a solution for S_2 into a solution for X_1. The transformed equation took the form:

$$3 = 1X_1 + 0S_1 \quad \text{equation II (second tableau).}$$

If the operation transforming the initial equation into the new solution form can be identified, this same operation can be applied to the entire equation to adjust the two unknown coefficients.

The apparent operation is a division by six. Initially, the equation was:

$$18 = 6X_1 + 3X_2 + 0S_1 + 1S_2.$$

Dividing by six provides the required elements of the new equation:

$$3 = 1X_1 \qquad + 0S_1.$$

Linear Programming: The Simplex Method

If this operation is applied to the entire equation, the two unknown coefficients are determined:

$$3 = 1X_1 + 3/6 \quad X_2 + 0S_1 + 1/6 \quad S_2.$$

The adjusted equation for the *new variable row* can always be obtained by *dividing the previous row for the new variable by the pivot coefficient value*. The *pivot coefficient* is the coefficient at the intersection of the row to be adjusted and the column for the new variable. In this case, the *pivot coefficient* is six:

C_j			100	80	0	0	
	Sol. Var.	Quantity	X_1	X_2	S_1	S_2	
0	S_1	20	4	5	1	0	
→0	S_2	18	⑥	3	0	1	eq. II
	Z_j	0	0	0	0	0	
	$C_j - Z_j$		100	80	0	0	

When the old row is divided by the pivot coefficient, the new row for the new variable in the second tableau becomes:

C_j			100	80	0	0	
	Sol. Var.	Quantity	X_1	X_2	S_1	S_2	
0	S_1						
100	X_1	3	1	$3/6$	0	$1/6$	eq. II
	Z_j						
	$C_j - Z_j$						

The other row can be adjusted by a similar procedure. Initially equation I was:

$$20 = 4X_1 + 5X_2 + 1S_1 + 0S_2 \quad \text{equation I.}$$

After the new variable was entered, it became:

$$8 = 0X_1 + 1S_1.$$

A multiplication or division, however, will not provide the proper transformation. A more complex set of *row operations* involving an addition or subtraction is required.[7] To allow an addition or subtraction, the other equation (the new row for the new variable) must be used.[8] To determine the adjustment, a listing

---

[7] Row operations consist of a valid set of additions, subtractions, multiplications, divisions, and combinations of these to transform an equation. The usual objective is to transform an equation (or set of equations) into solution form.

[8] The other equation could also be used in the initial tableau form. However, the most recent *new row for the new variable form* will be more efficient.

can be made of (1) the row to be adjusted, (2) the new row for the new variable and (3) the required elements of the adjusted row:

Row to be adjusted $\quad\quad\quad 20 = 4X_1 + 5X_2 + 1S_1 + 0S_2 \quad$ equation I

New row for new variable $\quad 3 = 1X_1 + \frac{3}{6}X_2 + 0S_1 + \frac{1}{6}S_2 \quad$ equation II

Adjusted row $\quad\quad\quad\quad\quad 8 = 0X_1 \quad\quad\quad\quad + 1S_1 \quad\quad\quad$ equation I.

The required operations will be to multiply the second equation by four and subtract the result from the first equation. This set of operations will provide precisely the required elements in the adjusted row:

$$20 = 4X_1 + 5X_2 + 1S_1 + 0S_2$$
$$-4(\ 3 = 1X_1 + \frac{3}{6}X_2 + 0S_1 + \frac{1}{6}S_2)$$
$$\overline{\quad\quad\quad\quad\quad\quad\quad\quad\quad\quad\quad\quad\quad\quad\quad}$$
$$8 = 0X_1 + 3X_2 + 1S_1 - \frac{4}{6}S_2.$$

There is also a more mechanical way of adjusting the *other rows* in the tableau. The value four used above is a *pivot coefficient*. The first row is being adjusted; the variable X_1 is being entered. At the intersection of the respective row and column is the *pivot coefficient* of four:

C_j			100	80	0	0
	Sol. Var.	Quantity	X_1	X_2	S_1	S_2
0	S_1	20	④	5	1	0
0	S_2	18	6	3	0	1

Rows other than the new variable row can be adjusted by:

(1) listing the row to be adjusted,

(2) listing beneath this row the new row for the new variable,

(3) multiplying the row for the new variable by the pivot coefficient, and

(4) subtracting the new variable row from the row to be adjusted.

The procedure is more easily performed in terms of a vector of the co-efficients than in terms of the entire equation:

$$3 \quad (20 \quad 4 \quad 5 \quad 1 \quad 0) \quad 1$$
$$-4 \quad (\ 3 \quad 1 \quad \frac{3}{6} \quad 0 \quad \frac{1}{6}) \quad 2$$
$$\overline{\quad\quad\quad\quad\quad\quad\quad\quad\quad\quad\quad\quad}$$
$$4 \longrightarrow (\ 8 \quad 0 \quad 3 \quad 1 \quad -\frac{4}{6}).$$

The adjusted second tableau becomes:

| C_j | | | 100 | 80 | 0 | 0 |
	Sol. Var.	Quantity	X_1	X_2	S_1	S_2
0	S_1	8	0	3	1	$-4/6$
100	X_1	3	1	$3/6$	0	$1/6$
	Z_j	300	100	50	0	$16\frac{2}{3}$
	$C_j - Z_j$		0	30	0	$-16\frac{2}{3}$

With the shaded *substitution coefficients* determined, the respective Z_j values and, ultimately, the $C_j - Z_j$ values for potential entry variables can be calculated. The desirability of adjacent corner points—the desirability of adding new variables—can be evaluated.

THE SIMPLEX ALGORITHM: AN ITERATIVE PROCESS

The simplex procedure starts at a corner point on a convex polyhedron of feasible alternatives and moves to improved adjacent feasible corner points on this polyhedron until the optimal solution has been reached. It is a systematic, iterative process. Given a feasible corner point expressed in tableau form, the desirability of entering a new variable (an improved corner point) is expressed in the *net economic evaluator row*. If a new variable is to be entered, the *substitution quantities* indicate which variable to remove. A new tableau is then formed with adjusted rows. The row for the new variable is adjusted first. It is divided by the associated *pivot coefficient*. The other rows are adjusted by multiplying the newly adjusted row for the new variable by the new *pivot coefficient* and subtracting the result from the row to be adjusted. This provides a new tableau complete with the information required to evaluate the economic effect of entering variables not in the solution. This entire process is then repeated until no new variables should be entered—until the optimal corner point has been reached.

Starting with a formulated problem, the step-by-step simplex procedure might be summarized as follows:

1. Add variables to produce an initial feasible solution.

2. Calculate the $C_j - Z_j$ to evaluate adjacent corner points—to evaluate the desirability of entering a new variable.

3. Select the variable with the most favorable $C_j - Z_j$ consistent with the objective.

4. Calculate the *substitution quantities* and remove the variable with the minimum positive ratio.

5. Adjust the row for the new variable by dividing it by the *pivot coefficient*.

6. Adjust all other rows by multiplying the new row for the new variable by the *pivot coefficient* and subtracting the result from the row to be adjusted.

7. Repeat step 2. through step 6. until no new variables improve the objective function.

Once the underlying logic of the procedure is understood, the simplex method becomes a simple set of logical steps that are repeated until the optimal solution is reached.

Obtaining the Optimal Solution

The simplex procedure can now be applied to the second tableau to obtain the optimal solution:

C_j			100	80	0	0
	Sol. Var.	q_0	X_1	X_2	S_1	S_2
0	S_1	8	0	3	1	$-4/6$
100	X_1	3	1	$3/6$	0	$1/6$
	Z_j	300	100	50	0	$16^2/3$
	$C_j - Z_j$		0	30	0	$-16^2/3$

The *net economic evaluators* $(C_j - Z_j)$ indicate that X_2 can be introduced to improve the solution. Specifically, every unit of X_2 entered into the solution will increase the objective function by \$30.

The *substitution quantities* are now formed to determine which variable should be removed. They are formed by dividing the solution values (q_0) by the *pivot coefficients*:

$S_1: 8/3 = 2\ 2/3*$
$X_1: 3\ 3/6 = 6.$

S_1 has the minimum positive ratio. It is the *removal variable*.

Next, the new row for the *new variable* is formed by dividing the removal variable row by the *pivot coefficient*:

$S_{1/3}:\quad 8/3 \quad 0/3 \quad 3/3 \quad 1/3 \quad -4\ 6/3$

providing

$X_2:\quad 8/3 \quad 0 \quad 1 \quad 1/3 \quad -2/9.$

The row for the *other variable* in the solution is adjusted for the new variable:

Old X_1:		3	1	$\frac{3}{6}$	0	$\frac{1}{6}$
$-$ New X_2 row times pivot coefficient:	$-\frac{3}{6}$	($\frac{8}{3}$	0	1	$\frac{1}{3}$	$-\frac{2}{9}$)
New X_1:		$1\frac{2}{3}$	1	0	$-\frac{1}{6}$	$\frac{5}{18}$

The new tableau representing the improved corner point becomes:

C_j			100	80	0	0
	Sol. Var.	q_o	X_1	X_2	S_1	S_2
80	X_2	$2\frac{2}{3}$	0	1	$\frac{1}{3}$	$-\frac{2}{9}$
100	X_1	$1\frac{2}{3}$	1	0	$-\frac{1}{6}$	$\frac{5}{18}$
	Z_j	380	100	80	10	10
	$C_j - Z_j$		0	0	-10	-10

The $C_j - Z_j$ for the variables not in the solution are negative. To enter either S_1 or S_2 would reduce the value of the objective function. This is the optimal solution:

$$X_2 = 2\ 2/3 \qquad S_1 = 0$$
$$f = \$380$$
$$X_1 = 1\ 2/3 \qquad S_2 = 0$$

The best allocation of the two workers is to have them work to capacity to product 2 2/3 units of product 2 and 1 2/3 units of product 1 for a profit of $380.

INTERPRETATION OF THE SIMPLEX ALGORITHM

Before any new concepts are introduced, the simplex solution to the previous problem will be carefully reviewed with a full interpretation. Figure 9.12 and Table 9.7 summarize the steps required to obtain the optimal solution. They should be studied carefully before proceeding. They should also be referred to frequently while reading this section.

The formulated problem with slack variables is restated in Figure 9.12. The alternative space contains the variables X_1, X_2, S_1, and S_2. The values of these variables are restricted by the resource and nonnegative constraints. The optimal solution is restricted to a corner point. The corner points can be defined by two variables at the intercepts and at the intersection of the constraint equations (Figure 9.12). The other two variables at these locations have values of zero.

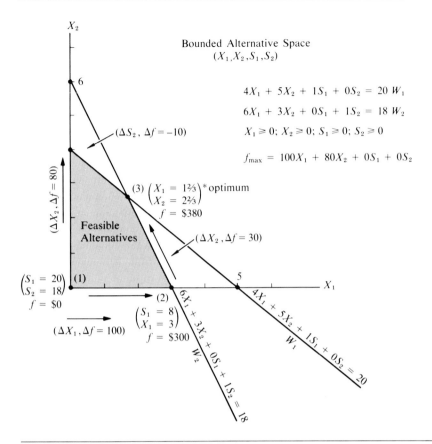

FIGURE 9.12

The Graphic Counterpart of the Simplex Solution

The simplex procedure starts with an initial feasible corner point solution. The slack variables S_1 and S_2 guarantee a feasible corner point. They are used as initial feasible solution variables in the first simplex tableau (Table 9.6). No adjustment of the constraint equations is required to provide the proper solution format for these variables.

The graphical counterpart for the initial feasible solution is the origin. The coordinate can be obtained by substituting values of zero for X_1 and X_2 into the resource constraint equations. The corner point is thus defined by $S_1 = 20$ and $S_2 = 18$.

The next step in the simplex procedure is the search for a better adjacent corner point. The information needed to evaluate the economic effect of entering a variable is provided by the net economic evaluator row ($C_j - Z_j$). If one unit of X_1 is entered, the objective function will be increased by 100 (Table 9.7). Similarly, for every unit of X_2 entered, the objective function will increase by 80. The solution can be improved by entering either X_1 or X_2.

(1)

C_j			100	80	0	0
	Sol. Var.	q_0	X_1	X_2	S_1	S_2
0	S_1	20	4	5	1	0
→ 0	S_2	18	6	3	0	1
	Z_j	0	0	0	0	0
	$C_j - Z_j$		100	80	0	0

S_1: 20/4 = 5
S_2: 18/6 = 3*

(2)

C_j			100	80	0	0
	Sol. Var.	q_0	X_1	X_2	S_1	S_2
→ 0	S_1	8	0	3	1	$-1/6$
100	X_1	3	1	$3/6$	0	$1/6$
	Z_j	300	100	50	0	$16\,2/3$
	$C_j - Z_j$		0	30	0	$-16\,2/3$

S_1: 8/3 = $2\,2/3$*
X_1: $3/{}^3\!/_6$ = 6

(3)

C_j			100	80	0	0
	Sol. Var.	q_0	X_1	X_2	S_1	S_2
80	X_2	$2\,2/3$	0	1	$1/3$	$-2/9$
100	X_1	$1\,2/3$	1	0	$-1/6$	$5/18$
	Z_j	380	100	80	10	10
	$C_j - Z_j$		0	0	-10	-10

TABLE 9.7
The Simplex Solution

Graphically, adjacent corner points are found by moving from the origin along either the X_1 or the X_2 axis. The economic effect of entering a variable can be read directly from the objective function. The move from the origin to include one unit of X_1 will increase the objective function by 100. Similarly, the addition of a unit of X_2 will provide an increase of 80. A movement in both directions is economically desirable.

Since the simplex procedure allows the entry of only one variable at a time, a somewhat arbitrary decision is made to enter X_1 into the solution—to move along the X_1 axis. This variable contributes more to profits per unit and, therefore, might possibly allow an optimal solution in fewer additional corner points. As can be seen in Figure 9.12, the entry of either variable would require three corner points.

Since every unit of X_1 entered will improve the solution, it is desirable to enter as many units of X_1 as possible. In the tableau, the maximum number of units allowable, and also the minimum number required, is indicated by the *minimum positive substitution quantity*. From the respective constraint equations:

$S_1: 20/4 = 5$
$S_2: 18/6 = 3^*.$

Three units of X_1 should be entered into the solution.

In the graphic counterpart, a move from the origin as far as possible along the X_1 axis must be consistent with the resource constraints. The availability of worker 1, the first resource constraint, restricts X_1 to five units. Similarly, the availability of worker 2, the second resource constraint, restricts X_1 to three units. Consistent with both constraints, the maximum move allowable is the smaller quantity of three units.

Three units of X_1 are entered into the solution. This will require the utilization of part of the present solution variables. From the X_1 column in the tableau or the constraint equations of the graph, every unit of X_1 will require four units of S_1 and six units of S_2. Every unit of product 1 will require 4 hours of worker 1's idle time and 6 hours of worker 2's idle time. In terms of the initial solution, worker 1 is idle for 20 hours ($S_1 = 20$), and worker 2 is idle for 18 hours ($S_2 = 18$). If three units of X_1 are entered, worker 1 will have to give up 12 hours of idle time ($3 \cdot 4$) and worker 2 18 hours ($3 \cdot 6$). Worker 1 will be left 8 hours of idle time ($S_1 = 20 - 12$) and worker 2 with 0 hours ($S_2 = 18 - 18$). Adding three units of X_1 into the solution moves the initial corner point to a new improved corner point:

$$\begin{matrix} S_1 = 20 \\ S_2 = 18 \end{matrix} \quad f = \$0 \quad \rightarrow \quad \begin{matrix} S_1 = 8 \\ X_1 = 3 \end{matrix} \quad f = \$300.$$

In order to evaluate adjacent corner points, the complete resource constraint equations must be adjusted in the body of the second tableau. A simple mechanical procedure will provide the new adjusted rows. In order, the row for the new variable is adjusted by dividing it by the pivot coefficient. Then the other variable row is obtained by multiplying the newly adjusted new variable row by the pivot coefficient and subtracting the result from the row to be adjusted. The adjusted rows provide the new corner point solution. They provide the second tableau with constraint equations in the proper solution format for the new set of variables (S_1, X_1). They provide the information required to evaluate adjacent corner points.

The addition of X_1 into the solution by graphical means is conceptually analogous. It consists of moving from the origin along the X_1 axis to the intersection of the worker 2 resource constraint. The coordinates for this corner point are derived by solving the two resource constraints for S_1 and X_1. The specific values are $S_1 = 8$ and $X_1 = 3$.

At this point, the procedure of moving from one corner point to the next is repeated. In the tableau, reference is made to the net economic evaluators to determine the economic desiderata for the variables not in the solution. If one unit of X_2 is entered, the objective function will be improved by $30. Graphically, this will represent a movement toward the intersection of the constraint equations. If one unit of S_2 is entered, the objective function will be decreased by $16 2/3. This is equivalent to a movement back toward the previous corner point at the origin. X_2 is entered to provide an improved adjacent corner point.

The maximum number of units of X_2 are entered. This information is provided again by the substitution quantities. According to the first resource constraint, the maximum is 2 2/3; according to the second, 6. In accordance with both constraints, the maximum is the minimum positive value:

S_1: $8/3 = 2 2/3*$
X_1: $3 3/6 = 6$.

This is graphically equivalent to moving from the second corner point along the second constraint equation. In accordance with the first constraint alone, the movement cannot exceed $X_2 = 2 2/3$. In accordance with the second constraint alone, the movement can be continued to the X_2 intercept ($X_2 = 6$) before violating the nonnegative constraint. In accordance with both constraints, the maximum movement is restricted to the minimum of these extremes at the intersection of the constraint equations, with $X_2 = 2 2/3$.

In entering X_2, both resources presently utilized to capacity to produce $S_1 = 8$ and $X_1 = 3$ will be reallocated. From the X_2 column in the tableau, every unit of X_2 entered will require a sacrifice of 3 units of S_1 and 3/6 units of X_1. If 2 2/3 units of X_2 are entered, 8 units of S_1 and 1 1/3 units of X_1 will be given up, leaving $S_1 = 0$ and $X_1 = 1 2/3$. The new corner point with the maximum amount of the new variable will be:

$X_1 = 1 2/3$
$$f = \$380.$$
$X_2 = 2 2/3$

From the third corner point (third tableau), the economic advantage of adjacent corner points (new variables) is again computed. If S_1 is reintroduced to move back toward the previous corner point, there will be a loss of $10 for every unit entered. If S_2 is introduced to provide a movement to a new adjacent corner point at the X_2 intercept, profits will again be reduced by $10 for every unit of S_2 entered. There is no advantage to entering any new variables. There is no better adjacent corner point. The optimal solution must be:

$X_1 = 1 2/3$ $S_1 = 0$
$$f_{max} = \$380.$$
$X_2 = 2 2/3$ $S_2 = 0$

After a decision maker has solved several small linear programming problems, the simplex algorithm will begin to flow from one logical step to the next. Except that computations increase, larger linear programming problems are solved in the same way. When a decision maker completely understands a small linear programming problem, he or she will understand the basics to solving any size linear programming problem.

AN ARTIFICIAL INITIAL FEASIBLE SOLUTION

The first step in the simplex procedure is to obtain an initial corner point on the surface of the convex polyhedron of feasible alternatives. If all constraints contain less-than-or-equal-to signs ($\leq$), the origin will always serve this purpose (Figure 9.13). However, a formulated linear programming problem may also contain *equal-to* constraints ($=$) and a *greater-than-or-equal-to* constraint ($\geq$) (Figure 9.14). If either of these occurs, the origin will be *infeasible*. A difficulty will exist in determining an initial feasible starting solution.

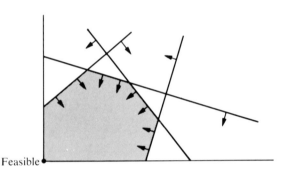

FIGURE 9.13

Less-Than-or-Equal-To Constraints: Origin Feasible

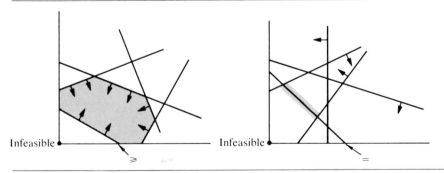

FIGURE 9.14

Equal-To or Greater-Than-or-Equal-To Constraints: Origin Infeasible

While it occurs in both maximization and minimization problems, a minimization problem will best demonstrate the difficulty. A feed company must blend 600 pounds of grain to satisfy a customer's weekly demand. The final product contains three ingredients: I_1, I_2, and I_3. Not more than 200 pounds of I_1 or less than 100 pounds of I_3 may be used. The ingredients cost, respectively, 10, 20, and 40 cents a pound. The problem is to find the blend of the ingredients satisfying the requirements at the lowest cost.

First, the problem must be structured in a proper linear programming (LP) format. The number of units (pounds) of I_1, I_2, and I_3 can be represented by the respective decision variables X_1, X_2, and X_3. The objective is to satisfy the overall mix requirements at a minimum cost. This objective can be represented by:

$$\text{Total Cost}_{\min} = 10(\text{number of units of } I_1)$$
$$+ 20(\text{number of units of } I_2) + 40(\text{number of units of } I_3).$$

Or more compactly by:

$$f_{\min} = 10X_1 + 20X_2 + 40X_3.$$

The values of X_1, X_2, and X_3 are restricted to the requirements of the mix. The total weight must be 600 pounds:

$$\frac{1X_1}{\text{lbs of } I_1} + \frac{1X_2}{\text{lbs of } I_2} + \frac{1X_3}{\text{lbs of } I_3} = \frac{600}{\text{total lbs}}.$$

There are also certain special restrictions on the ingredients:

$$\frac{X_1}{\text{lbs of } I_1} \leq \frac{200}{\text{maximum}}$$

$$\frac{X_3}{\text{lbs of } I_3} \geq \frac{100}{\text{minimum}}.$$

Adding the nonnegative constraints, the formulated LP problem becomes:

Find the best (X_1, X_2, X_3): $f_{\min} = 10X_1 = 20X_2 + 40X_3$

$$\begin{aligned}
\text{Subject to: } 1X_1 + 1X_2 + 1X_3 &= 600 && \text{equation I} \\
X_1 &\leq 200 && \text{equation II} \\
X_3 &\geq 100 && \text{equation III} \\
X_j \geq 0 \quad \text{for } j &= 1, 2, 3.
\end{aligned}$$

An Initial Feasible Solution: Adding Surplus and Artificial Variables

The first requirement in developing an initial feasible solution is to change the inequalities to equalities. This will reduce the alternative space to a finite number of extreme corner points. The first equation is already an equality and, therefore, need not be adjusted:

$$1X_1 + 1X_2 + 1X_3 = 600 \qquad \text{equation I.}$$

Since it has a less-than-or-equal-to sign ($\leq$), the second equation can be adjusted as before by adding a slack variable:

$$1X_1 + 1S_1 = 200 \qquad \text{equation II.}$$

The greater-than-or-equal-to sign in equation III must be treated differently:

$$X_3 \geq 100 \qquad \text{equation III.}$$

The quantity X_3 can exceed 100. In order to establish an equality, X_3 must be reduced to 100 by some *variable amount*. There are two possibilities:

$$X_3 - (\text{positive valued variable}) = 100$$
$$X_3 + (\text{a negative valued variable}) = 100.$$

To maintain the nonnegative constraint, the *only possibility* will be the introduction of *minus a positive valued surplus variable*:

$$X_3 - S_2 = 100.$$

With added variables, the problem formulation is:

$$f_{\min} = 10X_1 + 20X_2 + 40X_3 + 0S_1 + 0S_2$$
$$1X_1 + 1X_2 + 1X_3 + 0S_1 + 0S_2 = 600$$
$$1X_1 + 0X_2 + 0X_3 + 1S_1 + 0S_2 = 200$$
$$0X_1 + 0X_2 + 1X_3 + 0S_1 - 1S_2 = 100$$
$$X_j \geq 0;$$
$$S_1 \geq 0; S_2 \geq 0 \qquad \text{for } j = 1, 2, 3.$$

In the objective function, the contribution of the surplus variable will be zero. The nonnegative constraint also applies to surplus variables. With the problem formulated, the next step is to determine an initial feasible corner point solution. The initial solution and all following corner point solutions will contain three variables—one for each constraint equation. Three variables will exactly span the alternative space—exactly define each corner point.

In determining the initial feasible solution, the surplus variable will be considered as an initial feasible variable. As mentioned above, there will be a solution variable for each constraint equation. The surplus variable, S_2, appears in constraint equation III:

$$1X_3 - 1S_2 = 100 \qquad \text{equation III.}$$

This equation can be transformed into a solution format for S_2.

A single equation can only be solved for one variable at a time. If S_2 is the solution variable, the value of the $1X_3$ part of the equation must be zero. There are two possibilities. First, if X_3 is not one of the solution variables, the value of X_3 will be zero:[9]

$$1(0) - 1S_2 = 100.$$

Second, if X_2 is a solution variable for some other equation, the row operations to allow X_3 to be in the solution will produce a zero for the coefficient[10] for X_3 in equation III:

$$0X_3 - 1S_2 = 100.$$

In either case, the constraint equation will be:

$$0 - 1S_2 = 100.$$

To express the equation in a solution format for S_2, the equation can be multiplied by -1:

$$1S_2 = -100.$$

An S_2 of -100 violates the nonnegative constraint. It is not a feasible alternative. A surplus variable *cannot* be used as an initial feasible solution variable.

The slack variable in equation II, however, can be used as a solution variable. The second equation is:

$$1X_1 + 1S_1 = 200.$$

If the equation is solved for S_1, the contribution by $1X_1$ will be zero:[11]

$$0 + 1S_1 = 200.$$

or

$$1S_1 = 200.$$

---

[9] Variables not in the solution have values of zero.

[10] If an equation is in a solution format for a variable, the coefficient for the variable will be a one. All other equations containing this variable will be transformed to contain a coefficient of zero for the variable. The column coefficients for a variable in the solution will therefore contain a one and the rest zeros.

[11] The value of $1X_1$ will be zero for the same reasons that $1X_3$ was zero in equation III (footnotes 9 and 10).

The slack variable S_1 will provide an initial feasible solution variable for equation II.

With S_1 used as an initial solution variable for equation II, there is still the problem of determining initial feasible solution variables for equation I and equation III. This creates the difficulty encountered earlier in entering variables into the first tableau. If variables are arbitrarily selected, the equations can be solved mathematically for the variables. The resulting corner point solution, however, may be infeasible. If this occurs, the variables must be discarded and new ones selected.

For a small problem, this difficulty may be relatively minor.[12] It will increase substantially, however, with the size of the problem. For a very large problem, the proportion of infeasible corner points becomes immense. The probability of selecting an infeasible set of variables becomes almost certain. In the search for an initial feasible solution, there will tend to be a move from infeasible, to infeasible, to infeasible, ad infinitum. A procedure to provide a guaranteed initial feasible solution is essential.

There is an interesting way around this impasse. It is to develop an *artificial initial feasible solution*. This can be accomplished by the introduction of an *artificial variable*. In the problem, equation I and equation III do not contain any obvious feasible solution variables:

$$1X_1 + 1X_2 + 1X_3 + 0S_1 + 0S_2 = 600 \qquad \text{equation I}$$
$$0X_1 + 0X_2 + 1X_3 + 0S_1 - 1S_2 = 100 \qquad \text{equation III.}$$

The artificial variables A_1 and A_2 can be added as guaranteed initial feasible solution variables:

$$1X_1 + 1X_2 + 1X_3 + 0S_1 + 0S_2 + 1A_1 + 0A_2 = 600 \qquad \text{equation I}$$
$$0X_1 + 0X_2 + 1X_3 + 0S_1 - 1S_2 + 0A_1 + 1A_2 = 100 \qquad \text{equation III.}$$

The first simplex tableau with the artificial variables becomes:

C_j	Sol. Var.	q_o	10 X_1	20 X_2	40 X_3	0 S_1	0 S_2	☐ A_1	☐ A_2
☐	A_1	600				0		1	0
0	S_1	200				1		0	0
☐	A_2	100				0		0	1
	Z_j								
	$C_j - Z_j$								

---

[12] In this particular simple problem, the selection of feasible solution variables for equation I and equation III is not very difficult. If S_1 is to be the solution variable for equation II and the surplus variable is not allowed, the only allowable solution will be to solve equation I for X_2 and equation III for X_3. This forced solution will be feasible.

In equational form:

$$0S_1 + 1A_1 + 0A_2 = 600 \qquad \text{equation I}$$
$$A_1 = 600$$

$$1S_1 + 0A_1 + 0A_2 = 200 \qquad \text{equation II}$$
$$S_1 = 200$$

$$0S_1 + 0A_1 + 1A_2 = 100 \qquad \text{equation III}$$
$$A_2 = 200.$$

This represents an easily derived initial feasible corner point on the surface of a convex polyhedron containing the optimal solution. The simplex procedure will provide this solution.

The conceptual aspects of the introduction of artificial variables require explanation. The addition of an artificial variable will increase the number of variables that express the alternative space—increase the dimension of the problem. The domain of feasible alternatives will still be defined by a convex polyhedron. The polyhedron, however, will be expanded by the added dimensions. Of central importance to this approach, the newly expanded convex polyhedron of feasible alternatives will contain *a corner point at the origin.* This corner point can be used as an initial feasible solution. In essence, *artificial variables generate an expanded convex polyhedron of feasible alternatives with a guaranteed initial feasible solution at the origin.*

An illustration will add considerable clarity. A single-constraint equation will serve the purpose:

$$4X_1 + 2X_2 = 12.$$

The associated area of feasible alternatives is represented in Figure 9.15. For the equality, all feasible alternatives are along the line. The origin is not a feasible alternative.

With the introduction of an artificial variable, the constraint will be:

$$4X_1 + 2X_2 + 1A_1 = 12.$$

The *new expanded alternative space* is provided in Figure 9.16. With the artificial variable (A_1), the entire shaded area represents feasible alternatives. The area of feasible alternatives has been expanded to include the origin. For the single constraint, the artificial variable will represent an initial feasible solution at the origin:

$$4(0) + 2(0) + 1A_1 = 12$$
$$1A_1 = 12.$$

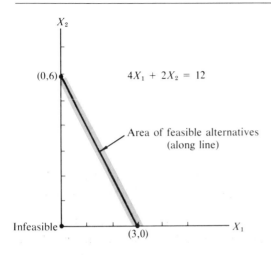

FIGURE 9.15

Equality Constraint: Origin Infeasible
Alternative Space (X_1, X_2)

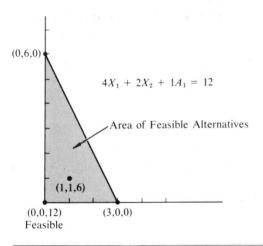

FIGURE 9.16

Equality Constraint with Artificial Variable: Origin Feasible
Alternative Space (X_1, X_2, A_1)

Artificial variables provide an expanded convex polyhedron of feasible alternatives. The expanded polyhedron will contain all earlier feasible alternatives plus feasible alternatives extending the original polyhedron downward to include the origin. The *same number of solution variables* will span the alternative space. The same number of solution variables will define all corner points in either polyhedron.

Therefore, the origin on the expanded polyhedron will provide an initial feasible starting solution. Movements can be made outward from the *artificial origin* to the surface of the *regular polyhedron*. If movements follow the simplex requirements for feasibility, the first corner point on the *regular* polyhedron must be feasible. Since the same number of variables defines corner points for both polyhedrons, and the regular polyhedron does not contain artificial variables, the return to the regular polyhedron will occur when artificial variables are no longer solution variables. Moreover, on the regular polyhedron with a feasible corner point solution, the eventual optimal solution can be obtained as before by the simplex method.

The only remaining difficulty is to guarantee a movement from the starting expanded polyhedron to the regular polyhedron. Since the regular polyhedron will not contain artificial variables, there must be a guaranteed removal of artificial variables.

A resolution is found in the internal operation of the simplex method. Movements are iteratively made from corner point to improved adjacent feasible corner point. Each movement involves the entry of one variable and the removal of another. All movements are made on an *economic basis*. Therefore, the assignment of the *worst conceivable contribution* to artificial variables will economically force them from the solution. An extremely large symbolic value of M will be assigned as the worth of artificial variables in the objective function. In a maximization problem, the per unit contribution (C_j) for the artificial variable will be $-M$. In a minimization problem, the assignment will be $+M$—the opposite of the desired objective. With such economically adverse values, the simplex procedure will quickly force the artificial variables from the solution.

The problem statement with artificial variables is:

$$f_{min} = 10X_1 + 20X_2 + 40X_3 + 0S_1 + 0S_2 + MA_1 + MA_2$$

$$1X_1 + 1X_2 + 1X_3 + 0S_1 + 0S_2 + 1A_1 + 0A_2 = 600 \qquad \text{equation I}$$

$$1X_1 + 0X_2 + 0X_3 + 1S_1 + 0S_2 + 0A_1 + 0A_2 = 200 \qquad \text{equation II}$$

$$0X_1 + 0X_2 + 1X_3 + 0S_1 - 1S_2 + 0A_1 + 1A_2 = 100 \qquad \text{equation III}$$

$$X_j \geq 0; S_k \geq 0; A_l \geq 0 \qquad j = 1, 2, 3; k = 1, 2; l = 1, 2.$$

In solution form, the first simplex tableau becomes:

C_j			10	20	40	0	0	M	M
	Sol. Var.	q_o	X_1	X_2	X_3	S_1	S_2	A_1	A_2
M	A_1	600				0		1	0
0	S_1	200				1		0	0
M	A_2	100				0		0	1
	Z_j	$700M$							

This is an initial feasible solution. The associated costs are, however, a very undesirable $700M$.

The Solution to the Minimization Problem: One Minor Variation

Once an initial feasible solution has been obtained, the simplex procedure moves from tableau to tableau by the previously outlined steps. The first complete tableau with an economic evaluation of potential entry variables is:

C_j			10	20	40	0	0	M	M
	Sol. Var.	q_0	X_1	X_2	X_3	S_1	S_2	A_1	A_2
M	A_1	600	1	1	1	0	0	1	0
0	S_1	200	1	0	0	1	0	0	0
M	A_2	100	0	0	1	0	-1	0	1
	Z_j	$700M$	M	M	$2M$	0	$-M$	M	M
	$C_j - Z_j$		$-M$ $+10$	$-M$ $+20$	$-2M$ $+40$	0	M	0	0

The next step is to enter a new variable. As was previously mentioned, $C_j - Z_j$ values provide the information needed for this decision. They indicate the effect on the objective function, Z_0, of adding a unit of the variable at the head of the column. Since the objective is to minimize cost, or make Z_0 as small as possible, variables improving the solution will have *negative $C_j - Z_j$* evaluators.

Three new variables are economically desirables: X_1, X_2, and X_3.[13] The one improving the solution most per unit (most negative $C_j - Z_j$) is chosen for entry. Variable X_3 will be introduced into the solution.

The reminder of the minimization problem follows the standard simplex format:

1. Locate the new variable to be entered.

2. Determine the variable to be removed.

3. Adjust the row for the new variable.

4. Adjust the rows for the other variables.

5. Compute the net economic evaluators to locate the new variable.

6. Repeat the process until no new variable should be entered.

Table 9.8 provides the computations and a step-by-step outline of the solution.

---

[13] If the $C_j - Z_j$ row contains the quantity M, the M should be stated before any other quantity to avoid a possible confusion of sign. Consider $C_1 - Z_1$, for example. $-M + 10$ is clearly a negative contribution to the objective function, whereas $10 - M$ might be carelessly interpreted as a positive quantity.

C_j			10	20	**40**	0	0	M	M
	Sol. Var.	q_0	X_1	X_2	X_3	S_1	S_2	A_1	A_2
M	A_1	600	1	1	1	0	0	1	0
0	S_1	200	1	0	0	1	0	0	0
M	A_2	100	0	0	1	0	-1	0	1
	Z_j	$700\,M$	M	M	$2M$	0	$-M$	M	M
	$C_j - Z_j$		$-M$ $+10$	$-M$ $+20$	$-2M$ $+40$	0	M	0	0

Removal Variable (arrow to A_2)

(1) Entry Variable (arrow to X_3 column)

(2) A_1: $600/1 = 600$

$\quad S_1$: $200/0 = $ Undefined

$\quad A_2$: $100/1 = 100*$

(3) New Variable Row Adjustment:

Row 3	A_2	1/1	(100	0	0	1	0	-1	0	1)
Pivot Coefficient										
Row 3 Adjusted	X_3		100	0	0	1	0	-1	0	1

(4) Other Variable Row Adjustments:

Row 1	A_1		600	1	1	1	0	0	1	0
New Row	X_3	-1	(100	0	0	1	0	-1	0	1)
Pivot Coefficient										
Row 1 Adjusted	A_1		500	1	1	0	0	1	1	-1

Row 2	S_1		200	1	0	0	1	0	0	0
New Row	X_3	-0	(100	0	0	1	0	-1	0	1)
Pivot Coefficient										
Row 2 Adjusted	S_1		200	1	0	0	1	0	0	0

TABLE 9.8

Tableau 1: An Initial Feasible Solution

All net economic evaluators have values greater-than-or-equal-to zero. There are no improved adjacent corner points. The fourth tableau in Table 9.8 contains the optimal solution:

$$X_1 = 200 \quad S_1 = 0 \quad A_1 = 0$$
$$X_2 = 300 \quad \quad \quad f_{\min} = 12,000.$$
$$X_3 = 100 \quad S_2 = 0 \quad A_2 = 0$$

C_j			10	20	40	0	0	M	M
	Sol. Var.	q_o	X_1	X_2	X_3	S_1	S_2	A_1	A_2
M	A_1	500	1	1	0	0	1	1	-1
0 →	S_1	200	1	0	0	1	0	0	0
40	$\widehat{X_3}$	100	0	0	1	0	-1	0	1
	Z_j	500M +4000	M	M	40	0	M -40	M	$-M$ $+40$
(5)	$C_j - Z_j$		$-M$ $+10$	$-M$ $+20$	0	0	$-M$ $+40$	0	$2M$ -40

└ Removable Variable

↑
(1) Entry
Variable

(2) A_1: 500/1 = 500

S_1: 200/1 = 200*

X_3: 100/0 = undefined

(3) New Variable Row Adjustment:

Row 2	S_1	1/1	(200	1	0	0	1	0	0	0)

Pivot Coefficient ↗

Row 2 Adjusted	$\widehat{X_1}$		200	1	0	0	1	0	0	0

(4) Other Variable Row Adjustments:

Row 1	A_1		500	1	1	0	0	1	1	-1
New Row	$\widehat{X_1}$	-1	(200	1	0	0	1	0	0	0)

Pivot Coefficient ↗

Row 1 Adjusted	A_1		300	0	1	0	-1	1	1	-1

Row 3	X_3		100	0	0	1	0	-1	0	1
New Row	$\widehat{X_1}$	-0	(200	1	0	0	1	0	0	0)

Pivot Coefficient ↗

Row 3 Adjusted	X_3		100	0	0	1	0	-1	0	1

TABLE 9.8

Tableau 2: An Improved Adjacent Feasible Solution

Two hundred pounds of ingredient 1, 300 pounds of ingredient 2, and 100 pounds of ingredient 3 should be used. The feed mix will cost $120:

$$f_{min} = \$.10(200) + \$.20(300) + \$.40(100)$$
$$= \$120.$$

It is the most economical means of satisfying the requirements.

C_j				10	20	40	0	0	M	M
	Sol. Var.		q_0	X_1	X_2	X_3	S_1	S_2	A_1	A_2
►M	A_1		300	0	1	0	-1	1	1	-1
10	Ⓧ$_1$		200	1	0	0	1	0	0	0
40	X_3		100	0	0	1	0	-1	0	1
	Z_j		300M +6000	10	M	40	$-M$ +10	M -40	M	$-M$ +40
(5)	$C_j - Z_j$			0	$-M$ +20	0	M -10	$-M$ +40	0	2M -40

└─ Removal Variable

(1) Entry Variable

(2) A_1: 300/1 = 300*

X_1: 200/0 = Undefined

X_3: 100/0 = Undefined

(3) New Variable Row Adjustment:

Row 1	A_1	1/1	(300	0	1	0	-1	1	1	-1)
Row 1 Adjusted	Ⓧ$_2$		300	0	1	0	-1	1	1	-1

(4) Other Variable Row Adjustments:

Row 2	X_1		200	1	0	0	1	0	0	0
New Row	Ⓧ$_2$	-0	(300	0	1	0	-1	1	1	-1)
Row 2 Adjusted	X_1		200	1	0	0	1	0	0	0
Row 3	X_3		100	0	0	1	0	-1	0	1
New Row	Ⓧ$_2$	-0	(300	0	1	0	-1	1	1	-1)
Row 3 Adjusted	X_3		100	0	0	1	0	-1	0	1

TABLE 9.8

Tableau 3: An Improved Adjacent Feasible Solution

ADDING NEW VARIABLES

To prevent any possible confusion, the addition of new variables to constraint equations will be summarized. Variables are entered for only two reasons:

(1) to convert an inequality to an equality, or

(2) to provide an initial feasible solution.

C_j			10	20	40	0	0	M	M
	Sol. Var.	q_o	X_1	X_2	X_3	S_1	S_2	A_1	A_2
20	X_2	300	0	1	0	−1	1	1	−1
10	X_1	200	1	0	0	1	0	0	0
40	X_3	100	0	0	1	0	−1	0	1
	Z_j	12000	10	20	40	−10	−20	20	20
	$C_j - Z_j$		0	0	0	10	20	M −20	M −20

TABLE 9.8

Tableau 4: The Optimal Solution

Three types of variables may be added to accomplish these objectives:

(1) slack variables (S_1),

(2) surplus variables $(-S_2)$, or

(3) artificial variables (A_1).

The slack variable is used when there is a less-than-or-equal-to sign ($\leq$):

$$1X_2 \leq 10.$$

The slack variable S_1 is added to increase the left side of the equation to form an equality:

$$1X_2 + 1S_1 = 10.$$

Besides converting the inequality into an equality, the slack variable is also used as an initial feasible solution variable. Since the X_j variable will be a nonsolution variable with a value of zero,[14] using S_1 as a solution variable:

$$1(0) + 1S_1 = 10$$
$$S_1 = 10.$$

The slack variable is used concurrently (1) to convert an inequality to an equality and (2) to provide an initial feasible solution.

---

[14] As a general rule, the initial feasible solution will contain all slack and artificial variables to avoid the difficulty of obtaining an infeasible corner point. The X_j variables, therefore, will not appear as initial solution variables.

The surplus variable is used when there is a greater-than-or-equal-to ($\geq$) constraint. It is used to convert the inequality into an equality:

$$1X_1 \geq 12$$
$$1X_1 - 1S_1 = 12.$$

Minus S_2 was added to reduce the left side of the equation to 12. Since the nonnegative constraint does not allow negative valued variables, the reduction of the left side of the equation must be made by minus a positive value ($-(+) = $ reduction).

The surplus variable $-S_2$ cannot be used in an initial feasible solution. If the foregoing equation were to be solved for S_2, the other variable would have a value of zero[15] and S_2 would be negative:

$$1(0) - 1S_2 = 12$$
$$- 1S_2 = 12$$
$$S_2 = -12.$$

Because it will violate the nonnegative constraint, a surplus variable can never be an initial feasible solution variable. A surplus variable can only be used to convert a $\geq$ into an $=$.

Slack and surplus variables can convert all inequalities into equalities. When an equality is without a guaranteed initial feasible solution variable, an artificial variable provides the initial feasible solution variable. This will occur when a surplus variable has been added:

$$1X_1 - 1S_2 \qquad = 12$$
$$1X_1 - 1S_2 + 1A_2 = 12.$$

The initial feasible solution will be:[16]

$$1(0) - 1(0) + 1A_2 = 12$$
$$1A_1 = 12.$$

Also, an artificial variable is customarily used when the constraint equation is an equality:

$$4X_1 + 8X_2 = 120.$$

---

[15] Again, for practical purposes, the X_j will not be in the initial solution mix and therefore will have an initial value of zero. Refer to footnote 14, page 292.
[16] Since X_1 and S_2 will not be initial solution variables, they will have initial values of zero. Refer to footnote 14, page 292.

This equation does not contain an easily obtained guaranteed initial feasible solution variable.[17] An artificial variable will guarantee feasibility:

$$4X_1 + 8X_2 + 1A_1 = 120.$$

Since the variables not in the solution have values of zero:

$$4(0) + 8(0) + 1A_1 = 120$$
$$1A_1 = 120.$$

The artificial variable provides a feasible starting solution.
Reconsidering the possible constraint variations:

$$4X_1 + 8X_2 = 120$$
$$X_1 \geq 12$$
$$X_2 \leq 10$$
$$f_{min} = 16X_1 + 14X_2.$$

With the addition of variables:

$$4X_1 + 8X_2 + A_1 = 120$$
$$1X_1 - S_1 + A_2 = 12$$
$$1X_2 + S_2 = 10$$
$$f_{min} = 16X_1 + 14X_2 + 0S_1 + 0S_2 + MA_1 + MA_2.$$

	Type of Variable and Reason for Use		
Type of Constraint	Convert Inequality into Equality	Initial Feasible Solution Variable	Value in Objective Function
Less-than-or-equal-to ($\leq$)	Slack Variable S_1: $\leq$ to =	Slack Variable (S_1)	Slack Variable: 0
Greater-than-or-equal-to ($\geq$)	Surplus Variable $-S_2$: $\geq$ to =	Artificial Variable (A_1)	Surplus Variable: 0
Equal-to (=)	None Required	Artificial Variable (A_2)	Artificial Variable: max. $-M$ min. $+M$

TABLE 9.9

The Addition of Variables

---

[17] Refer to page 284, not selective arbitrary initial solution variables.

Linear Programming: The Simplex Method

A_1 provides an initial feasible solution variable for equation I. Minus S_1 converts the greater-than-or-equal-to ($\geq$) into an equality. A_2 provides a solution variable for equation II. S_2 converts the less-than-or-equal-to ($\leq$) into an equality and also provides the solution variable for equation III. The slack variables are assigned a value of zero in the objective function. Since the objective is minimization, the artificial variables are assigned the exceedingly large positive quantity M. Table 9.9 summarizes the addition of new variables.

SUMMARY

The simplex algorithm is an exceedingly powerful quantitative model. It provides a decision maker with a means for solving linear programming problems—for solving allocation of resources problems.

The beauty of the simplex method is only too easily hidden by the complex of computation. The essential quality of the simplex method is the structured logic that restricts an inexhaustible set of alternatives.

The nature of linear constraints restricts alternatives to a convex polyhedron of feasible alternatives. The addition of slack and surplus variables converts the resource constraints from inequalities into equalities. This limits the alternatives to the surface of the convex polyhedron of feasible alternatives.

Alternatives are defined by one variable for each constraint equation. All other variables are assigned values of zero. This restricts alternatives to corner points on the surface of the convex polyhedron of feasible alternatives.

In an initial tableau, slack variables guarantee a feasible corner point at the origin. In problems with $\geq$ or $=$ constraints, artificial variables guarantee an initial feasible solution at the origin of an expanded convex polyhedron of feasible alternatives.

With an initial feasible corner point, the net economic evaluators indicate the economic desirability of new variables. They restrict adjustments to improved solutions. Moreover, to guarantee feasible corner points, only one new variable at a time is introduced into the solution. The search for the optimal solution is restricted to improved adjacent corner points on the surface of the convex polyhedron of feasible alternatives.

In the entry of a new variable, the substitution quantities maintain both the proper number of solution variables and the nonnegative constraints. Associated with the new entry variable, they indicate the removal variable. They indicate the required quantity of the new variable to define an adjacent feasible corner point. They guarantee that movements are made to adjacent feasible corner points.

Concisely, linear constraints form a convex polyhedron of feasible alternatives. The components of the simplex procedure restrict the search for the best alternative to feasible corner points on this polyhedron. The initial solution is a feasible corner point. The economic evaluators indicate the advantage of adjacent corner points. The substitution quantities restrict new solutions to corner points. The simplex algorithm starts at a corner point on the convex polyhedron of feasible alternatives. It makes movements from feasible corner point to better adjacent feasible corner point until the optimal solution has been reached. Not all corner points on this convex polyhedron require evaluation—only enough to locate the optimal solution.

The advantage of the restricted search can be fully appreciated only in the context of large problems. The number of corner points alone for a formulated problem containing 8 variables and 12 constraints (eight activities associated with 12 resources) exceeds a million. In a problem with 60 variables and 100 constraints, the number of corner points becomes astronomical: 3.8 times 10^{52}. Many organizations have hundreds or thousands of potential activities and tens or hundreds of thousands of resources. For such organizations, even in small problems, the number of alternative corner points will run into zillions.

From the myriad possibilities, the best alternative can be obtained by considering only part of the feasible alternatives. The simplex procedure reduces the search for the best alternative from an alternative space approaching infinity to an evaluable few alternatives. The value and beauty of the simplex method is that it solves the allocation of resources problem.

Bierman, H., Jr., C. P. Bonini, and W. H. Hausman. *Quantative Analysis for Business Decisions*. Homewood, Ill.: Richard D. Irwin, 1973.

Boulding, K. E., and W. A. Spivey. *Linear Programming and the Theory of the Firm*. New York: Macmillan Co., 1960.

Charnes, A., and W. W. Cooper. *Management Models and Industrial Applications of Linear Programming*, 2 Vols. New York: John Wiley & Sons, 1961.

Childress, R. L. *Mathematics for Managerial Decisions*. Englewood Cliffs, N.J.: Prentice-Hall, 1974.

Dantzig, G. B. *Linear Programming and Extensions*. Princeton: Princeton University Press, 1963.

Dorfman, R., P. A. Samuelson, and R. M. Solow. *Linear Programming and Economic Analysis*. New York: McGraw-Hill Book Co., 1958.

Gass, S. I. *Linear Programming: Methods and Applications*. New York: McGraw-Hill Book Co., 1969.

Gaver, D. P., and G. L. Thompson. *Programming and Probability Models in Operations Research*. Belmont, Calif.: Wadsworth Publishing Co., 1973.

Hadley, G. *Linear Programming*. Reading, Mass.: Addison-Wesley Publishing Co., 1962.

Hillier, F. S., and G. J. Lieberman. *Introduction to Operations Research*. San Francisco: Holden-Day, 1967.

Kim, C. *Introduction to Linear Programming*. New York: Holt, Rinehart and Winston, 1971.

Levin, R. I., and C. A. Kirkpatrick. *Quantitative Approaches to Management*. New York: McGraw-Hill Book Co., 1975.

Levin, R. I., and R. P. Lamone. *Linear Programming for Management Decisions*. Homewood, Ill.: Richard D. Irwin, 1969.

Loomba, N. P. *Linear Programming, An Introductory Analysis*. New York: McGraw-Hill Book Co., 1964.

Loomba, N. P., and E. Turban. *Applied Programming for Management*. New York: Holt, Rinehart and Winston, 1974.

Riley, V., and S. I. Gass. *Bibliography on Linear Programming and Related Techniques*. Baltimore: Johns Hopkins Press, 1958.

Spivey, W. A., and R. M. Thrall. *Linear Optimization*. New York: Holt, Rinehart and Winston, 1970.

Stockton, R. S. *Introduction to Linear Programming*. Homewood, Ill.: Richard D. Irwin, 1971.

Strum, J. E. *Introduction to Linear Programming*. San Francisco: Holden-Day, 1972.

Thierauf, R. J., and R. C. Klekamp. *Decision Making Through Operations Research*. New York: John Wiley & Sons, 1975.

Wagner, H. M. *Principles of Operations Research with Applications to Managerial Decisions*. Englewood Cliffs, N.J.: Prentice-Hall, 1969.

9.1. Two machines are available for specified hours daily to perform two activities. The linear programming formulation is as follows:

$f_{max} = 20X_1 + 24X_2$
subject to: $2X_1 + 6X_2 \leq 12$ machine 1
$4X_1 + 2X_2 \leq 8$ machine 2
$X_1 \geq 0; X_2 \geq 0.$

Optimally allocate the machines to maximize profit contributions.

9.2. The weekly allocation of two workers has been formally structured as a linear programming problem:

$f_{max} = 20X_1 + 40X_2$
subject to: $5X_1 + 3X_2 \leq 30$
$2X_1 + 6X_2 \leq 36$
$X_1 \geq 0; X_2 \geq 0.$

Solve by the simplex method.

9.3. One component of a large assembly operation has been structured on an allocation of two special-purpose pieces of equipment:

$f_{max} = 20X_1 + 40X_2$
subject to: $4X_1 + 2X_2 \leq 40$
$2X_1 + 4X_2 \leq 40$
$X_1 \geq 0; X_2 \geq 0.$

Determine all optimal corner points by the simplex method. How many different ways can the equipment be used appropriately?

9.4. In Chapter 8, the minimum-cost feed mix providing daily nutritional requirements for a herd of Herefords was formulated as:

$f_{min} = 15X_1 + 22X_2$
$4X_1 + 2X_2 \geq 20$
$1X_1 + 2X_2 \geq 14$
$1X_1 + 4X_2 \geq 16$
$X_1 \geq 0; X_2 \geq 0.$

Solve by the simplex method. Compare the optimal simplex solution with the graphic solution in Figure 8.7.

9.5. $f_{max} = 40X_1 + 50X_2$

subject to: $4X_1 + 3X_2 \leq 24$

$2X_1 + 4X_2 \leq 20$

$X_1 \geq 0; X_2 \geq 0.$

Reformulate with slack variables. Graphically represent the alternative space containing all four variables. From the new constraint equations, determine the coordinates for each corner point. How many variables acquire values other than zero to define corner points? How are feasible corner points distinguished from infeasible corner points?

9.6. Why do inequality constraints have to be converted to equalities?

9.7. How many corner points will be formed in a formulated problem containing 8 variables and 10 constraints? Using a hand calculator, determine how many corner points there will be with 20 variables and 20 constraints.

9.8. What part of the simplex tableau determines the desirability of adjacent corner points? Why are only adjacent corner points considered?

9.9. A surplus variable is always added to a $\geq$ to form an equality. Why can a surplus variable never be used as an initial feasible solution variable?

9.10. Slack variables, surplus variables, and artificial variables are added to initial constraint equations prior to the formation of the first simplex tableau. What are the two main reasons for adding variables? What are the specific reasons for adding each of these types of variables?

9.11. Why is the *removal variable* restricted to positive substitution quantities?

9.12. If the removal variable selected has a substitution quantity larger than the smallest positive substitution quantity, what will happen in the next tableau?

9.13. In applying the simplex method, only one variable at a time is introduced into each new tableau. If there is more than one economically desirable new entry variable, why doesn't the simplex procedure concurrently introduce more than one variable?

9.14. For even fairly small problems, why is a guaranteed initial feasible solution required?

9.15. If all constraints are initially $\leq$'s, where is the guaranteed initial feasible solution located on the surface of the convex polyhedron of feasible alternatives?

9.16. Why are artificial variables introduced into the solution? What do artificial variables do to the convex polyhedron of feasible alternatives?

9.17. What do the *substitution quantities* represent? Why is the removal variable associated with the smallest positive *substitution quantity*?

9.18. In terms of the logic of the simplex method, how does the addition of the symbolic M force artificial variables from the solution?

9.19. $f_{max} = 40X_1 + 30X_2$

subject to: $8X_1 + 6X_2 = 70$

$14X_1 + 9X_2 \leq 120$

$4X_1 + 8X_2 \geq 45$

$X_1 \geq 0; X_2 \geq 0.$

Add the required variables and provide the first simplex tableau.

9.20.

		10	28	0	0
Sol. Var.	q_0	X_1	X_2	X_3	X_4
	14		1	$1/3$	0
	8	$-1/3$		$4/3$	
$C_j - Z_j$			-4		

Complete this tableau.

9.21. $5X_1 + 4X_2 - 1X_3 + 1X_4 \qquad = 160$

$2X_1 + 8X_2 \qquad\qquad + 1X_5 = 200$

Variables X_3, X_4, and X_5 were added to these constraints.

1. What kind of variables do they represent?
2. Why were they introduced?

If any of these variables can be of more than one type, name all possibilities.

9.22.

C_j			40	42	0	0	M	0	M
	Sol. Var.	q_0	X_1	X_2	X_3	X_4	X_5	X_6	X_7
M	X_7	120	4	2	0	0	0	-1	1
M	X_5	140	2	6	-1	0	1	0	0
0	X_4	25	1	0	0	1	0	0	0

This represents the first simplex tableau. Represent the initial formulation of the problem prior to the inclusion of *additional variables*.

9.23. Next month a production manager will have two major resources available: 96 hours of unused machine time and 80 hours of labor. These resources can be used to manufacture product 1 and product 2:

1. One unit of product 1 requires four hours of machine time and eight hours of labor.
2. One unit of product 2 requires six hours of machine time and three hours of labor.
3. A company policy will not allow the manufacture of product 2 items in excess of forecasted demand. The forecasted demand is 10 items.
4. Product 1 is worth $220 and product 2, $260.

Formulate this decision environment as a linear programming problem and solve by the simplex method.

9.24. A company must combine ingredient X and ingredient Y to produce an item with a required weight of 100 pounds. At least 40 pounds of X and not more than 80 pounds of Y can be used. Ingredient X costs $25 and ingredient Y, $15.

Determine the optimal blend of ingredients to minimize costs by the simplex method.

9.25.

C_j			200	280	240	0	0	0
	Sol. Var.	q_0	X_1	X_2	X_3	S_1	S_2	S_3
280	X_2	40	$3/4$	1	$1/2$	$1/8$	0	0
0	S_2	100	$2^1/2$	0	3	$-2/8$	1	0
0	S_3	140	$-2^1/2$	0	1	$-3/4$	0	1
	Z_j							
	$C_j - Z_j$							

1. Express the objective function in equational form.
2. What is the solution quantity for each of the six variables for the corner point represented in the tableau?
3. What is the value of the objective function for this corner point?
4. If exactly 10 units of X_3 are introduced into the solution, what are the adjusted solution quantities for each of the present solution variables?
5. If X_1 is entered into the solution, which variable should be removed? If one of the other variables is removed, what will happen to the next tableau?
6. If X_3 is the entry variable, what is the maximum number of units of X_3 that can be entered? How many units of X_3 must be entered to define the new corner point?

9.26. A company would like to allocate its $120,000 advertising budget optimally among three competing media: TV program A, TV program B, and a large national magazine. A 60-second TV spot commercial on programs A and B costs $20,000 and $50,000 respectively. A four-color full-page magazine unit costs $14,000. Target market exposure is: TV program A, 450,000; TV program B, 2,200,000; and the magazine, 800,000. Relative exposure effectiveness per medium: TV program A, 1.8; TV program B, 2.6; and the magazine, 1.4. A commitment has already been made for one unit of the magazine.

Formulate this information as a linear programming problem maximizing target market exposure value. Solve by the simplex method. What adjustment will be required of the simplex solution?

10

Linear Programming: The Dual Solution

Because linear programming can be used to solve such a general category of important problems, it is perhaps the most developed quantitative tool in the field of operations research and management science. Linear programming has many extensions. This chapter and the next will consider two of the most important ones: *duality* and *sensitivity analysis*.

DUALITY

One of the most significant discoveries in the early development of linear programming was the concept of *duality*. Associated with every linear programming problem there is an intimately related companion problem. For every maximization problem there is a complementary minimization problem. For every minimization problem there is a complementary maximization problem. Linear programming problems exist in pairs—both leading to the same solution and the obtainment of the same objective. The original problem is termed the *primal* and the companion problem the *dual*.

Besides have a pure theoretical importance, duality is important for several pragmatic reasons. The dual formulation may greatly reduce computations. It often facilitates a more direct and useful economic interpretation. Finally, the dual concept has been fundamental to the development of several special algorithms and valuable extensions.

The mathematical relationship between the primal and dual can be most simply expressed in terms of an example. The worker allocation problem used in Chapter 9 will be reintroduced as the primal:

Primal $f_{max} = 100X_1 + 80X_2$
subject to: $4X_1 + 5X_2 \leq 20$
$\qquad\qquad 6X_1 + 3X_2 \leq 18$
$\qquad\qquad X_j \geq 0 \qquad j = 1, 2.$

With W_i representing the variables, the complementary dual minimization problem is represented by:

Dual $f_{min} = 20W_1 + 18W_2$
subject to: $4W_1 + 6W_2 \geq 100$
$\qquad\qquad 5W_1 + 3W_2 \geq 80$
$\qquad\qquad W_i \geq 0 \qquad i = 1, 2.$

The transformation of the primal into the dual can be performed by transposing the matrix of coefficients. The transpose of a matrix is determined by interchanging the rows and columns:

$$A = \begin{bmatrix} a_{11} & a_{12} & a_{13} \\ a_{21} & a_{22} & a_{23} \\ a_{31} & a_{32} & a_{33} \end{bmatrix}; \qquad A' = \begin{bmatrix} a_{11} & a_{21} & a_{31} \\ a_{12} & a_{22} & a_{32} \\ a_{13} & a_{23} & a_{33} \end{bmatrix}.$$

The a_{ij} components of the original matrix become a_{ji} components in the transpose.

Reconsidering the primal maximization problem in a partitioned matrix format:

$$P = \begin{bmatrix} 4 & 5 & \vdots & 20 \\ 6 & 3 & \vdots & 18 \\ \hdashline 100 & 80 & \vdots & 0 \end{bmatrix}.$$

The objective function has been expressed at the bottom with a zero entry in entry in the right-hand corner.

Interchanging rows and columns, the transpose becomes:

$$P' = \begin{bmatrix} 4 & 6 & \vdots & 100 \\ 5 & 3 & \vdots & 80 \\ \hdashline 20 & 18 & \vdots & 0 \end{bmatrix}.$$

The rows in the primal become the columns in the dual. The coefficients of the objective function become the right-hand resource values. The resource values become the new objective function coefficients.

In order to complete the transformation, new variables, inequalities, and *an optimization objective are required.* The X_j in the primal are replaced by W_i

in the dual. The direction of the inequalities in the primal are reversed. If the primal inequalities are $\leq$, the dual inequalities become $\geq$, and conversely. The sense of the objective is reversed. If the primal is maximization, the dual will be minimization, and conversely.

The dual matrix of coefficients, therefore, acquires the formulation:

Dual $\quad f_{min} = 20W_1 + 18W_2$
subject to: $4W_1 + 6W_2 \geq 100$
$\qquad\qquad 5W_1 + 3W_2 \geq 80$
$\qquad\qquad W_i \geq 0 \qquad i = 1, 2.$

The dual can be solved, as before, by the simplex algorithm. Moreover, if a finite optimal solution exists, the dual theorem states that there will be a *finite, identical, optimal solution to both forms.*

The essential correspondence in transforming the primal into the dual is summarized in Table 10.1. There are three potential difficulties. First, *the optimization objective may not correspond with the sense of the constraint inequalities.* For example, a primal maximization problem may have $\geq$ constraints. This difficulty can be resolved by multiplying the objective function by -1 to provide consistency with the sense of the constraints:

$$f_{max} = 8X_1 - 12X_2.$$

Equivalently,

$$f_{min} = -8X_1 + 12X_2.$$

A second difficulty is that *the inequalities of the primal must be in the same direction.* The sense of a constraint can be altered, however, by multiplying it by -1. Consider the maximization problem:

Primal $\quad f_{max} = 60X_1 + 50X_2$
subject to: $1X_1 + 2X_2 \leq 40$
$\qquad\qquad 2X_1 - 1X_2 \geq 6$
$\qquad\qquad 1X_1 + 1X_2 \leq 25$
$\qquad\qquad X_j \geq 0 \qquad j = 1, 2.$

Primal		Dual	
f_{max}	$\leq$	f_{min}	$\geq$
f_{min}	$\geq$	f_{max}	$\leq$
ith constraint	$=$	ith variable unrestricted in sign	
jth variable unrestricted in sign		jth constraint	$=$

TABLE 10.1

Correspondence of Primal and Dual

To reexpress this problem with $\leq$ constraints, the second constraint is multiplied by -1:

Primal $f_{max} = 60X_1 + 50X_2$
subject to: $1X_1 + 2X_2 \leq 40$
$-2X_1 + 1X_2 \leq -6$
$1X_1 + 1X_2 \leq 25$
$X_j \geq 0 \quad j = 1, 2.$

The corresponding dual formulation becomes:

Dual $f_{min} = 40W_1 - 6W_2 + 25W_3$
subject to: $1W_1 - 2W_2 + 1W_3 \geq 60$
$2W_1 + 1W_2 + 1W_3 \geq 50$
$W_i \geq 0 \quad i = 1, 2, 3.$

A third difficulty occurs when there is *an equality in the primal constraints.* Consider the following problem:

Primal $f_{max} = 24X_1 + 18X_2$
subject to: $4X_1 + 6X_2 = 48$
$X_1 \qquad \leq 9$
$X_2 \leq 7$
$X_j \geq 0 \quad j = 1, 2.$

As the primal-dual correspondence in Table 10.1 indicates, the formulation contains an *unconstrained variable*:

Dual $f_{min} = 48W_1 + 9W_2 + 7W_3$
subject to: $4W_1 + 1W_2 + 0W_3 \geq 24$
$6W_1 + 0W_2 + 1W_3 \geq 7$
$W_2, W_3 \geq 0$
W_1 unrestricted in sign.

To resolve this difficulty, an unconstrained variable can be expressed as the difference between two nonnegative variables.[1] Therefore, substituting the nonnegative variables $W_1' - W_1''$ for W_1, the formulation becomes:

Dual $f_{min} = 48W_1' - 48W_1'' + 9W_2 + 7W_3$
subject to: $4W_1' - 4W_1'' + 1W_2 + 0W_3 \geq 24$
$6W_1' - 6W_1'' + 0W_2 + 1W_3 \geq 7$
$W_i \geq 0 \quad i = 1, 2, 3.$

The simplex assumption of nonnegativity is maintained.

---

[1] Since the simplex procedure examines only feasible corner points, at least one of the newly introduced nonnegative variables will not be a solution variable with a corresponding value of zero.

THE ECONOMIC WORTH OF A RESOURCE

An important statistic for management decision making is the *economic worth of a resource*. The worth of a resource can be evaluated in terms of overhead allocations, depreciation, labor rates, and other accounting costs. It can also be evaluated in terms of *opportunity costs—the profits forgone by not having the resource available*.

The optimal simplex tableau provides this second means of evaluation. Although they are considered *opportunity costs* or *shadow prices*, the economic worths of the resources are an indirect by-product in the solution of a primal problem. Moreover, they represent the solution variables in the dual counterpart.

The following production problem will facilitate the development of three important concepts. First, the primal and the dual methods of determining the economic worth of resources. Second, the economic interpretation of the dual. Third, the direct comparison between the primal and the dual simplex solutions.

A small garage shop producer utilizes two machines (M_1, M_2) to manufacture two products. The formal statement of the decision environment is:

Find X_1, X_2 $f_{max} = \$24X_1 + \$32X_2$
subject to: $2X_1 + 4X_2 \leq 60$ M_1
              $3X_1 + 2X_2 \leq 54$ M_2
              $X_1, X_2 \geq 0.$

The machines are available for 60 hours and 54 hours per week, respectively. The net contribution to profits for product 1 is \$24; for product 2, \$32. Two hours of machine 1 and 3 hours of machine 2 are required to produce one unit of product 1. Four hours of M_1 and 2 hours of M_2 are required to produce one unit of product 2.

The producer has the opportunity to rent two identical machines for \$5 each per hour. He would like to know the economic worth of the machines in order to make an informed decision.

The Primal Evaluation of a Resource

The economic worth of a resource is easily obtained from the primal solution of a linear programming problem. The conceptual reasoning will build on the concept of an *opportunity loss* and the components of the simplex tableau.

In the primal evaluation of resources, the critical components are the *slack variables*. They represent the *slack or unproductive available time for a resource*. They are initially introduced to change inequalities into equalities and to provide an initial feasible solution. The machine rental problem with slack variables is:

$$f_{max} = 24X_1 + 32X_2 + 0S_1 + 0S_2$$

subject to:
$$\begin{aligned}
2X_1 + 4X_2 + 1S_1 \quad\quad &= 60 \quad M_1 \\
3X_1 + 2X_2 \quad\quad + 1S_2 &= 54 \quad M_2 \\
X_j \geq 0; S_j \geq 0 \quad j &= 1, 2.
\end{aligned}$$

S_1 represents the amount of idle time on machine 1; S_2, the idle time on machine 2.

The economic worth of a resource, again, can be thought of in terms of an opportunity loss—the profits forgone by not utilizing the resource in the best possible way. An opportunity loss implies a comparison between the best that could be done and a less desirable alternative.

In order to use the opportunity loss concept to evaluate a resource, a comparison must be made between one use of the resource and the best use of the resource. Therefore, it is necessary to know the best possible allocation of the resources. This information is contained in the *final simplex tableau*. Table 10.2 provides the complete set of simplex computations. The optimal allocation of the resources is to produce 12 units of product 1 and 9 units of product 2 for a profit of $576.

Specifically, the resource expenditures are represented by the respective constraint equations:

Resource 1: $2X_1 + 4X_2 + 1S_1 \quad\quad = 60 \quad M_1$
Resource 2: $3X_1 + 2X_2 \quad\quad + 1S_2 = 54 \quad M_2.$

In terms of the optimal allocation:

$$\begin{aligned}
X_1 &= 12 \quad S_1 = 0 \\
X_2 &= 9 \quad\; S_2 = 0.
\end{aligned}$$

Therefore,

Time on Product 1		Time on Product 2		Idle Time		Total Time for Resource	
2(12)	+	4(9)	+	1(0)	=	60	M_1
3(12)	+	2(9)	+	1(0)	=	54	M_2

In hours utilized by machine 1:

24	+	36	+	0	=	60	M_1.

Twelve units of product 1 at 2 hours each $(2 \cdot 12 = 24)$, nine units of product 2 at 4 hours each $(4 \cdot 9 = 36)$, and 0 hours of idle time consume the entire 60

Tableaus

Initial

S. Var.	q_0	X_1 (24)	X_2 (32)	S_1 (0)	S_2 (0)
S_1: 15* → 0 S_1	60	2	4	1	0
S_2: 28 0 S_2	54	3	2	0	1
Z_j	0	0	0	0	0
$C_j - Z_j$		24	32 ↑	0	0

Second

Sol. Var.	q_0	X_1 (24)	X_2 (32)	S_1 (0)	S_2 (0)
X_2: 30 32 X_2	15	½	1	$1/4$	0
S_2: 12* → 0 S_2	24	2	0	$-2/4$	1
Z_j	480	16	32	8	0
$C_j - Z_j$		8 ↑	0	-8	0

Optimal

Sol. Var.	q_0	X_1 (24)	X_2 (32)	S_1 (0)	S_2 (0)
32 X_2	9	0	1	$3/8$	$-1/4$
24 X_1	12	1	0	$-1/4$	$1/2$
Z_j	576	24	32	6	4
$C_j - Z_j$		0	0	-6	-4

TABLE 10.2
Primal Solution of Product Mix Problem

hours machine 1 is available. Similarly, the machine 2 allocation is 36 hours on product 1, 18 hours on product 2, and 0 hours of idle time. Both resources are being utilized to capacity. The idle times for machine 1 and machine 2 are both zero: $S_1 = 0$, $S_2 = 0$.

With this background, the basic economic question is reintroduced. What would be the *opportunity loss* associated with an hour of lost time on machine 1? How much would an additional hour of time on machine 1 contribute to profits? What is the economic worth of resource 1?

The effect on profits of not having machine 1 for the last hour of production can be obtained directly from the final simplex tableau (Table 10.2). A loss of one hour of production on machine 1 is equivalent to having *the resource idle for one hour*. In turn, an hour of idle time is equivalent to increasing the slack variable associated with the resource by one. The effect of a lost hour of productivity for machine 1 is, therefore, equivalent to *the introduction of one unit of S_1 into the solution.*

Reading directly from the S_1 column of the final tableau, if one unit of S_1 is entered into the solution, X_2 will be reduced by 3/8, and X_1 will be increased by 1/4. As indicated by the associated $C_j - Z_j$ evaluation, the net economic effect on the objective function will be a reduction of $6. If machine 1 is unproductive (idle) for one hour, profits will be reduced by $6. Within measurable limits, machine 1 has *an economic worth* of $6 an hour.

Increasing the availability of machine 1 by one hour leads to the same conclusion. It will allow an increased productivity of 3/8 units of X_2, a reduction of 1/4 units of X_1, and a resulting improvement in profits of $6. Within measurable limits, the $6 per hour evaluation is maintained.

The worth of the second resource, machine 2, can be evaluated in the same way. In the optimal allocation, machine 2 is utilized all 54 hours. If machine 2 is idle for 1 hour—if one unit of S_2 is entered into the solution—the $C_j - Z_j$ in the associated slack variable column indicates that profits will be reduced by $4. Specifically, X_1 will be reduced by 1/2 at a value of $24, and X_2 will be increased by 1/4 at a value of $32:

$$- 1/2 \, (\$24) + 1/4 \, (\$32) = - \$4.$$

An hour of idle time on machine 2—1 hour of lost productivity on the second resource—will cost $4. The second resource has an economic worth of $4 per hour.

To summarize, the economic contribution of a resource can be obtained from the final simplex tableau. The resource constraints will be $\leq$ inequalities. *Slack variables* are assigned to the resource constraints. The slack variables represent the difference between the time utilized and the time available for the associated resource—the unutilized time for the resource. If the resource is utilized to capacity in the final tableau, the associated slack variable will be *nonbasis* (a nonsolution variable) with a value of zero. To enter one unit of slack into the solution will require forfeiting an hour of productive utilization. The reallocation of the resource from productive to nonproductive use has an associated cost. The economic change in the objective function for entering one unit of the nonbasis slack variable into the solution is found in the associated $C_j - Z_j$ evaluator. The economic loss for not utilizing the resource—the economic worth of the resource—is evaluated directly by the absolute $C_j - Z_j$ evaluator for the slack variable assigned to the resource.

Another example is provided in Table 10.3. There are three resources with restrictions defined by three respective constraint equations. The slack variables S_1, S_2, and S_3 are introduced to convert the inequalities to equalities. Slack variable S_1 is associated with resource 1 (R_1); S_2 with R_2; and S_3 with R_3. As indicated by the $C_j - Z_j$ evaluators in the final tableau, to enter one unit of S_1 into the solution will reduce profits by $6 2/3. If resource 1 is idle for one hour, $6 2/3 will be lost. Resource 1 has an economic worth of $6 2/3. Resource 2 can likewise be evaluated. The associated slack variable is S_2 with an accompanying $C_j - Z_j$ evaluator of -21 2/3. To enter S_2 into the solution—to lose

$f_{max} = 120X_1 + 100X_2$

subject to:
$5X_1 + 2X_2 \leq 90 \quad R_1$
$4X_1 + 4X_2 \leq 80 \quad R_2$
$2X_1 + 5X_2 \leq 80 \quad R_3$

$5X_1 + 2X_2 + 1S_1 \qquad\qquad = 90 \quad R_1$
$4X_1 + 4X_2 \qquad + 1S_2 \qquad = 80 \quad R_2$
$2X_1 + 5X_2 \qquad\qquad + 1S_3 = 80 \quad R_3$

Tableaus

Initial

		Sol. Var.	q_0	120 X_1	100 X_2	0 S_1	0 S_2	0 S_3
S_1: 18* ➡	0	S_1	90	5	2	1	0	0
S_2: 20	0	S_2	80	4	4	0	1	0
S_3: 40	0	S_3	80	2	5	0	0	1
		Z_j	0	0	0	0	0	0
		$C_j - Z_j$		120 ⬆	100	0	0	0

Second

		Sol. Var.	q_0	120 X_1	100 X_2	0 S_1	0 S_2	0 S_3
X_1: 45	120	X_1	18	1	$2/5$	$1/5$	0	0
S_2: $3^1/3$* ➡	0	S_2	8	0	$2^2/5$	$-4/5$*	1	0
S_3: $10^{10}/21$	0	S_3	44	0	$4^1/5$	$-2/5$	0	1
		Z_j	2160	120	48	24	0	0
		$C_j - Z_j$		0	52 ⬆	-24	0	0

Optimal

		Sol. Var.	q_0	120 X_1	100 X_2	0 S_1	0 S_2	0 S_3
	120	X_1	$16^2/3$	1	0	$1/3$	$-1/6$	0
	100	X_2	$3^1/3$	0	1	$-1/3$	$5/12$	0
	0	S_3	30	0	0	1	$-1^3/4$	1
		Z_j	$2333^1/3$	120	100	$6^2/3$	$21^2/3$	0
		$C_j - Z_j$		0	0	$-6^2/3$	$-21^2/3$	0

TABLE 10.3

Resource Evaluation: Primal Tableau

the productivity of resource 2 for an hour—will reduce the objective function by $21 2/3. Within measurable limits, resource 2 is worth $21 2/3 per hour. Resource 3 has been assigned slack variable S_3 with a $C_j - Z_j$ of 0. Resource 3 has an imputed worth of $0.

The evaluation of resource 3 requires explanation. The utilization of resource 3 is expressed entirely in terms of the third constraint:

Time on Product 1		Time on Product 2		Idle Time		Total Time Available	
$2X_1$	+	$5X_2$	+	$1S_3$	=	80	R_3.

In terms of the optimal solution:

$X_1 = 16\ 2/3$
$X_2 = 3\ 1/3$
$S_3 = 30.$

The optimal resource utilization is:

Time on Product 1		Time on Product 2		Idle Time		Total Time Available	
$2(16\ 2/3)$	+	$5(3\ 1/3)$	+	30	=	80	R_3
33 1/3 hours	+	16 2/3 hours	+	30 hours	=	80 hours	

Optimally allocated, resource 3 is idle for 30 hours.

During the last hour of availability, resource 3 is idle. Therefore, if the last hour were lost, there would be no lost productivity. The last hour or the last 30 hours, for that matter, is of no economic consequence. If 1 additional hour of resource 3 could be obtained, it could not be put to profitable use. Resource 3 is termed a *free good* with an imputed worth of zero.

The Dual Evaluation of a Resource

The economic worth of a resource can also be obtained directly from the dual counterpart. The variables to be solved in the dual will be the economic worth of the resources. Consider an introductory single-constraint product mix problem. The primal formulation is:

$f_{max} = 8X_1 + 6X_2$
subject to: $2X_1 + 1X_2 \leq 10$ resource 1
             $X_1, X_2 \geq 0.$

There are 10 hours of time available on resource 1. It requires 2 hours to produce product 1 and 1 hour to produce product 2. The products are worth \$8 and \$6 respectively. The objective is to determine the economic worth of the resource.

Table 10.4 provides the accompanying primal simplex tableaus. Each extreme corner point production possibility is represented by a tableau. The initial tableau has a solution of $S_1 = 10$. The resource would be idle for all 10 hours, produce no products, and generate no profits. If allocated in this way, the resource obviously will have no economic worth. This is expressed in the tableau by the $C_j - Z_j$ of 0 for the slack variable (S_1) associated with the resource.

The second tableau provides an improved allocation. In this case, the resource is used entirely to produce units of product 1. As can be seen from the tableau or from the direct reference to the resource constraint, resource 1 can produce a maximum of five units of product 1 for a total profit of $40. With 10 hours of the resource producing $40, the allocation of the resource to produce product 1 will provide an imputed economic worth of $4 per hour. The absolute $C_j - Z_j$ evaluator for S_1 is 4.

The third tableau provides the optimal allocation of the resource. At a utilization rate of 1 hour per unit of product 2, the 10 hours of the resource should be used to product 10 units of product 2 for $60 profit. With 10 hours

Tableaus:

Initial

C_j		Sol. Mix	q_o	8 X_1	6 X_2	0 S_1
S_1: 5*	0	S_1	10	2	1	1
		Z_j	0	0	0	0
		$C_j - Z_j$		8 ↑	6	0

Second

C_j		Sol. Mix	q_o	8 X_1	6 X_2	0 S_1
X_1: 16*	8	X_1	5	1	$1/2$	$1/2$
		Z_j	40	8	4	4
		$C_j - Z_j$		0	2 ↑	−4

Optimal

C_j		Sol. Mix	q_o	8 X_1	6 X_2	0 S_1
	6	X_2	10	2	1	1
		Z_j	60	12	6	6
		$C_j - Z_j$		−4	0	−6

TABLE 10.4

Primal Resource Evaluation

producing $60, the resource must be worth $6 per hour. This conclusion is again confirmed by the $C_j - Z_j$ row. If the resource is allocated to idle time (S_1) rather than to the production of product 2, profits will be reduced by $6 per hour.

The alternative corner point allocations can be summarized as follows:

Product 1	Product 2	Profits	Value of Resource per Hour
0	0	$ 0	$0
5	0	$40	$4
0	10	$60	$6

The proper allocation, obviously, is to produce 10 units of product 2 with a $60 profit. If allocated in the best possible way, the resource has an *opportunity cost* evaluation of $6 per hour. Ceteris paribus, in a free market, the producer would be willing to bid up to $6 per hour for the resource—the resource is worth $6 per hour.

Once the primal problem is fully understood, the dual can be readily interpreted. The dual formulation can be obtained from the transpose of the primal:

$f_{min} = 10W_1$
subject to: $2W_1 \geq 8$ product 1
$\qquad\qquad 1W_1 \geq 6$ product 2
$\qquad\qquad W_1 \geq 0$.

The objective in the dual is to allocate the resource to the production of products so as to minimize total opportunity costs. Variable W_1 represents the opportunity cost or economic worth of the resource. The objective function is:

$f_{min} = \qquad 10 \qquad \cdot \qquad W_1$
$\qquad\qquad$ quantity $\qquad$ opportunity
$\qquad\qquad$ of resource $\quad$ cost of resource.

The quantity of the resource multiplied by the opportunity cost is the value to be minimized. Since the quantity is fixed at 10, the objective is to make W_1 as small as possible.

The value of W_1, however, is subject to the restriction imposed by the constraints:

	imputed cost			profit contribution	
2	·	W_1	≥	8	product 1
1	·	W_1	≥	6	product 2
quantity of	opportunity			value per	
resource	cost			unit	

Each constraint is related to the profitability of producing one of the products. The left-hand side of the inequality represents the total imputed cost. The right-hand side represents the contribution margin for the product.

The imputed cost for each product will be greater than or equal to ($\geq$) the profit contribution. If the *greater than* applies, the imputed costs for the product will exceed the attainable profits—the resource cannot be economically applied to the production of the product. If the *equality* exists, the imputed costs equal the profits for the product—the net opportunity cost for the product will be zero. *Since opportunity costs are relative to the best utilization of the resource, a net opportunity cost of zero will indicate the best allocation of the resource.* The product associated with the equality should be produced. Moreover, the value of W_1 producing the equality will be the opportunity cost solution for the resource.

The simplex algorithm allows a systematic optimization of the dual. As indicated in Table 8.5, the best allocation of the resource is:

$$W_1 = 6$$
$$S_1 = 4 \qquad f_{min} = \$60.$$

As was already confirmed by the primal, the economic worth of the resource is $6 per hour. The 10 hours of the resource have an opportunity cost (economic worth) of $60. Substituting the opportunity cost (economic worth) of the resource into the constraint equations:

imputed cost		profit contribution	
2(6)	>	8	product 1
1(6)	=	6	product 2

In allocating the resource to produce product 1, there is an imputed cost of $12 and a profit contribution of $8. Product 1 is unprofitable and should not be produced. Product 2 has an imputed cost of $6 and a profit contribution of $6. The *net opportunity cost* for producing product 2 is zero. There is no opportunity cost incurred in the production of product 2—the allocation of the resource cannot be improved. Product 2 is the best allocation of the resource.

Given this background, consider the machine rental problem (page 306) in the context of the dual. The formulation of the problem can be obtained directly from the problem statement. Two products can be manufactured. There will be a constraint for each product. Two resources are used to manufacture the products. There will be two variables representing the imputed opportunity costs of the resources. Resource utilization rates for product 1 are two hours for machine 1 and three hours for machine 2. The total imputed

$$f_{min} = 10W_1 + 0S_1 + 0S_2 + MA_1 + MA_2$$

subject to:
$$2W_1 - 1S_1 \qquad + 1A_1 \qquad = 8$$
$$1W_1 \qquad - 1S_2 \qquad + 1A_2 = 6$$

Tableaus:

Initial

	C_j	Sol. Mix	q_0	10 W_1	0 S_1	0 S_2	M A_1	M A_2
A_1: 4* →	M	A_1	8	2	−1	0	1	0
A_2: 6	M	A_2	6	1	0	−1	0	1
		Z_j	14M	3M	−M	−M	M	M
		$C_j - Z_j$		−3M +10 ↑	M	M	0	0

Second

	C_j	Sol. Mix	q_0	10 W_1	0 S_1	0 S_2	M A_1	M A_2
W_1: −8	10	W_1	4	1	−1/2	0	1/2	0
A_2: 4* →	M	A_2	2	0	1/2	−1	−1/2	1
		Z_j	2M +40	10	1/2M −5	−M	−1/2M +5	M
		$C_j - Z_j$		0	−1/2M +5 ↑	M	1 1/2M −5	0

Optimal

	C_j	Sol. Mix	q_0	10 W_1	0 S_1	0 S_2	M A_1	M A_2
	10	W_1	6	1	0	−1	0	1
	0	S_1	4	0	1	−2	−1	2
		Z_j	60	10	0	−10	0	10
		$C_j - Z_j$		0	0	10	M	$M - 10$

TABLE 10.5
The Dual Solution

cost to manufacture product 1 is therefore:

imputed cost   imputed cost
for machine 1   for machine 2

$$\overset{\text{utilization rate}}{\underset{\text{of resource}}{2W_1}} \quad + \quad \overset{\text{opportunity}}{\underset{\text{cost}}{3W_2}}.$$

The profit contribution for product 1 is \$24. The constraint representing the opportunity costs associated with product 1 will be:

$$\begin{array}{ccc} & \text{profit} & \\ \text{total imputed cost} & \text{contribution} & \\ 2W_1 + 3W_2 \quad \geq & 24 & \text{product 1.} \end{array}$$

Product 2 requires four hours on machine 1 and two hours on machine 2. The profit contribution is \$32. The constraint representing the opportunity costs associated with product 2 will be:

$$\begin{array}{ccc} & \text{profit} & \\ \text{total imputed cost} & \text{contribution} & \\ 4W_1 + 2W_2 \quad \geq & 32 & \text{product 2.} \end{array}$$

The optimization objective is the minimization of total opportunity costs. There are 60 hours of available time on machine 1 and 54 hours on machine 2. W_1 and W_2 are the respective opportunity cost evaluations of these resources. The objective function will be:

$$f_{min} = 60W_1 + 54W_2.$$

Of course, the dual could have been formulated by the transpose of the primal. With either approach, the dual formulation becomes:

$$f_{min} = 60W_1 + 54W_2$$
$$\text{subject to: } 2W_1 + 3W_2 \geq 24 \quad \text{product 1}$$
$$4W_1 + 2W_2 \geq 32 \quad \text{product 2}$$
$$W_1, W_2 \geq 0.$$

With the addition of surplus variables to provide equations and artificial variables for an initial feasible solution, the simplex solution of the dual is represented in Table 10.6:

$$\begin{array}{l} W_1 = 6 \\ W_2 = 4 \end{array} \quad f_{min} = \$576.$$

Machine 1 has an opportunity cost evaluation of \$6 per hour. Machine 2 has an evaluation of \$4 per hour. If properly allocated, the two resources have a total worth of \$576. In terms of the product constraints:

$$2(6) + 3(4) = 24 \quad \text{product 1}$$
$$4(6) + 2(4) = 32 \quad \text{product 2.}$$

With an equality indicating that the total opportunity costs to produce the product equal the profit contribution, both products should be manufactured.

Note, the $C_j - Z_j$ evaluators for the surplus variables are:

evaluator

$S_1 = \quad 12$
$S_2 = \quad \ 9.$

S_1 is the surplus variable for the first constraint, representing product 1. S_2 is the surplus variable for the second constraint, representing product 2. As will be demonstrated shortly, the 12 and 9 are the optimal product mix solution values for product 1 and product 2 in the primal.

Dual

	C_j	Sol. Mix	q_o	60 W_1	54 W_2	0 S_1	0 S_2	M A_1	M A_2
A_1: 12	M	A_1	24	2	3	-1	0	1	0
A_2: 8* →	M	A_2	32	4	2	0	-1	0	1
		Z_j	56M	6M	5M	$-M$	$-M$	M	M
		$C_j - Z_j$		$-6M$ $+60$	$-5M$ $+54$	M	M	0	0

	C_j	Sol. Mix	q_o	60 W_1	54 W_2	0 S_1	0 S_2	M A_1	M A_2
A_1: 4* →	M	A_1	8	0	2	-1	$1/2$	1	$-1/2$
W_1: 16	60	W_1	8	1	$1/2$	0	$-1/4$	0	$1/4$
		Z_j	8M $+480$	60	2M $+30$	$-M$	$1/2M$ -15	M	$-1/2M$ $+15$
		$C_j - Z_j$		0	$-2M$ $+24$	M	$-1/2M$ $+15$	0	$1 1/2M$ -15

	C_j	Sol. Mix	q_o	60 W_1	54 W_2	0 S_1	0 S_2	M A_1	M A_2
	54	W_2	4	0	1	$-1/2$	$1/4$	$1/2$	$-1/4$
	60	W_1	6	1	0	$1/4$	$-3/8$	$-1/4$	$3/8$
		Z_j	576	60	54	-12	-9	12	9
		$C_j - Z_j$		0	0	12	9	$M-12$	$M-9$

TABLE 10.6

The Dual Solution of the Product Mix Problem

The Economic Worth of a Resource

THE DUAL AND PRIMAL COMPARED

The primal and the dual are direct complements. They solve the same problem in different ways. They both provide the same information. In the primal product mix problem, the variables were product outputs with resource constraints. The objective was to allocate the resources to the product mix that would maximize profits. The simplex algorithm provided a solution for the product mix variables. Moreover, the economic worth of the resources could be obtained, in the final simplex tableau, from the $C_j - Z_j$ evaluator for the slack variable assigned to the resource. In the companion dual, the variables were the opportunity losses for the resources with product profitability constraints. The objective was to allocate the resources to the products that would minimize the total opportunity costs. The simplex algorithm provided a solution for the resource opportunity costs variables. Furthermore, the quantity of the products to manufacture could be obtained, in the final simplex tableau, from the $C_j - Z_j$ evaluator for the surplus variable assigned to the product.[2]

The primal and dual are intimately related—component for component. For the product mix problem (page 326), the formulated primal was:

Primal $f_{max} = 24X_1 + 32X_2$
subject to: $2X_1 + 4X_2 \leq 60 \leftarrow$ resource 1
$ 3X_1 + 2X_2 \leq 54 \leftarrow$ resource 2
$ \uparrow \uparrow$
$ $ product 1   product 2
$ X_1, X_2 \geq 0.$

The dual equivalence:

Dual $f_{min} = 60W_1 + 54W_2$
subject to: $2W_1 + 3W_2 \geq 24 \leftarrow$ product 1
$ 4W_1 + 2W_2 \geq 32 \leftarrow$ product 2
$ \uparrow \uparrow$
$ $ resource 1   resource 2
$ W_1, W_2 \geq 0.$

The rows in the primal are the columns in the dual and conversely. The primal can be converted to the dual or the dual to the primal by transposing the rows and columns.

The primal-dual interface of rows and columns is not restricted to the formulation. Disregarding artificial components, any simplex tableau can be

---

[2] Refer to Table 10.6. The surplus variables are S_1 for product 1 and S_2 for product 2. In the optimal tableau, the $C_j - Z_j$ values accompanying these surplus variables are 12 and 9 respectively. Corresponding to the primal solution in Table 10.2, the optimal product mix is 12 units of product 1 and 9 units of product 2.

Primal

Sol. Mix	q_0	X_1	X_2	S_1	S_2
X_1	12	1	0	$-1/4$	$1/2$
X_2	9	0	1	$3/8$	$-1/4$
Z_j	576				
$C_j - Z_j$				-6	-4

Dual

Sol. Mix	q_0	W_1	W_2	S_1	S_2
W_1	6	1	0	$1/4$	$-3/8$
W_2	4	0	1	$-1/2$	$1/4$
Z_j	576				
$C_j - Z_j$				12	9

TABLE 10.7

Primal-Dual Equivalence

transposed into the companion equivalaence. Table 10.7 demonstrates the component-by-component relationship between primal and dual final simplex tableaus of the product mix problem.[3] The rows of the primal tableau become the columns of the dual tableau. As a minor modification, the slack variable coefficients in the dual require a change of sign to allow nonnegative solution values.[4]

From the direct equivalence of primal and dual, an important inference can be drawn. *Since both provide the same information, either the primal or the dual can be used to solve a problem.* The simplex method can be applied to the form requiring the least computational effort.[5]

SUMMARY

An introduction to linear programming would not be complete without a consideration of several important extensions. This chapter has considered two

---

[3] In the primal tableau, the two rows have been interchanged to facilitate a direct comparison.
[4] The direct transpose of the S_1 primal column would produce -6 as a dual solution variable. The column is multiplied by -1 in the transposing to alter the sign to conform to nonnegativity of solution variables.
[5] A solution for a corner point requires the *inverse of the matrix of coefficients* for the solution variables. With a solution variable for each constraint equation, a problem containing 10,000 constraints and 100 variables will require the inverse of a 10,000 by 10,000 matrix of coefficients. If the problem is expressed in a dual form, there will be 100 solution variables. The inverse will be reduced to 100 by 100. Instead of 100,000,000 coefficients, only 10,000 are required per corner point solution—a significant improvement.

extensions: the determination of the economic worth of a resource and duality. The next chapter will consider another important extension: sensitivity analysis.

The economic worth of a resource is readily obtainable. This valuable information can be obtained in two ways. If the problem has a primal formulation, the economic worth of a resource is contained in the net economic evaluator $(C_j - Z_j)$ for the slack variable assigned to the resource. If the problem has a dual formulation, the economic worth of the resources are the decision variables. They are the solution values for the decision variables in the final tableau.

Duality is an important characteristic of linear programming problems. All linear programming problems come in pairs. For every primal problem, there is a companion dual problem. The two have a direct component-by-component transference: the rows of one are the columns of the other.

A standard allocation of resources problem can be formulated in two ways. The decision variables can represent the ways to use the resources. They will be restricted by resource availability constraints. The problem will be to find the best values for the decision variables, subject to the constraints, to maximize an objective. The decision environment can be structured from a different perspective. The decision variables can represent the opportunity losses associated with using the resources. These decision variables will be restricted by resource usage cost constraints. The problem will be to find the best values for the decision variables, subject to the constraints, to minimize opportunity usage costs. The two formulations arrive at an identical allocation of the resources via conceptually different routes. Their final simplex tableaus will both contain identical information. A decision maker can formulate and solve a linear programming problem either way.

THE DUAL SIMPLEX ALGORITHM

The component-by-component transference of primal and dual solutions allows a new solution procedure: the *dual simplex method*. This procedure consists of applying the simplex operations for the dual directly on the primal formulation. The procedure has the advantage of eliminating the need for artificial variables. In certain problems, and especially in postoptimality analysis (Chapter 11), this advantage may significantly reduce the number of tableaus required to reach an optimal solution.

The Dual Simplex Operations

The transference of the simplex operations applied to the dual into primal implications is illustrated in the following minimization problem:

Primal $\quad f_{\min} = 52X_1 + 40X_2$
subject to: $2X_1 + 4X_2 \geq 20$
$\qquad\qquad 5X_1 + 2X_2 \geq 18$
$\qquad\qquad X_1, X_2 \geq 0.$

To allow the application of the simplex algorithm, surplus and artificial variables are introduced:

Primal $\quad f_{\min} = 52X_1 + 40X_2 + 0S_1 + 0S_2 + MA_1 + MA_2$
subject to: $2X_1 + 4X_2 - 1S_1 \qquad\quad + 1A_1 \qquad\quad = 20$
$\qquad\qquad 5X_1 + 2X_2 \qquad\quad - 1S_2 \qquad\quad + 1A_2 = 18$
$\qquad\qquad X_1, X_2 \geq 0; S_1, S_2 \geq 0; A_1, A_2 \geq 0.$

The negative slack or surplus variables are added to change the inequalities into equalities. The artificial variables are introduced to provide an artificial initial feasible solution.

To avoid artificial components, the primal formulation can be transposed into the dual formulation:

Dual $\quad f_{\max} = 20W_1 + 18W_2$
subject to: $2W_1 + 5W_2 \leq 52$
$\qquad\qquad 4W_1 + 2W_2 \leq 40$
$\qquad\qquad W_1, W_2 \geq 0.$

Tableaus

Initial

	C_j			20	18	0	0
		Sol. Mix	q_0	W_1	W_2	S_1	S_2
S_1: 26 0		S_1	52	2	5	1	0
remove S_2: 10* → 0		S_2	40	4	2	0	1
		Z_j	0	0	0	0	0
		$C_j - Z_j$		20	18	0	0

enter ↑

Second

	C_j			20	18	0	0
		Sol. Mix	q_0	W_1	W_2	S_1	S_2
remove S_1 : 8* → 0		S_1	32	0	4	1	$-1/2$
W_1: 20 20		W_1	10	1	$1/2$	0	$1/4$
		Z_j	200	20	10	0	5
		$C_j - Z_j$		0	8	0	-5

enter ↑

Optimal

	C_j			20	18	0	0
		Sol. Mix	q_0	W_1	W_2	S_1	S_2
	18	W_2	8	0	1	$1/4$	$-1/8$
	20	W_1	6	1	0	$-1/8$	$5/16$
		Z_j	264	20	18	2	4
		$C_j - Z_j$		0	0	-2	-4

TABLE 10A.1
The Simplex Applied to the Dual

With the addition of slack variables, the dual can be readily solved by the simplex algorithm (Table 10A.1).

The simplex operations on the dual formulation in Table 10A.1 demonstrate two important conditions. First, each tableau for the dual will represent a feasible solution. Second, the simplex operations on the dual will lead to the optimal solution. Therefore, the following added condition will lead to an important conclusion. Since every component of the dual will have a complementary component in the primal, the dual operations must be applicable to the primal. They must also represent feasible solutions leading to the optimal solution.

The simplex operations of the dual will now be applied to the primal formulation. To avoid artificial variables, the primal is first reformulated:

Primal $\quad f_{min} = 52X_1 + 40X_2$
subject to: $-2X_1 - 4X_2 \le -20$
$\qquad\qquad -5X_1 - 2X_2 \le -18$
$\qquad\qquad X_1, X_2 \ge 0.$

Tableaus

Initial

	C_j	Sol. Mix	q_o	52 X_1	40 X_2	0 S_1	0 S_2
remove →	0	S_1	−20	−2	−4	1	0
	0	S_2	−18	−5	−2	0	1
		Z_j	0	0	0	0	0
		$C_j - Z_j$		52	40	0	0

$$X_1: \frac{52}{-2} = -26 \quad X_2: \frac{40}{-4} = -10^*$$

enter

Second

	C_j	Sol. Mix	q_o	52 X_1	40 X_2	0 S_1	0 S_2
	40	X_2	5	$1/2$	1	$-1/4$	0
remove →	0	S_2	−8	−4	0	$-1/2$	1
		Z_j	200	20	40	−10	0
		$C_j - Z_j$		32	0	10	0

$$X_1: \frac{32}{-4} = -8^* \qquad S_1: \frac{10}{-1/2} = -20$$

enter

Optimal

	C_j	Sol. Mix	q_o	52 X_1	40 X_2	0 S_1	0 S_2
	40	X_2	4	0	1	$-5/16$	$1/8$
	52	X_1	2	1	0	$1/8$	$-1/4$
		Z_j	264	52	40	−6	−8
		$C_j - Z_j$		0	0	6	8

TABLE 10A.2

The Dual Simplex Solution of the Primal

Adding slack variables and *momentarily* disregarding the nonnegativity requirement for solution variables, Table 10A.2 provides an initial solution.

To move from one tableau to an improved tableau, a new variable is entered and a solution variable removed. Refer to the first simplex tableau of the dual (Table 10A.1). The variable to be entered will have the largest positive $C_j - Z_j$ evaluator. Variable W_1, with the largest evaluator of 20, will be entered. The variable to be removed will have the smallest positive *substitution quantity*. S_2, with the smallest value of 10, will be removed.

These operations will produce acceptable adjustments of the dual. Complementary adjustments of the primal must be equally acceptable. Moreover, an analogous set of operations must exist to produce these acceptable adjustments. Using the primal-dual correspondence of the solution values and the $C_j - Z_j$ net economic evaluators,[1] the entry of the largest $C_j - Z_j$ net economic evaluator in the dual is equivalent to the removal of the most negative solution value in the primal. Therefore, the entry of W_1 in the dual with a $C_j - Z_j$ of 20 is equivalent to the removal of S_1 in the primal with a solution value of -20.

The removal of a variable in the dual also has an acceptable counterpart in the primal. The removal of the smallest positive *substitution quantity* in the dual corresponds to the entry of the least negative *evaluator ratio* ($C_j - Z_j$ row/ removal variable row). The removal from the dual of variable S_2 (with a substitution quantity of 10) is duplicated in the primal by the entry of X_2 with a negative *evaluator ratio* of -10.

After the variables to enter and to remove have been selected, the adjustment of the tableau follows the standard row operations prescribed by the simplex method. Table 10A.2 provides the second primal tableau adjusted by dual simplex operations.

The procedure of adjusting an *infeasible* primal through acceptable simplex operations on the dual is aptly termed the *dual simplex algorithm*. Two rules are added to the standard simplex operations:

Dual Simplex Rule 1.
Remove the variable with the most negative solution value.

Dual Simplex Rule 2.
Enter the variable with the least negative evaluator ratio. The evaluator ratios are formed by dividing the $C_j - Z_j$ evaluator row by the removal variable row.

Tableau 10A.2 provides the tableau-by-tableau application of the dual simplex algorithm to solve the problem. The first tableau is nonoptimal and primal infeasible.[2] The second tableau is still nonoptimal and primal infeasible. The third tableau is both optimal and primal feasible.

The Feasibility Requirement

The concept of feasibility requires a careful explanation. A corner point solution in a tableau must be feasible—must be on a convex polyhedron of feasible alternatives. Feasibility is maintained by nonnegative solution variables. As Table 10A.2 illustrates, the first and the second tableau of the primal solution

---

[1] The solution values of the primal are the negative $C_j - Z_j$ net economic evaluators in the dual, and conversely.
[2] It is nonoptimal because an entry variable will improve the solution. It is infeasible because of the violation of the nonnegative constraints.

contain negative valued solution variables. These two tableaus are infeasible primal solutions. They violate the feasibility requirement.

All linear programming problems, however, come in pairs: a primal and a dual. There will always be two separate, but intimately related, convex polyhedrons of feasible alternatives. A solution on either of these two convex polyhedrons will be feasible. The first two tableaus in Table 10A.2 are definitely not primal feasible. However, they may still be acceptable dual feasible solutions.

Dual feasibility is maintained by nonnegative dual solution variables. In a primal tableau, the dual solution variables are the $C_j - Z_j$ net economic evaluators.[3] They will be nonnegative when the $C_j - Z_j$ net economic evaluators in the primal are either (1) nonnegative for a primal minimization problem or (2) nonpositive for a primal maximization problem.

As Table 10A.2 illustrates, this primal minimization problem has non-negative $C_j - Z_j$ net economic evaluators in each of the three tableaus. Each of these solutions is dual feasible. The tableaus satisfy the requirement of feasibility. They represent corner points on a convex polyhedron of feasible alternatives.

At the point of optimality, and only at this point, will a solution be both *primal feasible and dual feasible*. The simplex and the dual simplex approach identical optimal *feasible* solutions from different directions. The simplex method starts with an economically poor, nonoptimal, initial feasible solution. It progressively moves to better and better feasible solutions until the optimal feasible solution is obtained. The dual simplex method starts with a definably optimal,[4] primal infeasible (dual feasible) solution. It progressively eliminates infeasbility until the solution becomes feasible and simultaneously optimal. The simplex method and the dual simplex method approach the search for the optimal solution from opposing directions that converge at identical optimal feasible solutions.

---

[3] Refer to Table 10.7 and the related discussion.
[4] By containing all unfavorable $C_j - Z_j$ net economic evaluators, the dual feasible solution satisfies the criterion for optimality.

Bierman, H., Jr., C. P. Bonini, and W. H. Hausman. *Quantitative Analysis for Business Decisions*. Homewood, Ill.: Richard D. Irwin, 1973.

Boulding, K. E., and W. A. Spivey. *Linear Programming and the Theory of the Firm*. New York: Macmillan Co., 1960.

Charnes, A., and W. W. Cooper. *Management Models and Industrial Applications of Linear Programming*, 2 Vols. New York: John Wiley & Sons, 1961.

Childress, R. L. *Mathematics for Managerial Decisions*. Englewood Cliffs, N.J.: Prentice-Hall, 1974.

Dantzig, G. B. *Linear Programming and Extensions*. Princeton: Princeton University Press, 1963.

Dorfman, R., P. A. Samuelson, and R. M. Solow. *Linear Programming and Economic Analysis*. New York: McGraw-Hill Book Co., 1958.

Gass, S. I. *Linear Programming: Methods and Applications*. New York: McGraw-Hill Book Co., 1969.

Gaver, D. P., and G. L. Thompson. *Programming and Probability Models in Operations Research*. Belmont, Calif.: Wadsworth Publishing Co., 1973.

Hadley, G. *Linear Programming*. Reading, Mass.: Addison-Wesley Publishing Co., 1962.

Hillier, F. S., and G. J. Lieberman. *Introduction to Operations Research*. San Francisco: Holden-Day, 1967.

Kim, C. *Introduction to Linear Programming*. New York: Holt, Rinehart and Winston, 1971.

Levin, R. I., and C. A. Kirkpatrick. *Quantitative Approaches to Management*. New York: McGraw-Hill Book Co., 1975.

Levin, R. I., and R. P. Lamone. *Linear Programming for Management Decisions*. Homewood, Ill.: Richard D. Irwin, 1969.

Loomba, N. P. *Linear Programming, An Introductory Analysis*. New York: McGraw-Hill Book Co., 1964.

Loomba, N. P., and E. Turban. *Applied Programming for Management*. New York: Holt, Rinehart and Winston, 1974.

Riley, V., and S. I. Gass. *Bibliography on Linear Programming and Related Techniques*. Baltimore: The Johns Hopkins Press, 1958.

Spivey, W. A., and R. M. Thrall. *Linear Optimization*. New York: Holt, Rinehart and Winston, 1970.

Stockton, R. S. *Introduction to Linear Programming*. Homewood, Ill.: Richard D. Irwin, 1971.

Strum, J. E. *Introduction to Linear Programming*. San Francisco: Holden-Day, 1972.

Thierauf, R. J., and R. C. Klekamp. *Decision Making Through Operations Research*. New York: John Wiley & Sons, 1975.

Wagner, H. M. *Principles of Operations Research with Applications to Managerial Decisions*. Englewood Cliffs, N.J.: Prentice-Hall, 1969.

10.1. During a period of business slowdown, two specially trained workers can be allocated to the joint production of two profitable activities. The *LP* formulation of the weekly allocation is as follows:

Primal $f_{\max} = 100X_1 + 120X_2$
subject to: $1X_1 + 3X_2 \leq 12$
$ 4X_1 + 2X_2 \leq 20$
$ X_1 \geq 0; X_2 \geq 0.$

Using W_i to represent the decision variables, construct the complementary dual formulation.

10.2. Consider the following primal formulation with regard to conformability of signs:

$f_{\max} = 40X_1 + 60X_2$
subject to: $2X_1 + 4X_2 \leq 120$
$ 4X_1 - 2X_2 \geq 18$
$ X_1 \geq 0; X_2 \geq 0.$

Using W_i to represent the decision variables, construct the complementary dual formulation.

10.3. Primal:

$f_{\max} = 20X_1 + 18X_2$
subject to: $8X_1 + 4X_2 = 40$
$ 1X_1 \leq 4$
$ X_1 \geq 0; X_2 \geq 0.$

Provide the dual formulation solvable by the simplex method.

10.4. Primal:

$f_{\min} = -10X_1 + 20X_2$
subject to: $-1X_1 + 1X_2 \leq 1$
$ 3X_1 + 2X_2 \leq 12$
$ X_1 \geq 0; X_2 \geq 0.$

Using W_i to represent the decision variables, construct the complementary dual formulation.

10.5. Primal:

$f_{max} = \$30X_1 + \$36X_2$
subject to: $2X_1 + 5X_2 \leq 40$ resource 1
              $6X_1 + 2X_2 \leq 48$ resource 2
              $X_1, X_2 \geq 0.$

By forming the shadow price in the primal, determine the per unit worth of resource 1.

10.6. Three machines are each being leased for 56 hours a week to manufacture two products. The weekly output levels of product 1 and product 2 are represented by the respective decision variables X_1 and X_2. The linear programming formulation is expressed as:

$f_{max} = \$100X_1 + \$140X_2$
subject to: $8X_1 + 5X_2 \leq 56$ M_1
              $7X_1 + 7X_2 \leq 56$ M_2
              $4X_1 + 8X_2 \leq 56$ M_3
              $X_1, X_2 \geq 0.$

What is the economic contribution to profit of the last hour for each of these resources? Will machine 1 always have this same per hour worth for all 56 hours?

10.7. Two workers have specialized in the manufacture of two products. Each worker is presently employed for 40 hours a week. The joint requirements to manufacture the products are summarized below:

$f_{max} = 50X_1 + 80X_2$
subject to: $2X_1 + 4X_2 \leq 40$ W_1
              $3X_1 + 2X_2 \leq 40$ W_2
              $X_1, X_2 \geq 0.$

Worker 1 has requested two hours of weekly overtime at $10 an hour. Delighted with the offer, the production manager grants the overtime. Worker 2 then makes the same request. He is refused. From an economic perspective, was the production manager's decision a pure act of discrimination or an act of sound economic discretion?

10.8. Primal:

$f_{max} = 22X_1 + 80X_2$
subject to: $2X_1 + 1X_2 \leq 24$
              $1X_1 + 4X_2 \leq 40$
              $1X_1 + 2X_2 \leq 34$
              $2X_1 + 1.4X_2 \leq 28$
              $4X_1 + 3X_2 \geq 24$
              $1X_1 \geq 2$
              $1X_2 \geq 4$
              $X_1, X_2 \geq 0.$

Construct the initial simplex tableau for this primal. After adjusting for conformability of sign, transform the primal formulation into the dual counterpart. Construct the initial simplex tableau for the dual.

10.9. Two machines are used to manufacture two products. The units of the manufactured products are represented by the decision variables X_1 and X_2. The first product requires 6 hours on machine 1 and 4 hours on machine 2. The second product requires 5 hours and 7 hours, respectively. The two machines are available for 54 hours and 72 hours, respectively. Product 1 contributes $240 to profits; product 2, $260. The primal formulation is:

$f_{max} = \$240X_1 + \$260X_2$
subject to: $6X_1 + 5X_2 \leq 54 \qquad M_1$
$\qquad\qquad 4X_1 + 7X_2 \leq 72 \qquad M_2$
$\qquad\qquad X_1, X_2 \geq 0.$

Transform the primal into the dual. Provide a complete component-by-component description of the dual.

10.10. Primal:

$f_{min} = 40X_1 + 60X_2$
subject to: $2X_1 + 4X_2 \geq 52$
$\qquad\qquad 5X_1 + 2X_2 \geq 60$
$\qquad\qquad X_1, X_2 \geq 0.$

Transform the primal into the dual. Provide the simplex solution of the dual. From the final dual tableau, construct the final primal tableau.

11

Linear Programming: Sensitivity Analysis

Linear programming can provide a decision maker with a wealth of information to facilitate the better allocation of resources. It can provide much more information than the optimal solution to a formulated linear programming problem. *It can provide virtually all resource allocation information.*

A formulated linear programming problem is a formal statement of a decision environment—a formal statement of the structured relationships that concern resource allocations. In concise cause-effect relationships, a formulated problem expresses the availability of the resources (R_i), the ways the resources can be used (X_j), the resource usage rates (a_{ij}), and the contributions to the objective (C_j) for resource allocations. It contains all relevant information for a resource allocation decision environment[1]—all relevant information for resource allocation decisions.

The simplex procedure and special adjustments of the simplex tableaus can make virtually any information about resource allocations readily available. With minimal computational effort, the final simplex tableau can be adjusted to incorporate any hypothesized change in the structural components of the decision environment. A manager, for example, may want to measure the economic effects of changing the level of output, hiring a worker overtime, adjusting a pricing policy, altering the means for production, or producing a new product. This information can be made readily available. A progressive decision maker can have the information needed to explore the creative potential for initiating change.

---

[1] A decision maker must remember that this decision environment is only an *abstraction* of the much more complex real world. Proper decisions may require adjustments for other important considerations not included in the abstraction.

This chapter will develop several models for obtaining important information from linear programming. It will consider the effect of changing the basic components (parameters) of a formulated linear programming problem.[2] This extension of linear programming is referred to as *optimality analysis*. Further subdivisions are *sensitivity analysis* and *parametric programming*. The former is concerned with discrete parameter changes, the latter with continuous parameter changes.

To illustrate parameter changes, several sensitivity analysis models will be developed on the product mix problem described on page 326:

$$f_{max} = 24X_1 + 32X_2$$
$$\text{subject to: } 2X_1 + 4X_2 \leq 60 \quad \text{resource 1}$$
$$3X_1 + 2X_2 \leq 54 \quad \text{resource 2.}$$

The optimal primal solution is presented in Table 11.1.

$$f_{max} = 24X_1 + 32X_2$$

subject to: $2X_1 + 4X_2 \leq 60 \quad R_1$
$3X_1 + 2X_2 \leq 54 \quad R_2$
$X_1, X_2 \geq 0.$

Optimal Tableau	C_j			24	32	0	0
		Sol. Var.	q_o	X_1	X_2	S_1	S_2
32		X_2	9	0	1	$3/8$	$-1/4$
24		X_1	12	1	0	$-1/4$	$1/2$
		Z_j	576	24	32	6	4
		$C_j - Z_j$		0	0	-6	-4

TABLE 11.1

The Product Mix Problem

CHANGES IN THE CONTRIBUTION COEFFICIENTS

In many situations, a decision maker needs to know the implications of a change in prices, in costs, or, more generally, in the *contributions of the decision variables to the objective*. In linear programming, the influence of contributions is expressed in the C_j coefficients in the objective function. The effect of contribution

---

[2] One approach for determining the effect of parameter changes is to resolve the linear programming problem with the new parameter. Especially when boundary limits must be determined in the context of large problems, resolving an entire linear programming problem is exceedingly inefficient. Special models have been developed to determine this information efficiently.

coefficient changes on the proper use of the resources and profitability can be determined directly from the final simplex tableau.

There are two categories of contribution coefficients—contribution coefficients for solution (basis) variables and contribution coefficients for nonsolution (nonbasis) variables. Change in each of these types of contribution coefficients will be considered separately.

A Change in a Nonbasis Variable Contribution Coefficient

In the product mix problem presented in Table 11.1, the optimal tableau contains two nonbasis variables: S_1 and S_2. They represent the amount of idle time on the respective resources. Both have contribution coefficients of zero. If the resources are idle and there is no other use for them, they will *contribute* nothing to profits.

In the present situation (Table 11.1), both resources are utilized to capacity to produce product 1 and product 2. There is no idle time—S_1 and S_2 are nonbasis variables with solution values of zero. The production manager, however, is confronted with a change in the decision environment. A new product development provides an alternative use for resource 1. Therefore, if resource 1 is not fully utilized for the present production, the idle time can be redirected profitably to the new product. The value of idle time for resource 1 is no longer zero. Furthermore, if the new use of the resource is sufficiently profitable, the resource should be directly allocated to this improved use.

Sensitivity analysis will determine the required profitability of the new usage of resource 1 that will redirect the allocation of the resources. Specifically, it will define the required *worth of* S_1 needed to change the present optimal solution—needed to enter S_1 into the solution.

The present maximization problem remains optimal as long as the $C_j - Z_j$ net economic evaluators remain nonpositive. If a $C_j - Z_j$ becomes positive, the associated variable is entered into the solution. Therefore, S_1 will be an entry variable when the associated $C_j - Z_j$ becomes positive. As indicated in Table 11.2, when an increment δ is added to the C_j for S_1, the net economic evaluator becomes $\delta - 6$. S_1 will enter the solution when:

$$\delta - 6 > 0.$$

The present product mix will change when $\delta > 6$.

The other nonbasis solution variable can be evaluated in the same way. The required change δ to introduce S_2 into the solution must be large enough to make the $C_j - Z_j$ positive. The old evaluator plus the increment must be positive:

$$(C_j - Z_j) + \delta > 0.$$

C_j			24	32	$(0+\delta)$	0
	Sol. Var.	q_0	X_1	X_2	S_1	S_2
32	X_2	9	0	1	$3/8$	$-1/4$
24	X_1	12	1	0	$-1/4$	$1/2$
	Z_j	576	24	32	6	4
	$C_j - Z_j$		0	0	$\delta - 6$	-4

enter S_1 for: $\delta > 6$

TABLE 11.2
Sensitivity of Nonbasis C_j

In terms of the increment:

$$\delta > -(C_j - Z_j).$$

With an evaluator of -4 (Table 11.1), the increment required to enter S_2 is:

$$\delta > -(-4)$$
$$\delta > 4.$$

If the C_j for S_2 is increased by 4 or more, the present product mix will no longer remain optimal

Change in a Basis Variable Contribution Coefficient (C_j)

The sensitivity of the optimal solution to changes in the contribution coefficients of solution (basis) variables is determined in a similar way. The optimal solution will be sensitive to changes that introduce a new variable into the solution. *Specifically, the optimal solution will be sensitive to a change that produces a positive net economic evaluator in a maximization problem or a negative net economic evaluator in a minimization problem.*

To illustrate with the product mix problem (Table 11.1), the producer is contemplating a new pricing strategy for product 1. The net effect is an anticipated increase in product 1's profit contribution by δ. In the tableau, this change increments the C_j for the X_1 *basis variable* by δ. The implications for the optimal tableau are indicated in Table 11.3. The net economic evaluators for both S_1 and S_2 have changed. For a *sufficiently* large δ, the evaluator for S_1 will become positive, indicating the required entry of the variable. Specifically, S_1 will enter

C_j			$24 + \delta$	32	0	0
	Sol. Var.	q_o	X_1	X_2	S_1	S_2
32	X_2	9	0	1	$^3/_8$	$-^1/_4$
$24 + \delta$	X_1	12	1	0	$-^1/_4$	$^1/_2$
	Z_j	576	$24 + \delta$	32	$6 - ^1/_4\delta$	$4 + ^1/_2\delta$
	$C_j - Z_j$		0	0	$-6 + ^1/_2\delta$	$-4 - ^1/_2\delta$

TABLE 11.3
Sensitivity of Basis C_j

the solution when:

$$-6 + 1/4\delta > 0$$

or

$$\delta > 24.$$

Also, for a *sufficiently* negative δ, the S_2 evaluator will become positive and S_2 will be entered into the solution:

$$-4 - 1/2\delta > 0$$

or

$$\delta < -8.$$

The present solution remains *insensitive* within the upper and lower boundaries of:

$$-8 \leq \delta \leq 24.$$

With an initial value of 24, the boundary for the new objective function coefficient becomes:

$$16 \leq C_1 \leq 48.$$

This contribution coefficient can be anywhere within these boundaries without changing the present corner point solution.

A Graphical Development of the Boundaries for Basis Variable Contribution Coefficients

The conceptual aspects of the boundaries for changes in basis variable contribution coefficients are best demonstrated graphically. An important preliminary property of the objective function, however, must first be developed.

The objective function $(f = 24X_1 + 32X_2)$ measures the profitability of different alternatives (X_1, X_2). Graphically for a specified value of f, it is plotted as a single straight line. The worths of alternatives anywhere along this line are all the same. The larger the specified value of f, the further to the right the objective function will be plotted. Also, the larger f is, the higher the profitability for the alternatives along this line. Therefore, the highest graphically constructed objective function (the one with the largest specified value of f) that still contains a feasible alternative isolates the optimal corner point solution.

In Figure 11.1, the highest objective function with a feasible alternative intersects the optimal corner point at $(X_1 = 12, X_2 = 9)$. The specified value of the objective function (f) at this point is \$576. The construction of a higher objective function will not contain any feasible alternatives. The construction of lower objective functions will contain better feasible alternatives to the right.

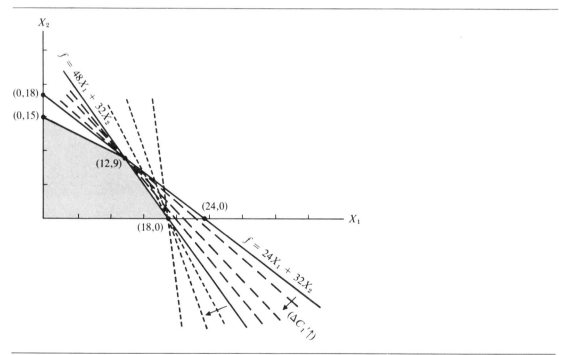

FIGURE 11.1

Shift in Objective Function for Incremental Increases in C_1 Coefficient

With this understanding, the conceptual aspects of the boundaries for the basis variable contribution coefficients will be developed. Figure 11.1 illustrates the graphical effect of a change in C_1 on the optimal solution. With no change in C_1, the objective function ($f = 24X_1 + 32X_2$) passes through the optimal corner point ($X_1 = 12$, $X_2 = 9$; $f = \$576$).

As C_1 is increased (Figure 11.1), new objective functions will be formed. They will pivot around the optimal corner point (12, 9). If the increase in C_1 is not too large, the optimal corner point will remain unchanged with a higher profit.

When C_1 reaches the boundary value of 48, the corresponding objective function line will take the same form as the second constraint equation. The optimal solution will be represented by two corner points: ($X_1 = 12$, $X_2 = 9$) and ($X_1 = 18$, $X_2 = 0$). The optimal solution will be at either of these or at any point on the constraint joining them.

If C_1 is increased beyond the boundary of 48, the corresponding objective function lines will pivot ($X_1 = 18$, $X_2 = 0$). A new optimal corner point will be determined. The present optimal solution is sensitive to C_1 increased beyond the upper boundary of 48.

Figure 11.2 illustrates the lower boundary for C_1. As C_1 is decreased, the corresponding objective function lines pivot around the corner point

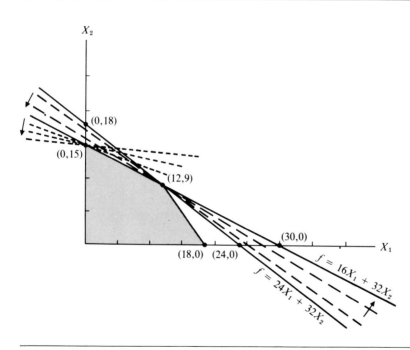

FIGURE 11.2

Shift in Objective Function for Incremental Decreases in C_1 Coefficient

Linear Programming: Sensitivity Analysis

(12, 9). When C_1 falls below the lower boundary of 16, the respective objective functions begin to pivot around a new corner point solution (0,15). For C_1 below the lower boundary of 16, the optimality of the present solution is changed.

A CHANGE IN THE AMOUNT OF A RESOURCE OR A REQUIREMENT

In a simplex solution to a problem, the resource and requirement quantities on the right-hand side of the constraint equations are assumed constant. In many situations, especially in the long run, an organization has control over the supply of labor, materials, equipment, or any other resource. Moreover, it can typically change output requirement restrictions. When there is sufficient incentive, *an organization may want to alter the right-hand side R_i values in the constraint equations.*

The effect on the optimal solution for right-hand-side constraint alterations can be readily measured. Within definable limits, R_i can be changed without altering the principal components of the final tableau. These limits are specified by the requirements to maintain the present solution variables.

If more of a resource is made available, it will be allocated in the best possible way. Since the optimal solution has defined the best way to allocate the previous resources, it will also define the best way to allocate the additional resources. They will be used to produce more of the same proportional output. A continued proportional increase in output, however, cannot be continued indefinitely. As the increased resource increases output, one of the other resources will eventually be depleted. Any further attempt to increase the level of output will be infeasible.

This can be expressed in terms of the present solution variables. As more of a resource is made available, the solution variables will be adjusted by the *proportionality correspondence* between these variables. If this process continues, the proportional changes in the solution variables will eventually force one of the variables to become negative. Since this would violate the nonnegativity constraint, a new variable must be introduced into the solution—the final tableau will be materially changed.

Refer again to the product mix problem in Table 11.1. Sixty hours of resource 1 and 54 hours of resource 2 are available. The quantity of resource 1 will be increased by one hour. This additional hour will then be allocated in the best possible way.

Initially, the additional hour is assigned to idle time for resource 1. The net economic evaluators indicate the economic effect of entering a nonsolution variable. If one unit of S_1 is entered into the solution, the objective function will decrease by $6. The allocation of the additional hour to idle time (S_1) is uneconomical.

Without resolving the entire problem, the one hour of idle time $(S_1 = 1)$ can be used for the production of the solution variables X_1 and X_2. The utilization of idle time for resource 1 to produce the solution mix output is expressed in the a_{ij} column for variable S_1:

Sol. Mix	$S_1\downarrow$
X_2	$3/8$
X_1	$-1/4.$

An additional hour of resource 1 will *increase* X_2 by $3/8$ and *reduce* X_1 by $1/4$. Allocating the additional hour as the first 60 hours were allocated provides a new optimal solution:

	previous	addition	new
$X_2 =$	9	$+ \dfrac{3}{8}$	$= 9\dfrac{3}{8}$
$X_1 =$	12	$- \dfrac{1}{4}$	$= 11\dfrac{3}{4}$
$f_{max} =$	576	$+ \quad 6$	$= 582.$

Allocated according to the optimal solution quantity proportions, an added hour increase in resource 1 will have the following constant effect:

$$X_2\uparrow \quad \frac{3}{8}$$

$$X_1\downarrow \quad \frac{1}{4}$$

$$f_{max}\uparrow \quad \$6.$$

These adjustments, however, are restricted. Product 1 (X_1) can be reduced only to zero. With 12 units of product 1 and a reduction of $1/4$ unit per hour increase in the resource, this type of allocation cannot exceed 48 additional hours. The new solution, with the maximum 48 additional hours of resource 1, would be:

$$X_2 = 9 + \frac{3}{8}(48) = 27$$

$$X_1 = 12 - \frac{1}{4}(48) = 0$$

$$f_{max} = 576 + 6(48) = 864.$$

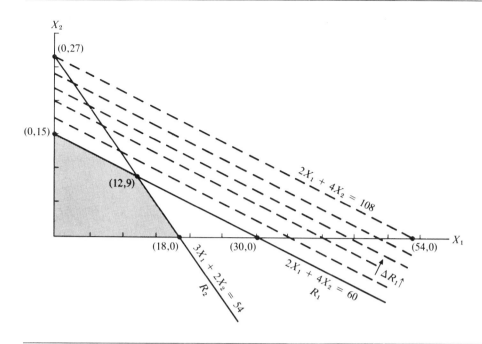

FIGURE 11.3
Increase in Resource 1

Figure 11.3 illustrates the shift in the optimal solution for increases in resource 1. As resource 1 is increased, the constraint associated with resource 1 shifts upwards. The optimal corner point $(12, 9)$ will correspondingly shift along the resource 2 constraint to a new optimal point of intersection. Once resource 1 is available for 108 hours, the optimal solution reaches a new corner point $(0, 27)$. At this point X_1 becomes zero. It is forced from the solution. Any additional amounts of resource 1 will produce a new set of solution variables—a new final tableau.

There is also a lower limit to reductions in resource 1 that can be made without altering the solution mix variables and the body of the optimal tableau. If resource 1 is reduced by one unit, the solution variables will be adjusted in the opposite direction to the previous increase in resource 1:

$$\Delta X_2 \downarrow \qquad \frac{3}{8}$$

$$\Delta X_1 \uparrow \qquad \frac{1}{4}$$

$$f_{max} \downarrow \qquad \$6.$$

As resource 1 is reduced further, X_2 will be depleted to zero. With a present solution of 9 for X_2 and a depletion rate of 3/8, resource 1 can be reduced by 24 hours before altering the solution variables:

$$X_2 = 9 - \frac{3}{8}(24) = 0$$

$$R_1 = 60 - 24$$
$$= 36$$

$$X_1 = 12 + \frac{1}{4}(24) = 18$$

$$f_{max} = 576 - 6(24)$$
$$= 432.$$

Figure 11.4 provides the graphical counterpart to the reduction in resource 1. As resource 1 is reduced, the associated optimal solutions move down the resource 2 constraint. At a reduction of 24 hours (18, 0), any further reduction will force X_2 from the solution mix.

Consequently, resource 1 can be changed within specified boundaries without requiring the development of a new tableau. Only the quantities of the

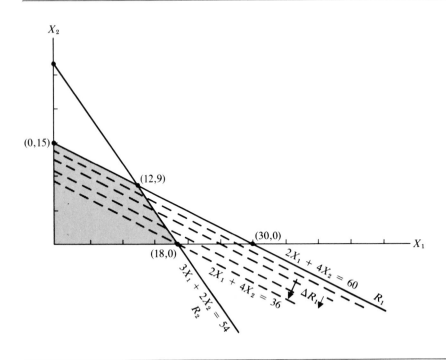

FIGURE 11.4

Reduction in Resource 1

　　　　　　　　　　　　　　　Linear Programming: Sensitivity Analysis

solution mix variables and the value of the objective function require adjustment. The boundaries of change δ are:

$$-24 \leq \delta \leq 48.$$

For resource 1 with 60 initial hours, the resource boundaries are:

$$36 \leq R_1 \leq 108.$$

A mathematical approach will facilitate the construction of boundary limits for larger problems. For the product mix problem, the initial constraint equations with slack variables are:

$$2X_1 + 4X_2 + 1S_1 + 0S_2 = 60 \qquad R_1$$
$$3X_1 + 2X_2 + 0S_1 + 1S_2 = 54 \qquad R_2.$$

The slack variables that form an *identity matrix* serve as initial feasible solution variables:

$$
\begin{array}{cc}
S_1 & S_2
\end{array}
\quad \text{Sol. Mix}
$$
$$
\begin{pmatrix} 1 & 0 \\ 0 & 1 \end{pmatrix} = \begin{pmatrix} 60 \\ 54 \end{pmatrix}
$$

A number of *row operations* were performed on the constraint equations to form the final tableau in a solution format for variables X_1 and X_2 (Table 11.1):

$$
\begin{array}{cc}
X_1 & X_2
\end{array}
\quad \text{Sol. Mix}
$$
$$
\begin{pmatrix} 0 & 1 \\ 1 & 0 \end{pmatrix} = \begin{pmatrix} 9 \\ 12 \end{pmatrix}
$$

These same row operations performed on the slack variable components produced the adjusted form (Table 11.1):[3]

$$
\begin{array}{cc}
& \begin{array}{cc} S_1 & \quad S_2 \end{array}
\end{array}
$$
$$
B^{-1} = \begin{pmatrix} 3/8 & -1/4 \\ -1/4 & 1/2 \end{pmatrix}.
$$

In the conversion of the identity matrix into the adjusted form, the new coefficients summarize the operations performed on the two equations. If these

---

[3] B^{-1} is the inverse of the initial matrix of basis variable coefficients.

same operations are performed on the initial solution quantities, the final solution values will be produced:

$$\begin{pmatrix} 3/8 & -1/4 \\ -1/4 & 1/2 \end{pmatrix} \begin{pmatrix} 60 \\ 54 \end{pmatrix} = \begin{pmatrix} 9 \\ 12 \end{pmatrix}.$$

Performing these coded operations on any column of the initial tableau will provide the counterpart in the final tableau.

The *matrix of coded row operations*, therefore, should allow the determination of the effect on the solution quantities for a change in the resource column. If an increment δ is added to resource 1, the final tableau with proper row operation adjustments will be:

$$\begin{pmatrix} 3/8 & -1/4 \\ -1/4 & 1/2 \end{pmatrix} \begin{pmatrix} 60 + \delta \\ 54 \end{pmatrix} = \begin{pmatrix} 9 + 3/8\,\delta \\ 12 - 1/4\,\delta \end{pmatrix}.$$

Since the present variables will remain in the solution as long as non-negativity is maintained, the requirements for the new solution variables are:

$$9 + \frac{3}{8}\delta \geq 0$$

$$12 - \frac{1}{4}\delta \geq 0.$$

The limits for δ can be calculated. In the first δ statement, a value of -24 or less will violate the requirement. In the second, any δ longer than 48 will change the solution variables. The boundaries of δ for which the final solution is *insensitive* are thus:

$$-24 \leq \delta \leq 48.$$

And in terms of R_1:

$$36 \leq R_1 \leq 108.$$

The boundaries for resource 1 are between 36 and 108.

CHANGES IN THE TECHNICAL COEFFICIENTS OF PRODUCTION

The usage rate of a resource to perform an activity does not always remain constant. Machines may become less productive with age. Workers may become more productive with experience. Management may consider the possibility of purchasing a new machine or the possibility of a training program for workers.

Changes in the *technical coefficients of production* (a_{ij}) may have a considerable impact on profits and on the proper way to allocate resources. The effect of changes in these coefficients can be measured by adjusting the final tableau.

In the product mix problem (Table 11.1), several new components allow resource 1 and resource 2 to produce product 2 more efficiently. While the old process required four hours on resource 1 and two hours on resource 2, the *new process* reduces the times to three hours and one hour respectively. The X_2 *column* has changed from:

$$X_2 \qquad\qquad X_2'$$

$$\binom{4}{2} \quad \text{to} \quad \binom{3}{1}.$$

The improved productivity expressed in the X_2' column needs to be incorporated into the optimal tableau. The constraint equations, however, are not in the original form. A series of row operations has been performed to transform the original equations into a solution format for variables X_1 and X_2. The new X_2' column cannot be inserted without performing an equivalent set of row operations.

As was mentioned in the preceding section, the row operations that convert the initial constraint equations into the final tableau expression are *coded* in B^{-1}:

$$B^{-1} = \begin{pmatrix} 3/8 & -1/4 \\ -1/4 & 1/2 \end{pmatrix}.$$

Initially, the X_2 column was:

$$X_2$$

$$\binom{4}{2}.$$

Performing the adjusting operations on this column:

$$\begin{pmatrix} 3/8 & -1/4 \\ -1/4 & 1/2 \end{pmatrix} \binom{4}{2} = \binom{1}{0}.$$

The initial X_2 column is converted into the X_2 column in the final tableau.

If the same coded operations are performed on the new column, it will be transformed appropriately for the final tableau:

$$\begin{array}{ccc} & X_2 & X_2 \\ B^{-1} & \text{initial} & \text{final} \end{array}$$

$$\begin{pmatrix} 3/8 & -1/4 \\ -1/4 & 1/2 \end{pmatrix} \binom{3}{1} = \binom{7/8}{-1/4}.$$

The final tableau with the new X_2' column is provided in Table 11.4.

	C_j			24	32	0	0
		Sol. Mix	q_o	X_1	X_2'	S_1	S_2
→ X_2: $10^2/_7$	32	X_2	9	0	$^7/_8$	$^3/_8$	$-^1/_4$
X_1: -48	24	X_1	12	1	$-^1/_4$	$-^1/_4$	$^1/_2$
		Z_j	576	24	22	6	4
		$C_j - Z_j$		0	10	-6	-4
					↑		

TABLE 11.4

Changing a Column

The constraint equation rows in the tableau are now properly adjusted to incorporate the new column information. Standard simplex procedures are applied to move from the presently *nonoptimal tableau* ($C_2 - Z_2 = 10$) to the optimal tableau. The new optimal corner point solution is presented in Table 11.5.

C_j			24	32	0	0
	Sol. Var.	q_o	X_1	X_2'	S_1	S_2
32	X_2'	$10^2/_7$	0	1	$^3/_7$	$-^2/_7$
24	X_1	$14^4/_7$	1	0	$-^1/_7$	$^3/_7$
	Z_j	$678^6/_7$	24	32	$10^2/_7$	$1^1/_7$
	$C_j - Z_j$		0	0	$-10^2/_7$	$-1^1/_7$

TABLE 11.5

Adjusting the Tableau to a Corner Point Solution

A graphical illustration will clarify the conceptual aspects of introducing a new column into the final tableau. The new technical coefficients for the X_2 column change both resource constraint equations. Since a_{12} in the first constraint and a_{22} in the second constraint have been reduced, more units of product 2 can be produced with the available resources. As illustrated in Figure 11.5, both constraint equations will be shifted proportionally upward with respect to variable X_2. The new optimal corner point will remain at the intersection of the constraint equations—the same variables will remain in the solution. The new corner point will be moved upward and to the right to an improved position.

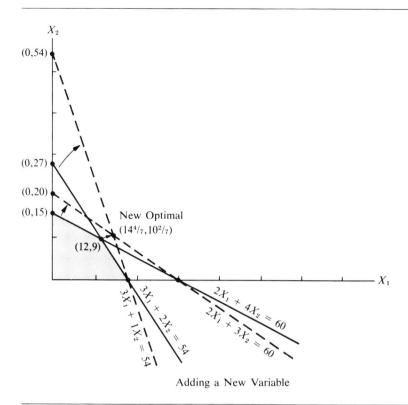

X_2
$(0,54)$
$(0,27)$
$(0,20)$
$(0,15)$
New Optimal
$(14^4/_7, 10^2/_7)$
$(12,9)$
X_1
$3X_1 + 1X_2 = 54$
$3X_1 + 2X_2 = 54$
$2X_1 + 4X_2 = 60$
$2X_1 + 3X_2 = 60$
Adding a New Variable

FIGURE 11.5
Reducing the Technical Coefficients of Production

ADDING A NEW VARIABLE

The usage of the resources do not always remain constant. New products replace old products. New products are added to existing product lines. New ingredients are introduced into blends. The effect of introducing a *new decision variable* (X_j) on the proper allocation of existing resources is often exceedingly important information. This information can be obtained from adjustments of the final tableau.

In the product mix problem (Table 11.1), the introduction of a third product is under consideration. The new product will require one hour on resource 1 and two hours on resource 2. The column of structural coefficients for the new product represented by X_3 will be:

C_3
X_3

$$\begin{pmatrix} 1 \\ 2 \end{pmatrix}.$$

C_j			24	32	C_3	0	0
	Sol. Mix	q_0	X_1	X_2	X_3	S_1	S_2
32	X_2	9	0	1	$-1/8$	$3/8$	$-1/4$
24	X_1	12	1	0	$3/4$	$-1/4$	$1/2$
	Z_j	576	24	32	14	6	4
	$C_j - Z_j$		0	0	$C_3 - 14$	-6	-4

TABLE 11.6

Adding a New Variable

The constraint equations in the optimal tableau have already been adjusted by the row operations coded in:

$$B^{-1} = \begin{pmatrix} 3/8 & -1/4 \\ -1/4 & 1/2 \end{pmatrix}.$$

Applying these same operations on the new column vector (A_{n+1}) will allow the introduction of the adjusted column directly into the optimal tableau. Performing the row operations:

$$B^{-1}A_{n+1} = \begin{pmatrix} 3/8 & -1/4 \\ -1/4 & 1/2 \end{pmatrix} \begin{pmatrix} 1 \\ 2 \end{pmatrix} = \begin{pmatrix} -1/8 \\ 3/4 \end{pmatrix}.$$

The tableau containing the new variables is presented in Table 11.6.

After the new column vector has been adjusted to the requirements of the tableau, the simplex procedure again becomes applicable. Unless X_3 is an entry variable, the present solution will remain optimal. If the net economic evaluator for X_3 is positive, the new variable will be entered:

$$C_j - Z_j > 0.$$

In this case, X_3 will be entered when:

$$C_3 - 14 > 0$$

or

$$C_3 > 14.$$

If the new product contributes more than \$14 per unit, it will be introduced into the solution.

INTRODUCING A NEW CONSTRAINT

In many business situations, the impact of adding or deleting a constraint may require investigation. Rather than resolving the entire problem, *a new constraint can be added directly to the final tableau.*

In the product mix problem (Table 11.1), a special contract requires each product to be processed on an additional machine. To maintain specifications, product 1 requires 1/2 hour on the new machine and product 2, 1 hour. The new resource is available for 20 hours a week. In essence, the initial problem now has a third constraint:

$$\frac{1}{2} X_1 + 1 X_2 \leq 20 \qquad R_3.$$

The new constraint can have several implications for the optimal tableau. First, *the constraint may be redundant—may not restrict the area of feasible alternatives.* In this case, the optimal solution will remain unaffected.

Redundancy is easily identified by substituting the values of the optimal solution directly into the new constraint. Substituting the solution values (Table 11.1) into the constraint:

$$\frac{1}{2}(12) + 1(9) < 20 \qquad R_3$$

$$15 < 20.$$

The new constraint does not alter the alternative space (Figure 11.6). It is redundant and can be left out of the analysis.

The new constraint can also restrict the area of feasible alternatives without altering the optimal solution. This is exemplified by a new constraint of:

$$\frac{1}{2} X_1 + \frac{10}{7} X_2 \leq 20 \qquad R_3.$$

As Figure 11.7 illustrates, the alternative space is reduced and (12, 9) remains optimal. This situation can also be identified by substituting the optimal solution into the constraint equation:

$$\frac{1}{2}(12) + \frac{10}{7}(9) < 20 \qquad R_3$$

$$18\frac{6}{7} < 20.$$

The new constraint is not violated. The present corner point remains feasible and optimal.

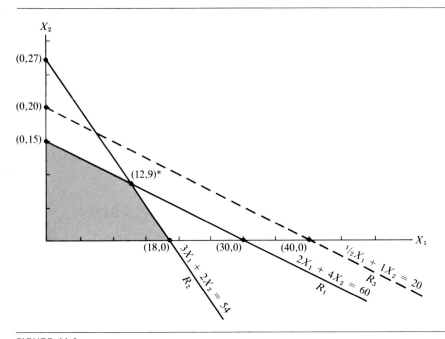

FIGURE 11.6

A Redundant New Constraint

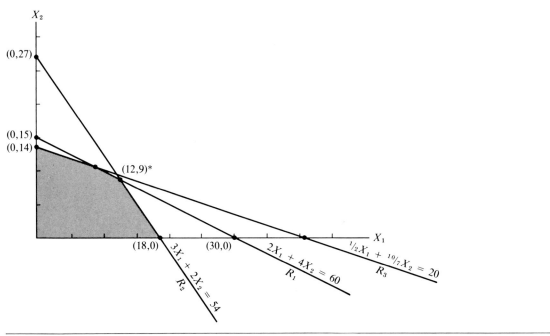

FIGURE 11.7

Reduced Alternative Space: Optimal Corner Point Unchanged

A third possibility occurs when *the new constraint makes the optimal corner point infeasible.* If the new constraint is:

$$\frac{1}{2} X_1 + 2X_2 \leq 20 \qquad R_3,$$

the optimal solution values violate this new requirement.

$$\frac{1}{2} (12) + 2(9) \nleq 20$$

$$24 > 20.$$

The graphical counterpart is provided in Figure 11.8. The new constraint must be introduced into the final tableau and a new optimal tableau produced.

In order to introduce the new constraint, the inequality must be converted to an equality by the addition of a slack variable:

$$\frac{1}{2} X_1 + 2X_2 + 1S_3 = 20 \qquad R_3.$$

Table 11.7 provides the adjusted tableau with the new constraint equation.

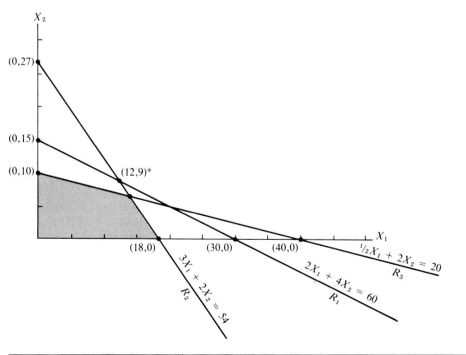

FIGURE 11.8
Reduced Alternative Space: Optimal Corner Point Infeasible

Introducing a New Constraint

C_j			24	32	0	0	0
	Sol. Mix	q_o	X_1	X_2	S_1	S_2	S_3
32	X_2	9	0	1	$3/8$	$-1/4$	0
24	X_1	12	1	0	$-1/4$	$1/2$	0
0	S_3	20	$1/2$	2	0	0	1
	Z_j	576	24	32	6	4	0
	$C_j - Z_j$		0	0	-6	-4	0

TABLE 11.7

Tableau with New Constraint

Simply adding the constraint is not sufficient. Although equation III is in a solution format for variable S_3, equations I and II are no longer properly expressed as solution variables. The structural coefficients (a_{ij}) in equation III, columns 1 and 2, must both be zeros. Row operations are required to transform equation III into an acceptable form.

To maintain the required solution format, the solution variables must contain the elements of an identity matrix:

$$\begin{array}{c} \\ X_2 \\ X_1 \\ S_3 \end{array} \begin{array}{ccc} X_1 & X_2 & S_3 \\ \begin{pmatrix} 0 & 1 & 0 \\ 1 & 0 & 0 \\ 0 & 0 & 1 \end{pmatrix} \end{array}.$$

The present form is:

$$\begin{array}{c} \\ X_2 \\ X_1 \\ S_3 \end{array} \begin{array}{ccc} X_1 & X_2 & S_3 \\ 0 & 1 & 0 \\ 1 & 0 & 0 \\ 1/2 & 2 & 1 \end{array}.$$

The first two elements in the third row must be converted:

$$\begin{array}{ccc} 0 & 1 & 0 \\ 1 & 0 & 0 \\ 1/2 & 2 & 1 \end{array} \begin{array}{c} \text{to} \\ \rightarrow \end{array} \begin{pmatrix} 0 & 1 & 0 \\ 1 & 0 & 0 \\ 0 & 0 & 1 \end{pmatrix}.$$

The following row operations are required: (1) multiply row 2 by one-half and subtract from row 3 and (2) multiply row 1 by two and subtract from row 3.

The result will be the required matrix form:

$$
\begin{array}{c}
\quad\;\; X_1 \;\; X_2 \;\; S_3 \\
\begin{array}{c} X_2 \\ X_1 \\ S_3 \end{array}
\left(
\begin{array}{ccc}
0 & 1 & 0 \\
1 & 0 & 0 \\
0 & 0 & 1
\end{array}
\right).
\end{array}
$$

Once the proper row operations have been discovered, they are applied to the *entire operation* to provide an acceptable new row:

	20	$1/2$	2	0	0	1	R_3
$-1/2 R_2$	$-1/2\,(12$	1	0	$-1/4$	$1/2$	0)	
	14	0	2	$1/8$	$-1/4$	1	R_3
$-2R_1$	$-2\,(\;9$	0	1	$3/8$	$-1/4$	0)	
	-4	0	0	$-5/8$	$1/4$	1	R_3

Table 11.8 represents the new tableau with the adjusted third row constraint.

Since the evaluators are all nonpositive and the solution mix contains a negative solution variable, the tableau is not *primal feasible*. Primal feasibility can be restored by either of two approaches. In the first approach, the third equation is multiplied by -1 and an artificial variable is introduced as a solution variable. The corresponding tableau is presented in Table 11.9. The simplex procedure can now be applied to this primal feasible solution to proceed to the optimal solution.

The second approach avoids the introduction of an artificial component. Since the net economic evaluators are nonpositive, the solution is dual feasible. The *dual simplex algorithm* presented in the Appendix to Chapter 10 can be applied. Refer to Table 11.8, the variable with the largest negative solution

C_j			24	32	0	0	0
	Sol. Mix	q_o	X_1	X_2	S_1	S_2	S_3
32	X_2	9	0	1	$3/8$	$-1/4$	0
24	X_1	12	1	0	$-1/4$	$1/2$	0
0	S_3	-4	0	0	$-5/8$	$1/4$	1
remove	Z_j	576	24	32	6	4	0
	$C_j - Z_j$		0	0	-6	-4	0

$$S_1 : 9\,3/5$$
$$\uparrow$$
$$\text{enter}$$

TABLE 11.8
Tableau with Adjusted Constraint—Infeasible Primal

C_j		Sol. Mix	q_o	24 X_1	32 X_2	0 S_1	0 S_2	0 S_3	$-M$ A_1
X_2: 24	32	X_2	9	0	1	$3/8$	$-1/4$	0	0
X_1: -48	24	X_1	12	1	0	$-1/4$	$1/2$	0	0
A_1: $6\frac{1}{4}$* $\rightarrow$	$-M$	A_1	4	0	0	$5/8$	$-1/4$	-1	1
remove		Z_j	576 $+\,4M$	24	32	$6 - 5/8\,M$	$4 + 1/4\,M$	M	$-M$
		$C_j - Z_j$		0	0	$5/8\,M -6$	$-1/4\,M -4$	$-M$	0

$$\uparrow$$
$$\text{enter}$$

TABLE 11.9

Regaining Primal Feasibility with an Artificial Variable

value will be removed: S_3. Considering only negative a_{ij} structural constraints, the variable with the minimum absolute *dual substitution quantity* is entered: S_1. The solution will be pivoted around row 3, column 3.

The next tableau is optimal and feasible. It is presented in Table 11.10. This is the same final tableau that will eventually be derived from Table 11.9. The new constraint has reduced profits by \$37 4/5 to \$538 1/5.

C_j		Sol. Var.	q_o	24 X_1	32 X_2	0 S_1	0 S_2	0 S_3
32		X_2	$6^3/_5$	0	1	0	$-^1/_{10}$	$^3/_5$
24		X_1	$13^3/_5$	1	0	0	$^2/_5$	$-^2/_5$
0		S_1	$6^2/_5$	0	0	1	$-^2/_5$	$-1^3/_5$
		Z_j	$538^1/_5$	24	32	0	$6^2/_5$	$9^3/_5$
		$C_j - Z_j$		0	0	0	$-6^2/_5$	$-9^3/_5$

TABLE 11.10

The Optimal Tableau

SUMMARY

Sensitivity analysis is an important extension of linear programming. By adjusting the final simplex tableau, any component of a linear programming problem can be changed and the resulting effect on resource allocations and profitability measured. This has profound importance for decision makers. A formulated linear programming problem is a formal statement of the decision environment for the resources. Any component of the decision environment can be changed and the effect on all other components measured.

A decision maker can obtain the information needed to make proper resource allocation decisions. All relevant information is summarized in the final simplex tableau or a minor modification of the final tableau. If this wealth of information is put at a manager's fingertips on a computer typewriter terminal, a manager can instantly obtain the information vital to responsible resource decisions.

Bierman, H., Jr., C. P. Bonini, and W. H. Hausman. *Quantitative Analysis for Business Decisions*. Homewood, Ill.: Richard D. Irwin, 1973.

Boulding, K. E., and W. A. Spivey. *Linear Programming and the Theory of the Firm*. New York: Macmillan Co., 1960.

Charnes, A., and W. W. Cooper. *Management Models and Industrial Applications of Linear Programming*, 2 Vols. New York: John Wiley & Sons, 1961.

Childress, R. L. *Mathematics for Managerial Decisions*. Englewood Cliffs, N.J.: Prentice-Hall, 1974.

Dantzig, G. B. *Linear Programming and Extensions*. Princeton: Princeton University Press, 1963.

Dorfman, R., P. A. Samuelson, and R. M. Solow. *Linear Programming and Economic Analysis*. New York: McGraw-Hill Book Co., 1958.

Gass, S. I. *Linear Programming: Methods and Applications*. New York: McGraw-Hill Book Co., 1969.

Gaver, D. P., and G. L. Thompson. *Programming and Probability Models in Operations Research*. Belmont, Calif.: Wadsworth Publishing Co., 1973.

Hadley, G. *Linear Programming*. Reading, Mass.: Addison-Wesley Publishing Co., 1962.

Hillier, F. S., and G. J. Lieberman. *Introduction to Operations Research*. San Francisco: Holden-Day, 1967.

Kim, C. *Introduction to Linear Programming*. New York: Holt, Rinehart and Winston, 1971.

Levin, R. I., and C. A. Kirkpatrick. *Quantitative Approaches to Management*. New York: McGraw-Hill Book Co., 1975.

Levin, R. I., and R. P. Lamone. *Linear Programming for Management Decisions*. Homewood, Ill.: Richard D. Irwin, 1969.

Loomba, N. P. *Linear Programming, An Introductory Analysis*. New York: McGraw-Hill Book Co., 1964.

Loomba, N. P., and E. Turban. *Applied Programming for Management*. New York: Holt, Rinehart and Winston, 1974.

Riley, V., and S. I. Gass. *Bibliography on Linear Programming and Related Techniques*. Baltimore: Johns Hopkins Press, 1958.

Spivey, W. A., and R. M. Thrall. *Linear Optimization*. New York: Holt, Rinehart and Winston, 1970.

Stockton, R. S. *Introduction to Linear Programming*. Homewood, Ill.: Richard D. Irwin, 1971.

Strum, J. E. *Introduction to Linear Programming*. San Francisco: Holden-Day, 1972.

Thierauf, R. J., and R. C. Klekamp. *Decision Making Through Operations Research*. New York: John Wiley & Sons, 1975.

Wagner, H. M. *Principles of Operations Research with Applications to Managerial Decisions*. Englewood Cliffs, N.J.: Prentice-Hall, 1969.

11.1. This is the optimal tableau for a product mix problem:

C_j			60	40	0	0
	Sol. Var.	q_0	X_1	X_2	S_1	S_2
60	X_1	4	1	0	$1/2$	$-1/2$
40	X_2	12	0	1	$-1/2$	1
	Z_j	720	60	40	10	10
	$C_j - Z_j$		0	0	-10	-10

The first resource is worth \$5 an hour on another project. Therefore, if the C_j associated with S_1 is increased to 5, will the present solution change? If it is increased to 10, what is the optimal solution?

11.2.

C_j			10	12	0	0
	Sol. Var.	q_0	X_1	X_2	S_1	S_2
10	X_1	14	1	0	$-1/3$	$2/3$
12	X_2	14	0	1	$2/3$	$-1/3$
	Z_j	308	10	12	$4^2/3$	$2^2/3$
	$C_j - Z_j$		0	0	$-4^2/3$	$-2^2/3$

Construct a table indicating the upper and lower boundaries for the C_j values within which the present product mix will remain *optimal*.

11.3. An organization allocates resources to those activities contributing the highest profit contribution. Two resources are presently allocated as follows:

C_j			32	40	0	0
	Sol. Var.	q_0	X_1	X_2	S_1	S_2
32	X_1	36	1	0	$-1/2$	1
40	X_2	27	0	1	$3/4$	$-1/2$
	Z_j	2232	32	40	14	12
	$C_j - Z_j$		0	0	-14	-12

Two units of resource 1 can be used for another activity. In order to redirect resource 1 to this activity, how much profit must this activity contribute per unit of the resource used? Within what resource availability boundaries will the foregoing evaluation apply?

11.4. A marketing manager has recommended a new distribution strategy for product 1. If it is effective, the per unit profit contribution should increase by $10. The production manager is concerned about the potential effect of this strategy on the present product mix. More specifically, he would like to know if the two resources involved in production will remain optimally allocated. The present allocation is made with the following optimal tableau:

C_j			80	60	0	0	
	Sol. Var.	q_o	X_1	X_2	S_1	S_2	
80	X_1	30	1	0	$1/4$	$-1/7$	resource 1
60	X_2	10	0	1	$-1/4$	$2/7$	resource 2
	Z_j	3000	80	60	5	$5^5/_7$	
	$C_j - Z_j$		0	0	-5	$-5^5/_7$	

Will the new distribution strategy alter the product mix? How effective would the new strategy have to be to cause a change in the product mix? If the strategy turns out to be more costly than anticipated, how much can the profit contribution decrease before an adjustment is required in the allocation of the resources?

11.5. An allocation of resources problem has the following formulation:

$$f_{max} = 12X_1 + 10X_2$$
subject to:
$$5X_1 + 2X_2 \leq 270$$
$$4X_1 + 4X_2 \leq 240$$
$$2X_1 + 5X_2 \leq 240$$
$$X_1, X_2 \geq 0.$$

The initial tableau is:

C_j			12	10	0	0	0
	Sol. Var.	q_o	X_1	X_2	S_1	S_2	S_3
0	S_1	270	5	2	1	0	0
0	S_2	240	4	4	0	1	0
0	S_3	240	2	5	0	0	1
	Z_j	0	0	0	0	0	0
	$C_j - Z_j$		12	10	0	0	0

The final simplex tableau is:

C_j			12	10	0	0	0
	Sol. Var.	q_o	X_1	X_2	S_1	S_2	S_3
12	X_1		1	0	$1/3$	$-1/6$	0
10	X_2		0	1	$-1/3$	$5/12$	0
0	S_3		0	0	1	$-1^3/_4$	1
	Z_j		12	10	$2/3$	$2^1/_6$	0
	$C_j - Z_j$		0	0	$-2/3$	$-2^1/_6$	0

Find the 3 by 3 matrix of coded row operations. Use this matrix to determine the solution quantities for the three optimal solution variables.

11.6. Two machines are each available for 56 hours weekly for the manufacture of two products. The relevant production information is summarized as follows:

$$f_{max} = 160X_1 + 140X_2$$
$$\text{subject to: } 8X_1 + 4X_2 \leq 56 \quad M_1$$
$$7X_1 + 7X_2 \leq 56 \quad M_2$$
$$X_1, X_2 \geq 0.$$

Solve by the simplex procedure to determine the optimal product mix and the associated profit contribution.

Four additional hours on machine 1 are available. Without resolving, determine the new adjusted final tableau. Find the new optimal product mix and the new profit contribution.

Add four hours directly to the initial machine 1 constraint. Solve by the simplex method. Compare this tableau with the previous adjusted tableau.

If machine 1 is made available for a total of 64 hours, determine the final simplex tableau. What is the gain in profit from the 8 hours of the new resource? Could this value have been determined without adjusting the tableau? Will the addition of 2 more hours have the same proportionate effect on the profit contribution?

11.7. Two resources are utilized to produce two activities. The linear programming formulation is:

$$f_{max} = 50X_1 + 40X_2$$
$$\text{subject to: } 6X_1 + 3X_2 \leq 54 \quad R_1$$
$$4X_1 + 5X_2 \leq 60 \quad R_2$$
$$X_1, X_2 \geq 0.$$

The optimal tableau is:

C_j			50	40	0	0
	Sol. Var.	q_o	X_1	X_2	S_1	S_2
50	X_1	5	1	0	$5/18$	$-1/6$
40	X_2	8	0	1	$-2/9$	$1/3$
	Z_j	570	50	40	5	5
	$C_j - Z_j$		0	0	-5	-5

An improvement in the first resource (R_1) has reduced the resource utilization rate for activity 1 from six to four. From the previous optimal tableau, find the new optimal tableau. Find the new levels of the activities and the associated objective contribution.

11.8. Two resources were initially allocated to two activities as follows:

$$f_{max} = 60X_1 + 60X_2$$
$$\text{subject to: } 4X_1 + 5X_2 \leq 120 \quad R_1$$
$$6X_1 + 3X_2 \leq 108 \quad R_2$$
$$X_1, X_2 \geq 0.$$

The final tableau:

C_j	Sol. Var.	q_o	60 X_1	60 X_2	0 S_1	0 S_2
60	X_2	16	0	1	$1/3$	$-2/9$
60	X_1	10	1	0	$-1/6$	$5/18$
	Z_j	1560	60	60	10	$3^1/3$
	$C_j - Z_j$		0	0	-10	$-3^1/3$

Activity 2 has been replaced by an improved substitute. Instead of contributing $60 and requiring five units of resource 1 and three units of resource 2, the new activity will contribute $80 and require only four units and two units of the respective resources.

Using the initial final tableau, construct the new optimal tableau. Find the new product mix and the new profit contribution. From the new activities, what is the increased per unit worth of each of the resources?

11.9. A company is presently manufacturing two products with three resources. The optimal product mix is represented by:

C_j	Sol. Var.	q_o	20 X_1	16 X_2	0 S_1	0 S_2	0 S_3
20	X_1	50	1	0	$1/3$	0	$-1/6$
0	S_2	90	0	0	1	1	$-1^3/4$
16	X_2	10	0	1	$-1/3$	0	$5/12$
	Z_j	1160	20	16	$4/3$	0	$4^1/6$
	$C_j - Z_j$		0	0	$-4/3$	0	$-4^1/6$

Engineering can design a third product to satisfy Marketing's request for a fuller product line. The resource requirements will be: two units of resource 1, four units of resource 2, and two units of resource 3. The profit contribution is uncertain. If the contribution is $22 per unit, express the new optimal product mix in tableau format.

Determine the lowest possible contribution (C_j) that will allow the product to be a profitable consideration.

11.10. A pharmaceutical company processes pills in lots of 100,000. Each lot must pass through three processing and inspection areas. With X_j representing the number of group j, the linear programming statement is:

$$f_{max} = 1500X_1 + 2200X_2 + 1800X_3 + 1000X_4$$

subject to:
$$1X_1 + 3X_2 + 0X_3 + 1X_4 \leq 80 \qquad \text{area 1}$$
$$2X_1 + 1X_2 + 0X_3 + 0X_4 \leq 60 \qquad \text{area 2}$$
$$0X_1 + 1X_2 + 4X_3 + 1X_4 \leq 60 \qquad \text{area 3}$$
$$X_1, X_2, X_3 \geq 0.$$

Subject to the area requirements, the optimal product mix is:

C_j			1500	2200	1800	1000	0	0	0
	Sol. Var.	q_0	X_1	X_2	X_3	X_4	S_1	S_2	S_3
1000	X_4	50	0	$5/2$	0	1	1	$-1/2$	0
1500	X_1	30	1	$1/2$	0	0	0	$1/2$	0
1800	X_3	2.5	0	$-3/8$	1	0	$-1/4$	$1/8$	$1/4$
	Z_j	99500	1500	2575	1800	1000	550	475	450
	$C_j - Z_j$		0	-375	0	0	-550	-475	-450

The Federal Drug Administration has recently established a new inspection regulation. A fourth area can be constructed to satisfy this regulation:

$$1X_1 + 1X_2 + 1X_3 + 1X_4 \leq 60 \qquad \text{area 4.}$$

Excluding construction and operating costs, what will be the effect of this regulation on the present product mix?

12

The Transportation Model

The allocation of resources is an exceedingly general problem area. Problems in this area can be formulated and solved by the simplex method. This general problem area, however, contains several important specialized allocation of resources problems. One of these is the transportation problem. While it can be solved by the simplex method, several special characteristics allow a more efficient special version of the simplex method—the transportation model.

The transportation problem is concerned with the economic shipping of homogeneous units from supply sources to demand destinations. The objective is to maintain the supply and demand requirements with minimum shipping costs. The transportation problem is as inclusive as those situations that involve allocating costs to equate supply and demand. Problems in this area include: the shipment of products from factories to warehouses; the assignment of workers to jobs; the placement of work orders on machines; the assignment of missiles to targets; the deployment of warships to locations; the allocation of water from Northern California rivers to Southern California cities; and the movement of Long Island commuters to New York City offices.

THE TRANSPORTATION PROBLEM:
A SPECIAL LINEAR PROGRAMMING PROBLEM

A single transportation problem will be used throughout the chapter to illustrate the conceptual and the computational aspects of the transportation model. Three factories supply a standard product to meet the weekly demand requirements of three warehouses. The relevant information is summarized in Table 12.1. The factories can supply 42, 30, and 28 units respectively. The warehouses have respective demands for 35, 40, and 25 units. A unit corresponds to a

Supply (Truckloads)	Factories (Source)		Warehouses (Destination)	Demand (Truckloads)

42   F_1 $80 W_1 35

$90 $100 $90 $110 $110 $100 $120 $90

30   F_2 W_2 40

28   F_3 W_3 25

100   100

TABLE 12.1

A Transportation Problem

truckload of the product. It costs $80 to send one truckload (1 unit) from factory 1 (F_1) to warehouse 1 (W_1); $90 from F_1 to W_2; and $100 from F_1 to W_3. The other costs are specified in Table 12.1. The problem is to satisfy warehouse demands from factory supplies at the lowest transportation cost.

With the decision environment specified in Table 12.1, the transportation problem can be formulated as a linear programming problem. The purpose of the analysis is to determine the number of units to send from F_1 to W_1, F_1 to W_2, ..., F_3 to W_3. These are the *decision variables*. They can be expressed as X_{ij}, with i representing the factory and j the warehouse. For example, the number of units sent from F_1 to W_1 is denoted by X_{11}. In this problem, there are nine decision variables.

The objective function measures the total transportation cost. It has a minimization direction and contains each decision variable and the associated cost contribution coefficients:

$$f_{min} = 8X_{11} + 9X_{12} + 10X_{13} + 9X_{21} + 11X_{22} + 11X_{23} + 10X_{31} + 12X_{32} + 9X_{33}.$$

The *objective* is to *find the best values for the X_{ij} to minimize the total transportation costs.*

The choice of the X_{ij} value, however, is not without restriction. The warehouse demands and the factory supplies impose constraints. Warehouse 1 demands exactly 35 units. Any other number of units will create either an undesirable shortage (underage cost) or an undesirable excess (overage cost from inventory). The units can be supplied from F_1, F_2, or F_3:

$$1X_{11} \quad + \quad 1X_{21} \quad + \quad 1X_{31} \quad = \quad 35 \qquad W_1.$$
$$\text{supply } F_1 \quad \text{supply } F_2 \quad \text{supply } F_3 \quad \text{demand } W_1$$

Similarly, for the other two warehouses:

$$1X_{12} \quad + \quad 1X_{22} \quad + \quad 1X_{32} \quad = \quad 40 \qquad W_2.$$
$$1X_{13} \quad + \quad 1X_{23} \quad + \quad 1X_{33} \quad = \quad 25 \qquad W_3.$$

Factory supplies also restrict the values of the X_{ij}. Factory 1 cannot supply more than the 42 available units. Neither can it supply less than 42 units. The supply from the three factories equals the demand of the three warehouses. If F_1 does not ship all items, one or more of the warehouse demand requirements cannot be met. Therefore, the sum of the goods sent from F_1 must be exactly 42 units. The F_1 constraint is:

$$X_{11} \quad + \quad X_{12} \quad + \quad X_{13} \quad = \quad 42 \qquad F_1.$$
$$\text{demand } W_1 \quad \text{demand } W_2 \quad \text{demand } W_3 \quad \text{total} \\ \text{supply}$$

For the other two factories:

$$1X_{21} \quad + \quad 1X_{22} \quad + \quad 1X_{23} \quad = \quad 30 \qquad F_2$$
$$1X_{31} \quad + \quad 1X_{32} \quad + \quad 1X_{33} \quad = \quad 28 \qquad F_3.$$

A linear programming formulation will also require *nonnegative constraints*. All values of X_{ij} must be greater than or equal to zero:

$$X_{ij} \geq 0.$$

Negative units cannot be shipped.

The *tentative linear programming formulation* of the problem becomes:

$$f_{\min} = 80X_{11} + 90X_{12} + 100X_{13} + 90X_{21} + 110X_{22} + 110X_{23} + 100X_{31} + 120X_{32} + 90X_{33}$$

$$
\begin{array}{lllll}
1X_{11} + & & 1X_{21} + & & 1X_{31} + & & = 35 & W_1 \\
& 1X_{12} + & & 1X_{22} + & & 1X_{32} + & = 40 & W_2 \\
& & 1X_{13} + & & 1X_{23} + & & 1X_{33} = 25 & W_3 \\
1X_{11} + & 1X_{12} + & 1X_{13} & & & & = 42 & F_1 \\
& & & 1X_{21} + & 1X_{22} + & 1X_{23} & = 30 & F_2 \\
& & & & & 1X_{31} + & 1X_{32} + 1X_{33} = 28 & F_3
\end{array}
$$

$$X_{ij} \geq 0 \qquad i = 1, 2, 3; j = 1, 2, 3.$$

Removing a Redundant Constraint

One unique characteristic of this formulation is *redundancy in the structural constraints*. For the entire set of six constraints, the information expressed in one of the constraints is already determined by the others. The constraint is redundant. If there are three factories and three warehouses and the shipments from two factories are known, the shipments from the third factory will be forced, restricted, known values. The value of each *variable* in the third factory constraint is a predetermined *constant*. The third factory constraint will not contain *variables* and therefore must be removed from the analysis.

This characteristic is clarified by Table 12.2. Given the demand and supply requirements, the shipments from F_1 and F_2 determine the shipments from F_3. If F_1 and F_2 supply all 35 units to W_1, F_3 cannot supply any. If F_1 and F_2 supply W_2 with 37 of the required 40 units, F_3 must supply 3 units. And if F_1 and F_2 do not supply any units to W_3, F_3 must supply all 25.

In equation form, the F_3 constraint is:

$$1X_{31} + 1X_{32} + 1X_{33} = 28 \qquad F_3.$$

Given the shipments from F_1 and F_2, the three variables are forced constants. They are *no longer variables*:

$$0 + 3 + 25 = 28 \qquad F_3.$$

The equation must be removed from the analysis.

F_1 and F_2 Shipments

Supply			Demand	Received	Required
42	F_1 — 5 → W_1		35	35	0
30	F_2 — 30 — 37 → W_2		40	37	3
28	F_3	W_3	25	0	25

Required Shipment from F_3

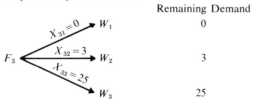

	Remaining Demand
$X_{31} = 0 \to W_1$	0
$X_{32} = 3 \to W_2$	3
$X_{33} = 25 \to W_3$	25

TABLE 12.2
A Forced Solution for One Factory

A similar argument can be made for any single constraint. If the demand received by two of the warehouses is known, the demand received by the third warehouse is also known. Consequently, the third warehouse constraint could be considered a candidate for removal from the analysis.

For the set of formulated constraints, one of the constraints must be removed. An acceptable solution will contain a constraint for each factory (F) and each warehouse (W) minus one. *There will be $F + W - 1$ constraint equations.*

Arbitrarily selecting the F_3 constraint for removal, the formulated problem becomes:

$$f_{min} = 80X_{11} + 90X_{12} + 100X_{13} + 90X_{21} + 110X_{22} + 110X_{23} + 100X_{31} + 120X_{32} + 90X_{33}$$

$$
\begin{array}{llllll}
1X_{11} + & & 1X_{21} + & & 1X_{31} + & & = 35 & W_1 \\
& 1X_{12} + & & 1X_{22} + & & 1X_{32} + & = 40 & W_2 \\
& & 1X_{13} + & & 1X_{23} + & & 1X_{33} = 25 & W_3 \\
1X_{11} + & 1X_{12} + & 1X_{13} & & & & = 42 & F_1 \\
& & & 1X_{21} + & 1X_{22} + & 1X_{23} & = 30 & F_2
\end{array}
$$

$$X_{ij} \geq 0 \quad i = 1, 2, 3; j = 1, 2, 3.$$

The Simplex Tableau

To obtain an initial feasible simplex tableau, *artificial variables* are added to the constraints and the objective function. The cost associated with the artificial variables will again be a large positive quantity M, which will economically force them from the final solution. With artificial variables, the formulated problem becomes:

$$f_{min} = 80X_{11} + 90X_{12} + 100X_{13} + 90X_{21} + 110X_{22} + 110X_{23} + 100X_{31} + 120X_{32} + 90X_{33} + MA_1 + MA_2 + MA_3 + MA_4 + MA_5$$

$$
\begin{array}{llllll}
1X_{11} + & & 1X_{21} + & & 1X_{31} + & & 1A_1 & & = 35 & W_1 \\
& 1X_{12} + & & 1X_{22} + & & 1X_{32} + & & 1A_2 & = 40 & W_2 \\
& & 1X_{13} + & & 1X_{23} + & & 1X_{33} & & 1A_3 & = 25 & W_3 \\
1X_{11} + & 1X_{12} + & 1X_{13} + & & & & & & 1A_4 & = 42 & F_1 \\
& & & 1X_{21} + & 1X_{22} + & 1X_{23} + & & & & 1A_5 = 30 & F_2.
\end{array}
$$

$$X_{ij} \geq 0 \quad i = 1, 2, 3; j = 1, 2, 3.$$
$$A_k \geq 0 \quad k = 1, 2, \ldots, 5.$$

The initial and final simplex tableaus are provided in Tables 12.3 and 12.4. Note the unique character of the initial tableau. *All of the coefficients are zeros or ones.* In fact, every row has 4 ones and 10 zeros. This greatly simplifies the adjustment of one tableau to the next. The row for the new variable is divided by a pivot coefficient of one—it therefore remains unchanged. Most of the other rows have pivot coefficients of zero which produce no adjustment— they remain unchanged. In fact, it is sometimes possible to add a new variable,

The Transportation Model

C_j			80	90	100	90	110	110	100	120	90	M	M	M	M	M
	Sol. Var.	q_0	X_{11}	X_{12}	X_{13}	X_{21}	X_{22}	X_{23}	X_{31}	X_{32}	X_{33}	A_1	A_2	A_3	A_4	A_5
M	A_1	35	1	0	0	1	0	0	1	0	0	1	0	0	0	0
M	A_2	40	0	1	0	0	1	0	0	1	0	0	1	0	0	0
M	A_3	25	0	0	1	0	0	1	0	0	1	0	0	1	0	0
M	A_4	42	1	1	1	0	0	0	0	0	0	0	0	0	1	0
M	A_5	30	0	0	0	1	1	1	0	0	0	0	0	0	0	1
	Z_j	172M	2M	2M	2M	2M	2M	2M	M	M	M	M	M	M	M	M
	$C_j - Z_j$		-2M +80	-2M +90	-2M +100	-2M +90	-2M +110	-2M +110	-M +100	-M +120	-M +90	0	0	0	0	0

TABLE 12.3

The Initial Simplex Tableau

to move from one tableau to the next, without adjusting the coefficients in any of the rows.[1]

From Table 12.4, the final solution is:

$X_{11} = 2$ $X_{21} = 30$ $X_{33} = 25$
$X_{12} = 40$ $X_{31} = 3$ $f_{min} = \$9,010$.

The actual allocation is more easily visualized in Table 12.5.

C_j			80	90	100	90	110	110	100	120	90	M	M	M	M	M
	Sol. Var.	q_0	X_{11}	X_{12}	X_{13}	X_{21}	X_{22}	X_{23}	X_{31}	X_{32}	X_{33}	A_1	A_2	A_3	A_4	A_5
100	X_{31}	3	0	0	-1	0	0	-1	1	1	0	1	1	0	0	0
90	X_{12}	40	0	1	0	0	1	0	0	1	0	0	1	0	0	0
90	X_{33}	25	0	0	1	0	0	1	0	0	1	0	0	1	0	0
80	X_{11}	2	1	0	1	0	-1	0	0	-1	0	0	-1	0	1	0
90	X_{21}	30	0	0	0	1	1	1	0	0	0	0	0	0	0	1
	Z_j	9010	80	90	70	90	100	80	100	110	90	100	110	90	80	90
	$C_j - Z_j$		0	0	30	0	10	30	0	10	0	M -100	M -110	M -90	M -80	M -90

TABLE 12.4

The Final Simplex Tableau

---

[1] Consider X_{31}, X_{32}, X_{33} as entry variables in the initial tableau (Table 12.3).

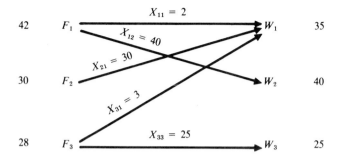

TABLE 12.5
The Lowest-Cost Shipments

THE TRANSPORTATION TABLEAU

The initial feasible simplex tableau in Table 12.3 has three notable characteristics. First, this rather small transportation problem produces a rather large simplex tableau. With three factories sending units to three warehouses, there are 60 coefficients in the body of the tableau. Second, all of these coefficients are either ones or zeros. Most of them are zeros. Third, all of the solution variables are artificial variables. At least five new tableaus are required to move to a potentially optimal corner point.

The size of the tableau produces cumbersomeness in the movement from tableau to improved tableau. The artificial variables require many additional larger tableaus to reach the optimal solution. The ones and zeros provide a means to avoid these difficulties. The artificial variables and *all of the zero coefficients* can be removed from the simplex tableau. All of the relevant information can be restructured in a compact transportation tableau.

Table 12.6 illustrates the more compact transportation tableau. The structural constraints in the simplex tableau are presented without zero coefficient decision variables. For example, the factory 1 constraint in the simplex tableau is:

$$1X_{11} + 1X_{12} + 1X_{13} + 0X_{21} + 0X_{22} + 0X_{23} + 0X_{31} + 0X_{32} + 0X_{33} = 42 \qquad F_1.$$

In the first row of the transportation tableau, this constraint is:

$$1X_{11} + 1X_{12} + 1X_{13} = 42 \qquad F_1.$$

The warehouse 1 simplex constraint is:

$$1X_{11} + 0X_{12} + 0X_{13} + 1X_{21} + 0X_{22} + 0X_{23} + 1X_{31} + 0X_{32} + 0X_{33} = 35 \qquad W_1.$$

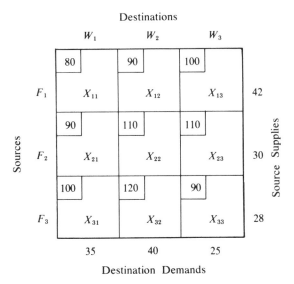

Destinations

TABLE 12.6
The Transportation Tableau

In the first column of the transportation tableau, this constraint is:

$$1X_{11} + 1X_{21} + 1X_{31} = 35 \qquad W_1.$$

The other four constraints have similar correspondence.

The objective function is also housed in the transportation tableau. In the simplex formulation, the objective function is the sum of the decision variables multiplied by their respective contribution coefficients:

$$f = 80X_{11} + 90X_{12} + 100X_{13} + 90X_{21} + 110X_{22}$$
$$+ 110X_{23} + 100X_{31} + 120X_{32} + 90X_{33}.$$

In the transportation tableau, the contribution coefficients are housed in the corner of the decision variable locations. The sum of the decision variables multiplied by their respective contribution coefficients will similarly provide an objective function evaluation.

The transportation tableau contains all of the informational components of the simplex tableau. It is more compact and more amenable to adjustment from tableau to improved tableau. Instead of applying the simplex method on a standard simplex tableau, the transportation problem can be solved by a streamlined version of the simplex method applied to the transportation tableau—the transportation model.

The Transportation Tableau

A Special Simplex Procedure for the Transportation Tableau

The operations performed in the transportation model are directly analogous to those for the simplex method. Both follow the same reasoning. They both start at an initial corner point on a convex polyhedron of feasible alternatives. They both move from corner point to improved adjacent feasible corner point. Improved corner points are determined by evaluating the economic effect of entering a new decision variable into the solution. In both, if a new variable is entered, the constraint equations determine the existing solution variable to be removed. In both, the process of entering a variable and removing another—the process of moving from one corner point to a better adjacent feasible corner point—is repeated until no new variables should be entered. In both, this isolates the optimal solution.

The transportation model follows the simplex method step by step. The specifics of the steps are different. The basic operations are the same. There is one difference between the two methods. The simplex method performs the operations on a simplex tableau. The transportation model performs the same operations on a transportation tableau. The *transportation model is a specially designed simplex method.*

AN INITIAL FEASIBLE CORNER POINT SOLUTION

The transportation model starts at an initial corner point on a convex polyhedron of feasible alternatives. This starting solution must satisfy two requirements. First, it must be *a corner point.* It must be defined in the proper number of solution variables. Second, it must be *feasible.* It must maintain the factory and warehouse constraints.

In the simplex method, a specified number of solution variables define all corner points. This number is equal to the number of structural constraints. The same property holds for the transportation model. Since the transportation problem formulation requires the removal of a redundant constraint (Tables 12.2 and 12.3), *the number of solution variables equals the number of constraints minus one.* For a problem with F factories and W warehouses, all corner point solutions will have $F + W - 1$ solution variables.

The Northwest-Corner Method

Several procedures provide an initial feasible corner point solution. Probably the simplest is the *northwest-corner method.* The factory supplies are allocated in respective order to satisfy the warehouse demands in respective order. The demand for W_1 is satisfied first, followed by the demand for W_2 and finally W_3. The supply sources are respectively F_1, F_2, and F_3.

To maintain corner points and feasibility, the allocations from the factories to the warehouses must be the maximum permissible within the constraints. If less than the maximum quantity is allocated, the starting solution will contain more than the proper number of variables. It will be feasible. However, it will not be a corner point solution. If more than the maximum quantity is allocated, the starting solution will contain negative-valued solution variables. It will violate the constraints. It will not be feasible, nor will it be a corner point solution.

The northwest-corner method is applied to the problem in Table 12.7. W_1 has a demand for 35 and F_1 a potential supply of 42. Subject to both constraints, the maximum allocatable to W_1 will be the smaller quantity, 35. W_1 is satisfied; the second warehouse (W_2) is considered next. F_1 has a remaining supply of 7 units, W_2 has a demand for 40. The maximum allowable will be 7 units. F_1 is now depleted. The next source is used. F_2 can supply 30 units and W_2 has a remaining demand for 33. F_2 will supply W_2 with 30. This depletes F_2 and leaves W_2 with a remaining demand for 3 units. These must come from F_3, which must also supply W_3 with 25 units. The warehouse supplies have been satisfied in respective order from shipments from the factories in respective order. This initial feasible corner point solution meets all of the demand and supply requirements and uses exactly $F + W - 1$ locations. It is an initial feasible corner point solution.

In terms of all of the variables, the first solution is:

$$X_{11} = 35 \quad X_{12} = 7 \quad X_{13} = 0$$
$$X_{21} = 0 \quad X_{22} = 30 \quad X_{23} = 0$$
$$X_{31} = 0 \quad X_{32} = 3 \quad X_{33} = 25$$

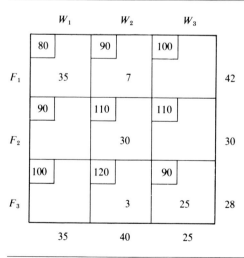

TABLE 12.7

An Initial Feasible Solution: The Northwest-Corner Method

Total Cost = $80(35) + $90(7) + $110(30) + $120(3) + $90(25)
Total Cost = $9,340.

There are $F + W - 1$ solution variables with filled locations. Variables not in the solution are represented by unfilled locations with values of zero.

The Lowest-Cost Method

Another easily applied procedure for obtaining an initial feasible corner point solution is the *lowest cost method*. Allocations are made on the basis of economic desirability. As many units as possible are allocated to the location that has the lowest associated cost. For the remaining locations that can still receive allocations, this procedure is repeated.

The lowest-cost method is applied in Table 12.8. The lowest allocation cost of $80 is associated with location $F_1 W_1$. Subject to the factory and warehouse constraints, the maximum of 35 units are allocated to this location. The next lowest cost of $90 is associated with locations $F_2 W_1$, $F_1 W_2$, and $F_3 W_3$. $F_2 W_1$ is considered first. Since the previous allocation has satisfied W_1 completely, no allocation is possible. In fact, the W_1 column can be removed from further consideration. $F_1 W_2$ is considered next. Seven units can be allocated without violating the constraints. The remaining allocations, in respective order, are 25 units to $F_3 W_3$, 30 units to $F_2 W_2$, and 3 units to $F_3 W_2$. The procedure has satisfied the rim requirements with exactly $F + W - 1$ filled locations. The solution is a feasible corner point.

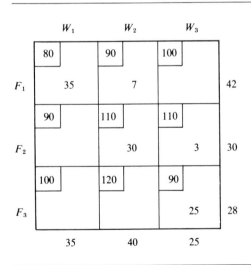

TABLE 12.8
An Initial Feasible Solution: The Lowest-Cost Method

The Transportation Model

In selecting a preferable method for obtaining an initial feasible corner point solution, it is necessary to consider the tradeoff between starting time and solution time.[2] In this problem, the lowest-cost method and the northwest-corner method provide the same starting solution. These solutions are typically not the same. The lowest-cost method tends to require more time than the northwest-corner method. However, it tends to provide a better starting solution —one that requires less solution time.

AN IMPROVED ADJACENT FEASIBLE CORNER POINT

The initial feasible corner point solution contains five solution variables and four nonsolution variables. It contains five filled locations and four empty locations. In order to move to an improved adjacent feasible corner point, nonsolution variable must be entered into the solution and an existing solution variable must be removed.

A nonsolution variable can be entered into the solution by allocating items into the associated empty location. This should be done, however, only when the entry of the nonsolution variable provides an economically improved solution. In the simplex method, the economic effect of an entry variable is measured by the net economic evaluators ($C_j - Z_j$). Analogous measures of the economic effect of an entry variable are available for the transportation tableau.

Three methods for measuring the economic effect of an entry variable will be presented. They are:

(1) the cost-savings method,

(2) the direct-indirect cost method, and

(3) the modified-distribution method.

Although it is computationally inefficient, the cost-savings method provides an easily understood basis for economic evaluation. It establishes the fundamentals for the direct-indirect cost method. In turn, this method provides the background for the most efficient and operationally desirable modified distribution method.

---

[2] Vogel's approximation method and Russell's approximation both tend to provide better initial feasible solutions. They take much more time to provide the starting solution. Especially when applied on smaller problems, the computational effort required of these methods to provide a very good starting solution often outweighs the eventual benefit.

The Cost-Savings Method

There are four empty locations (Table 12.8). There are four nonsolution variables that represent adjacent feasible corner points—four potential entry variables that require an economic evaluation: X_{21}, X_{31}, X_{23}, and X_{13}.

Consider the entry variable X_{21}. Trucks are dispatched from the factories. Therefore, in order to get units into F_2W_1, they must be sent from F_2. Presently, F_2 is sending all of its supply to W_2. It will have to reallocate at least part of the shipments to W_1.

	W_1	W_2	W_3	
F_1	35	7		42
F_2	R	30 − R		30
F_3		3	25	28
	35 + R	40 − R	25	

TABLE 12.9

Allocating Units into F_2W_1: A Violation of Demand Requirements

If R units are reallocated from F_2W_2 to F_2W_1, however, the warehouse demand requirements are not maintained. W_1 will receive a surplus of R units, and W_2 will suffer a deficiency of R units (Table 12.9).

To maintain these requirements, compensating allocations are required from F_1W_1 to F_1W_2. To allocate units into F_2W_1, a set of reallocations is required.

The economic effect of this reallocation is easily measured (Table 12.11). If *one unit* is moved to F_2W_1, there is a cost of $90 for the unit entered in F_2W_1 and a savings of $110 for the unit removed from F_2W_2. Likewise, the reallocation

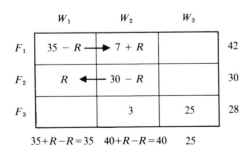

	W_1	W_2	W_3	
F_1	35 − R	7 + R		42
F_2	R	30 − R		30
F_3		3	25	28
	35+R−R=35	40+R−R=40	25	

TABLE 12.10

Reallocating One Unit

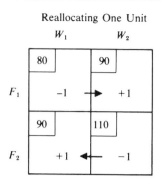

The Economic Effect

	W_1	W_2
F_1	$-80	+$90
F_2	+$90	$-110

TABLE 12.11

The Economic Effect of Reallocating One Unit

from $F_1 W_1$ to $F_1 W_2$ generates a cost of $90 for the unit added to $F_1 W_2$ and a savings of $80 for the unit transferred from $F_1 W_1$. The net economic effect is:

	Cost		Savings
$F_2 W_1$	$ 90	$F_2 W_2$	$110
$F_1 W_2$	90	$F_1 W_1$	80
	$180		$190

The savings exceed the cost by $10.[3] The allocation of units into $F_2 W_1$ is economical. The nonsolution variable X_{21} is associated with an improved adjacent feasible corner point. X_{21} is a desirable entry variable.

Moving to an Improved Adjacent Feasible Corner Point

Units should be allocated into $F_2 W_1$. For every unit reallocated into $F_2 W_1$, the total transportation cost will be reduced by $10. It is desirable to enter as many units of the new variable as possible. According to the supply constraint for F_2, the maximum reallocation from $F_2 W_2$ to $F_2 W_1$ is 30 units. According to the constraint for F_1, the maximum reallocation from $F_1 W_1$ to $F_1 W_2$ is 35 units.

---

[3] The cost minus the savings of $-10 is analogous to a net economic evaluator $(C_j - Z_j)$ of -10 in the corresponding simplex tableau. Since this is a minimization problem, the negative net economic evaluator indicates a desirable entry variable.

The maximum allowable in both directions is the smaller of these amounts:[4]

30* F_2 constraint
35   F_1 constraint.

There is an additional requirement. To be at a corner point, there must be $F + W - 1$ variables in the solution. *If a new variable is added, one of the solution variables must be reduced to zero or removed from the solution.* If 30 units are entered, X_{22} is removed (Table 12.12).

If more than 30 units are entered, X_{22} will become negative, violating the nonnegative constraint. The new solution will be infeasible. If less than 30 units are entered, there will be too many variables in the solution. While the solution will be feasible, it will not represent a corner point.

With the entry of the required 30 units, Table 12.12 illustrates the improved adjacent feasible corner point solution. The values for each variable and the

	W_1	W_2	W_3	
F_1	80 — 5	90 — 37	100 —	42
F_2	90 — 30	110 —	110 —	30
F_3	100 —	120 — 3	90 — 25	28
	35	40	25	

TABLE 12.12
An Improved Adjacent Feasible Corner Point
Solution

---

[4] The maximum reallocatable quantities are the *substitution quantities* in the simplex method. There are two potential *removal variables.* The quantities of the entry variable to force them from the solution are:

X_{22} : 30*
X_{11} : 35.

To maintain the nonnegativity constraints, the solution variable to be removed must have the minimum positive substitution quantity. X_{22} will be removed. Thirty units of the entry variable will be introduced into the solution.

The Transportation Model

total cost are:

$$X_{11} = 5 \qquad X_{12} = 37 \qquad X_{13} = 0$$
$$X_{21} = 30 \qquad X_{22} = 0 \qquad X_{23} = 0$$
$$X_{31} = 0 \qquad X_{32} = 3 \qquad X_{33} = 25$$

$$TC = 80(5) + 90(37) + 90(30) + 120(3) + 90(25) = \$9,040.$$

The total cost has been reduced from \$9,340 to \$9,040, an improvement of \$300.

The Stepping-Stones Procedure

To locate another adjacent feasible corner point, the nonsolution variables are again evaluated. Nonsolution variable X_{31}—empty location F_3W_1—will be evaluated. Since goods flow from the factories, there are two locations from which units could enter F_3W_1. They could be moved from F_3W_2 or from F_3W_3. Each of these has several exploratory sets of reallocations.

If units are entered into F_3W_1 from F_3W_2, there are two possible reallocations (Table 12.13). The second of these is not acceptable. The reallocation maintains the rim requirements. It is *feasible*. Before the reallocation, however, there were two filled locations. After the reallocation there are three. An extra

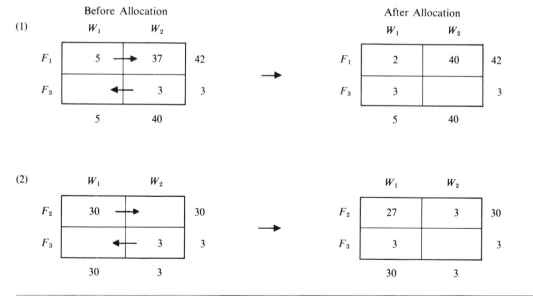

TABLE 12.13
Entering Units into F_3W_1 from F_3W_2

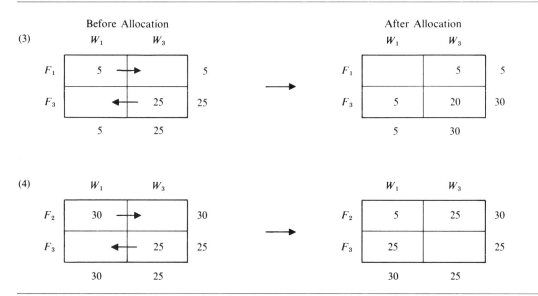

TABLE 12.14
Entering Units into F_3W_1 from F_3W_3

filled location—an extra solution variable—has been introduced. This violates the requirement for $F + W - 1$ solution variables. It is *not a corner point*.

The other two ways to allocate units into F_3W_1 create the same difficulty (Table 12.14). Both start with two filled locations and end up with three. Both introduce an extra solution variable. Both create unacceptable noncorner point solutions.

While there are numerous ways to reallocate units into an empty location, *only one route for reallocation* will maintain (1) the rim requirements and (2) the proper number of solution variables. *Only one route for reallocation* will provide *feasibility* and *a corner point*. Associated with each empty location, there is *only one adjacent feasible corner point*.

To eliminate the search for the only acceptable route for reallocation, the *stepping-stones procedure* has been developed. It consists of the following steps:

1. Start at the location to be evaluated.

2. Move to a filled location. Filled locations are referred to as *stepping stones*.

3. Once at a stepping stone, change direction and move to another stepping stone. It is acceptable to jump either filled or empty locations.

4. Continue to move from stepping stone to stepping stone, returning finally to the location to be evaluated.[5]

5. The stepping stones define the locations involved in the reallocation.

_____
[5] If the initial leaving direction is horizontal, the final returning direction must be vertical, and conversely.

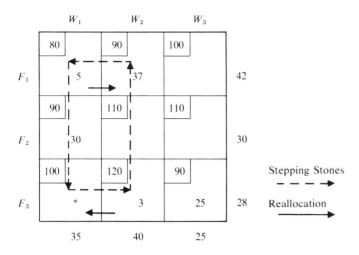

TABLE 12.15
The Stepping-Stones Procedure

The stepping-stones procedure is used to locate the reallocation route for F_3W_1 in Table 12.15. The first step is to move over to the stepping stone F_3W_2. With a change in direction, the move is to stepping stone F_1W_2. With another change in direction, the move is to stepping stone F_1W_1. The final move is back to F_3W_1—the location to be evaluated. The three stepping stones and the location to be evaluated define the single route for reallocation.[6]

The actual reallocation will require moving units into F_3W_1. They will be moved from F_3W_2 to F_3W_1. To maintain the rim requirements, a second move will be made from F_1W_1 to F_1W_2.

With the route for reallocation identified, the economic effect of entering X_{31} into the solution is easily obtained. If one unit is moved from F_3W_2 to F_3W_1, there is a cost of $100 and a savings of $120. If one unit is moved from F_1W_1 to F_1W_2, there is a cost of $90 and a savings of $80. The net economic effect is a savings of $10:

	Cost		Savings
F_3W_1:	$100	F_3W_2:	$120
F_1W_2:	90	F_1W_1:	80
	$190		$200

[6] Since allocations only come from the sources, the reallocation arrows always run horizontally. If the first stepping stone is selected in a horizontal direction, the reallocation arrows will point in the opposite direction to the horizontal stepping-stone arrows. If the first stepping stone is selected in a vertical direction, the reallocation arrows will point in the same direction as the horizontal stepping-stone arrows.

	W_1		W_2		W_3		
	80		90		100		
F_1		2		40			42
	90		110		110		
F_2		30					30
	100		120		90		
F_3		3				25	28
	35		40		25		

TABLE 12.16
An Improved Corner Point Solution

Variable X_{31} represents an improved adjacent feasible corner point. It should be entered into the solution.

Determining the number of units to reallocate is straightforward. The maximum that can be moved one way is three. The maximum that can be moved the other way is five. The maximum that can be moved in both directions is the smaller quantity—three units. Table 12.16 provides the improved adjacent feasible corner point. Since three units are reallocated at a net savings of $10 each, the total cost will be reduced from $9,040 to $9,010.

To continue the search for the optimal solution, each of the potential new entry variables—each of the empty locations—requires an economic evaluation. Using the stepping-stones procedure, the cost-savings evaluations of the empty locations are:

F_2W_2		F_3W_2		F_1W_3		F_2W_3	
C	S	C	S	C	S	C	S
$110	$ 90	$120	$100	$100	$ 90	$110	$ 90
80	90	80	90	100	90	100	90
$190	$180	$200	$190	$200	$180	$210	$180

The cost exceeds the savings in each case. There are no economically desirable entry variables. There are no improved adjacent feasible corner points. The optimal solution is:

$$X_{11} = 2 \qquad X_{12} = 40 \qquad X_{13} = 3$$
$$X_{21} = 30 \qquad X_{22} = 0 \qquad X_{23} = 0$$
$$X_{31} = 3 \qquad X_{32} = 0 \qquad X_{33} = 25$$

$$TC = \$9,010.$$

Note this is the exact minimum-cost solution provided by the simplex method (Table 12.4).

The Direct-Indirect Cost Method

The direct-indirect cost method is a second procedure for measuring the economic effect of entering a nonsolution variable into the solution. It is not quite as logically straightforward as the cost-savings method. It will, however, introduce the terminology and cost concepts needed to understand the modified-distribution method.

Reconsider the northwest-corner initial feasible solution in Table 12.7. The nonsolution variable X_{21} offers a suitable empty location $(F_2 W_1)$ to evaluate. The stepping-stones procedure defines the other locations involved in a reallocation (Table 12.17).

Before location $F_2 W_1$ is evaluated, a *forced allocation concept* will be developed. All of the allocations to locations involved in the reallocation are internally related to the maintenance of the rim requirements. A change in the allocation to one location will *force adjusted allocations* in the others. For example, if 30 units are assigned to $F_2 W_1$, $F_2 W_2$ will be *forced* to 0 to maintain F_2's supply; $F_1 W_2$ will be *forced* to 37 to maintain W_2's demand; and $F_1 W_1$ will be *forced* to 5 to maintain the requirements of W_1 and F_1 (Table 12.18).

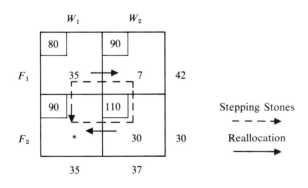

TABLE 12.17
The Reallocation for Location $F_2 W_1$

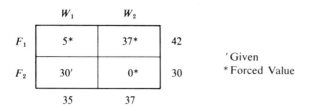

	W_1	W_2	
F_1	5*	37*	42
F_2	30'	0*	30
	35	37	

' Given
* Forced Value

TABLE 12.18
Internally Related Forced Allocations

This concept of forced allocations, with associated forced costs, will be an inherent part of the direct-indirect cost method.

The direct-indirect cost method provides *two alternative* ways in which units can be allocated to the location to be evaluated. First, the location can be filled—*a direct allocation*. Second, the location can be left empty—*an indirect allocation*. The direct allocation has an associated *direct cost*. The indirect allocation has an associated *indirect cost*. The best way to allocate units to the location—the alternative with the lowest cost—is selected.

The alternatives for location F_2W_1 are presented in Table 12.19. The cost comparison is made on a one-unit basis. If F_2W_1 is filled (a direct allocation), the total cost to maintain all rim requirements is $6,720. If F_2W_1 is left empty (an indirect allocation), the total cost is $6,730. The filled location is preferable to the empty location. The *direct allocation* is preferable to the *indirect allocation*. The direct allocation should be used. Units should be allocated into F_2W_1. Variable X_{21} is a desirable entry variable that represents an improved adjacent feasible corner point.

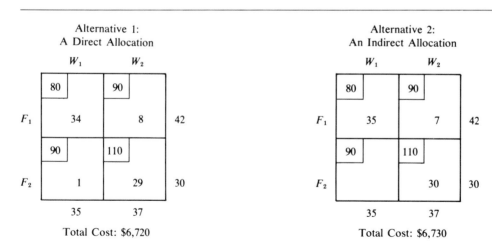

TABLE 12.19
Direct-Indirect Allocations

The Transportation Model

Table 12.20 more clearly illustrates the cost comparison. The direct cost of having one unit in the location is $90. To avoid having this unit in the location entails three *forced* effects: one more unit in $F_1 W_1$; one less unit in $F_1 W_2$; and one more unit in $F_2 W_2$. The net economic effect is: $+\$80 - \$90 + 110 = \$100$. The two alternatives are:

Direct Allocation Direct Cost	Indirect Allocation Indirect Cost
$90*	$100.

A direct allocation is better than an indirect allocation. Units should be allocated into the location. X_{21} is a desirable entry variable.[7]

In the direct-indirect cost comparison, the direct cost is obtained simply, from the location to be evaluated. The indirect cost is not obtained so easily. There is, however, a systematic procedure for determining the indirect cost. Before the costs are considered, the locations involved in the reallocation are determined by the stepping-stones procedure. Each stepping stone will contribute to the indirect cost. Assign a plus to the cost in the first stepping stone; assign a

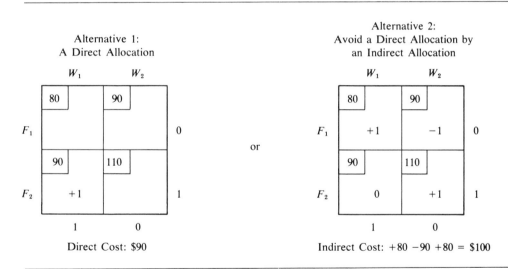

TABLE 12.20

Direct-Indirect Cost Comparison

---

[7] The direct-indirect cost method provides the same information as the cost-savings method. The difference between the direct cost ($90) and the indirect cost ($100) is the same as the difference between the cost ($190) and the savings ($200). They both provide the equivalent of the net economic evaluator $(C_J - Z_J)$ of $-\$10$ for the X_{21} entry variable.

minus to the second; assign alternating signs for all others. The indirect cost is the sum of these costs. Refer to the direct cost and indirect cost in Table 12.20.

More Complex Reallocations

In order to obtain an optimal solution, all nonsolution variables must be evaluable. In some cases, especially in larger problems, the evaluations will include complex routes for reallocation. Consider the evaluation of location F_2W_3 in Table 12.21.

Since allocations come only from the factories, units can enter F_2W_3 only from F_2W_1. If R units are moved from F_2W_1 to F_2W_3, there will be R too many units in W_3 and R too few in W_1 (Table 12.22). The solution will be

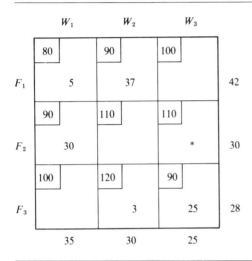

TABLE 12.21
A More Complex Route for Reallocation

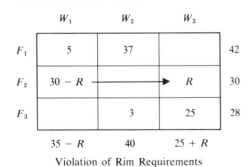

Violation of Rim Requirements

TABLE 12.22
An Infeasible Solution

The Transportation Model

	W_1	W_2	W_3	
F_1	5	37		42
F_2	5		(25)	30
F_3	(25)	3		28
	35	40	25	

TABLE 12.23

A Non–Corner Point Solution

infeasible. If allocations are made from F_3W_3 to F_3W_1 to maintain the warehouse requirements (feasibility), there will be more than $F + W - 1$ filled locations (Table 12.23). The solution will not be a corner point. A more complex route for reallocation must be considered.

The only acceptable reallocation will involve three sets of adjustments. First, to allocate items into F_2W_3, a movement from F_2W_1 to F_2W_3 is required. Then, in order to maintain the rim requirements, there will be two adjusting movements. There will be a movement from F_1W_2 to F_1W_1 to rebalance the W_1 requirement. And there will be a movement from F_3W_3 to F_3W_2 to rebalance the W_2 and W_3 requirements (Table 12.24)

The route for more complex reallocations can be determined easily with the stepping-stones procedure. Refer to Table 12.25. Starting at the location to be evaluated (F_2W_3), a movement is made to a stepping stone (F_2W_1). From here, movements are made to stepping stone (F_1W_1), to stepping stone (F_1W_2), to stepping stone (F_3W_2), to stepping stone (F_3W_3), back to the initial location. These are the locations for the reallocation.[8]

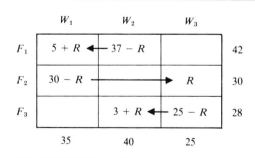

	W_1	W_2	W_3	
F_1	$5 + R$ ←	$37 - R$		42
F_2	$30 - R$ →		R	30
F_3		$3 + R$ ←	$25 - R$	28
	35	40	25	

TABLE 12.24

Allocating R Units to F_2W_3

[8] If the reallocation were made, the new solution variables would be: $X_{11} = 30$; $X_{12} = 12$; $X_{21} = 5$; $X_{23} = 25$; and $X_{32} = 28$. The reallocation, however, is not economical: direct cost: $110; indirect cost: $90 − $80 + $90 − $120 − $90 = $70. Or comparably, the evaluation is: cost: $110 + $80 + $120 = $310; savings: $90 + $90 + $90 = $270.

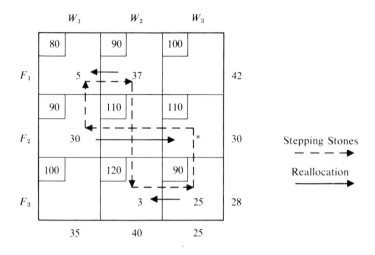

TABLE 12.25
A More Complex Stepping-Stones Route

The larger the problem, the more numerous and more complex the routes for reallocation (Appendix). Even for large problems, the stepping-stones procedure can be used to isolate the single reallocation route for a nonsolution variable from the myriad possibilities.

The Modified-Distribution Method

The modified-distribution method (Modi method) is a third procedure for evaluating the economic desirability of an entry variable. The evaluation is again based on the comparison of direct and indirect costs. The modified-distribution method, however, provides the indirect cost almost by inspection. The significant added efficiency of this method for larger problems is considered in the Appendix.

Consider the feasible corner point solution presented in Table 12.26. The four nonsolution variables have the following cost comparisons:

	DC	IC
F_2W_1	$ 90*	$100
F_3W_1	100*	110
F_1W_3	100	60*
F_2W_3	110	80*

	W_1	W_2	W_3	
F_1	80 · 35	90 · 7	100 ·	42
F_2	90 ·	110 · 30	110 ·	30
F_3	100 ·	120 · 3	90 · 25	28
	35	40	25	

TABLE 12.26

A Feasible Corner Point Solution

Using this cost information, a *cost table* can be developed (Table 12.27). The direct costs are entered for the locations with *direct allocations*. The calculated indirect costs are then entered and circled for the locations with *indirect allocations*.

At this point, three unique relationships become apparent. *First, there is a constant difference between the columns*:

column 1	(W_1)	80	100	110
column 2	(W_2)	90	110	120

$+10$

column 1	(W_1)	80	100	110
column 3	(W_3)	60	80	90

-20

column 2	(W_2)	90	110	120
column 3	(W_3)	60	80	90

-30

	W_1	W_2	W_3
F_1	80	90	(60)
F_2	(100)	110	(80)
F_3	(110)	120	90

TABLE 12.27

A Cost Table

An Improved Adjacent Feasible Corner Point

385

Second, there is a constant cost difference between the rows:

row 1 (F_1) = row 2 (F_2) − 20
row 2 (F_2) = row 3 (F_3) − 10
row 1 (F_1) = row 3 (F_3) − 30

And third, the sum of any two diagonals is equal:

$$F_1W_1 + F_2W_2 = F_1W_2 + F_2W_1$$
$$80 + 110 = 90 + 100$$

$$F_1W_2 + F_2W_3 = F_1W_3 + F_2W_2$$
$$90 + 80 = 60 + 110$$

$$F_1W_1 + F_3W_2 = F_1W_2 + F_3W_2$$
$$80 + 120 = 90 + 110$$

$$\cdots$$

$$F_1W_1 + F_3W_3 = F_1W_3 + F_3W_1$$
$$80 + 90 = 60 + 110.$$

These special relationships[9] allow an easy determination of the *indirect costs* from the readily available *direct-cost* information. The direct costs for the direct allocations (filled locations) are inserted into the *Modi cost table* (Table 12.28). The indirect costs for the empty locations need to be determined. The difference between column 2 and column 1 is $−10. F_2W_2 is $110—$F_2W_1$ must be $100. F_3W_2 is $120—$F_3W_1$ must be $110. The other two indirect

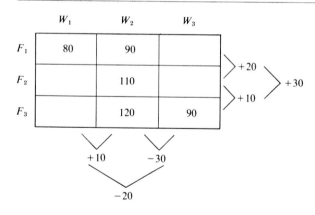

TABLE 12.28

The Direct Costs Relationships

---

[9] A proof of these relationships can be obtained from the dual formulation of the simplex method.

The Transportation Model

	W_1	W_2	W_3
F_1	80	90	(60)
F_2	(100)	110	(80)
F_3	(110)	120	90

TABLE 12.29

The Modi Cost Table

costs are as easily determined.[10] The entire Modi cost table is presented in Table 12.29.

With the indirect costs determined, the direct costs (DC) and the indirect costs (IC) can be compared:

	DC	IC
F_2W_1	$90*	$100
F_3W_1	100*	110
F_1W_3	100	60*
F_2W_2	110	80*.

The lowest-cost means for allocation is preferred. F_2W_1 and F_3W_1 should have direct allocations. F_1W_3 and F_2W_2 should have indirect allocations. Either X_{21} or X_{31} can be used as an entry variable. Either will provide an improved adjacent feasible corner point.

DEGENERACY

Transportation problems have one special difficulty. *Degenerate solutions* occur with *frequency*. A degenerate solution occurs when a corner point is defined in fewer than $F + W - 1$ nonzero solution variables. It produces a difficulty in the evaluation of adjacent feasible corner points.

Degeneracy may occur at any time. Refer to the segment of a larger problem presented in Table 12.30. Units are allocated into $F_{14}W_4$. The segment

---

[10] Once the procedure is clearly understood, the essential cost components can be formed directly in the transportation tableau.

Before Allocation

	W_4	W_9
F_{14}	6	9
		20
F_{17}	8	7
	20	10

After Allocation

	W_4	W_9
F_{14}	6	9
	20	
F_{17}	8	7
		30

TABLE 12.30
Degeneracy

started with three filled locations. After the allocation had been made, the segment has only two filled locations. If the overall problem initially had $F + W - 1$ filled locations, after the allocation, it would contain $F + W - 2$: a degenerate solution.

Degeneracy may also appear in the initial feasible solution. The earlier problem has been modified to allow F_3 to send its entire supply to satisfy W_3's entire demand.[11] The northwest-corner initial feasible solution is provided in Table 12.31. There are four filled locations instead of the required five. The corner point has been defined in fewer than five nonzero variables. The initial feasible corner point solution is degenerate.

A requirement for the obtainment of the optimal solution is the evaluability of all adjacent feasible corner points—the evaluability of all empty locations. Degeneracy produces a difficulty in the obtainment of these required evaluations. Consider the empty location $F_3 W_1$, variable X_{31}, in Table 12.31. An evaluation can be made by any of the three methods: the cost-savings method, the direct-indirect cost method, or the modified distribution method. In applying the first two methods, the relevant cost considerations are derived via the stepping-stones procedure. Starting at location $F_3 W_1$, the first stepping stone is $F_3 W_3$. From here, changing direction, there is no other stepping stone—no place to go. The procedure breaks down: $F_3 W_1$ cannot be evaluated.

If the modified distribution method is attempted, a similar difficulty is encountered (Table 12.32). The relationships among the rows, columns, and diagonals are insufficient to evaluate $F_3 W_1$.

Further inquiry will reveal that $F_3 W_2$, $F_1 W_3$, and $F_2 W_3$ are also un-evaluable. If a location cannot be evaluated, there is no systematic procedure for

---

[11] Degeneracy can also be defined as a solution that has fewer nonzero solution variables than the number of nonredundant constraints. In this problem, F_3 and W_3 both provide constraints. They are both satisfied by the single variable X_{33}.

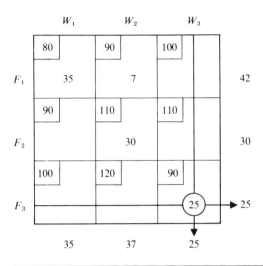

	W_1	W_2	W_3	
F_1	80	90	100	42
	35	7		
F_2	90	110	110	30
		30		
F_3	100	120	90	25
			25	
	35	37	25	

TABLE 12.31

A Degenerate Initial Feasible Corner Point

	W_1	W_2	W_3
F_1	80	90	
F_2	(100)	110	
F_3			90

TABLE 12.32

Insufficient Cost Information

adding a new variable—there is no systematic means of obtaining an optimal solution.

Evaluations will require $F + W - 1$ filled locations. To obtain the needed filled location (the needed stepping stone), some units are added to one of the empty locations. Since the evaluating procedures do not distinguish between the number of units necessary for a filled location, an *exceedingly small quantity* d is added.[12]

If the quantity d is placed in F_3W_2 (Table 12.33), there will be $F + W - 1$ filled locations. There will be enough stepping stones. All empty locations will be evaluable.

---

[12] The symbol d is selected to indicate degeneracy. The literature contains a number of other analogous notations such as a *symbolic unit*, a *zero stone*, or some Greek letter.

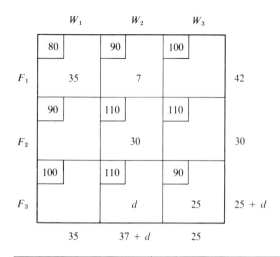

TABLE 12.33
Add a Small Quantity d

Using any of the evaluating procedures, the evaluations are:

	DC	IC
F_2W_1	$ 90*	$100
F_3W_1	100*	110
F_1W_3	100	60*

The evaluation of entry variables—the evaluation of adjacent feasible corner points—can be made. The optimal solution can eventually be obtained.

One additional note: *The* d *cannot be placed in any empty location.* For example, if the *d* is placed in F_2W_1 (Table 12.34). The remaining empty locations still will not be evaluable; degeneracy still will exist.

	W_1	W_2	W_3
F_1	35	7	
F_2	d	30	
F_3			25

TABLE 12.34
An Inappropriately Placed d

The d must be placed where it will remove degeneracy. *Any nonevaluable locations will serve this purpose.* In Table 12.34, the d can be introduced into F_3W_1, F_3W_2, F_2W_3, or F_1W_3. Any of these will allow the entry variable evaluations.

Therefore, *the degeneracy problem can be resolved simply by adding a small quantity* d *to one of the unevaluable empty locations.* In terms of actual truckloads of products to be dispatched, the quantity d represents an immateriality. When the optimal solution has defined the allocations, it is assigned an appropriate value of zero.

UNBALANCED PROBLEMS

In many, if not most, situations, the total supply and the total demand are not equal. The problem is *unbalanced.* The added complications are easily resolved by a minor modification.

Table 12.35 illustrates an unbalanced problem—factory supplies exceed the warehouse demands. The difficulty is the inability to satisfy rim requirements. With a northwest-corner initial feasible solution (Table 12.35), F_3 cannot satisfy the rim requirement of 45.

This difficulty is easily overcome by adding a *dummy* warehouse (W_4) to absorb the excess supply (Table 12.36). The new warehouse locations are

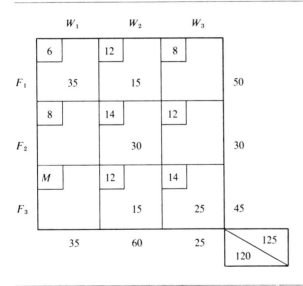

TABLE 12.35

An Unbalanced Problem: Supply Exceeds Demand

	W_1	W_2	W_3	W_4	
F_1	6 35	12 12	8	0	50
F_2	9	14 30	17	0	30
F_3	M	12 15	14 25	0 5	45
	35	60	25	5	125 / 125

TABLE 12.36

Adding a Dummy Facility

	W_1	W_2	W_3	W_4	
F_1	6 35	12 12	8	0	50
F_2	9	14 30	17	0	30
F_3	M	12 15	14 25	0 5	45
	35	60	25	5	125 / 125

TABLE 12.37

The Optimal Tableau

assigned *a cost of zero.*[13] Shipments can never really be made to W_4. There can never really be any costs.

The modified problem can be solved with standard transportation pro-

---

[13] The assigned cost of zero will attract allocations to the dummy warehouse. In the optimal solution, this will determine the most economical supply locations for excesses.

cedures. The optimal solution is provided in Table 12.37.[14] Since W_4 is actually nonexistent, F_3 has a nonshipable excess supply of five units.

Total demand may also exceed total supply. This difficulty can be handled analogously. A dummy factory is added to equate supply and demand. The dummy facility locations will again have zero costs.[15]

SUMMARY

The transportation problem is an important special allocation of resources problem. The problem is the economic transportation of homogenous units from supply sources to demand destinations. The objective is to maintain the supply and demand requirements at the lowest transportation costs.

This special allocation of resources problem allows a special adaption of the simplex method. Instead of being expressed in a simplex tableau, the relevant informational components are expressed more efficiently in a transportation tableau. Instead of applying the regular simplex procedures designed for a simplex tableau, an analogous set of procedures is developed for a transportation tableau. The simplex method and the transportation model follow the same steps. Both start at a corner point on a convex polyhedron of feasible alternatives. Both evaluate the economic desirability of entry variables—the economic desirability of adjacent feasible corner points. Both move from corner point to improved corner point—from tableau to improved tableau—until the optimal allocation has been reached.

In the transportation model, an initial feasible corner point can be obtained by the northwest-corner method or the lowest-cost method. The economic evaluation of improved corner points—of entry variables—can be obtained by combining the stepping-stones procedure with either the cost-savings method or the direct-indirect cost method. They can also be obtained by the modified-distribution method. The reallocations required to move to an improved corner point are made by the stepping-stones procedure.

Two major difficulties are frequently encountered in using the standard transportation model. One difficulty is degeneracy. It causes the breakdown of the procedures for evaluating entry variables. This difficulty can be easily resolved. A small quantity d is introduced into an unevaluable empty location. The other difficulty is an unbalanced supply and demand. This difficulty is also easily resolved. A dummy facility is introduced to absorb the excesses.

---

[14] Shipments from F_3 to W_1 are physically impossible. *An exceedingly high cost M* was assigned to F_3W_1. The entry variable X_{31} will never be economically favorable—units will never enter F_3W_1.

[15] The linear programming counterpart of the unbalanced problem is equivalent to inequalities in the constraint equations. In defining corner points, slack variables are added to convert the inequalities into equalities. These slack variables with zero contribution coefficients correspond to the dummy facility locations.

THE MODIFIED DISTRIBUTION METHOD:
A SIGNIFICANT ADDED EFFICIENCY

In direct- and indirect-cost comparisons for entry variables, the modified distribution method provides a substantially improved computational procedure for determining the indirect costs. The important advantage of the method, however, is the evaluation of entry variables without the closed loop of stepping stones.

The importance of circumventing stepping stones increases substantively for larger problems. Even the seven-by-seven problem in Figure 12A.1 is large enough to indicate the difficulty of forming the closed loop of stepping stones. The evaluation of empty location S_4D_4 will demonstrate this difficulty.

Following the stepping-stones procedure, an initial move is made from S_4D_4 to S_4D_3. Changing direction, a move downward is attempted. There are no stepping stones—a terminus path. The search for a stepping stone continues upward. A move is made to the stepping stone S_2D_3. From here, a move is attempted to the left—no stepping stone; a terminus path. The search continues to the right.

By the time the ninth stepping stone (S_3D_5) has been reached as many as 10 terminus paths could have been discovered. From S_5D_5, all directions are terminus. *This set of stepping stones cannot form a closed loop.* Backtracking to the preceding stepping stone, the search for the closed loop is continued. All new directions are terminus. The preceding stepping stone is then tried.

All the way back to the first stepping stone (S_4D_3), all new directions are terminus. The search has proceeded full cycle. An additional attempt can be made to move to the right—no stepping stone. Now the last possible attempt can be made to the left—a stepping stone. Only after 18 paths have been attempted is the closed loop ($S_4D_4 \rightarrow S_4D_1 \rightarrow S_7D_1 \rightarrow S_7D_4$) discovered. Clearly, the search for the required closed loop can be exceedingly inefficient. For this small problem, 17 terminus paths were attempted. For larger problems, the number may be much larger.

A few inefficient searches may be tolerable. The difficulty, however, is magnified by the number of entry variable evaluations. Each tableau will have entry variable evaluations for each nonsolution variable. In turn, numerous improved tableaus may be required to reach the optimal solution. Even the small problem (Table 12A.1) will require 36 entry variable evaluations in the final tableau alone.

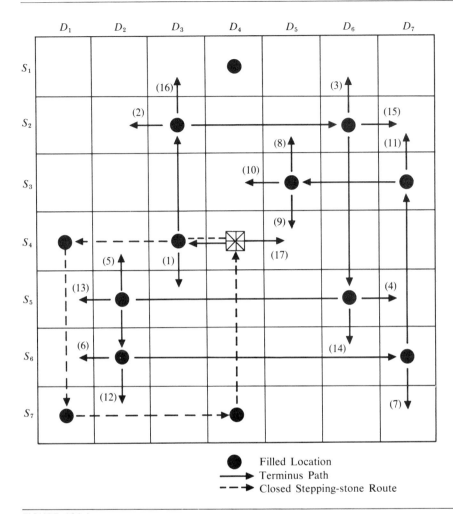

FIGURE 12A.1

The Inefficiency of Forming the Closed Loop of Stepping Stones

The modified distribution method requires the closed loop of stepping stones for only one variable per tableau: the entry variable. An inefficient search for stepping stones is reduced from hundreds or thousands of attempts to only a few.

BIBLIOGRAPHY

Bierman, H., Jr., C. P. Bonini, and W. H. Hausman. *Quantitative Analysis for Business Decisions.* Homewood, Ill.: Richard D. Irwin, 1973.

Boulding, K. E., and W. A. Spivey. *Linear Programming and the Theory of the Firm.* New York: Macmillan Co., 1960.

Charnes, A., and W. W. Cooper. *Management Models and Industrial Applications of Linear Programming*, 2 Vols. New York: John Wiley & Sons, 1961.

Childress, R. L. *Mathematics for Managerial Decisions.* Englewood Cliffs, N.J.: Prentice-Hall, 1974.

Dantzig, G. B. *Linear Programming and Extensions.* Princeton: Princeton University Press, 1963.

Dorfman, R., P. A. Samuelson, and R. M. Solow. *Linear Programming and Economic Analysis.* New York: McGraw-Hill Book Co., 1958.

Gass, S. I. *Linear Programming: Methods and Applications.* New York: McGraw-Hill Book Co., 1969.

Gaver, D. P., and G. L. Thompson. *Programming and Probability Models in Operations Research.* Belmont, Calif.: Wadsworth Publishing Co., 1973.

Hadley, G. *Linear Programming.* Reading, Mass.: Addison-Wesley Publishing Co., 1962.

Hillier, F. S., and G. J. Lieberman. *Introduction to Operations Research.* San Francisco: Holden-Day, 1967.

Kim, C. *Introduction to Linear Programming.* New York: Holt, Rinehart and Winston, 1971.

Levin, R. I., and C. A. Kirkpatrick. *Quantitative Approaches to Management.* New York: McGraw-Hill Book Co., 1975.

Levin, R. I., and R. P. Lamone. *Linear Programming for Management Decisions.* Homewood, Ill.: Richard D. Irwin, 1969.

Loomba, N. P. *Linear Programming, An Introductory Analysis.* New York: McGraw-Hill Book Co., 1964.

Loomba, N. P., and E. Turban. *Applied Programming for Management.* New York: Holt, Rinehart and Winston, 1974.

Riley, V., and S. I. Gass. *Bibliography on Linear Programming and Related Techniques.* Baltimore: Johns Hopkins Press, 1958.

Spivey, W. A., and R. M. Thrall. *Linear Optimization.* New York: Holt, Rinehart and Winston, 1970.

Stockton, R. S. *Introduction to Linear Programming.* Homewood, Ill.: Richard D. Irwin, 1971.

Strum, J. E. *Introduction to Linear Programming.* San Francisco: Holden-Day, 1972.

Thierauf, R. J., and R. C. Klekamp. *Decision Making Through Operations Research.* New York: John Wiley & Sons, 1975.

Wagner, H. M. *Principles of Operations Research with Applications to Managerial Decisions.* Englewood Cliffs, N.J.: Prentice-Hall, 1969.

12.1. Three factories (S_1, S_2, S_3) ship goods to three warehouses (D_1, D_2, D_3). The weekly factory supplies are 50, 40, and 47 units respectively. The respective weekly warehouse demands are 60, 35, and 42 units. The associated transportation costs are:

Joint Cost Table

	S_1	S_2	S_3
D_1	15	10	16
D_2	11	10	11
D_3	13	14	12

Optimally allocate the items from the factories to the warehouses.

12.2. Items are manufactured on three machines (M_1, M_2, M_3) and transported to three assembly locations (L_1, L_2, L_3). The supply, demand, and transportation costs are as follows:

Supply (quantity)

	$M_1(40)$	$M_2(66)$	$M_3(68)$
$L_1(62)$	6	8	7
$L_2(42)$	7	8	9
$L_3(70)$	2	8	8

Form the associated transportation tableau and:

1. Evaluate location $M_3 L_2$ by the cost-savings method and the direct-indirect cost method.
2. Evaluate $M_1 L_3$ by the two preceding methods. If it is economically desirable, make the reallocation.

12.3. Three Western dispatching stations allocate large earth-moving diesel trucks to construction operations. The construction operation demands, truck supplies, and transportation costs are summarized below:

	D_1	D_2	D_3	
J_1	50	100	40	5
J_2	90	70	60	7
J_3	90	80	80	12
	6	10	8	

Start with the lowest-cost method initial feasible solution. Use direct-indirect cost economic evaluators. Optimally allocate the trucks to the construction projects. If there is more than one optimal way, indicate the other possibility.

12.4. The following tableau summarizes the supply, demand, and cost information for three factories (F_1, F_2, F_3) producing goods for three warehouses (W_1, W_2, W_3):

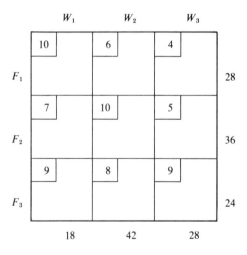

	W_1	W_2	W_3	
F_1	10	6	4	28
F_2	7	10	5	36
F_3	9	8	9	24
	18	42	28	

Starting with a lowest-cost method initial feasible solution, determine the optimal allocation of the goods from the factories (F_i) to the warehouses (W_j).

The Transportation Model

12.5.

Destination

Source	D_1	D_2	D_3	D_4	D_5	
S_1	10	7 (10)	5	5	7 (6)	16
S_2	12	9	8 (10)	10 (12)	9	22
S_3	7 (9)	6	4	8	12	9
S_4	10	8 (8)	5	8 (14)	10	22
S_5	8 (16)	6	4	4	8 (7)	23
	16	18	10	26	13	

Evaluate the economic desirability of location S_3D_3 (variable X_{33}). If this location is desirable, make the appropriate set of reallocations.

12.6. Three grain elevator complexes provide wheat to four large wholesalers as indicated below. The shipping costs are represented by relative values and the shipments are in tons.

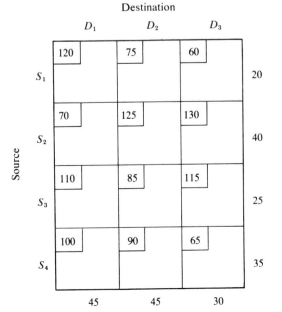

Destination

Source	D_1	D_2	D_3	
S_1	120	75	60	20
S_2	70	125	130	40
S_3	110	85	115	25
S_4	100	90	65	35
	45	45	30	

Determine an initial feasible solution by the lowest-cost method. Calculate the associated total cost.

For comparison, find the northwest-corner starting solution with associated total cost. What are the specific advantages of each method?

12.7. Consider the following transportation problem, in which a factory (F_1) supplies two warehouses (W_1, W_2):

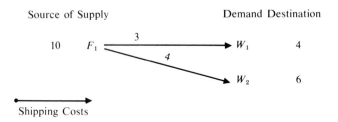

Source of Supply   Demand Destination

Shipping Costs

Formulate as a linear programming problem with one factory and two warehouse constraints. Remove any of the three constraints and solve by the simplex method.

If the redundant constraint is not removed before beginning the simplex procedure, what will happen?

12.8. Truckloads of finished products are shipped from two production facilities (F_i) to three warehouse destinations (W_j). The supply, demand, and shipping costs are summarized as follows:

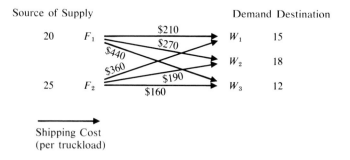

Source of Supply   Demand Destination

Shipping Cost
(per truckload)

Formulate as a solvable linear programming problem. Add the required *additional* variables and provide the initial simplex tableau. Then develop the improved second simplex tableau.

The Transportation Model

12.9. Three factories can supply three warehouses as follows:

	W_1	W_2	W_3	
F_1	4	7	10	30
		18	12	
F_2	8	5	7	25
	10	15		
F_3	8	9	6	20
			20	
	10	33	32	

The transportation model represents a streamlined version of the simplex method for this special category of problems. The analogous simplex representation of the allocation to F_1W_1 is the value of the variable X_{11}. In the present tableau, X_{11} *is not a solution variable* with a value of zero. Using both the cost-savings method and the direct-indirect cost method, determine the economic desirability of allocating units into F_1W_1. What would be the corresponding net economic evaluator $(C_j - Z_j)$ for the entry variable X_{11}? In the transportation model, how many units can be allocated into location F_1W_1? This same information is provided by the substitution quantities in the simplex tableau. What are the corresponding substitution quantities?

12.10. A transportation problem can be represented as follows:

	S_1	S_2	S_3	S_4	
D_1	7	6	6	9	25
		25			
D_2	7	9	6	9	35
		15	20		
D_3	8	9	7	12	32
	18			14	
D_4	9	8	7	8	30
	12		18		
D_5	8	5	4	6	16
				16	
	30	40	38	30	

Evaluate all empty locations (potential entry variables) by the direct-indirect cost method. DO NOT REALLOCATE.

Make the same direct-indirect cost comparisons using the Modi method to facilitate indirect-cost calculations.

12.11.

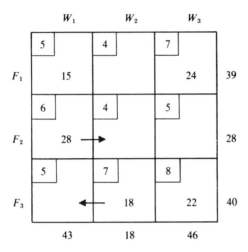

An attempt is commonly made to move units into location F_3W_1 by the route illustrated above. If this reallocation is made, which requirement for an acceptable solution will be violated? What difficulty, if any, will this cause?

12.12. Three factories can supply three warehouses as follows:

	W_1	W_2	W_3	
F_1	7	10	5	50
F_2	6	8	10	50
F_3	9	6	6	70
	60	60	50	

Starting with the lowest-cost initial feasible solution, use the Modi method to determine the optimal allocation. Find the minimum total cost.

The Transportation Model

	W_1	W_2	W_3	
F_1	5	6 4	5 6	10
F_2	8 4	5 8	5	12
F_3	12	6	7 6	6
	4	12	12	

Find the optimal allocation of the items from the factories to the warehouses. Find the minimum total cost.

12.14.

	F_1	F_2	F_3	Demand
R_1	1.40	1.30	1.00	200
R_2	1.20	2.10	1.20	150
R_3	1.60	1.80	1.60	250
R_4	2.10	2.00	1.40	180
Supply	400	300	350	

Three small manufacturers provide products to four large retail outlets. The tableau gives supply, demand, and shipping cost per case. Determine the best allocation of the production facility supply to meet retail outlet demand.

12.15. Three categories of union workers (W_1, W_2, W_3) are available for four types of jobs (J_1, J_2, J_3, J_4). In the first work pool (W_1), there are 34 man days of available time at a rate of $28 for work on J_1 and J_2 and a rate of time-and-a-half for J_3. These workers cannot be used on J_4 projects. In the second work pool (W_2), there are 18 man days available, at rates of $32 a day for J_1 and J_2 and $38 a day for J_3 and J_4. In the third pool (W_3), there are 22 man days available at a rate of $42 a day for any type of job.

The four jobs have respective requirements of 16, 22, 20, and 16 man days. Allocate the workers to minimize total costs.

12.16. Two work groups (W_1, W_2) can be assigned to three projects (P_1, P_2, P_3). The workers are always willing to work overtime at the improved pay scale: W_1 receives 1.5 and W_2 receives 1.3 times normal pay. However, not more than 200 hours of overtime can be scheduled for either group. With the information provided below, allocate the workers to the projects at a minimum total cost.

Project requirements:

Work group availability:

		hours	cost/hr
Project 1	280 hours		
Project 2	460 hours		
Project 3	340 hours		

	hours	cost/hr
Group 1	400	3.00
Group 2	400	4.00

12.17. Joe, Mike, and Guy have been hired and paid to work 32, 40, and 30 hours respectively. During the week, four service locations (J_1, J_2, J_3, J_4) require 25, 30, 35, and 20 hours of respective attendance. Without specialized training, Joe cannot perform J_3, or Mike J_2. If the J_1 location is filled, the associated profit contributions are $10 per hour for Joe and Mike and $12 for Guy. On J_2, Joe can bring in $8 and Guy $10. J_3 will return $8 regardless of the attendant. J_4 will return $7, $6, and $14 for Joe, Mike, and Guy respectively. Allocate the workers to *maximize* profit contributions.

13

Project Planning, Scheduling, and Control: PERT and CPM Network Models

Confronted with the need to plan, schedule, and control the Polaris Weapons System, the Special Projects Office of the U.S. Navy, Lockheed Aircraft Corporation, the consulting firm of Booz-Allen and Hamilton developed a new method to coordinate the development. Developed in 1958–59, the new method was labeled Project Evaluation Research Task. It was soon renamed *Program Evaluation Review Technique* and commonly referred to by the acronym PERT.

The application of PERT on the Polaris project was credited with the successful coordination of 250 prime contractors, over 9,000 subcontractors, numerous agencies, and literally hundreds of thousands of individuals. The Navy Department credited PERT with bringing the Polaris missile submarine to combat readiness two full years ahead of schedule. As a result of its demonstrated success, the government applied PERT to such forthcoming projects as the Air Force's Minuteman, Skybolt, and Dyna-Soar, and the Army's Nike-Zeus. Since then, PERT has spread rapidly throughout the defense and aerospace industry. The marked importance accorded PERT as an effective planning method is clearly reflected in the government's decision (1962) to require PERT on most government sponsored research and development contracts.[1]

At about the same time as the Navy was developing PERT, the Du Pont Company (1957) was independently developing a similar planning tool for

---

[1] Office of the Secretary of Defense and the National Aeronautics and Space Administration, *DOD and NASA Guide*, *PERT Cost Systems Design* (Washington, D.C.: U.S. Government Printing Office, June 1962).

the construction of a chemical plant. The model has come to be known as the Critical Path Method (CPM).[2] CPM has widespread industrial application with major concentration in the construction industry.

PERT and CPM are conceptually similar. They both provide a network of sequence information with a *critical path*. As initially developed, they differ in emphasis. Because it was intended for application to research and development projects, the original PERT focused on incorporating uncertainties into completion time estimates. On the other hand, CPM was intended for industrial projects in which time estimates could be made with reasonable certainty. The emphasis was placed on tradeoffs between completion time and project costs. The objective was to optimize the total cost of the project.

Since the introduction of PERT and CPM, a number of variations and extensions have evolved. Many of the new forms combine the features of both methods (*e.g.*, PERT/Cost). The distinguishing aspects of the original models have been so obscured that the distinction has all but disappeared in practice. The term PERT presently denotes any network scheduling model featuring a *critical path*.

PERT and CPM network models are fundamentally *methods of project management*. They facilitate the basic functions of *planning*, *scheduling*, and *control*. *The planning phase* separates an entire project into a well-defined list of associated jobs. Each job is further specified by clearly defined requirements for materials, manpower, and equipment. These are accompanied by associated estimates of time and cost. *The scheduling phase* is concerned with arranging the well-defined jobs into a time sequence of performance. *The control phase* focuses on a review, analysis, and adaptive correction for differences between scheduled and actual performance.

PERT and CPM provide management with a clear definition of time, cost, and resource requirements; an operational network that relates all activities in a time dimension; and a method for pinpointing critical and subcritical activities. They provide management with a tool to isolate and minimize potential trouble areas—a tool to reduce bottlenecks, interruptions, conflicts, and delays. They provide a systematic means for better coordinating and synchronizing of the component parts of a large project. By relating individual efforts to total project requirements, they facilitate communication, coordination, and cooperation of diverse project team efforts. By their reporting of favorable and unfavorable developments, PERT and CPM keep management informed as to where they are and where they need to be. They facilitate a smoothly coordinated, on-time completion of often vastly complex, one-time projects.

The application of these networking models has been extensive. It includes such diverse areas as: the development and distribution of a new product; the construction of a building, a computer, an aircraft, a missile, or a highway;

---

[2] The essentials of CPM were first published in 1959: James E. Kelly and Morgan R. Walker, *Critical Path Planning and Scheduling*, 1959 Proceedings of the Eastern Joint Computer Conference.

the maintenance and repair of a ship, a plant, or a weapons system; the timing of important activities in a merger; the installation of a computer system; or planning the economy of an underdeveloped nation.

FUNDAMENTAL CONCEPTS OF NETWORK MODELS

PERT and CPM have similar frameworks. They both start with a planning stage. The project is separated into specified work components. Each individual segment of the project is clearly defined to allow a precise identification of *activities and events. An activity is defined in terms of the time and resources required to complete a specified event. An event is the completion of a definable segment of the project.*

Once the project has been separated into these basic elements, the *activities* and *events* are structured sequentially to form *an operational network* diagrammatically depicting the flow of work. The operational network specifies each activity (job) required to complete an event (finished segment) and the required order of completion. Implicit in the definition of an activity is an estimated completion time. The operational network will contain these time estimates and subsequently provide a time dimension to all components of the project.

After the operational network has been developed, the *critical path* and subcritical *slack paths* are identified. *The critical path represents the longest set of adjoining activities in the project.* Any delay along this path will cause a similar delay in the completion of the project. *The slack paths indicate the activities that allow delays without lengthening the duration of the project.* They represent a potential for rescheduling resources from noncritical activities to critical activities to reduce the project completion time.

THE OPERATIONAL NETWORK

The operational network focuses on scheduling. It identifies each activity in terms of a formal sequence. It determines which activities can be started when, and which must be completed before others can be started.

The network is formed by representing the activities and associated events in their order of occurrence. The *starting event* is represented by a numbered circle (①). Subsequent events are numbered serially according to completion time and joined to *successor events* by arrowed lines. The activities are denoted by the lines joining two events. The arrowed line between event 2 and event 3 represents activity 2–3.

Predecessor Events	Successor Events	Time Estimate (weeks)
1	2	3
1	3	5
2	4	5
3	4	6
3	5	3
4	5	7
4	6	3
4	7	5
6	7	0
5	8	4
7	8	2

TABLE 13.1

Network Components

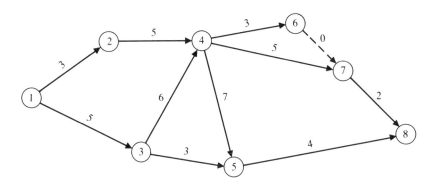

FIGURE 13.1

The Operational Network

The project presented in Table 13.1 will demonstrate the construction of a network. The events are already in proper sequence. Beginning with the starting event, *predecessor* and *successor events* are joined by arrowed lines representing activities. The *terminal event* completes the network (Figure 13.1). The expected times for the activities are inserted midway along the activity arrows. Once constructed, the operational network graphically represents the interrelationship and flow of the major components of the project.

Note, activity 6–7 is represented by a broken arrow with zero duration (Figure 13.1). In this case, two activities are required for the completion of event 7:

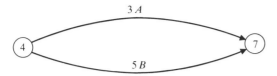

Since activities are defined in terms of adjoining events, both activities would be designated as A_{4-7}. Therefore, to maintain internal logic and to define each individual activity, a dummy activity with zero duration is introduced:

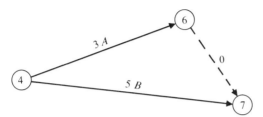

A_{6-7} prevents any confusion in identification.

A dummy activity can serve a second purpose. If two sequentially independent jobs require the same resource, a dummy activity will guarantee that both jobs are not attempting to use the same resource at the same time:

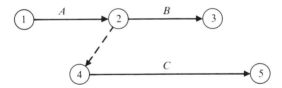

The zero time dummy activity 2–4 guarantees that activity C will not begin until activity A has relinquished the critical resource.

A dummy activity is also used when one activity depends only partially on another. For example, activity C must be preceded by activities A and B:

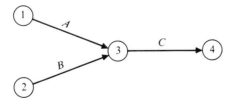

However, a more detailed analysis reveals that C depends only partially on the completion of A. Activity C can begin before A is entirely completed. To allow C to start earlier, A can be separated into two segments: A_1, which must be completed before C can begin, and A_2, which has no effect on C. The dummy activity D enables the network to express fully the appropriate requirements:

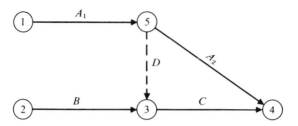

THE CRITICAL PATH

After the construction of the operational network, the next objective is the determination of the critical path. The critical path is the longest route through the network. The sum of the activity times along this path is longer than the sum of any others. *The length of the critical path, therefore, will represent the earliest project completion time.* Any increase in the duration of an activity on this path will result in a similar increase in the duration of the project. The activity times along the critical path are *critical* to the project completion time.

The critical path may be readily identified by applying the basic *model for decision making*:

1. Define and list the alternatives.

2. Evaluate them.

3. Select the best.

The alternatives are the routes through the network. The measure of evaluation is the total time for the route. The criterion for *best* is maximum time.

For the example illustrated in Figure 13.1, the alternative routes are listed in Table 13.2. The longest path, the critical path, is 1–3–4–5–8, which takes 22 weeks.

Listing all possibilities and selecting the longest is conceptually straightforward. As the size of the project increases, however, the number of alternative routes increases more than proportionally. As can be seen from Figure 13.2 and 13.3, the addition of event E to the network increases the number of alternative paths from 7 to 17—a substantial change. In large projects, the addition of a single event may contribute thousands of new alternative routes through the network. For even a moderate-sized project, the enumeration

Project Planning, Scheduling, and Control: PERT and CPM Network Models

Route	Time (weeks)	Total Time	
1-2-4-6-7-8	3+5+3+0+2	13	
1-2-4-7-8	3+5+5+2	15	
1-2-4-5-8	3+5+7+4	19	Critical
1-3-4-5-8	5+6+7+4	22*	Path
1-3-5-8	5+3+4	12	
1-3-4-7-8	5+6+5+2	18	
1-3-4-6-7-8	5+6+3+0+2	16	

TABLE 13.2

Alternative Paths Through the Network

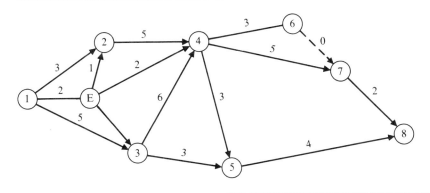

FIGURE 13.2

The Addition of Event E

technique breaks down. A procedure is required to restrict the alternatives to a measurable number.

A model has been developed to locate the critical path. In a *forward pass* through the network, the *earliest completion time* (T_E) is calculated for each event. *The T_E for the terminal event will indicate the earliest completion time for the project.* The earliest completion time is then set equal[3] to the latest completion time (T_L) for the terminal event. In a *backward pass* through the network, the *latest completion time* (T_L) is calculated for each event. *The T_L is the latest time an event can be completed to complete the project in the earliest time. The critical path is identified by the events with the same earliest and latest times: $T_E = T_L$.*

---

[3] If T_L is set greater than T_E, there will be a potential for slippage on all routes. If T_L is set less than T_E, the project will be behind schedule on the starting date. In terms of concepts to be clarified shortly, these two possibilities represent, respectively, *positive* and *negative* slack on the critical path.

The Critical Path

Route	Time (weeks)	Total Time	
1-2-4-6-7-8	3+5+3+0+2	13	
1-2-4-7-8	3+5+5+2	15	
1-2-4-5-8	3+5+7+4	19	Critical
1-3-4-5-8	5+6+7+4	22*	Path
1-3-5-8	5+3+4	12	
1-3-4-7-8	5+6+5+2	18	
1-3-4-6-7-8	5+6+3+0+2	16	
Addendum for event E			
1-E-2-4-6-7-8	2+1+5+3+0+2	13	
1-E-2-4-7-8	2+1+5+5+2	15	
1-E-2-4-5-8	2+1+5+7+4	19	
1-E-4-6-7-8	2+2+3+0+2	9	
1-E-4-7-8	2+2+5+2	11	
1-E-4-5-8	2+2+7+4	15	
1-E-3-4-6-7-8	2+2+6+3+0+2	15	
1-E-3-4-7-8	2+2+6+5+2	17	
1-E-3-4-5-8	2+2+6+7+4	21	
1-E-3-5-8	2+2+3+4	11	

TABLE 13.3

The Alternative Paths Through the Adjusted Network

The latest time the event has to be completed is equal to the earliest time the event can be completed. There is no leeway. Any slippage along the critical path will mean slippage for the entire project.

Earliest Times: T_E

For the project in Figure 13.1, the earliest times are presented in Figure 13.3. The starting event is assigned an earliest time of zero. Activity 1–2 requires 3 weeks for completion, providing a T_E of 3 for event 2. Similarly, the T_E for event 3 is 5. Event 4 (E_4) has two predecessors requiring the completion of both activity 2–4 and activity 3–4 (A_{2-4} and A_{3-4}). The earliest time the A_{2-4} part can be completed is 8 weeks:

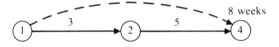

Project Planning, Scheduling, and Control: PERT and CPM Network Models

The earliest time the A_{3-4} part can be completed is 11 weeks:

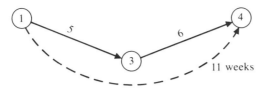

The earliest time both A_{2-4} and A_{3-4} can be completed is 11 weeks—the longer of the two component times.

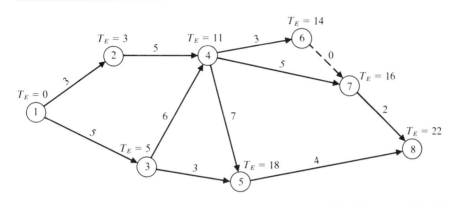

FIGURE 13.3
Earliest Times: T_E

There is a simple rule for calculating the earliest time for an event with more than one predecessor. Calculate the earliest time for each adjoining activity and select the longest. For example, event 5 has two predecessors: event 3 and event 4. To move from E_3, 5 weeks are required to get to E_3 and 3 more weeks to accomplish A_{3-5}—a total of 8 weeks. Similarly, to move from E_4, 11 weeks are required to get to E_4 and 7 weeks to accomplish A_{4-5}—a total of 18 weeks. Event 5 requires both activities. The earliest time for A_{3-5} is 8 weeks; for A_{4-5}, 18 weeks. The earliest time for both will be the *longest time*—18 weeks.

To conclude the forward pass T_E computations (Figure 13.3): the earliest completion time for the terminal event is 22 weeks. The longest path through the network and the shortest project duration is 22 weeks.

Latest Times: T_L

Following a similar logic, the latest time calculations begin with the terminal event and proceed back through the network. The latest times (T_L) represent the latest time the events can be completed to allow the earliest project

The Critical Path

completion time. The T_L for the terminal event is set equal to the earliest completion time. In this case, T_L for event 8 is set equal to 22 weeks.

The latest time event 7 can be completed to allow a project completion in 22 weeks is $T_L = 20$. Since activity 7–8 requires 2 weeks, E_7 cannot be completed later than 20 weeks to allow the 22-week project completion. The latest time for even 5 is similarly derived: $T_L = 22 - 4 = 18$.

The latest time for E_4, with three successors, requires a more thorough consideration:

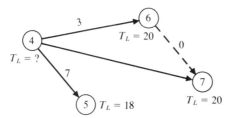

Event 6 must be completed by the end of the 20th week, and activity 4–6 requires 3 weeks. For the path connecting E_4 and E_6, E_4 must be completed by the end of the 17th week to allow E_6 by the end of the 20th week. Similarly, for the path connecting E_4 and E_7, the T_L for E_4 equals 15. For the path connecting E_4 and E_5, the T_L for E_4 equals 11. To assure the required completion time of all three successors, the latest time for E_4 must be the smallest of these values:

$E_6–E_4$	17 weeks
$E_7–E_4$	15 weeks
$E_5–E_4$	11 weeks*

If E_4 is completed in 11 weeks, all three connecting paths can meet the earliest project completion time. If the completion of E_4 exceeds 11 weeks, one or more of the connecting paths will be extended beyond the 22-week limit. For example, if E_4 is completed in 17 weeks, the earliest project completion time will be extended to 28 weeks:

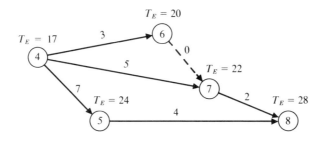

There is a simple rule for calculating the latest time for an event with more than one immediate successor: Subtract the associated activity times from the

Project Planning, Scheduling, and Control: PERT and CPM Network Models

successor events and select the smallest total. For example, in calculating the T_L for E_3:

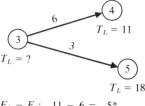

$$E_4 - E_3: \quad 11 - 6 = \quad 5*$$
$$E_5 - E_3: \quad 18 - 3 = \quad 15$$

E_3 must be completed by the end of the fifth week.

The calculation of T_L for E_2 and E_1 concludes the backward pass through the network. The complete set of T_L computations is provided in Figure 13.4.

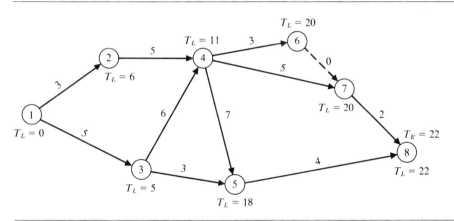

FIGURE 13.4

Latest Times: T_L

The Critical Path: $T_E = T_L$

Once the earliest and latest times are presented on the operational network (Figure 13.5), the critical path is identified by the events with equal earliest and latest times ($T_E = T_L$). As Figure 13.5 illustrates, events 1, 3, 4, 5, and 8 have equal earliest and latest times. Joining these with a double-shaded arrow identifies the critical path: $1 \to 3 \to 4 \to 5 \to 8$. If the estimated times along the critical path are maintained, the project can be completed in the earliest completion time of 22 weeks. If a delay occurs for any activity along the critical path, the total project will be correspondingly delayed. Moreover, if the duration of an activity on the critical path can be shortened, the total project can be shortened correspondingly.

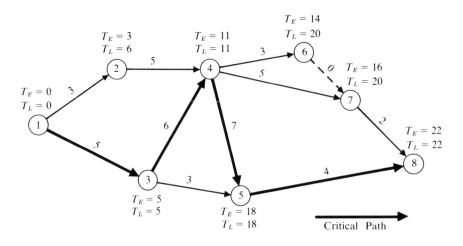

FIGURE 13.5

The Critical Path

SLACK PATHS

An important counterpart to the critical path is the *slack paths* and their associated *slack times*. The slack paths have some flexibility in completion time. The slack time quantifies the allowable *slippage, float, slack,* or *delay*. The activities on the slack path can be delayed by as much as the slack time without delaying the duration of the project.

The activities on the critical path have no allowable delay and therefore contain zero slack time. All other activities contain measurable slack. The slack paths and accompanying slack times can be determined from the operational network (Figure 13.5). The slack for activity 3–5, for example, can be measured in several ways. Probably the simplest approach is to *compare the activity time with the associated critical path activity times:*

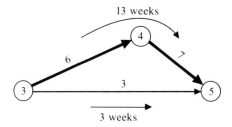

To move from E_3 to E_5 on the critical path requires 13 weeks. To move from E_3 to E_5 via A_{3-5} requires only 3 weeks:

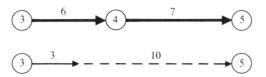

A_{3-5} can slip for 10 weeks without affecting the completion time of E_5 and ultimately the duration of the project. A_{3-5} has a slack of 10 weeks.

A second approach is to *use the T_E and T_L calculations:*

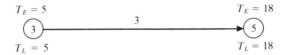

The earliest time A_{3-5} can be started is 5 weeks. The activity requires 3 weeks. Therefore, the A_{3-5} component of E_5 can be completed in 8 weeks. Considering the other requirement on E_5, the latest time required for completion is 18 weeks. A_{3-5} has an allowable slack of 10 weeks.

Activities 1–2 and 2–4 have a *combined total slack* of 3 weeks. To move from E_1 to E_4 on the critical path requires 11 weeks. To move from E_1 to E_2 to E_4 requires only 8 weeks:

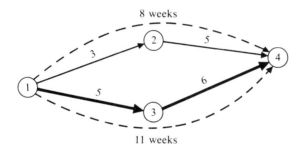

The path 1–2–4 has a slack of 3 weeks.

In terms of the other procedure, the allowable slack for A_{1-2} is three weeks:

$T_E = 0$

1 ——— 3 ———→ 2

$T_L = 6$

$$\text{Slack } (S) = T_{L2} - (T_{E1} + A_{1-2})$$
$$S = 6 - (0 + 3)$$
$$S = 3 \ .$$

E_2 can be completed by the end of the third week $(T_{E_1} + A_{1-2})$ and must be completed by the end of the sixth week (T_{L_2}). There are three weeks of possible slippage or delay—A_{1-2} has a slack of three weeks. A_{2-4} also has a calculated slack of three weeks:

$T_E = 3$

$T_L = 11$

$$S = T_{L4} - (T_{E2} + A_{2-4})$$
$$= 11 - (3 + 5)$$

One important qualification must be emphasized. A_{1-2} has a calculated slack of three, A_{2-4} has a calculated slack of three, and the path containing A_{1-2} and A_{2-4} has a total slack of three weeks. A_{1-2} was calculated under the assumption of zero slack for A_{2-4}. The A_{2-4} computation similarly assumed zero slack for A_{1-2}. The two activities on the path 1–2–4 share *a common total slack* of three weeks. Any combination of slack can be allocated between the two activities *as long as the total allocation does not exceed three weeks*.

Note, if there is a series of activities between two events on the critical path, the *total slack for the activities can be determined by directly comparing the T_E and T_L for the intermediary event*. Reconsider the path 1–2–4 (Figure 13.5). Event 2 has a T_E of three and T_L of six. The path 1–2–4 has a total allowable slack represented by the difference between T_{L2} and T_{E2} (6–3) of three weeks.

The complete slack report and slack summary report are presented in Tables 13.4 and 13.5. The critical path is 1–3–4–5–8 with zero slack. There are four noncritical paths containing specified limits within which activity delays will not affect the duration of the project.

Predecessor Events	Successor Events	T_e	T_E	T_L	Slack
1	2	3	3	6	3
1	3	5	5	5	0
2	4	5	8	11	3
3	4	6	11	11	0
3	5	3	8	18	10
4	5	7	18	18	0
4	6	3	14	20	6
4	7	5	16	20	4
6	7	0	14	20	6
5	8	4	22	22	0
7	8	2	18	22	4

TABLE 13.4

Slack Report

Project Planning, Scheduling, and Control: PERT and CPM Network Models

Slack				
$\underline{0}$	$\underline{3}$	$\underline{4}$	$\underline{6}$	$\underline{10}$
1 ↓	1 ↓	4 ↓	4 ↓	3 ↓
3 ↓	2 ↓	7 ↓	6 ↓	5
4 ↓	4 ↓	8	7	
5 ↓				
8				

TABLE 13.5
Slack Summary Report

One more important point requires consideration. To proceed from E_4 to E_8 on the critical path requires 11 weeks:

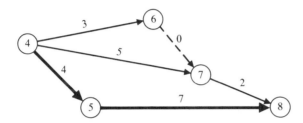

On the noncritical path of 4–6–7–8, the required time is 5 weeks. The maximum total allocatable slack is 6 weeks ($11 - 5 = 6$). Moreover, the noncritical path of 4–7–8 requires 7 weeks with a total allocatable slack of 4 weeks.

These two noncritical paths have *activity 7–8 in common*. A_{7-8} is subject to a double set of restrictions. The maximum allowable slack on 4–6–7–8 is six weeks; on 4–7–8, four weeks. Therefore, the maximum for A_{7-8} subject to both restrictions is the smaller allowable quantity of four weeks.

To illustrate, if A_{7-8} is extended by six weeks to form a new total of eight weeks, the path 4–7–8 will take two weeks longer than the critical path and therefore extend the duration of the project:

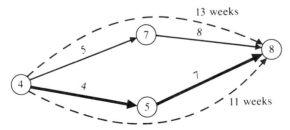

A_{7-8} cannot be extended by more than four weeks without delaying the project. A_{7-8} has an allowable slack of only four weeks. Therefore, in the slack summary report, activities 4–6–7 will have a slack of six and activities 4–7–8 a slack of four.

As a simple rule, the slack for a noncritical path can be calculated by comparing it with the critical path. If two or more noncritical paths have an *activity in common*, the noncritical path with the lowest slack will contain the common activity.

For example, consider the new network in Figure 13.6. The critical path is 1–2–6, requiring 16 weeks. There are two noncritical paths: 1–3–6, with 9 weeks, and 1–3–5–6, with 13 weeks. These paths have slacks of 7 and 3 weeks, respectively. The common activity 1–3 is subject to both requirements. It will have the smaller slack of the two: *a maximum slack of 3 weeks*. The path 1–3–5–6 has *a total allocatable slack of 3 weeks*. The path 1–3–6 has *a total allocatable slack of 7 weeks*. Not more than 3 of these 7 weeks can be allocated to A_{1-3}.

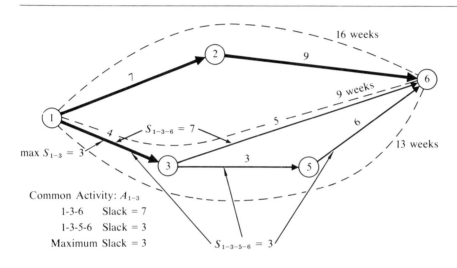

FIGURE 13.6
Maximum Slack for a Common Activity

INFORMATION FROM NETWORK MODELS

PERT and CPM network analysis is not complete with the construction of the operational network, the critical path or paths, and the slack paths. Proper use of these techniques requires a continual review, readjustment, and formulation of new networks. PERT is a *process of planning, replanning, and evaluating progress directed at better coordination and control*. A proper application of this process implies *corrective action by* responsible project managers.

With information from the network model, a manager can concentrate his or her efforts on maintaining or shortening the duration of activities along the critical path. Interchangeable resources and funds from slack activities might be reallocated to critical-path activities. Pretesting or some other technical constraint might be relaxed for a critical-path activity. Alternatively, the sequencing on the critical path might be carefully reevaluated. Activities initially connected in a series might possibly be reorganized on a parallel or concurrent basis. New resources or overtime use of present resources might provide desired flexibility.

As the project progresses, numerous variations from the initial schedule should be anticipated. An estimating error may cause a noncritical activity to become critical; an unforeseen activity may be required; an unprecedented material shortage may arise; a required breakthrough may not materialize. The activities of a complex project will be in a continual state of flux. The system will require constant updating and reanalysis. The manager must conceptualize a dynamic process flexibly adaptive to change.

THE PERT MODEL

PERT and CPM are both based on network fundamentals: the construction of an operational network and the concept of critical and slack paths. In application, extensions have diminished or eliminated the major differences between the two models. Traditionally, however, as a result of independent development in different industrial settings, each model has emphasized a particular aspect of the scheduling problem.

PERT was developed for research and development projects in the aerospace industry. This industry is characterized by rapidly changing technology and nonstandard products. The development of an ICBM, the Saturn V rocket, or a space platform requires new developments in materials and technology. Planning and scheduling must occur before all technological problems have been solved. Such large-scale, one-time projects entail substantial uncertainties. Little of no historical information is available for time estimates and network construction.

Consequently, the original PERT team focused on providing means to account specifically for uncertainties. They devised a special procedure to measure the expected time and the uncertainty of activity durations. By statistically combining these activity estimates and their variability, they developed a method for making *probability statements* about the duration of the project.

Estimating Activity Time and Variation

Instead of a traditional single best estimate of the duration of an activity, the PERT team recommended three estimates:

a = optimistic time
m = most likely time
b = pessimistic time

The optimistic time is the minimum estimated duration, assuming that everything goes right the first time. *The most likely time is the normal or most likely estimated duration. The pessimistic time is the maximum estimated duration,* assuming bad luck. It does not, however, consider catastrophic events such as fire, strike, or material shortage, unless these are an inherent risk in the particular activity.

More formally, *the optimistic time (a) is chosen so that the probability of a shorter duration is 1 in 100:*

$$P(t \leq a) = .01.$$

The pessimistic time (b) is chosen so that the probability of a longer duration is also 1 in 100:

$$P(t \geq b) = .01.$$

The most likely time (m) is chosen to represent the duration with the highest probability of occurrence.

The PERT team selected a *Beta distribution* as a reasonably approximate expression of activity duration. The Beta distribution is not necessarily symmetrical. It is unimodal with finite and nonnegative end points. The optimistic a and pessimistic b time estimates represent extremes on the distribution. The most likely time m represents the mode or peak of the distribution.

The mean (t_e)[4] and standard deviation (σ)[5] for the Beta distribution are reasonably approximated by:

$$t_e = \frac{a + 4m + b}{6}$$

$$\sigma = \frac{b - a}{6}.$$

---

[4] The *expected time t_e approximates the mean.* It is a special weighted average of the most likely and midrange estimates. It represents the 50th percentile on the distribution, dividing the area into two equal parts. The *expected time t_e is truly the median* of the Beta distribution, which will typically serve as a reasonable approximation of the mean.

[5] The standard deviation is an approximation based on the observation that almost all of a unimodal distribution is contained within three standard deviations from the mean. For the normal distribution, the percentage within $\pm 3\sigma$ is 99.7. Furthermore, Tchebyshev's inequality indicates that no distribution can have less than 88.9 percent. Therefore, the standard deviation of a unimodal distribution is frequently measured as roughly one-sixth the range $(b - a)$ of the distribution:

$$6\sigma \simeq b - a; \sigma \simeq \frac{b - a}{6}.$$

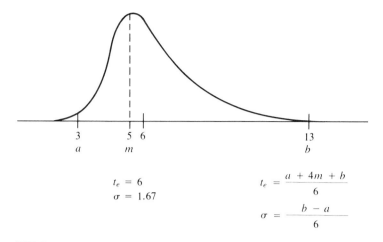

FIGURE 13.7

The Beta Distribution of Activity Duration

If an activity has ($a = 3$, $m = 5$, $b = 13$), the *expected lapsed time* and standard deviation will be:

$$t_e = \frac{3 + 4(5) + 13}{6} \qquad \sigma = \frac{13 - 3}{6}$$

$$t_e = 6 \qquad\qquad \sigma = 1.67.$$

The corresponding Beta distribution is in Figure 13.7.

Probability Statements of Project Duration

To facilitate bidding, compliance with contracted dates, and the general requirements of planning, scheduling, and controlling, a decision maker must know when the project will be completed. The inherent variability in activity times however, creates an estimation problem. To cope with this difficulty, *the project duration can be expressed in terms of a probability distribution. The uncertainties can be measured and probability statements can be made for completion times.*

First, the duration of each activity is represented by a Beta distribution with an *approximate mean* (t_e) and *standard deviation* (σ). Second, the activities most strategic to the length of the project are those along the critical path. Third, the expected times and variability along the critical path are *pooled* statistically. They will form a probability distribution with known parameters for the duration of the critical path—for the duration of the project.[6] Probability statements, therefore, can be made for any project completion time.

In statistical theory, the *central limit theorem* implies that the sum of n independent activity distributions will tend to be normally distributed with a mean equal to the sum of the activity means and variance equal to the sum of activity variances:

Critical Path mean: $\quad T_E = \sum t_{ei-j}$

Critical Path variance: $\quad \sigma_{TE}{}^2 = \sum \sigma_{i-j}^2$

Distribution of critical
Path duration: $\quad\quad\quad N(T_E, \sigma_{TE})$.

The expected activity times and variances along the critical path can be aggregated to form a normal distribution of project duration with mean T_E and standard deviation σ_{TE}.

Table 13.6 provides the time estimates of the critical path activities on the previously considered operational network. The critical path mean is equal to the earliest completion time for the network:

$$T_E = \sum t_{ei-j}$$
$$T_E = t_{e1-3} + t_{e3-4} + t_{e4-5} + t_{e5-8}$$
$$T_E = 5 + 6 + 7 + 4$$
$$T_E = 22.$$

Activities	a	m	b	$t_e = \dfrac{a + 4m + b}{6}$	$\sigma = \dfrac{b - a}{6}$	σ^2
A_{1-3}	2	5	8	5	1	1
A_{3-4}	3	5	13	6	1.67	2.79
A_{4-5}	6	7	8	7	.33	.11
A_{5-8}	1	4	7	4	.83	.69
				$T_E = \Sigma t_e = 22$		$\sigma^2{}_{TE} = 4.59$

TABLE 13.6

Time Estimates of Critical Path Activities

---

[6] Excessive variation in noncritical activities may lengthen the duration of the project. Due to the number of possible paths in most networks, initial estimates customarily consider only critical path variations. While computationally expedient, this simplifying assumption will tend to bias an early estimated completion date.

Project Planning, Scheduling, and Control: PERT and CPM Network Models

The variance and standard deviation are:

$$\sigma_{TE}^2 = \sum \sigma_{i-j}^2$$
$$= \sigma_{1-3}^2 + \sigma_{3-4}^2 + \sigma_{4-5}^2 + \sigma_{5-8}^2$$
$$= 1 + 2.79 + .11 + .69$$
$$= 4.59$$
$$\sigma_{TE} = \sqrt{4.59}$$
$$= 2.14.$$

The normal distribution with parameters for the project completion time is presented in Figure 13.8.[7] Once the basics of the normal distribution are understood,[8] the probability of obtaining any specified completion date or *directed date* (T_D) can be easily derived. The probability of completing the project on or before the end of the 26th week can be obtained by measuring the shaded area in Figure 13.8. For the normal distribution, the area is measured in terms of standard units—the number of standard deviations from the mean. The directed date (T_D) of 26 weeks is four units from the mean of 22. The standard deviation is 2.14. The value 26 is 4/2.14 or 1.87 standard units from the mean. This same measure can be obtained from the familiar Z transformation:[9]

$$Z = \frac{T_D - T_E}{\sigma}.$$

In this case,

$$Z = \frac{26 - 22}{2.14}$$

$$= 1.87.$$

$$P(Z \le 1.87) = .96926.$$

The probability of randomly obtaining a result less than or equal to 1.87 standard deviations from the mean is .9693. The probability of completing the project on time with a directed date of 26 weeks is reasonably certain.

---

[7] In this case, the assumption of a normal distribution would be extremely weak and justifiable only for sake of convenience and illustration. The four activities along the critical path are insufficient to presuppose the convergence implicit in the central limit theorem. Most large projects, however, do have many activities on the critical path.
[8] Refer to any basic statistics text.
[9] For the random variable X, the Z requires the more familiar form:

$$Z = \frac{X - \mu_x}{\sigma_x}.$$

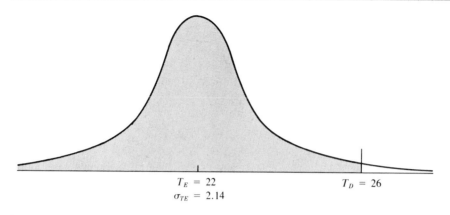

$$T_E = 22 \qquad\qquad T_D = 26$$
$$\sigma_{TE} = 2.14$$

FIGURE 13.8

Normal Approximation of Project Completion Time

Consider the probability that the project will be completed on or before the T_E time of 22 weeks. This is the *expected* duration—the most likely completion time. If the project is contracted for 22 weeks with a penalty for noncompliance, however, the probability of not meeting this date and of having to pay the penalty is .50. A probability distribution might provide valuable insight into better contract negotiations.

A project manager may also want to determine the completion date with a specified risk for noncompliance. For example, he or she may want to know the latest directed date that has only a .05 chance of the noncompliance penalty.

This information is obtained by reversing the computation required for the probability of maintaining a specified directed date. Instead of a directed date being given and an area sought, an area is given and a directed date sought. Instead of measuring the number of standard deviations from the mean and determining the area from the normal distribution table, the decision maker refers to the given area in the table to determine the number of standard deviations from the mean.

The directed date with a .05 chance of noncompliance is illustrated in Figure 13.9. From the standard normal distribution table (Appendix I), the 95 percent area to the left of the unknown directed date is associated with a Z of approximately 1.64. The T_D is therefore 1.64 standard deviations to the right of the mean. The standard deviation is 2.14 weeks. The distance is 1.64 standard deviations of size 2.14 weeks: $1.64(2.14) = 3.51$ weeks. With a mean of 22 weeks, the desired T_D must be $22 + 3.51$: $T_D = 25.51$ weeks.

There is a second more mechanistic approach. The measure of area for the normal distribution is the number of standard deviations from the mean (Z):

$$Z = \frac{T_D - T_E}{\sigma_{TE}}.$$

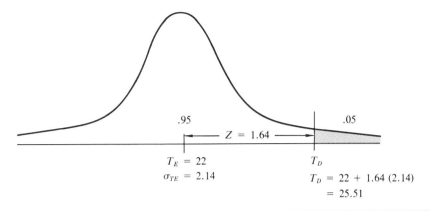

FIGURE 13.9
The Directed Date with Probability of Noncompliance

Since T_E and σ_{TE} are knowns and Z is obtainable from a table, this expression forms a single equation with T_D as the single unknown. For an area of .95, the Z from the table is 1.64. T_E and σ_{TE} are givens of 22 and 2.14, respectively. The T_D required to maintain these specifications is:

$$1.64 = \frac{T_D - 22}{2.14}$$

$$T_D = 22 + 1.64(2.14)$$
$$= 25.51.$$

The project manager will incur a late penalty only 5 percent of the time for a contracted completion date of 25.5 weeks.

THE CPM MODEL

The critical path method was developed for an industrial setting. It is most commonly used in construction projects where materials and activities are fairly standard. Instead of focusing on measuring the uncertainty of time estimates, it focused primarily on minimizing project costs.

CPM employs the basic networking fundamentals: the operational network, the critical path or paths, and slack paths. Instead of being probabilistic, as in PERT, the time estimates are assumed known with reasonable certainty. Two time estimates with associated costs are made for each activity: a *normal time* to reflect typical conditions and a *crash time* to reflect stepped-up, overtime, no-cost-spared, crash conditions. The basic contention is that time can be saved by applying added resources at an increased cost. The times and costs for each activity is analyzed in terms of *time-cost tradeoffs*.

Time-Cost Relationships

The *time-cost* relationship for the activities may take a variety of forms. As a simplifying assumption, the typically nonlinear time-cost curve is approximated by a linear equation (Figure 13.10). *The linear approximation infers a constant increase in cost per unit reduction in time.* In situations where the actual cost curve departs materially from linearity, a *piecewise linear approximation* can be used (Figure 13.11). The linear representation substantially facilitates analysis without materially affecting precision.

The *exact time-cost tradeoff* for reducing the duration of an activity can be obtained from the linear time-cost equation. *It is the absolute value of the slope.* More specifically, with a crash cost (C_C), a normal cost (C_N), a crash time (T_C), and a normal time (T_N), the *incremental cost* (I_C) *of crashing an activity is*:

$$I_C = \frac{\Delta \text{ cost}}{\Delta \text{ time}}$$

$$= \frac{C_C - C_N}{T_N - T_C}.$$

In effect, the incremental cost represents the cost increase per unit of time decrease. If an activity has a T_N of six weeks, a T_C of two weeks, a C_N of \$4,000,

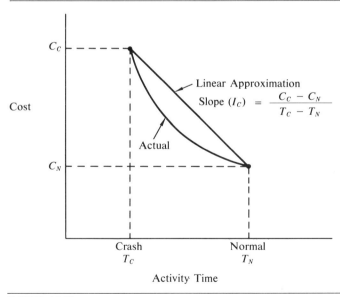

FIGURE 13.10

A Linear Approximation of the Time-Cost Relation

Project Planning, Scheduling, and Control: PERT and CPM Network Models

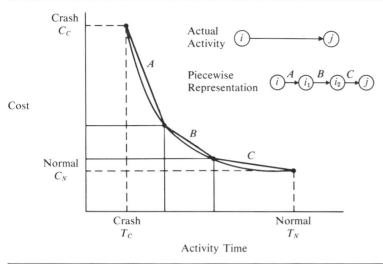

A Piecewise Linear Time-Cost Curve

and a C_C of \$6,000:

$$I_C = \frac{6,000 - 4,000}{6 - 2}$$

$$I_C = \$500.$$

As demonstrated in Figure 13.12, for every week the activity is crashed, there is an incremental expediting cost of \$500.

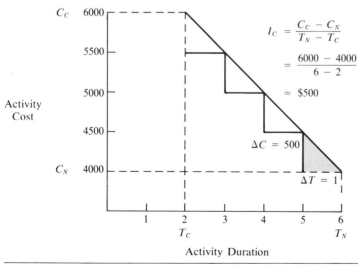

Incremental Expediting Cost

The Operational Network with Time-Cost Requirements

The operational network for CPM requires four estimates: normal time (T_N), crash time (T_C), normal cost (C_N), and crash cost (C_C). Table 13.7 contains the information for a representative project. The more descriptive network counterpart is presented in Figure 13.13. The time estimates are inserted above, and the cost estimates below the activity arrows.

Activity	Time (weeks)		Cost ($000)		Possible Time ΔT Reduction	Cost ΔC Increase	Incremental Expediting Cost ($I_C = \Delta C/\Delta T$)
	Normal	Crash	Normal	Crash			
1-2	6	3	4	5	3	$1000	$ 333
1-3	6	2	4	6	4	2000	500
2-4	7	5	4	6	2	2000	1000
3-4	5	2	4	6	3	2000	667
2-5	5	3	3	6	2	3000	1500
4-5	9	6	5	10	3	5000	1667
4-6	6	4	3	6	2	3000	1500
5-7	4	1	2	5	3	3000	1000
6-7	2	1	2	4	1	2000	2000

TABLE 13.7

Project Time-Cost Information

The project information may also be expressed in an operational network with incremental expediting costs inserted below the activity line (Figure 13.14). By emphasizing the cost of crashing an activity, this representation facilitates the implementation of time-cost tradeoffs.

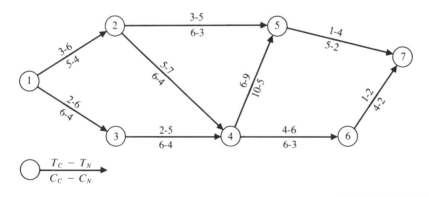

FIGURE 13.13

Operational Network with Time-Cost Estimates

Project Planning, Scheduling, and Control: PERT and CPM Network Models

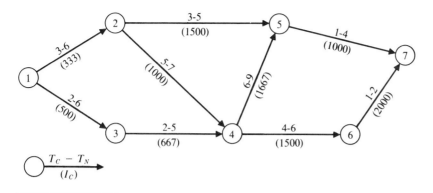

FIGURE 13.14

Operational Network with Incremental Expediting Costs

The Normal-Time and Crash-Time Schedules

A number of project schedules can be developed. At one extreme, a *normal-time schedule* can be designed to minimize the total cost of the activities. At the other extreme, a *crash-time schedule* can be constructed to minimize the duration of the project. Between these extremes, *intermediate-time schedules* can also be developed.

The scheduling process typically begins with the construction of the normal-time and crash time schedules. The normal-time schedule represents the project with all activities taking place under normal conditions. Figure 13.15 illustrates the normal-time schedule with critical and slack paths. Under normal-time

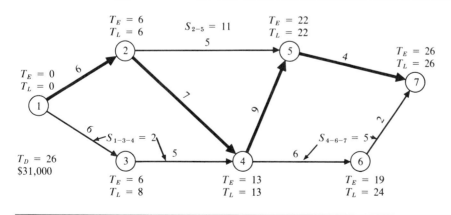

FIGURE 13.15

Normal-Time Schedule

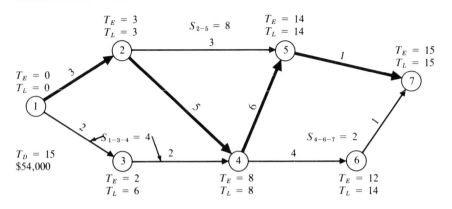

FIGURE 13.16
Crash-Time Schedule

conditions, the project will have a duration of 26 weeks and cost $31,000. The total cost is simply the sum of all normal activity costs.

The crash-time schedule is presented in Figure 13.16. By crashing all activities, the duration of the project can be reduced to 15 weeks. However, the cost is increased to $54,000.

The normal-time and crash-time schedules provide the scheduling bounds for the project. *The normal-time schedule gives the lowest cost and the longest duration. The crash-time schedule gives the highest cost and the shortest duration.* As will be demonstrated shortly, these extremes can be compromised into other scheduling alternatives: (1) time reductions on the normal-time schedule by crashing activities on the critical path; or (2) cost reduction of the crash time schedule by uncrashing some activities.

The Least-Cost Crash-Time Schedule

The crash time schedule provides a directed date of 15 weeks at a cost of $54,000. While it allows the minimum completion time, it also has the maximum project cost. The schedule can be substantially improved. Several adjustments can reduce costs without increasing the project completion time.

The central concept of reducing the cost, or *least costing* a schedule, is straightforward: activities that need not be expensively crashed should be assigned low-cost normal times. In the crash-time schedule in Figure 13.16, all activities are on crash times with crash costs. If the directed date of 15 weeks is to be maintained, the activities on the critical path must remain crashed. *Activities on noncritical paths, however, can be extended by the amount of associated slack without affecting the directed date.* These activities can be extended toward normal times with incremental cost savings.

Crash:

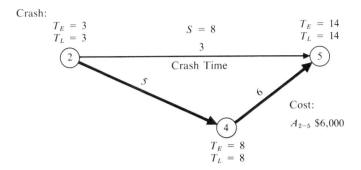

Least Cost:

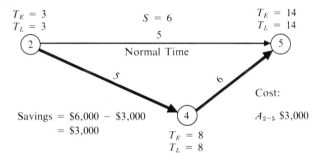

FIGURE 13.17

Extending from Crashing to Normal Time

Activity 2–5, for example, is presently crashed in three weeks at a cost of $6,000. The job has eight weeks of slack—the duration can be increased by eight weeks before the project completion date will be affected. There is no reason to crash A_{2-5}. It should be converted to the normal time of five weeks with a cost $3,000 (Figure 13.17). The total cost of the schedule will be correspondingly reduced from $54,000 to $51,000—*with no change in the directed date*.

The other noncritical activities should be uncrashed in the same way. Activities 1–3 and 3–4 have a total slack of four weeks. Their present crash times can be relaxed to realize a savings (Figure 13.18). For every week A_{1-3} is extended, the total activity cost will be reduced by $500. For every week A_{3-4} is extended, the cost will be reduced by $667. Because it offers the greater cost benefit, A_{3-4} should be uncrashed as much as possible. Since the normal time is five weeks, A_{3-4} will be extended from two to five weeks. The remaining week of slack is allocated to extend A_{1-3} from two to three weeks. The total savings from the two extended activities is $2,500.

The slack along the path containing A_{1-3} and A_{3-4} has been reduced to zero. These activities are now part of the critical path—any further extension will extend the duration of the project correspondingly.

The CPM Model

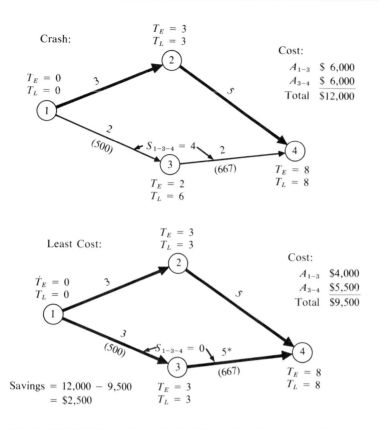

FIGURE 13.18
Uncrashing Noncritical-Path Activities

Activities 4–6 and 6–7 represent a noncritical path with a shared slack of two weeks (Figure 13.19). The activities can be profitably uncrashed with the extensions being applied to the activity with the larger incremental benefit. A_{4-6} has an incremental benefit of $1,500; A_{6-7}, of $2,000. A_{6-7} will be uncrashed by one week to the normal time limit of two weeks. A_{4-6} will be extended by the remaining week of slack. With all of the slack utilized, A_{4-6} and A_{6-7} also become part of the critical path. The uncrashing has saved $3,500.

All activities have now been extended toward low-cost normal times as far as possible without altering the directed date. Figure 13.20 provides the least-cost crash time schedule. The new schedule has the same directed date of 15 weeks. The uncrashing of noncritical activities has reduced the total cost from $54,000 to $45,000.

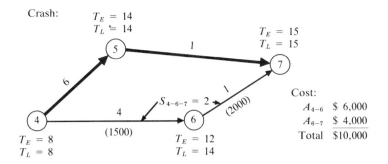

Crash:

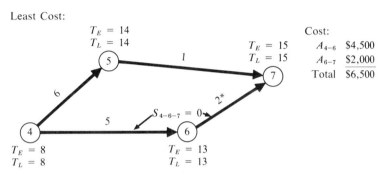

Least Cost:

Savings = $10,000 − $6,500
        = $3,500

FIGURE 13.19
Uncrashing Noncritical-Path Activities

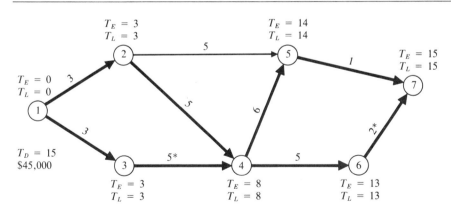

FIGURE 13.20
Least-Cost Crash-Time Schedule

Least-Cost Intermediate-Time Schedules

In most situations, the project planners will not be content with the extremes specified by the normal-time schedule or the least-cost crash time schedule. They will want some intermediate position between a low-cost long duration and a high-cost short duration. A compromise can be made between time and cost in a *least-cost intermediate-time schedule*.

Several least-cost intermediate-time schedules will be developed. They will be used later to form an *optimal total project cost schedule*. Developments will begin with the normal-time schedule (Figure 13.15) with a directed date of 26 weeks and a cost of $31,000. The directed date will be progressively reduced by crashing activities at an increase in cost. The schedule construction will conclude with the least-cost crash-time schedule (Figure 13.20) with a directed date of 15 weeks and a cost of $45,000. *These least-cost intermediate-time schedules will span the alternative space of time and cost options.*

The normal-time schedule (Figure 13.15) is a least-cost schedule with a duration of 26 weeks. If the duration must be shortened to 24 weeks, what is the most economical means of providing the 2-week reduction? Shortening the duration of noncritical activities will not reduce the project completion time. The critical path must be shortened. The 2-week reduction must be made by crashing one or more of the activities on the critical path.

The costs of crashing critical-path activities are:

Incremental Cost of Crashing

A_{1-2}	$ 333*
A_{2-4}	1,000
A_{4-5}	1,667
A_{5-7}	1,000.

A_{1-2} is the most economical choice. It can be shortened by two weeks at an increased cost of only $666.

Since the normal-time schedule has activities on a lowest-cost normal basis, no secondary adjustments are required to form the least-cost schedule. Figure 13.21 illustrates the least-cost intermediate-time schedule with a directed date of 24 weeks and a cost of $31,666.

If the desired directed date is 23 weeks, the critical path will have to be reduced by another week. A_{1-2} still has the lowest crashing cost of $333. To crash A_{1-2} for an additional week, however, will not reduce the duration of the project (Figure 13.22). A_{1-3} and A_{3-4} are part of a *parallel critical path* which must also be considered (Figure 13.23). To reduce the duration of the project, it will be necessary to crash an activity on both of the parallel paths:

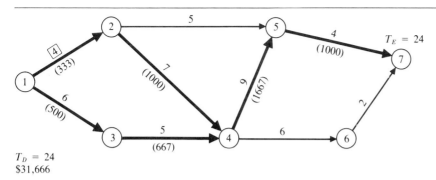

FIGURE 13.21
Least-Cost Intermediate-Time Schedule ($T_D = 24$)

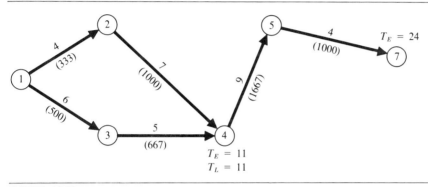

FIGURE 13.22
Parallel Critical Paths

Total Incremental Cost

A_{1-2} and A_{1-3}	$ 833*
A_{1-2} and A_{3-4}	1,000
A_{2-4} and A_{1-3}	1,500
A_{2-4} and A_{3-4}	1,667.

Crashing A_{1-2} and A_{1-3} is the most economical choice. Comparing this choice with the critical-path activities in the rest of the operational network:

Total Incremental Cost

A_{1-2} and A_{1-3}	$ 833*
A_{4-5}	1,667
A_{5-7}	1,000.

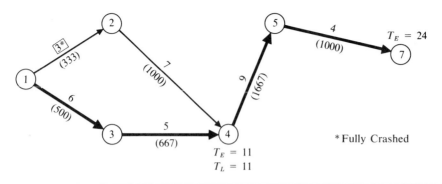

FIGURE 13.23

Crashing A_{1-2} Will Not Shorten the Duration of the Project

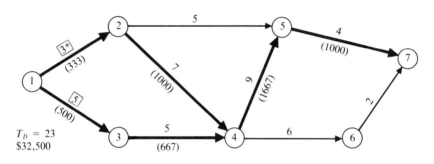

FIGURE 13.24

Least-Cost Intermediate-Time Schedule ($T_D = 23$)

Crashing A_{1-2} and A_{1-3} is still the most economical means of reducing the duration of the project.

The new least-cost intermediate-time schedule with a directed date of 23 weeks is presented in Figure 13.24. Both A_{1-2} and A_{1-3} have been crashed by 1 week, reducing the duration and increasing the total cost to $32,500.

The directed date will now be reduced to 20 weeks. The critical path must be shortened by 3 weeks. Consider the possibilities (Figure 13.24):

Total Incremental Cost

A_{1-2} and A_{1-3}	$ 833*
A_{1-2} and A_{3-4}	1,000
A_{2-4} and A_{1-3}	1,500
A_{2-4} and A_{3-4}	1,667
A_{4-5}	1,667
A_{5-7}	1,000.

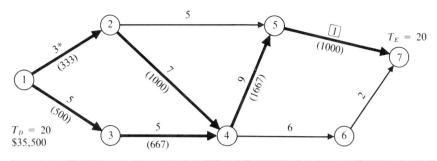

FIGURE 13.25

Least-Cost Intermediate-Time Schedule ($T_D = 20$)

A_{1-2} and A_{1-3} is the lowest-cost choice. However, A_{1-2} is already fully crashed. It cannot be reduced any further. The alternatives are restricted to:

Total Incremental Cost

A_{2-4} and A_{1-3}	$1,500
A_{2-4} and A_{3-4}	1,667
A_{4-5}	1,667
A_{5-7}	1,000*.

A_{5-7} should be crashed.

Expediting A_{5-7} by 3 weeks provides the least-cost intermediate-time schedule for 20 weeks (Figure 13.25). The added cost of the 3-week time reduction is $3,000, raising the total cost to $35,500.

Three additional least-cost intermediate-time schedules are presented in Figures 13.26, 13.27, and 13.28. They complete the time span from normal time to crash time.

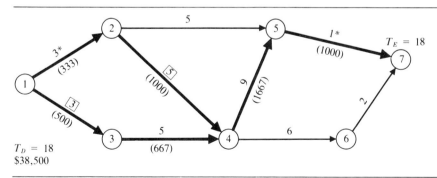

FIGURE 13.26

Least-Cost Intermediate-Time Schedule ($T_D = 18$)

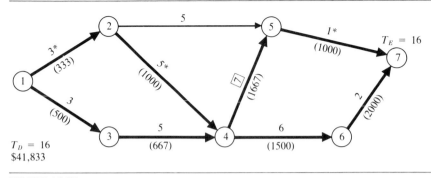

FIGURE 13.27

Least-Cost Intermediate-Time Schedule ($T_D = 16$)

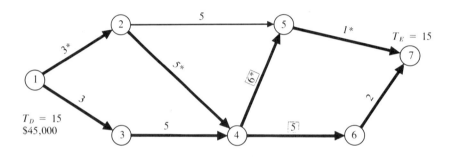

FIGURE 13.28

Least-Cost Intermediate-Time Schedule ($T_D = 15$): Least-Cost Crash-Time Schedule

An Optimal Total Project Cost Schedule

The analysis is extended one final step. Project costs that are not attributed directly to the separate activities are introduced into the analysis. Considering all costs, a *minimum total-cost schedule* will be identified.

The least-cost intermediate-time schedules indicate the costs attached directly to network activities. The *project time cost curve* in Figure 13.29 summarizes this direct activity cost information. Direct activity costs, however, are not usually the only cost consideration. There are time related costs that are not directly tied to network activities. *Indirect costs* (such as equipment rental or supervisory salaries) and *utility costs* (such as bonus or penalties related to the completion date) may materially affect the best target date.

All project costs are expressed in a total-cost curve. Direct costs, indirect costs, and utility costs are aggregated over the range of possible directed dates. To illustrate, this project has an indirect cost of $1,000 per week. The project is contracted for completion in 20 weeks. A penalty clause stipulates a $2,000-per-week change for any delays in completion. The total project cost over time appears in Figure 13.30. The optimal schedule—the lowest total project cost schedule—is the least-cost intermediate-time schedule with a 20-week duration.

Project Planning, Scheduling, and Control: PERT and CPM Network Models

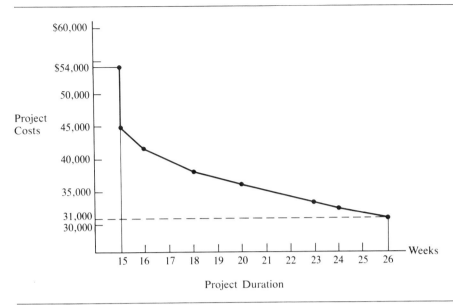

FIGURE 13.29

Project Time-Cost Curve for Direct Activity Costs

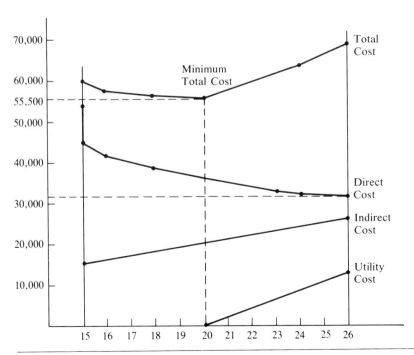

FIGURE 13.30

Total Project Cost Curve

SUMMARY

In the development and distribution of a new product, the construction of an office building, the design and implementation of a strategic national defense system, or the planning of the economy of an underdeveloped country, PERT and CPM are fundamental models of planning, scheduling, and control. They separate a vastly complex project into clearly defined, manageable, subcomponent parts. They structurally relate these myriad subcomponent parts in a single time-ordered network for the whole project. They measure uncertainties. They evaluate time-reducing expediting costs. They produce essential information for interchanging and reallocating resources. They specify where the project is now and where the project needs to be. They isolate potential conflict, interruptions, and delay. When they are used as part of a continual process of planning, replanning, and progress evaluation, PERT and CPM provide management with a tool for better project management.

A LINEAR PROGRAMMING SOLUTION TO NETWORK PROBLEMS

While network problems are most frequently solved with PERT and CPM, they can also be solved with linear programming. A linear programming solution is much less efficient computationally. Small network problems result in large linear programming problems. When it has been extended by sensitivity analysis, however, a linear programming solution provides a decision maker with an extensive wealth of information.

THE NETWORK PROBLEM

The network problem focuses on time considerations in determining critical and slack paths. The conventional PERT and CPM procedures require the calculation of the earliest completion time (T_E) and the latest completion time (T_L) for each event. The critical path is identified by those events which have the same earliest and latest completion times. Activities not on the critical path constitute slack paths. The amount of slack is measured by the difference in duration between the noncritical-path activities and the associated critical-path activities.

Figure 13A.1 represents a small project. The earliest completion time and

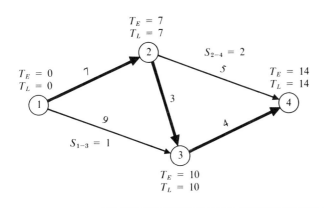

FIGURE 13A.1

An Operational Network with Network Information

the latest completion time calculations define the critical path: $1 \to 2 \to 3 \to 4$. A_{1-3} and A_{2-4} are noncritical-path activities containing slack. To move from event 1 to event 3 on the critical path requires 10 weeks. To proceed on the noncritical path of A_{1-3} requires only 9 weeks. The noncritical path is 1 week shorter: A_{1-3} contains a slack of 1 week. Similarly, to move from event 2 to event 4 on the critical path requires 7 weeks. The noncritical path of A_{2-4} requires 5 weeks. The noncritical path is 2 weeks shorter: A_{2-4} has 2 weeks of slack.

A LINEAR PROGRAMMING FORMULATION

The network problem will be formulated as a linear programming problem. The decision variables X_i will represent the earliest times for each of the $i = 1, \ldots, n$ events. The objective is to minimize the completion time of the project—to minimize the difference between X_n and X_1. The X_i values are restricted to the logic of earliest time computations. The difference between the duration of an event must be at least equal to the duration of connecting activities (A_{i-j}). The general linear programming formulation becomes:[1]

$$f_{min} = X_n - X_1$$
$$\text{subject to: } X_j - X_i \geq A_{i-j} \quad \text{for all } i, j$$
$$X_i \geq 0 \quad \text{for all } i.$$

The formulation of the problem for all i in Figure 13A.1 provides:

$$f_{min} = X_4 - X_1$$
$$\text{subject to: } X_2 - X_1 \geq 7$$
$$X_3 - X_1 \geq 9$$
$$X_3 - X_2 \geq 3$$
$$X_4 - X_2 \geq 5$$
$$X_4 - X_3 \geq 4$$
$$X_i \geq 0 \quad i = 1, 2, 3, 4.$$

With the addition of negative slack and artificial variables,[2] the first and final simplex tableaus are presented in Tables 13A.1 and 13A.2.

---

[1] The X_i are unconstrained in sign. Assignment of a value to any X_i will determine the values of the others. The simplex algorithm will lead to a solution of zero for X_1 forcing all the others to be $\geq$ to zero.

[2] Artificial variables can be avoided by the dual simplex algorithm.

Project Planning, Scheduling, and Control: PERT and CPM Network Models

C_j			-1	0	0	1	0	0	0	0	0	M	M	M	M	M
	Sol. Mix	q_0	X_1	X_2	X_3	X_4	S_{12}	S_{13}	S_{23}	S_{24}	S_{34}	A_1	A_2	A_3	A_4	A_5
M	A_1	7	-1	1	0	0	-1	0	0	0	0	1	0	0	0	0
M	A_2	9	-1	0	1	0	0	-1	0	0	0	0	1	0	0	0
M	A_3	3	0	-1	1	0	0	0	-1	0	0	0	0	1	0	0
M	A_4	5	0	-1	0	1	0	0	0	-1	0	0	0	0	1	0
M	A_5	4	0	0	-1	1	0	0	0	0	-1	0	0	0	0	1
	Z_j	$28M$	$-2M$	$-M$	M	$2M$	$-M$	$-M$	$-M$	$-M$	$-M$	M	M	M	M	M
	$C_j - Z_j$		$2M$ -1	M	$-M$	$-2M$ $+1$	M	M	M	M	M	0	0	0	0	0

TABLE 13A.1
The Initial Simplex Tableau

From Table 13A.2, the earliest times (X_i) are:

solution variables
(basis)

$$X_2 = 7$$
$$X_3 = 10 \qquad S_{13} = 1$$
$$X_4 = 14 \qquad S_{24} = 2$$

nonsolution variables
(nonbasis)

$$S_{12} = 0$$
$$X_1 = 0 \qquad S_{23} = 0$$
$$S_{34} = 0.$$

The critical path contains events 1, 2, 3, and 4 with respective earliest completion time and latest completion times of 0, 7, 10, and 14. Since each constraint has a direct activity association, the slack variables are the associated activity slack

C_j			-1	0	0	1	0	0	0	0	0	M	M	M	M	M
	Sol. Mix	q_0	X_1	X_2	X_3	X_4	S_{12}	S_{13}	S_{23}	S_{24}	S_{34}	A_1	A_2	A_3	A_4	A_5
0	X_2	7	-1	1	0	0	-1	0	0	0	0	1	0	0	0	0
0	S_{24}	2	0	0	0	0	0	0	-1	1	-1	0	0	1	-1	1
0	S_{13}	1	0	0	0	0	-1	1	-1	0	0	1	-1	1	0	0
0	X_3	10	-1	0	1	0	-1	0	-1	0	0	1	0	1	0	0
1	X_4	14	-1	0	0	1	-1	0	-1	0	-1	1	0	1	0	1
	Z_j	14	-1	0	0	1	-1	0	-1	0	-1	1	0	1	0	1
	$C_j - Z_j$		0	0	0	0	1	0	1	0	1	$M-1$	M	$M-1$	M	$M-1$

TABLE 13A.2
The Final Simplex Tableau

times.[3] The slack for the two noncritical-path activities A_{1-3} and A_{2-4} is represented by $S_{13} = 1$ and $S_{24} = 2$. The final linear programming tableau contains the same information as the conventional network model presented (Figure 13A.1).

A DUAL LINEAR PROGRAMMING FORMULATION

If the linear programming formulation in Table 13A.1 is labeled the primal, it must have an analogous dual counterpart. While a mathematical statement of the dual can be obtained by simply transposing the primal, the dual has its own interesting development and interpretation.

The dual gives the network problem a *network flow interpretation*. The starting event is viewed as the *source* and the terminal event as the *sink*. The decision variables w_{ij} are the flow through the activity branch A_{i-j}. The activity durations are the costs t_{ij} of sending one unit of flow from i to j. The objective of finding the longest path (the critical path) is equivalent to finding the highest cost route through the flow network.

With flow w_{ij} at cost t_{ij}, the objective function becomes:

$$f_{max} = \sum_{ij} t_{ij} w_{ij}.$$

The w_{ij} are restricted to the flow in the network. With positive flows into an event and negative flows out, the constraints imposed on w_{ij} are *balancing equations*. The starting event has a *flow out* of -1. The terminal event has a *flow in* of 1. Therefore,

$$-\sum_{j} w_{1j} = -1$$

$$\sum_{i} w_{in} = 1.$$

For all others, the *flow in* will equal the *flow out*:

$$\sum w_{ik} - \sum w_{kj} = 0 \qquad \text{for all } k \neq 1, n.$$

Each event will contain a constraint representing a flow balance.

---

[3] The entire slack for a sequence of activities on a noncritical path is assigned to one of the activities.

The network flow formulation is:

$$f_{max} = \sum_{ij} t_{ij} w_{ij}$$

subject to:
$$-\sum w_{1j} = -1 \qquad \text{for all } j$$
$$\sum w_{ik} - \sum w_{kj} = 0 \qquad \text{for all } k \neq 1, n$$
$$\sum w_{in} = 1 \qquad \text{for all } in$$
$$w_{ij} \geq 0 \qquad \text{for all } i, j.$$

Applied to the problem in Figure 13A.1, the formulation becomes:

$$f_{max} = 7w_{12} + 9w_{13} + 3w_{23} + 5w_{24} + 4w_{34}$$

subject to:
$$-w_{12} - w_{13} \qquad\qquad\qquad = -1$$
$$w_{12} \qquad - w_{23} - w_{24} \qquad\quad = 0$$
$$w_{13} + w_{23} \qquad\quad - w_{34} = 0$$
$$w_{24} + w_{34} = 1$$
$$w_{ij} \geq 0 \qquad \text{for } i, j = 1, 2, 3, 4.$$

Tables 13A.3 and 13A.4 provide the first and final simplex tableaus.[4] The solution is:

solution variables (basis)	nonsolution variables (nonbasis)
$w_{12} = 1$	$w_{13} = 0$
$w_{23} = 1$	$w_{24} = 0$
$w_{34} = 1$	

objective function: $f_{max} = 14$.

C_j			7	9	3	5	4	$-M$	$-M$	$-M$	$-M$
	Sol. Mix	q_0	w_{12}	w_{13}	w_{23}	w_{24}	w_{34}	A_1	A_2	A_3	A_4
$-M$	A_1	1	1	1	0	0	0	1	0	0	0
$-M$	A_2	0	1	0	-1	-1	0	0	1	0	0
$-M$	A_3	0	0	1	1	0	-1	0	0	1	0
$-M$	A_4	1	0	0	0	1	1	0	0	0	1
	Z_j	$-2M$	$-2M$	$-2M$	0	0	0	$-M$	$-M$	$-M$	$-M$
	$C_j - Z_j$		$2M$ $+7$	$2M$ $+9$	3	5	4	0	0	0	0

TABLE 13A.3
The Initial Simplex Solution

---

[4] The dual simplex will avoid artificial components.

C_j			7	9	3	5	4	$-M$	$-M$	$-M$	$-M$
	Sol. Mix	q_0	w_{12}	w_{13}	w_{23}	w_{24}	w_{34}	A_1	A_2	A_3	A_4
4	w_{34}	1	0	0	0	1	1	0	0	0	1
7	w_{12}	1	1	1	0	0	0	1	0	0	0
3	w_{23}	1	0	1	1	1	0	0	0	1	1
$-M$	A_2	0	0	0	0	0	0	-1	1	1	1
	Z_j	14	7	10	3	7	4	$M+7$	$-M$	$-M+3$	$-M+7$
	$C_j - Z_j$		0	-1	0	-2	0	$-2M-7$	0	-3	-7

TABLE 13A.4

The Final Simplex Tableau

The unit flow will proceed through branches w_{12}, w_{23}, and w_{34}. The longest route in the network is along the critical path: $1 \to 2 \to 3 \to 4$. The total project completion time is 14 weeks.

The *slack* for noncritical-path activities is obtained from the $C_j - Z_j$ row in the final tableau. If one unit of w_{13} is entered into the solution, the $C_j - Z_j$ indicates that the objective function will be reduced by 1. If w_{13} is entered into the solution, the new route will have a duration of 13 instead of 14 weeks. The new route is 1 week shorter than the critical path—activity 1-3 has a slack of 1 week. Activity 2-4 is not on the critical path either. The $C_j - Z_j$ for w_{24} is -2. A new route with w_{24} will be 2 weeks shorter than the critical path: A_{2-4} has a slack of 2 weeks. The dual provides the same network information as the primal.

Avots, F. "The Management Side of PERT." *California Management Review*. 4 (1962): 16–27.

Baker, B. N., and R. L. Eric. *An Introduction to PERT/CPM*. Homewood, Ill.: Richard D. Irwin, 1964.

Bierman, H., Jr., C. P. Bonini, and W. H. Hausman. *Quantitative Analysis for Business Decisions*. Homewood, Ill.: Richard D. Irwin, 1973.

Blickstein, S. "How to Put PERT into Marketing (And Aid Planning)." *Printer's Ink*, Oct. 1964, pp. 27–29.

Boulanger, D. "Program Evaluation and Review Technique (PERT): A Case Study Application With Analysis." *Advanced Management*, July–August, 1961, pp. 7–12.

Davis, E. W. "Resource Allocations in Project Network Models—A Survey." *Journal of Industrial Engineering*, April 1966, pp. 177–88.

Evarts, H. F. *Introduction to PERT/CPM*. Boston: Allyn and Bacon, 1964.

Ford, L. R., Jr., and D. R. Fulkerson. *Flows in Networks*. Princeton, N.J.: Princeton University Press, 1962.

Giffin, W. C. *Introduction to Operations Engineering*. Homewood, Ill.: Richard D. Irwin, 1971.

Gisser, P. "Taking the Chances Out of Product Introduction (Using the PERT Technique)." *Industrial Marketing*, May 1965, pp. 86–91.

Hein, L. W. *The Quantitative Approach to Managerial Decisions*. Englewood Cliffs, N.J.: Prentice-Hall, 1967.

Hillier, F. S., and G. J. Lieberman. *Introduction to Operations Research*. San Francisco: Holden-Day, 1974.

Levin, R. I., and C. A. Kirkpatrick. *Planning and Control with PERT/CPM*. New York: McGraw-Hill Book Co., 1966.

————. *Quantitative Approaches to Management*. New York: McGraw-Hill Book Co., 1975.

Levy, F. K., G. L. Thompson, and J. D. Wiest. "The ABC's of the Critical Path Method." *Harvard Business Review*, 41 (1963): 98–108.

Miller, R. W. "How to Plan and Control with PERT." *Harvard Business Review*, 40 (1962): 93–104.

————. *Scheduling, Cost, and Profit Control with PERT*. New York: McGraw-Hill Book Co., 1963.

Moder, J. J., and C. R. Phillips. *Project Management with CPM and PERT*, 2d ed. New York: Van Nostrand, 1970.

Muth, J. F., and G. L. Thompson, eds. *Industrial Scheduling*. Englewood Cliffs, N.J.: Prentice-Hall, 1963.

O'Brien, J. J. *CPM in Construction Management*. New York: McGraw-Hill Book Co., 1965.

Paige, H. W. "How PERT/Cost Helps the General Manager." *Harvard Business Review*, 41 (1963): 87–95.

Roman, D. D. "The PERT Systems: An Appraisal of Program Evaluation Review Technique." *J. Acad. Management*, 5, 1 (1962): 57–65.

Schoderbek, P. P. "A Study of the Applications of PERT." *J. Acad. Management*, 8, 3 (1965): 199–210.

Shaffer, L. R., J. B. Ritter, and W. L. Meyer. *Critical Path Method*. New York: McGraw-Hill Book Co., 1965.

Thierauf, R. J., and R. C. Klekamp. *Decision Making Through Operations Research*. New York: John Wiley & Sons, 1975.

Wagner, H. M. *Principles of Operations Research with Applications to Managerial Decisions*. Englewood Cliffs, N.J.: Prentice-Hall, 1969.

Wiest, J. D., and F. K. Levy. *A Management Guide to PERT/CPM*. Englewood Cliffs, N.J.: Prentice-Hall, 1969.

Wong, Y. "Critical Path Analysis for New Product Planning." *Journal of Marketing*, October 1964, pp. 53–59.

13.1.

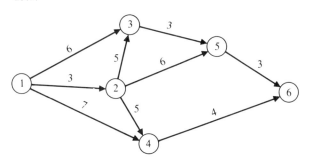

Using the fundamental approach specified by the model for decision making, determine the critical path and all slack paths.

13.2. An assembly operation is represented by the following network (time is given in hours):

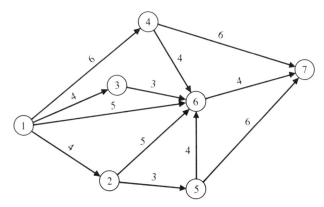

What is the earliest completion time for event 6? What is it for the project?

13.3. One part of a larger network has been represented as follows:

Referring to the three activities (*A, B, C*) required to proceed from *E*9 to *E*10, structure a network that will clearly define the activities in terms of predecessor and successor events.

13.4.

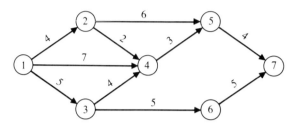

Determine the critical path by T_E and T_L calculations. Insert the amount of slack along slack paths.

13.5.

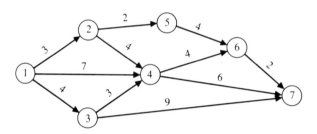

Determine the critical path or paths and the slack paths.

13.6. A small segment of a much larger network is represented below:

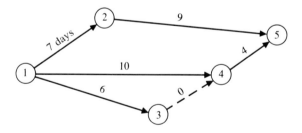

With regard to the master network, this small segment will contain a slack of four days. For the overall project, what is the maximum allowable slack, if any, along activity 1–4?

13.7. A small project is represented by the network components given below. Construct the operational network. Locate the critical path and slack paths.

Network Components

Predecessor Events	Successor Events	Time Estimates (weeks)
1	2	4
1	3	6
2	4	3
3	4	3
3	5	4
4	5	2
2	6	8
5	6	4

13.8. A small project consists of seven activities. The time estimates and order are as follows:

Activities	Most Optimistic Time	Most Likely Time	Most Pessimistic Time
A_{1-2}	2	4	6
A_{1-3}	4	5	6
A_{1-4}	6	7	8
A_{2-3}	1	5	8
A_{2-5}	3	5	7
A_{3-5}	4	7	12
A_{4-5}	1	2	3

Determine the operational network, the critical path, and the probability distribution for the critical path. What is the probability of completing the project later than T_E? What is the probability of completing the project in more than 20 weeks? There is a .10 probability that the project will exceed what duration?

13.9. A small project consists of the following activities and time estimates:

Predecessor Event	Successor Event	Most Optimistic Time	Most Likely Time	Most Pessimistic Time
1	2	4	8	12
1	3	8	10	12
1	4	8	14	24
2	5	5	8	10
3	4	2	5	8
3	5	2	4	8
4	5	6	10	14
5	6	1	3	6

Construct the operational network. Locate the critical path. Calculate the mean and standard deviation for the critical path. From this distribution, what is the probability of completing the project in more than 26 weeks? Along the noncritical path $1 \rightarrow 4 \rightarrow 6$, what is the probability of exceeding 26 weeks? What is the probability of exceeding 26 weeks along the noncritical path $1 \rightarrow 2 \rightarrow 5 \rightarrow 6$? What characteristics will increase the probability that a noncritical path will delay the project completion time?

13.10.

Project Time–Cost Information

Activity	Time (weeks)		Cost ($000)	
	Normal	Crash	Normal	Crash
1–2	10	6	7	9
1–7	10	7	6	8
2–4	9	6	7	9
3–4	11	9	7	10
3–5	9	7	7	10
4–6	10	8	6	10
4–5	13	10	11	14
6–8	6	5	6	9
5–7	4	2	3	6
5–8	8	5	8	12
7–8	4	3	4	5

1. Construct an operational network containing all information components.
2. Construct the normal-time schedule. Find the expected completion time and cost.
3. Construct the crash-time schedule. Find the expected completion time and cost.
4. Construct the least-cost crash-time schedule.
5. Construct the 40-week, least-cost intermediate-time schedule.
6. Construct the 36-week, least-cost intermediate-time schedule.

13.11. A project has the following operational network and time-cost information.

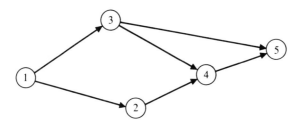

Project Planning, Scheduling, and Control: PERT and CPM Network Models

Activity	Time (weeks) Normal	Crash	Cost ($000) Normal	Crash
1–3	10	5	5	10
1–2	7	4	3	8
2–4	3	2	2	4
3–4	4	2	5	6
3–5	6	3	5	7
4–5	5	2	4	8

1. Construct the normal-time schedule with completion time and cost estimate.
2. Construct the crash-time schedule with completion time and cost estimate.
3. Construct the least-cost crash time schedule.
4. Develop the least-cost intermediate-time schedules to allow the construction of a direct-cost curve for the project.
5. The project has an accruing indirect cost of $2,000 a week. If the project exceeds 14 weeks, there is a contractual penalty of $4,000 a week until completion. Determine the total cost curve for the project. What schedule should the company use for the project?

INVENTORY AND QUEUING THEORY

PART THREE

14

Inventory Control: Deterministic Models

Because of their very size and complexity, many present-day organizations must maintain an often staggering number of items. If there is a stockout of a critical input material, a manufacturer may be forced to halt production. Excessive shortages will stimulate customers to find new sources of supply. The maintenance of abundant inventories, however, has a price. Handling, storage, insurance, taxes, obsolescence, deterioration, and interest on capital are some of the costs associated with holding resources in inventory reserve.

In the last two decades, an increased concern for better inventory management has inspired the development of many quantitative models to aid the decision maker. The models are as varied as the vast variety of inventory types. Chapters 14 and 15 will consider only the most basic models and the most fundamental concepts. It will provide the decision maker with a sound foundation in concept and terminology with which to explore further the plentiful literature on inventory control.

THE INVENTORY PROBLEM

The decision-making objective of an inventory system is *how to minimize total inventory related costs*. The *critical total cost* (T_C) components can be represented as a summation of *order costs* (C_O), *carrying costs* (C_C), *underage costs* (C_U), and *the cost of the inventory* (C_I):

$$T_C = C_O + C_C + C_U + C_I.$$

The ordering, acquisition, or setup costs (C_O) for getting items into inventory include the costs of requisition, trucking, receiving and inspection, placing in storage, and accounting. Carrying or holding costs (C_C) include such expenses as storage, handling, insurance, protection, taxes, obsolescence, deterioration, and the cost of capital. The underage or stockout costs (C_U) include the opportunity losses from direct lost sales, lost customers, and damaged good will resulting from insufficient supply. For inventory used in production, stockout costs include expenses associated with lost production, bottlenecks, or production shutdowns. The cost of the inventory (C_I) represents the actual purchase costs of items placed in inventory. The per unit cost may vary with quantity discounts or with the size of production runs.

The *inventory policy decision* consists of selecting the best values for *two decision variables:* (1) *how much to order* (or produce), the *economic order quantity* (q), and (2) *when to order*, the *reorder point* (R). The selection of the order quantity and the reorder point directly influences the components of the total cost.

A change in the economic order quantity (q) will generally produce the following effects:

order quantity	order cost	carrying cost	underage cost	inventory cost
$q\uparrow$:	$C_O\downarrow$	$C_C\uparrow$	$C_U\downarrow$	$C_I\downarrow$
$q\downarrow$:	$C_O\uparrow$	$C_C\downarrow$	$C_U\uparrow$	$C_I\uparrow.$

An increased order quantity will mean a larger average inventory with fewer orders and a corresponding reduction in order costs ($C_O\downarrow$). A larger inventory will increase carrying costs ($C_C\uparrow$). Moreover, a larger inventory will mean fewer inventory cycles and fewer accompanying periods of potential stockout ($C_U\downarrow$). If there are purchaser quantity discounts or producer economies of scale, an increase in the order quantity will reduce the costs of items in inventory ($C_I\downarrow$).

The selection of the reorder point (R) will also substantially influence total costs. For a specified order quantity:

reorder point	carrying cost	underage cost
$R\uparrow$:	$C_C\uparrow$	$C_U\downarrow$
$R\downarrow$:	$C_C\downarrow$	$C_U\uparrow.$

An increase in the order point (R) will raise the level of safety stock and the average level of inventory. This will increase carrying costs ($C_C\uparrow$) and reduce the chance of a stockout ($C_U\downarrow$). Furthermore, the reorder point (R) will affect the optimality of the order quantity (q), which will have a corresponding influence on all cost components.

The inventory problem, therefore, might be expressed as a policy decision: *determine the optimal order point* (R) *and the economic order quantity* (q) *that will minimize total inventory related costs.* Reexpressed, the policy decision is:

Find (R, q): $TC_{min} = C_O + C_C + C_U + C_I$.

This decision-making objective will be explored in several characteristic decision environments.

THE BASIC DETERMINISTIC MODEL

Inventory models have been designed for almost every special type of problem. The most basic problem is characterized by *deterministic demand with uniform depletion, fixed lead time,* and *infinite production rate* (Figure 14.1). A deterministic demand with uniform depletion infers a known demand with a constant rate of usage. A fixed lead time represents a constant duration between placing and receiving an order. An infinite production rate simply means the instantaneous arrival of the entire ordered quantity. This type of inventory system most commonly resembles a purchaser's receipt of orders from a supplier.

This inventory system is represented in Figure 14.1 in terms of the decision variables (R, q). The order quantity (q) is received from a supplier at the end of the lead time (L_T). The inventory is depleted at a constant rate until the reorder point level (R) has been reached. At this time, an order for q items is placed, with anticipated arrival at the end of the lead time.

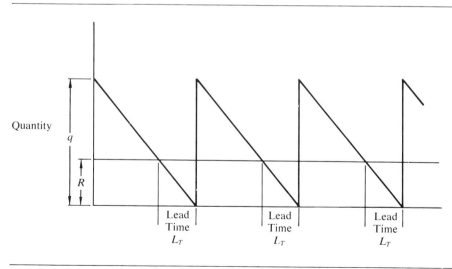

FIGURE 14.1
Deterministic Demand

The objective is to determine the optimal values for *the economic order quantity (q)* and *the reorder point (R)* that minimize inventory related costs:

$$T_C = C_O + C_C + C_U + C_I.$$

When the demand is known, the underage cost (C_U) will be zero. With a fixed annual demand and constant per unit cost, the annual cost of inventory items (C_I) will remain constant. The relevant inventory related costs are restricted to the ordering costs (C_O) and the carrying cost (C_C):

$$T_C = C_O + C_C.$$

In expressing the relationship between the decision variables and the relevant cost components, the notation is defined as follows:

q = economic order quantity
R = reorder point
D = demand during period T
T = time period (typically one year)
K_O = cost of placing an order
K_C = carrying cost for one unit over the time period
L_T = lead time

In terms of the defined variables, the *total annual order cost (C_O) consists of the cost per order (K_O) multiplied by the number of orders.* If the demand for the period is D and the order size is q, the number of orders required to satisfy demand must be:

number of orders = D/q.

The total ordering cost becomes:

$$C_O = \underset{\substack{\text{cost per} \\ \text{order}}}{K_O} \cdot \underset{\substack{\text{number} \\ \text{of orders.}}}{D/q}$$

The total annual cost of carrying inventory (C_C) is similarly reexpressed. *The annual carrying cost will consist of the cost of carrying a unit multiplied by the average number of units carried annually.* With a starting inventory of q uniformly depleted to zero, the average number of units carried in inventory will be $q/2$ items. The total annual carrying cost will be:

$$C_C = \underset{\substack{\text{carrying} \\ \text{cost}}}{K_C} \cdot \underset{\substack{\text{number} \\ \text{carried.}}}{q/2}$$

The total relevant inventory related costs are represented by:

$$\begin{array}{cccc}
 & \text{order cost} & & \text{carrying cost} \\
T_C = & C_O & + & C_C \\
T_C = & K_O D/q & + & K_C q/2 \quad .
\end{array}$$

A value for q exists that will minimize this total-cost expression.

The Economic Order Quantity: A Numerical Search Procedure

Although there are several acceptable procedures, the most basic approach for selecting the optimal order quantity is the general *model for decision making.* This procedure, however, must usually be accompanied by some form of logic to restrict a potentially inexhaustible alternative space to a measurably few realistic options.

The application of the general *model for decision making* is best demonstrated in the context of a specific problem. The critical information in the selection of an order quantity are demand (D), the cost of placing an order (K_O), the carrying costs per unit (K_C), and the lead time (L_T). They are:

$$\begin{array}{ll}
D = 1,000 & K_O = \$20 \\
L_T = 5 \text{ days} & K_C = \$4.
\end{array}$$

One thousand items are demanded annually. The cost to place and expedite an order is $20. Carrying one unit in inventory for a year has an expected cost of $4. Orders are received at the end of a five-day lead time.

The objective is to determine the value of the order quantity (q) that will minimize total inventory related costs:

$$\begin{array}{cccc}
 & \text{ordering cost} & & \text{carrying cost} \\
 & (C_O) & & (C_C) \\
TC = & K_O D/q & + & K_C q/2 \quad .
\end{array}$$

The alternative space of all values of q can be evaluated by separately substituting each possible value of q into the total-cost function. One difficulty with this enumeration technique is the number of alternatives requiring evaluation. With an annual demand for 1,000 units, the order quantity may take on any value from 1 to 1,000. There will be 1,000 alternatives requiring separate evaluation.

To simplify the evaluation, the alternatives must be restricted. Some definable relationship must be discovered. The total-cost function provides some information. The cost components vary directly with the order quantity. As

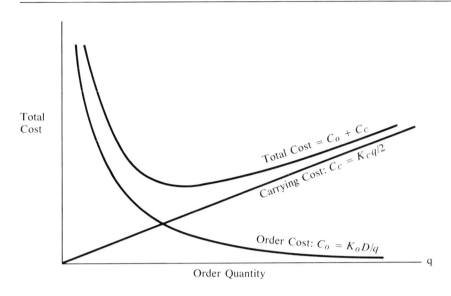

Total Cost = C_o + C_c

Carrying Cost: C_c = $K_c q/2$

Order Cost: C_o = $K_o D/q$

Total Cost

Order Quantity

q

FIGURE 14.2
Total Cost and Order Quantity

the order quantity increases, ordering costs will decrease and carrying costs will increase:

order quantity   ordering cost   carrying cost

$q\uparrow$: $K_o D/q\downarrow$ $K_c q/2\uparrow$.

The net effect on total cost of an increase in ordering quantity is best depicted graphically (Figure 14.2). As q increases, the total-cost curve begins by approximating ordering costs, decreases rapidly, flattens near the minimum, rises slowly, and ends by approximating carrying costs. An important relationship: *The total-cost curve decreases to a minimum and then rises.*

Equipped with this knowledge, the decision maker can restrict the alternatives requiring evaluation. Instead of evaluating each alternative, he or she can make several evaluations over the range of possibilities. This will isolate the area that warrants further investigation. Table 14.1 provides several evaluations for the present problem. The q of 100 has the lowest total cost—$400. The q of 50 and the q of 200 are next best, with a total cost of $500 each. Since the total cost curve decreases to the minimum before increasing, and since $400 is less than $500, the optimal q must be between 50 and 200 units. Presently, the best single estimate is for 100 units.

Alternative evaluations can now be conducted on both sides of $q = 100$. If a q of 101 has a lower cost, the optimal alternative is restricted to:

$$101 \leq q < 200.$$

Inventory Control: Deterministic Models

Order Quantity (q)	Number of Orders (D/q)	Order Cost ($C_o = K_o D/q$)	Average Inventory ($q/2$)	Carrying Cost ($C_c = K_c q/2$)	Total Inventory Related Cost ($T_c = C_o + C_c$)
1	1,000	20,000	.5	2	20,002
50	20	400	25	100	500
100*	10	200	50	200	400*
200	5	100	100	400	500
400	2.5	50	200	800	850
1,000	1	20	500	2,000	2,020

TABLE 14.1
Total Inventory Related Costs

If a q of 99 has a lower cost, the optimal will be between:

$50 < q \leq 99.$

As Table 14.2 illustrates, both evaluations have higher total costs than $q = 100$.[1] Because of the shape of the total-cost curve, the value of 100 must be optimal. Figure 14.3 illustrates that the order quantity of 100 units produces the minimum total inventory related cost of $400.

Order Quantity (q)	Number of Orders (D/q)	Order Cost ($C_o = K_o D/q$)	Average Inventory ($q/2$)	Carrying Cost ($C_c = K_c q/2$)	Total Inventory Related Cost ($T_c = C_o + C_c$)
99	10.101	202.02	49.5	198.00	400.02
100*	10.000	200.00	50	200.00	400.00*
101	9.910	198.20	50.5	202.00	400.20

TABLE 14.2
Total Inventory Related Costs

---

[1] If $q = 100$ is not optimal, the evaluation will indicate the direction of the restricted area. The middle value of this area can then be evaluated. If this leads to an improvement, values on both sides will be evaluated and the procedure will be repeated. If it does not lead to an improvement, the proper new area will be divided and evaluated. This approach will continually divide the alternative space in half until the optimal alternative has been isolated.

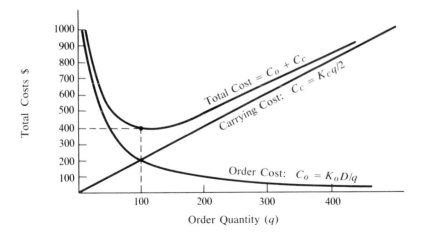

FIGURE 14.3
The Optimal Order Quantity

The Economic Order Quantity: An Algebraic Solution

A more *efficient* method for obtaining the optimal order quantity is to *structure a formal set of logic* (*a model*) that will allow a direct determination. This will be accomplished by expressing the optimal order quantity in terms of the required relationships of the input variables.

The optimal order quantity will minimize total inventory related costs:

$$
\begin{array}{ccc}
\text{ordering costs} & \text{carrying costs} \\
T_C = \quad C_O & + & C_C
\end{array}
$$

In terms of input variables,

$$T_C = K_O D/q + K_C q/2.$$

The total-cost curve takes a special form:

$$Y = aX^{-1} + bX$$

or

$$T_C = (K_O D)q^{-1} + (K_C/2)q.$$

For any curve of this form, the minimum will be found by setting aX^{-1} equal to bX. Specifically, the minimum total cost is located where the ordering costs and the carrying costs are equal:

$$\frac{K_O D}{q} = \frac{K_C q}{2}.$$

With reference to Figures 14.2 and 14.3, the order quantity with the minimum total cost is located at the intersection of the ordering-costs and carrying-costs curves. Solving for this minimum total-cost order quantity:

$$q = \sqrt{\frac{2K_O D}{K_C}}.$$

Applying the economic order quantity (EOQ) model to the foregoing problem:

$$D = 1,000; \ K_O = 20; \ K_C = 4$$

$$q = \sqrt{\frac{2(20)(1,000)}{4}}$$

$$q = 100.$$

The total inventory related costs are:

$$T_C = K_O D/q + K_C q/2$$
$$T_C = 20(1,000/10) + 4(100/2)$$
$$T_C = \$400.$$

The EOQ model allows a direct determination of the optimal order quantity and total inventory related costs.

The Economic Order Quantity: A Differentiation Solution

For those familiar with calculus, there is a more commonly used procedure for obtaining the economic order quantity. The minimization (or maximization) of a function with respect to a variable is obtained by *setting the first derivative equal to zero and solving for the variable*.

The objective is to find the value of q that will minimize total inventory related costs:

$$T_C = K_O D/q + K_C q/2.$$

Determining the first derivative with respect to q:[2]

$$\frac{dT_C}{dq} = -K_O D\, q^{-2} + \frac{K_C}{2}\, q^o.$$

Setting this equal to zero and solving for q:[3]

$$-K_O D\, q^{-2} + \frac{K_C}{2}\, q^o = 0$$

$$\frac{K_C}{2} = \frac{K_O D}{q^2}$$

$$q = \sqrt{\frac{2K_O D}{K_C}}.$$

The economic order quantity is defined directly by the cost per order, the carrying cost per unit, and the demand. With these input parameters, the *EOQ* model provides the direct derivation of the optimal order quantity.

Sensitivity of the Economic Order Quantity

One difficulty in applying the *EOQ* model is obtaining reliable parameter estimates. Accounting records are not usually designed to provide accessible information for making sound estimates of the cost per order (K_O) and the cost to carry a unit in inventory for a year (K_C). These costs are typically nonlinear and complex. A great deal of subjective guess work may enter into the final assessments.

With error prone input information, the reliability of the *EOQ* model may be seriously questioned. The sensitivity of the minimum total-cost objective to error inputs in the *EOQ* model will indicate the potential severity of the situation.

In the *EOQ* model considered above, the parameter inputs were:

$$D = 1,000; \qquad K_O = \$20; \qquad K_C = \$4.$$

---

[2] The derivative of Y with respect to X for a function of the form $Y = aX^n$ is

$$\frac{dY}{dX} = naX^{n-1}.$$

[3] The second derivative is:

$$\frac{d^2 T_C}{dq^2} = \frac{\cdot\, 2K_O D}{q^3}.$$

Since K_O, D, and q are positive, the second derivative will be greater than zero, indicating a minimization.

The optimal order quantity and associated total inventory related costs were:

$$q = \sqrt{\frac{2K_O D}{K_C}} \qquad\qquad T_C = K_O D/q + K_C q/2$$

$$q = \sqrt{\frac{2(20)(1,000)}{4}} \qquad T_C = 20(1,000/100) + 4(100/2)$$

$$q = 100 \qquad\qquad\qquad T_C = \$400.$$

For the sake of comparison, these parameters will be assumed accurate. The ordering costs will be assumed to have been overestimated by 50 percent: K_O is thus increased to an incorrect \$30. The estimation error in the ordering cost changes the order quantity:

$$q = \sqrt{\frac{2K_O D}{K_C}}$$

$$q = \sqrt{\frac{2(30)(1,000)}{4}}$$

$$q = 123.$$

The *EOQ* will be overstated by 23 units. The 50 percent error in K_O has produced a 23 percent error in the order quantity.

The use of a nonoptimal order quantity will, in turn, affect the total inventory related costs. Using the new order quantity, the total cost becomes:

$$T_C = K_O D/q + K_C q/2$$
$$T_C = 20(1,000/123) + 4(123/2)$$
$$T_C = \$408.60.$$

The 50 percent overestimate of K_O results in a total cost of \$408.60. It has produced an increase in total cost of \$8.60, or only 2.15 percent. The total cost is insensitive to fairly large errors in the parameter input information.

The *insensitivity* of total cost to parameter errors is the result of two dampening factors. *The order quantity will change only by the square root of the multiple increase caused by an error in parameter estimation.*[4] And, as Figures 14.2 and 14.3 demonstrate, *the total-cost curve is reasonably flat for moderate errors in the order quantity.* In essence, large errors in parameter estimates will

---

[4] A 50 percent overestimate will increase the new parameter to 1.50 times the correct value. The order quantity will increase by $\sqrt{1.50}$ or 1.23: a 23 percent increase. A 100 percent overestimate will double the correct value, with an associated order quantity increase of $\sqrt{2}$, or 1.41 times: a 41 percent increase.

produce small to moderate errors in the order quantity. Small or moderate errors in the order quantity will produce minimal increases in total costs. Total costs are rather insensitive even to substantial errors in parameter input. As long as the parameters are reasonably accurate, the EOQ model will serve as an effective tool.

The Economic Reorder Point

In forming an optimal inventory policy, there are two decision variables: *the economic order quantity (q)* and the *reorder point (R)*. For a purchaser with deterministic demand, the order quantity is provided by the EOQ model:

$$q = \sqrt{\frac{2K_o D}{K_C}}.$$

As was mentioned earlier, the reorder point represents the level of inventory at which an order is placed for q items. The period between the requisition and the receipt of the new order quantity is the lead time (L_T). For this type of inventory system, the lead time is a known constant with uniform demand. Demand will exactly equal supply with no stockouts or remaining inventory at the end of the lead time (Figure 14.1).

For this deterministic system, the reorder point is easily determined. Defining the daily utilization rate as U_R, the reorder point will be:

$$R = \underset{\substack{\text{no. days}}}{L_T} \cdot \underset{\substack{\text{utilization} \\ \text{per day}}}{U_R} .$$

The optimal reorder point (R) is equal to the demand during the lead time: the number of days in the lead time multiplied by the demand per day.[5]

To find R in the foregoing problem, reconsider the following information:

$$D = 1,000 \qquad K_O = \$20 \qquad q = 100$$
$$L_T = 5 \text{ days} \qquad K_C = \$4.$$

The uniform daily utilization rate will be:

$$U_R = \frac{D}{\text{no. of days}}.$$

---

[5] The inventory system assumes that the lead time is less than the time required to deplete the total order quantity.

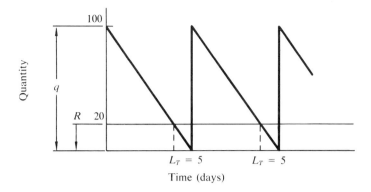

FIGURE 14.4
The Optimal Inventory Policy

If there are 250 working days:

$$U_R = \frac{1{,}000}{250}$$

$U_R = 4$ per day.

Four items are demanded daily over the five-day lead time. The demand during the lead time will be:

$$R = L_T \cdot U_R$$
$$= 5 \cdot 4$$
$$= 20.$$

The decision variables that minimize total inventory related costs are ($R = 20$, $q = 100$). The inventory system with optimal decision variables is presented in Figure 14.4. When the level of inventory reaches 20 items, an order is placed for 100 items. The order will arrive in five days, when the inventory has just been depleted.

QUANTITY DISCOUNTS

The *EOQ* model allows a systematic derivation of the order quantity for a purchaser with deterministic demand. The model is restricted, however, to the underlying assumptions of a known uniform demand, known constant lead time, constant values of K_O and K_C, and a constant purchase price for the products. A frequent exception to these assumptions occurs when a *quantity discount* is available. In this case price no longer remains constant, but varies with the quantity purchased.

If quantity discounts are allowed, the total inventory related costs will include the cost of the inventory (C_I):

$$T_C = C_O + C_C + C_I.$$

The total cost of inventory will be the price per item multiplied by the number of items. Using K_P to represent the purchase price of an item, the total annual cost of inventory becomes:

$$C_I = \underset{\text{price}}{K_P} \cdot \underset{\substack{\text{no.} \\ \text{demanded.}}}{D}$$

Total inventory related costs can be expressed as:

$$T_C = \underset{\text{ordering costs}}{K_O\, D/q} + \underset{\text{carrying costs}}{K_C\, q/2} + \underset{\text{cost of inventory}}{K_P D}.$$

The purchase of larger-than-normal quantities to obtain a quantity discount will have several effects on total cost. Purchasing the larger quantity will decrease the number of orders per year and therefore the ordering costs. Also the price reduction accompanying the larger purchase will reduce the cost of inventory. On the other hand, the larger quantity will increase the average inventory, resulting in increased carrying costs. The effect of purchasing larger-than-normal quantities at a discount may be summarized as:

$$T_C = K_O\, D/q\uparrow\downarrow + K_C\, q\uparrow/2\uparrow + K_P\downarrow D\downarrow.$$

The critical question is *whether the net economic effect will be an increase or a decrease in total costs* (T_C).

The objective, again, is to select a decision variable that will minimize total costs. Although a mathematical model can be developed to determine whether the *EOQ* or a larger quantity at discount price is preferable, a simpler approach to the problem is provided by the basic *model for decision making*:

1. List the alternatives.

2. Evaluate them.

3. Select the best.

In the present problem, the required input parameters are:

$$D = 4{,}000; \quad K_O = \$16; \quad K_C = \$5.$$

Price Break Quantity	Unit Price	Discount
401 or more	$ 9.00	10%
201 – 400	$ 9.50	5%
1 – 200	$10.00	0% (base price)

TABLE 14.3
Quantity Discounts

The discounts for quantity purchases are listed in Table 14.3. The alternatives are:

A_1: Use EOQ
A_2: Stock 201 for a 5 percent discount
A_3: Stock 401 for a 10 percent discount.

The criterion for evaluation is:

min. $T_C = K_O D/q + K_C q/2 + K_P D$.

Alternative 1 uses the EOQ model:

$$q = \sqrt{\frac{2K_O D}{K_C}}$$

$$q = \sqrt{\frac{2(16)(4,000)}{5}}$$

$$q = 160.$$

For an order of 160 items, there is no quantity discount. The total inventory related cost will be:

$T_C = K_O D/q + K_C q/2 + K_P D$
$T_C = 16(4,000/160) + 5(160/2) + 10(4,000)$
$T_C = \$40,800.$

Alternative 2 is to order 201 items to obtain a 5 percent discount. An order of 201 items exceeds the economic order quantity. The combination of ordering and carrying costs will increase. The cost of the inventory, however, will decrease by 5 percent. The total inventory related cost will be:

$T_C = 16(4,000/201) + 5(201/2) + 9.50(4,000)$
$T_C = \$38,820.90.$

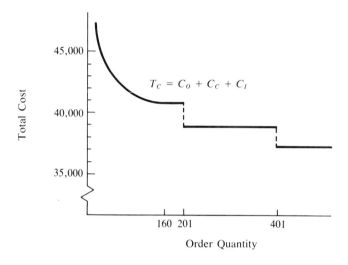

FIGURE 14.5
Total Cost with Quantity Discounts

Alternative 3 is to order 401 items to obtain a 10 percent discount. The total inventory related cost will be:

$$T_C = 16(4,000/401) + 5(401/2) + 9.00(4,000)$$
$$T_C = \$37,161.85.$$

Comparing the alternatives:

A_1: EOQ, $q = 160$—$T_C = \$40,800$
A_2: 5 percent discount, $q = 201$—$T_C = \$38,820.90$
A_3: 10 percent discount, $q = 401$—$T_C = \$37,161.85^*$.

The minimum total-cost selection is A_3, with a total inventory related cost of $37,161.85 (Figure 14.5). Alternative 3 offers a $3,638.15 savings over the economic order quantity by providing the option of a *nonoptimal order quantity* with a compensating price discount. Because the total inventory related cost curve flattens out near the economic order quantity, a small discount will frequently compensate for a reasonably large increase in the order quantity above the *EOQ* value.

THE DETERMINISTIC PRODUCTION RUN MODEL

A second basic inventory system is the *deterministic production run system*. The underlying assumptions, decision variables (R, q), and minimum total cost

Inventory Control: Deterministic Models

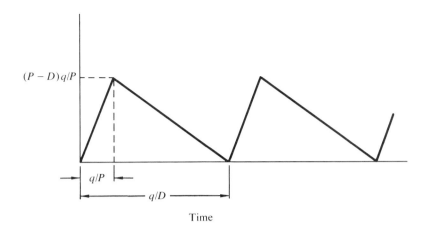

Time

FIGURE 14.6
The Deterministic Production Run System

objective of this system correspond to those of the deterministic system considered above. K_O, however, will no longer represent the ordering cost. In this model, it will represent the planning and setup costs for a production run. Also, the rate of production (P) will be constant and will exceed demand.

The deterministic production run system is represented in Figure 14.6. Since the rate of production exceeds demand, inventory will be accumulated during the production period. When the production run terminates, the accumulated level of inventory will be depleted to zero.[6] Upon depletion, the production cycle will be repeated.

The total inventory related costs are those of the deterministic model:

$$
\begin{array}{ccc}
\text{ordering} & \text{carrying} \\
\text{costs} & \text{costs} \\
T_C = & C_O & + & C_C & .
\end{array}
$$

The total ordering costs (C_O) might more appropriately be considered the total planning and setup costs. To be consistent, however, the notation used earlier will be retained:

$$
\begin{array}{cccc}
C_O = & K_O & \cdot & D/q \\
& \text{setup} & & \text{no. of} \\
& \text{cost} & & \text{setups.}
\end{array}
$$

---

[6] Since demand is known, no stockouts will occur.

The carrying-cost component (C_C) will require a new expression. The carrying cost was represented earlier by:

$$C_C = \underset{\underset{\text{per item}}{\text{cost}}}{K_C} \cdot \underset{\underset{\text{items.}}{\text{no. of}}}{q/2}$$

K_C still appropriately represents the cost of carrying an item over the time period. The average inventory, however, will no longer be $q/2$.

During the production period, items are produced at a rate P and demanded at a rate D.[7] Inventory will be accumulating at a rate $P - D$. The duration of the production run can be represented by:

duration of production run $= q/P$.

It is equal to the *quantity produced per production run divided by the rate of production*. For example, if 200 items are produced per production run at a production rate of 2,000 per year, the *time* required for a production run is .10 years:

$$\begin{aligned} \text{duration of production run} &= q/P \\ &= 200/2{,}000 \\ &= .10. \end{aligned}$$

Therefore, the size of the inventory at the end of the production run is expressed by:

$$\text{maximum inventory} = \underset{\underset{\text{accumulation}}{\text{rate of}}}{(P - D)} \cdot \underset{\text{time.}}{q/P}$$

To avoid confusion regarding the average level of inventory, the items in inventory can be separated into two categories: (1) inventory during the production run and (2) inventory after the production run. The separation is illustrated in Figure 14.7. During the production run period, the inventory level starts at zero and accumulates to $(P - D)q/P$. The average inventory level will be the maximum minus the minimum divided by two:

$$\begin{aligned} \frac{\text{average inventory level}}{\text{production cycle}} &= \frac{(P - D)q/P - 0}{2} \\ &= \frac{(P - D)q}{2P}. \end{aligned}$$

---

[7] Both terms are expressed for the same period: *e.g.*, annual production rate and annual demand.

Inventory Control: Deterministic Models

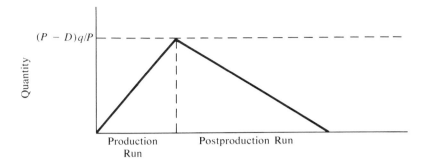

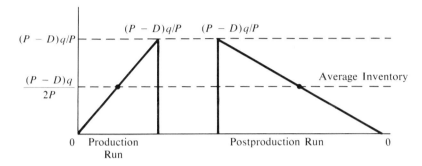

FIGURE 14.7

Average Inventory Level

During the post–production run period, the inventory starts at a maximum cf $(P - D)q/P$ and is uniformly depleted to zero. The average inventory level again becomes half of the maximum level:

$$\text{average inventory level} \atop \text{post production cycle} = \frac{(P - D)q}{2P}.$$

The average inventory carried during the production run is the same as the average level following the production run. *The average amount of inventory carried by the inventory system will be:*

$$\text{average inventory level} = \frac{(P - D)q}{2P}.$$

At a per unit cost of K_C, the *carrying cost* becomes:

$$C_C = K_C \frac{(P - D)q}{2P}.$$

With defined components, the *total inventory related cost* function is:

$$T_C = \overset{\text{ordering cost}}{K_O D/q} + \overset{\text{carrying cost}}{K_C \frac{(P-D)q}{2P}}.$$

The objective is to define the order quantity that minimizes T_C. As in the basic deterministic system, the *minimum total cost will occur at the intersection of the ordering-cost curve and the carrying-cost curve*—where the ordering costs equal the carrying costs (Figures 14.2 and 14.3). Setting C_O and C_C equal and solving for q:

$$C_O = C_C$$

$$K_O D/q = K_C \frac{(P-D)q}{2P}$$

$$q = \sqrt{\frac{2K_O D}{K_C}\left(\frac{P}{P-D}\right)}.$$

The more familiar calculus solution will verify this result. The minimum of the total-cost function with respect to order quantity is obtained by (1) calculating the first derivative, (2) setting the derivative equal to zero, and (3) solving for q. The total-cost function is:

$$T_C = K_O D/q + \frac{K_C(P-D)}{2P}.$$

The first derivative is:

$$\frac{dT_C}{dq} = \frac{-K_O D}{q^2} + \frac{K_C(P-D)}{2P}.$$

Setting this equal to zero and solving:[8]

$$\frac{-K_O D}{q^2} + \frac{K_C(P-D)}{2P} = 0$$

$$q = \sqrt{\frac{2K_O D}{K_C}\left(\frac{P}{P-D}\right)}.$$

———

[8] The second derivative is:

$$\frac{d^2 T_C}{dq^2} = \frac{2K_O D}{q^3} > 0.$$

Since the second derivative is positive, the first derivative has located a minimum.

Inventory Control: Deterministic Models

The Reorder Point and Number of Production Runs

The second decision variable is the reorder point. In the deterministic production system, a lead time (L_T) is required for the planning and setup of a production run. Since inventory will be depleted during the lead time, enough inventory must be available to prevent stockouts. The reorder point level of inventory will provide exactly for the demand during the lead time.[9] It can be calculated as:

$$R = \underset{\text{lead time}}{L_T} \cdot \underset{\substack{\text{utilization} \\ \text{rate}}}{U_R} .$$

The lead time (L_T) multiplied by the utilization rate provides the demand during the lead time.

It is sometimes necessary to know the *optimal number of production runs for a year* (N_R). This is easily determined. There should be ample production runs to satisfy annual demand (D). If the economic order quantity (q) is to be produced each time, then the optimal number must be:

$$N_R = D/q.$$

This formulation presupposes a knowledge of the optimal order quantity. A separate model can be constructed to express N_R directly in terms of the input parameters. Substituting the economic order quantity model solution for q and solving for N_R:

$$N_R = \frac{D}{\sqrt{\dfrac{2K_O D}{K_C}\left(\dfrac{P}{P-D}\right)}}$$

$$N_R{}^2 = \frac{D^2 K_C(P-D)}{2K_O DP}$$

$$N_R = \sqrt{\frac{DK_C(P-D)}{2K_O P}}.$$

The following example will demonstrate these models and the entire inventory system. The parameters of the system are: K_O, K_C, P, L_T, and D. The planning and setup cost is $40; the average annual carrying cost is $5 per item; the production rate is 15,000 per year; the lead time is four days; and demand is 6,000 per year. The problem is to determine the order quantity (q), the reorder point (R), and the number of production runs per year (N_R).

---

[9] This definition of the reorder point assumes the simplest case, in which the lead time demand is less than the pure demand portion of the inventory cycle. A similar model for the case in which lead time demand exceeds pure demand can be constructed.

From the *EOQ* model:

$$q = \sqrt{\frac{2K_oD}{K_C}\left(\frac{P}{P - D}\right)}$$

$$q = \sqrt{\frac{2(40)(6,000)}{5}\left(\frac{15,000}{15,000 - 6,000}\right)}$$

$$q = 400.$$

The reorder point is:

$$R = L_T \cdot U_R.$$

The daily utilization rate for a 250-day work year is:

$$U_R = D/250$$
$$U_R = 24.$$

The reorder point becomes:

$$R = 4 \cdot 24$$
$$R = 96.$$

The number of production runs will be:

$$N_R = D/q \qquad\qquad N_R = \sqrt{\frac{DK_C(P - D)}{2K_oP}}$$

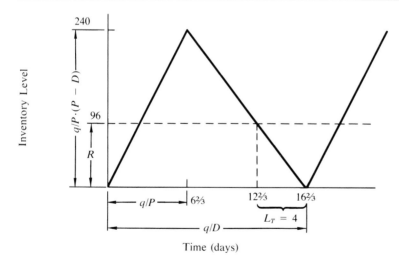

FIGURE 14.8

A Deterministic Production Run Inventory System

Inventory Control: Deterministic Models

$$N_R = 6{,}000/400 \qquad N_R = \sqrt{\frac{6{,}000 \cdot 5(15{,}000 - 6{,}000)}{2(40)(15{,}000)}}$$

$$N_R = 15 \qquad\qquad N_R = 15.$$

Figure 14.8 illustrates the first full cycle of the system. With an annual production rate of 15,000 and an annual demand of 6,000, the 250-day work year will require the production of 60 units per day with an accompanying daily demand for 24 units. Throughout the production run, inventory will accumulate at a rate of 36 items per day. The production run will continue for 6 2/3 days, providing an accumulated inventory of 240 items. Once production has stopped, the inventory will be depleted at a rate of 24 per day for another 6 days. At the end of this time, the reorder point level of 96 will be reached, signaling the beginning of the 4-day planning and setup period for the next production run. At the end of the lead time, the inventory will be completely depleted and the next production run will be started. The complete inventory cycle is 16 2/3 days, or 15 cycles in the 250-day year.

SUMMARY

In the past two decades, concern for better inventory management has stimulated the extensive development of quantitative models. The inventory problem focuses on the selection of two decision variables: the reorder point (R) and the order quantity (q). The criterion for selecting these variables is the minimization of total inventory related costs: ordering costs (C_O), carrying costs (C_C), underage costs (C_U), and inventory costs (C_I). While specifics vary with the type of decision environment, the proper decision variables provide an economic balance between the cost of keeping too many and keeping too few items in inventory reserve.

The variations in inventory decision environments are considerable. The most basic is a deterministic demand with uniform depletion, fixed lead time, and infinite production rate. The major inventory decision is to determine the economic order quantity (q) that will minimize inventory cycle costs ($C_O + C_C$). Several methods determine this value: the model for decision making, an algebraic solution for the special form of the cost function, and a differentiation of total costs. The other inventory decision is to determine the reorder point (R). It will simply be equal to the demand during the lead time.

An important variation of the deterministic inventory system occurs when quantity discounts are available. The inventory cycle costs are extended to include the cost of the inventory (C_I). The model for decision making provides a simple means for selecting the most economic quantity to purchase.

If items are produced instead of being purchased, the basic deterministic inventory system is easily converted to the deterministic production run system. The carrying costs during the production period are included in the economic order quantity (q). The reorder point (R) is again equal to the demand during the lead time. The number of annual production runs (N_R) is easily derived from the economic order quantity model (q).

BIBLIOGRAPHY

Arrow, K., S. Karlin, and H. Scarf. *Studies in the Mathematical Theory of Inventory and Production.* Stanford, Cal.: Stanford University Press, 1958.

Bierman, H., Jr., C. P. Bonini, and W. H. Hausman. *Quantitative Analysis for Business Decisions.* Homewood, Ill.: Richard D. Irwin, 1973.

Bock, R. H., and W. K. Holstein. *Production Planning and Control.* Columbus, Ohio: Charles E. Merrill Books, 1963.

Bowman, E. H., and R. B. Fetter. *Analysis of Production and Operations Management.* Homewood, Ill.: Richard D. Irwin, 1967.

Broom, H. N. *Production Management.* Homewood, Ill.: Richard D. Irwin, 1962.

Buchan, J., and E. Koenigsberg. *Scientific Inventory Management.* Englewood Cliffs, N.J.: Prentice-Hall, 1963.

Buffa, E. S. *Models for Production and Operations Management.* New York: John Wiley & Sons, 1963.

————. *Operations Management: Problems and Models.* New York: John Wiley & Sons, 1968.

————, and W. H. Taubert. *Production Inventory Systems: Planning and Control.* Homewood, Ill.: Richard D. Irwin, 1972.

Groff, G. K., and J. F. Muth. *Operations Management Analysis for Decisions.* Homewood, Ill.: Richard D. Irwin, 1972.

Hadley, G., and T. Whitin. *Analysis of Inventory Systems.* Englewood Cliffs, N.J.: Prentice-Hall, 1963.

Hanssmann, F. *Operations Research in Production and Inventory Control.* New York: John Wiley & Sons, 1962.

Hillier, F. S., and G. T. Lieberman. *Introduction to Operations Research.* San Francisco: Holden-Day, 1974.

Holt, C., F. Modigliani, J. Muth, and H. Simon. *Planning Production, Inventories, and Work Force.* Englewood Cliffs, N.J.: Prentice-Hall, 1960.

Killeen, L. M. *Techniques of Inventory Management.* New York: American Management Association, 1969.

Levin, R. I., and C. A. Kirkpatrick. *Quantitative Approaches to Management.* New York: McGraw-Hill Book Co., 1975.

Magee, J. F. *Production Planning and Inventory Control.* New York: McGraw-Hill Book Co., 1958.

————, and D. M. Boodman. *Production Planning and Inventory Control.* New York: McGraw-Hill Book Co., 1967.

Morris, W. T. *Analysis for Materials Handling Management.* Homewood, Ill.: Richard D. Irwin, 1962.

Naddor, E. *Inventory Systems.* New York: John Wiley & Sons, 1968.

Paik, C. M. *Quantitative Methods for Managerial Decisions.* New York: McGraw-Hill Book Co., 1973.

Prichard, J. W., and R. H. Eagle. *Modern Inventory Management.* New York: John Wiley & Sons, 1965.

Starr, M. K., and D. W. Miller. *Inventory Control: Theory and Practice.* Englewood Cliffs, N.J.: Prentice-Hall, 1962.

Stockton, R. *Basic Inventory Systems: Concepts and Analysis.* Boston: Allyn and Bacon, 1965.

Thierauf, R. J., and R. C. Klekamp. *Decision Making Through Operations Research.* New York: John Wiley & Sons, 1975.

Wagner, H. M. *Principles of Operations Research with Applications to Managerial Decisions.* Englewood Cliffs, N.J.: Prentice-Hall, 1969.

14.1. The costs associated with ordering, receiving, and inspecting items and placing them in inventories average around $2 per item. Orders arrive in shipments of 150 items. The annual demand is for 1,200 items. What is the annual ordering cost?

14.2. For a duration of one month, storage, handling, insurance, cost of capital, and breakage average 10 cents per item. Orders arrive each month in lots of 250 items. What is the total *annual* carrying cost?

14.3. The costs associated with requisitioning materials and placing them in inventory average $8. Every two months, orders arrive in truck-loads of 450 items. The items are purchased from a supplier for a delivered price of $12 each. Monthly storage, handling, and carrying costs per item average 14 cents. Calculate the total annual inventory costs for these materials.

14.4. The costs associated with placing an order are $10. Demand has been forecast for 1,000 units. It will be depleted uniformly over the next 12 months. The annual carrying cost per unit is $15. Determine the economic order quantity (*EOQ*).

14.5. Four hundred items are demanded annually. The cost of placing and expediting an order is $4. Carrying one unit in inventory for a year has an expected cost of 50 cents. Use the *model for decision making* to determine the optimal order quantity.

14.6. Two hundred items are demanded uniformly throughout the year. The cost of placing and expediting a purchase order is $10. Annual carrying costs are $1 per item. For different order quantities, graph the associated order cost, carrying cost, and total cost curves. Locate the optimal order quantity on the graph.

14.7. During the 250 working days, there will be a uniform demand for 1,250 units of a special input material. Ordering costs for the material are $10. The annual carrying cost is $2 per unit of the material. The lead time from requisition to receipt of order is 4 days. Determine the optimal inventory policy decision variables (q, R).

14.8. In determining the economic order quantity (*EOO*), the parameter estimates are:

$D = 800; K_O = \$20; K_C = \$9.$

The ordering cost (K_O) and carrying costs per unit (K_C) may contain estimating errors as large as 10 percent. What is the potential change in the economic order quantity? What dollar and percentage changes in total costs will be produced for the range of potential economic order quantities? Use the initial estimates for K_O and K_C.

14.9. The following order quantity information is available:

Demand for the next four months = 720
Lead time = 8 days
Ordering costs = $24
Annual carrying costs = $6
320 working days per year.

Determine the optimal values for the inventory policy decision variables.

14.10. An organization requires 2,500 units of a specially manufactured part to be used in the production of several main products. The units can be purchased more economically from a supplier. The estimated ordering cost is $9. The annual carrying cost is $2 per unit.

If sufficient quantities are ordered, the supplier is willing to provide a discount. The first 100 units must be purchased at the regular price of $20 each. If more than 100 units are ordered, the number exceeding 100 can be purchased at a 4 percent reduction from the regular price. The number exceeding 250 can be purchased at a 7 percent reduction.

Given the possibility of these quantity discounts, what is the most economical order quantity?

14.11. The following production information is available:

Demand for the next six months = 820
Annual production rate = 4,800
Lead time for planning, scheduling, and setup = 2 days
Setup costs = $50
Annual inventory carrying charge = $10
300 working days per year.

Determine the proper production quantity (q), the reorder point (R), and the number of production runs (N_R) per year.

What is the length of the cycle between production runs? In each cycle, how many days will be spent on production? What will be the maximum size of the inventory?

14.12. An organization's available inventory supply is reduced uniformly. The organization periodically sets up for a production run to replenish inventory. For the 300-day work year, the annual production rate is 10,000 units. The demand for the finished product is 4,000 annually. The lead time required to set up for a production run is 5 days. The estimated setup costs are $90. The annual inventory carrying cost for items is $4 per unit.

1. What is the most economical production quantity?
2. At what level of inventory should the planning and setup for a new production run begin?
3. What is the optimal number of production runs per year?
4. What is the length of the cycle between production runs?
5. A production run will continue for how many days?

6. At what rate will inventory accumulate during the production run?
7. What will be the maximum inventory at the end of a production run?
8. What will be the rate of depletion of inventory after the production run?

14.13. An organization manufactures and assembles a major subcomponent for later use in final assembly. For the 300-day work year, there is a projected annual usage requirement of 12,000 subcomponents. The annual cost of maintaining a subcomponent in inventory reserve is $14.

The subcomponents can be produced by either of two production systems. Large lots can be produced by a mass assembly system with an annual capacity of 100,000 subcomponents. The setup costs are $280. Smaller lots can be produced by a sub-assembly system with a setup cost of only $70. The production rate, however, is reduced to an annual capacity of 40,000 subcomponents. The daily cost of the mass assembly system is $510. The subassembly system can be operated at a daily cost of $340.

How should the subcomponent parts be produced?

14.14. You must decide whether to purchase or produce a required subcomponent. For the 250-day work year, the annual demand is estimated at 2,500. If you purchase the subcomponent, the ordering costs will average $12 and the annual inventory carrying costs will be around $2 per subcomponent. The lead time for deliveries will be 7 days. The product can be purchased for a regular price of $22. Moreover, if you purchase losts of 200 or more, you can obtain a quantity discount of 5 percent off the regular price. For lots of 400 or more, there is a quantity discount of 10 percent.

If the subcomponents are produced in-house, the setup time is two days, with an associated cost of $104. With present equipment, the annual rate of production is 15,000. The subcomponents can be produced for $18 each. The annual inventory carrying cost for the subcomponents will remain at $2. However, maintaining an adequate supply of raw materials to produce the subcomponents entails an added annual cost of $240.

Should you purchase or produce the subcomponents? If you were to purchase, what values would you use for the inventory decision variables? If you were to produce, what values would you use for the decision variables?

15

Inventory Control:
Stochastic Models

In the inventory models previously described, the parameters of the inventory system were assumed to be known constants—the decision environment was assumed deterministic. In most actual situations, the decision environment cannot be defined with complete certainty. Carrying and ordering (or setup) costs may not be easily assessed or simply stated. The lead time may not be a fixed constant. Transportation problems, strikes, or shortages of raw materials may cause unavoidable supplier delays. Product demand may not be easily estimated. It may not follow a uniform rate of depletion. Numerous internal and external environmental influences may cause demand to fluctuate appreciably: seasonal variations, new competition, advertising, distribution expansion, inflation, recession, and the like. More realistically, the decision environment will not be deterministic. It will be stochastic.

The *abstraction* of the real world to be formally modeled can be extended to incorporate these uncertainties. *Stochastic inventory models* have been developed to cope with the inherent uncertainties of inventory systems. This chapter will present several common and basic stochastic inventory models.

INVENTORY WITH STOCHASTIC DEMAND

Under conditions of demand uncertainty, the inventory policy decision variables remain the same: the determination of an optimal reorder point (R) and order quantity (q) to minimize inventory related costs. The essential difference is that *the decision environment is more complex*. As illustrated in Figure 15.1, a quantity of q items is ordered when the level of inventory is depleted to the reorder point R. The order of q items to replenish inventory supplies will arrive

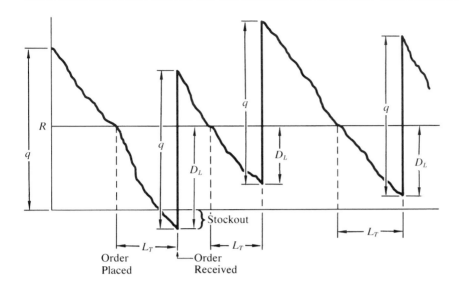

FIGURE 15.1
The Stochastic Demand System

at the end of the lead time period L_T.[1] When the new supply is received, the cycle is repeated.

The stochastic nature of demand will produce an added dimension to the decision environment: the possibility of *stockouts* and *surpluses*. If *lead time demand* (D_L) is higher than average, the items demanded (D_L) will exceed the available inventory supply (R): *A stockout of* $(D_L - R)$ *items.* If *lead time demand* is lower than average, the items demanded will not exceed the available inventory supply: *A surplus of* $(R - D_L)$.

Either a stockout or a surplus will produce an inventory related cost. If there is a stockout, customers will be required to wait.[2] Associated with the delay, there will be a *stockout (or underage) cost of K_U per item*. If there is a surplus, excess items will be carried in inventory. There will be an *annual carrying (or overage) cost of K_C per item*.

The possibility of stockouts and surpluses complicates the decision environment considerably. The total inventory related cost function must be extended to include the stockout (or underage) costs (C_U) and additional carrying costs (C_{CS}) for surpluses:

$$TC = \overset{\text{ordering cost}}{C_O} + \overset{\text{carrying cost}}{C_C + C_{CS}} + \overset{\text{underage cost}}{C_U}$$

[1] As a simplification, the lead time period is assumed to be of constant duration. Stochastic lead times have been incorporated into more complex models.
[2] This model assumes no lost sales from backorders. A proportion of lost sales and lost customers can be incorporated into a more elaborate model.

Inventory with Stochastic Demand

The ordering cost (C_O) and carrying cost (C_C) were defined in Chapter 14:

$$C_O = K_O D/q \qquad C_C = K_C q/2.$$

The two new cost components will be defined in terms of the basic parameters.

The underage cost (C_U) is considered first. If demand during the lead time exceeds the reorder point quantity, a stockout will occur. The size of the stockout will be the difference between the demand (D_L) and the supply (R):

stockout quantity $= (D_L - R)$.

If the stockout cost is K_U per item, the total stockout cost for the period will be:

period stockout cost $= \underset{\text{cost per item}}{K_U} \cdot \underset{\text{no. of items.}}{(D_L - R)}$

Since demand during the lead time is probabilistic, there will be several possible levels of demand (D_{L_i}) with associated probabilities ($P(D_{L_i})$). Therefore, considering all of the lead time demands that exceed supply, the *expected underage cost per cycle* can be represented by:

expected underage cost per cycle $= \underset{\text{cost per item}}{K_U} \cdot \underset{\text{expected stockout quantity.}}{\sum_i (D_{L_i} - R)P(D_{L_i})}$

With D/q cycles per year, the *expected annual underage costs* will be:

$$C_U = \underset{\substack{\text{no. cycles}\\ \text{per year}}}{D/q} \cdot \underset{\text{expected cost per cycle .}}{K_U \sum_i (D_{L_i} - R)P(D_{L_i})}$$

The added carrying cost from surplus inventory (C_{CS}) must also be parametrized. If the reorder point is set at the *expected level of demand during the lead time* (as in the deterministic counterpart to this model), there will be two opposing effects. During some inventory cycles, the actual lead time demand will exceed the expected demand. Stockout periods will result with favorable carrying costs. During other inventory cycles, the actual lead time demand will be less than the expected demand. Periods of excessive inventory will result with unfavorable carrying costs. Therefore, over a sufficient number of cycles, the net effect of stockouts and excesses on the average level of inventory will largely tend to balance out. *If the order point is set equal to the expected lead time demand, the carrying costs will remain approximately the same.*

Unfortunately, measuring the carrying cost is not quite so simple. If the reorder point is set at the expected lead time demand, stockouts will occur frequently. To avoid excessive underage costs (C_U), a safety or buffer stock will

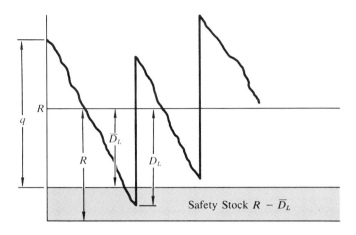

FIGURE 15.2
The Level of Safety Stock $(R - D_L)$

be carried. *The safety stock will consist of those items exceeding the expected lead time demand $(\bar{D}_L)$:*

safety stock $= (R - \bar{D}_L)$.

Compared with a policy of no safety stock, the increased carrying cost for maintaining a buffer against stockouts is approximately:[3]

safety stock carrying cost $(C_{CS}) = \underset{\substack{\text{carrying cost} \\ \text{per item}}}{K_C} \cdot \underset{\substack{\text{no. carried in} \\ \text{safety stock}}}{(R - \bar{D}_L)}$.

The added carrying cost for maintaining safety stock is the cost per item multiplied by the size of the safety stock. Additions to safety stock (Figure 15.2) are made by increasing the value of the order point (R) for the expected lead time demand $(\bar{D}_L)$.

Now that the cost components are expressed in terms of basic parameters, the inventory problem might conveniently be restated. Under conditions of demand uncertainty, the total inventory related costs are again:

$$T_C = \underset{\text{ordering cost}}{C_O} + \underbrace{C_C + C_{CS}}_{\text{carrying cost}} + \underset{\text{underage cost}}{C_U}.$$

---

[3] This expression of C_{CS} will produce an underestimate by $K_C \sum (D_{L_i} - R)P(D_{L_i})$. Since the expected stockout quantity $(\sum (D_{L_i} - R)P(D_{L_i}))$ will typically be very small, the approximation is customary.

In terms of parameters,

$$T_C = \underbrace{K_O D/q}_{\text{ordering cost}} + \underbrace{K_C q/2 + K_C(R - D_L)}_{\text{carrying cost}} + \underbrace{K_U D/q \sum_i (D_{L_i} - R)P(D_{L_i})}_{\text{underage cost}}$$

The policy decision is to find the values of the decision variables (R and q) that will make the new total inventory related cost as small as possible.

Before defining a procedure to determine the optimal decision variables, the internal relationships of the inventory systems will be examined. This will establish the concepts for several important conclusions. In the deterministic inventory system, the total inventory related costs contained two components related to the number of annual inventory cycles:

$$T_C = \overbrace{\underbrace{C_O}_{\text{ordering cost}} + \underbrace{C_C}_{\text{carrying cost.}}}^{\text{cycle costs}}$$

For this deterministic system, the objective was to derive an optimal order quantity (q) to define the number of inventory cycles that would minimize ordering and carrying costs.

With the introduction of uncertainty in demand, stockouts become possible. A safety stock is required to control stockout related costs (C_U). The safety stock increases inventory with related carrying costs (C_{CS}). The uncertainty in demand contributes two new opposing cost components:

$$\overbrace{\underbrace{C_{CS}}_{\text{carrying cost}} + \underbrace{C_U}_{\text{underage cost.}}}^{\text{Safety Stock Costs}}$$

The decision variable that directly influences the level of safety stock is the reorder point (R). An optimal order point (R) will provide a safety stock that minimizes the total safety stock costs.

In summary, total inventory related costs consist of two segments:

$$T_C = \overbrace{C_O + C_C}^{\text{cycle costs}} + \overbrace{C_{CS} + C_U}^{\text{safety stock costs}}.$$

First, the cycle costs are a *direct* function of the order quantity:

$$T_C = \overbrace{C_O + C_C}^{\text{cycle costs}}$$

$$T_C = \underset{\underset{f(q)}{\uparrow}}{K_O D/q} + \underset{\underset{f'(q)}{\uparrow}}{K_C q/2}.$$

The decision variable q will define the proper number of inventory cycles needed to minimize cycle related costs. Second, *for a given q*, the proper level of safety stock is a *direct* function of the reorder point (R):

$$\overbrace{C_{CS} \quad + \quad C_U}^{\text{safety stock costs}}$$

$$\underset{\underset{f(R)}{\uparrow}}{K_C(R - D_L)} + \underset{\underset{f'(R)}{\uparrow}}{K_U D/q \sum_i (D_{L_i} - R)P(D_{L_i})}.$$

The decision variable R will define the level of safety stock needed to minimize safety stock related costs.

There is one complication: *The decision variables contain a joint dependence.* For a given q, the safety stock problem is solved by the selection of an optimal R. The optimal q, however, will not be known initially, and the level of q will effect the optimality of R.

The interdependence of q and R occurs in the underage cost component. If q is not a given value, the underage costs are a function of both decision variables:

$$C_U = K_U D/q \sum_i (D_{L_i} - R)P(D_{L_i})$$

$$C_U = f(q, R).$$

The selection of q determines the number of annual inventory cycles (D/q). The number of cycles defines the number of periods when stockouts are possible. The order quantity (q) significantly affects underage costs (C_U). In turn, the selection of R defines the best safety stock level. It directly affects underage costs (C_U). Through the double dependency on underage costs, a cycle of interdependence is created: a change in q will require a different best R, and conversely, a change in R will require a different best q.

A circular dependence exists among the decision variables and all of the cost components. A change in the order quantity will demonstrate the dynamics of the interreactive system components:

$$\Delta q \uparrow \rightarrow C_O \downarrow C_C \uparrow$$
$$\rightarrow C_U \downarrow$$
$$C_U \downarrow \rightarrow R \downarrow$$
$$R \downarrow \rightarrow C_{CS} \downarrow C_U \uparrow$$
$$C_U \uparrow \rightarrow \Delta q.$$

An increase in the order quantity directly affects the cycle costs: ordering costs (C_O) will decrease, and carrying costs (C_C) will increase. By decreasing the number of annual inventory cycles, an increase in q will decrease underage costs (C_U). A decrease in underage costs will lower the best selection of R for the given q. In turn, a lower R will affect the safety stock costs: carrying costs (C_{CS}) will decrease, and underage costs (C_U) will increase. The new upward movement of underage costs will change the best selection of q. The process of adjustment has gone full circle. A change in one decision variable has stimulated adjustments in each cost component and the other decision variable. In turn, this sets off a second round of repercussions.

If q was not at the optimal value when it was increased, the second-round best selection of q will move toward the optimal value. The cycle of cost component and decision variable adjustments will continually produce a better q with an accompanying best R. The incremental total cost improvements will get smaller and smaller until the system has regained equilibrium with an optimal q and an accompanying optimal R.

Because the decision variables are interdependent, a theoretically exact order quantity and reorder point must be derived simultaneously from the total cost equation. To avoid some knotty mathematics, however, the conventional simplification will provide a reasonably accurate approximation.[4] The decision variables will be *assumed independent*. A good approximation of the optimal order quantity will be obtained from the *EOQ* model that considers only cycle costs. This value of q will then serve as a given in the derivation of the optimal reorder point to minimize safety stock costs.

INVENTORY WITH DEMAND UNCERTAINTY: A FUNDAMENTAL APPROACH

There are several procedures for obtaining an optimal order point and reorder quantity for conditions of demand uncertainty. The approach previously outlined will provide a reasonable approximation:

1. Determine q to minimize inventory cycle costs:

$$q = \sqrt{\frac{2K_O D}{K_C}}.$$

2. With the approximate optimal q, determine the best R to minimize safety stock costs.

---

[4] An iterative model can be constructed to provide an exact solution for the two parameters. q can be redefined as a function of R. For an initial assessment of q(*EOQ* model), a corresponding optimal R can be determined. With this R, a new q can be calculated. The new q will lead to a new R which, in turn, will provide an improved q. The iterative improvements quickly produce the optimal parameters.

Demand During the Lead Time (D_L)	$P(D_L)$	$P(\leqslant D_L)$
61	.02	.02
62	.14	.16
63	.23	.39
64	.24	.63
65	.21	.84
66	.12	.96
67	.04	1.00

TABLE 15.1

Probability of Demand During the Lead Time

One difficulty remains in applying this procedure. The order quantity is readily obtained from the *EOQ* model. The reorder point that minimizes safety stock costs, however, is not obvious: a model will be required to derive the best *R*. If the number of alternatives is not excessive, the *fundamental model for decision making* may be used.

The economic order quantity model and the fundamental model for decision making will be used to derive the optimal set of decision variables in the following example. From accounting records and other sources, a product under inventory management has an estimated annual demand (*D*) of 3,200 items. Costs per order (K_O) are estimated at \$16; annual carrying costs per item (K_C) average \$4, stockout costs (K_U) are estimated to average \$10:

$$D = 3,200 \qquad K_C = \$4$$
$$K_O = \$16 \qquad K_U = \$10.$$

The estimated uncertainty of demand during the 5-day lead time ($L_T = 5$) is presented in Table 15.1. There are 250 working days per year.

The proper order quantity is easily determined by applying the *EOQ* model:

$$q = \sqrt{\frac{2K_O D}{K_C}}$$

$$= \sqrt{\frac{2(16)(3,200)}{4}}$$

$$= 160.$$

One hundred and sixty items will be ordered at the reorder point of each inventory cycle.

Determining the reorder point is not so simple. The reorder point will define the proper level of safety stock. The selection of R must properly balance the cost of carrying safety stock units and the cost of stockouts in an environment of uncertain demand.

In applying the fundamental model for decision making to determine a best R, the first step is a clear definition of the alternatives. The level of safety stock, the value of R, is selected to provide sufficient supply during the lead time period. Refer to the demand during lead time (Table 15.1). There are seven potentially acceptable values of R:

$$61 \leq R \leq 67.$$

In no previous case had demand been less than 61 or more than 67.

Before these values of R are evaluated, the alternatives will be further restricted. The expected demand during the lead time is calculated as:

$$\bar{D}_L = \sum_i D_{L_i} P(D_{L_i})$$

$$= 64.$$

If R is set at 64, it will be equivalent to the R for the deterministic system (Chapter 14). There will be no safety stock. The probability demand will exceed this amount and required safety stock is .37. The probability of a stockout with associated underage costs is high. If R is set at 65, a safety stock of one unit will be carried:

$$\text{safety stock} = (R - \bar{D}_L)$$
$$= (65 - 64)$$
$$= 1.$$

This decision rule will reduce the likelihood of a stockout to .16. Underage costs will be reduced at the cost of carrying the safety stock unit. Any further increase in the level of safety stock will produce the anticipated effects:

$$C_{CS}\uparrow \qquad C_U\downarrow.$$

The problem is to find the level of R that will minimize the combination of C_{CS} and C_U.

Since stockout costs are generally high relative to carrying costs, some level of safety stock is usually warranted. Therefore, it would be advisable to restrict the alternative search for an optimal R to zero or more units of safety stock:

$$64 \leq R \leq 67.$$

Reorder Point (R)	Safety Stock $(R - D_L)$	Annual Carrying Cost $(K_C = \$4)$
64	0	\$0
65	1	4
66	2	8
67	3	12

TABLE 15.2

Reorder Point Carrying Costs

If the analysis of these values leads to 64 as the best selection, then evaluations of R below 64 will be required.

The alternative space of potential reorder points will consist of:

A_0	A_1	A_2	A_3
$R = 64$	$R = 65$	$R = 66$	$R = 67$

Each alternative requires evaluation in terms of the total inventory related cost criterion:

$$T_C = \underbrace{K_C(R - D_L)}_{\substack{C_{CS} \\ \text{carrying costs}}} + \overbrace{K_U D/q \underbrace{\sum_i (D_{L_i} - R)P(D_{L_i})}_{\text{underage costs}}}^{\substack{C_U}}$$

$$\text{Safety Stock Costs}$$

The carrying costs for the alternatives are evaluated in Table 15.2. If the reorder point is set at the expected demand during the lead time, there will be no safety stock and zero carrying costs. If R is set at 65 with a safety stock of one, there will be an annual carrying cost of \$4. As R is increased above the expected demand, the carrying costs will increase by increments of \$4.

The underage cost evaluations are slightly more complicated. If R is set at 64 with no safety stock, there are several possible levels of demand with specific associated costs. If demand during the lead time (D_L) is 64 or less, there will be no need for a safety stock and the underage costs will be zero. If D_L exceeds 64, several calculable costs may occur. The larger the value of D_L, the more stockouts will occur with associated losses. With R at 64, D_L could be 65, 66, or 67 with associated stockouts of one, two, or three items respectively. With a stockout cost per item of \$10 and the probability of lead time demand (Table 15.1), the expected underage cost *per cycle* can be determined:

$$E(C_U)\text{per cycle} = K_U \sum_i (D_{L_i} - R)P(D_{L_i}).$$

Reorder Point (R)	Lead-Time Demand (D_L)	Stockouts $(D_L - R)$	Prob. of Stockout $P(D_L)$	Expected Stockout Cost Per Cycle $K_U \Sigma (D_L - R)P(D_L)$	Annual Expected Stockout Costs $D/qK_U\Sigma(D_L - R)P(D_L)$
64	64	0	.63	$10(0)(.63) = 0.00$	$20(5.70) = \$114.00$
	65	1	.21	$10(1)(.21) = 2.10$	
	66	2	.12	$10(2)(.12) = 2.40$	
	67	3	.04	$10(3)(.04) = 1.20$	
				Total $\Sigma = 5.70$	
65	65	0	.84	$10(0)(.84) = 0.00$	$20(2.00) = \$ 40.00$
	66	1	.12	$10(1)(.12) = 1.20$	
	67	2	.04	$10(2)(.04) = .80$	
				Total $\Sigma = 2.00$	
66	66	0	.96	$10(0)(.96) = 0.00$	$20(0.40) = \$ 8.00$
	67	1	.04	$10(1)(.04) = 0.40$	
				Total $\Sigma = 0.40$	
67	67	0	1.00	$10(0)(1.0) = 0.00$	$20(0.00) = \$ 0.00$

TABLE 15.3

Stockout Costs for the Alternatives

For the decision rule of $R = 64$:

$$E(C_U)\text{per cycle} = \$10[(65 - 64)(.21) + (66 - 64)(.12) + (67 - 64)(.04)]$$
$$= \$5.70.$$

The expected underage costs *per cycle* for the other alternatives are presented in Table 15.3.

The required *annual expected underage cost* is derived by multiplying the cycle costs by the number of annual cycles. As before, the number of annual inventory cycles will be:

$$\text{annual inventory cycles} = D/q$$
$$= 3{,}200/160$$
$$= 20.$$

Therefore, the annual expected stockout cost for R of 64 is:

$$C_U(R = 64) = D/q \, K_U \sum_i (D_{L_i} - R)P(D_{L_i})$$
$$= 20(5.70)$$
$$= \$114.00.$$

Alternative Reorder Point (R)	Safety Stock $(R - D_L)$	Annual Carrying Cost (C_{CS})	Annual Expected Stockout Cost (C_U)	Total Safety Stock Costs
A_0: $R = 64$	0	$0	$114	$114
A_1: $R = 65$	1	4	40	44
A_2: $R = 66$	2	8	8	16
A_3: $R = 67$	3	12	0	12*

TABLE 15.4

Total Safety Stock Costs for Alternatives

The other alternatives are listed in Table 15.4. The annual expected stockout costs for the alternatives are:

R	C_U
64	$114
65	40
66	8
67	0

Increasing the safety stock more than proportionally decreases the annual expected stockout costs.

Once carrying and underage costs have been determined, the total safety stock costs for the decision variable alternatives are easily evaluated (Table 15.4). The lowest cost alternative is to set the reorder point at 67. This is a decision to carry a safety stock of three items with an annual cost of $12. There will be no possibility of a stockout.

DEMAND UNCERTAINTY WITH A SPECIFIED SERVICE LEVEL

The cost of a stockout cannot always be easily assessed. For a wholesaler or retailer, the assessment is difficult for several reasons. The customer may await the arrival of the new shipment. In many cases, however, the customer may find another supplier. Besides a lost sale, the customer too may be lost. Possibly only some customers will be lost. Others may remain, but with an increased propensity to seek a new supplier. Any new shortages may be more costly.

For a manufacturer, assessing the cost of a stockout may be even more difficult. The real value of a single unit in a large process may be difficult to assess. A stockout may cause a production shutdown—a machine may be

Demand (D_L)	$P(D_L)$	$P(\leqslant D_L)$
5	.03	.03
6	.07	.10
7	.18	.28
8	.28	.56
9	.24	.80
10	.12	.92
11	.06	.98
12	.02	1.00

TABLE 15.5
Demand During the Lead Time

temporarily idle or the entire production line may be abruptly halted. On the other hand, if two items are out of stock, the cost will not necessarily be doubled. A constant underage cost (K_U) may not be the most realistic assumption.

Because of this difficulty in assessment and because of the number of items in inventory, many organizations adopt a *service level policy*. For different products or product groups, the organization establishes a *probability of a stockout* that they are willing to live with. The level of safety stock is then chosen to conform with the probability specification.

A retailer maintaining a large inventory of products for direct consumer purchase illustrates the application of a service level policy. The following inventory parameters have been established: $D = 500$; $K_O = 8$; $K_C = 5$. A probability distribution representing demand during the 4-day lead time is presented in Table 15.5. There are 250 selling days per year. Products in this category have been assigned a 95 percent service level.

The order quantity is obtained directly from the *EOQ* model:

$$q = \sqrt{\frac{2K_O D}{K_C}}$$

$$= \sqrt{\frac{2(8)(500)}{5}}$$

$$= 40.$$

The reorder point must provide sufficient safety stock to avoid stockouts 95 percent of the time. The desired value is determined directly from the cumulative probability distribution of lead time demand (Table 15.5). With the specified service requirement, the order point (R) must be 11. An R of 11 will service the lead time demand without a stockout 98 percent of the time. If R is 10, the lead time demands will be satisfied only 92 percent of the time—insufficient for the 95 percent requirement.

With a specified service level, the inventory policy decision is simplified. The *EOQ* model determines the order quantity. The cumulative probability of lead time demand indicates the location of the reorder point.

AN ECONOMIC REORDER POINT MODEL FOR PROBABILISTIC DEMAND

In the deterministic inventory system with known demand (Chapter 14), the order quantity was the only decision variable that was difficult to obtain. The economic order quantity model was developed to solve this problem. The determination of the reorder point was straightforward. With a known demand, the reorder point was set equal to the demand during the lead time period. The value of R was simply the lead time period multiplied by the utilization rate.

Under conditions of uncertain demand, the problem is just the opposite. With the reasonable assumption of independence between the decision variables, a sufficiently accurate order quantity is provided by the economic order quantity model. *The difficulty is to determine an optimal reorder point.*

As was demonstrated earlier, the best reorder point was obtained by using the fundamental model for decision making: 1. List all potentially desirable reorder points. 2. Evaluate each in terms of the total safety stock costs. 3. Select the one with the lowest total safety stock costs. A severe drawback to this approach, however, is the often enormous number of alternatives requiring evaluation. Therefore, *an economic reorder point model* (*ERP*) will be constructed. It will directly define the optimal reorder point.

The model will structure a set of logic to restrict the alternatives to the single best choice. The criterion for evaluation will be the minimization of total safety stock related costs.

The reorder point indicates the safety stock needed to provide a buffer against stockouts. There are two opposing cost considerations. As the safety stock is increased, the cost of carrying the safety stock (C_{CS}) will increase, and the costs associated with stockouts (C_U) will decrease:

safety stock $\uparrow$: $C_{CS}\uparrow$ $C_U\downarrow$.

The objective is to determine the safety stock that minimizes both of these opposing cost components.

One logical approach for defining the best safety stock is to increase the safety stock by unit increments. If the reduction in underage costs (C_U) exceed the increase in carrying costs (C_{CS}), the total safety stock cost will be reduced—the added unit of safety stock will be economical. The addition of another unit to safety stock is then considered. As long as the reduction in C_U exceeds the increase in C_{CS}, the additions to safety stock are economical and they should continue.

The cost of adding one unit to the safety stock is readily approximated. Except when it is used to prevent a stockout,[5] the unit added to safety stock will be carried throughout the year. The annual unit carrying cost is K_C. Adding one unit to the safety stock will increase the carrying cost by:

$\Delta R\uparrow$ by 1 unit: $C_{CS}\uparrow$ by K_C.

The *savings* produced by adding one unit to safety stock is a more complex avoidance cost. If the added unit is not required, then no savings will occur. If the added unit is required to prevent a stockout, then there will be a direct savings of the underage cost (K_U). Since demand is probabilistic, the addition of the unit to safety stock will prevent stockouts only part of the time. It will prevent stockouts only when *the earlier safety stock level (R) produces a stockout.*

To quantify the expected savings from adding one unit to safety stock, the probability of a stockout with a reorder point R is defined as $P_S(R)$:

$P_S(R)$ = Probability of a stockout with a reorder point R.

In terms of lead time demand:

$P_S(R) = P(D_L > R)$.

The probability of a stockout with reorder point R is equal to the probability that lead time demand will exceed the reorder point R. In terms of a probability distribution of lead time demand, $P_S(R)$ represents the *right* tail of the distribution (Figure 15.3).

Adding one unit to safety stock provides a $P_S(R)$ probability of preventing a stockout costing K_U. The *expected per cycle* benefit of the added unit is:

expected cycle savings $= K_U P_S(R)$.

If the added safety stock unit is carried throughout the year, there will be D/q cycles of potential benefit. The *expected annual* savings produced by the safety stock unit becomes:

expected annual savings $= D/q\ K_U P_S(R)$.

Adding one unit to safety stock, the underage cost component of *safety stock costs* will decrease by:

$\Delta R\uparrow$ by 1 unit: $C_U\downarrow$ by $D/q\ K_U P_S(R)$.

---

[5] This period will be extremely short. It will last only from the time the unit is needed to the time the order quantity arrives.

Inventory Control: Stochastic Models

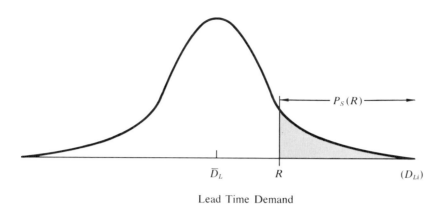

Lead Time Demand

FIGURE 15.3

$P_S(R)$: The Right Tail of the Probability Distribution of Lead Time Demand

To summarize, an incremental increase in the reorder point will have the following effect on total safety stock costs:

$$\Delta R\uparrow: C_{CS}\uparrow \qquad C_U\downarrow$$
$$\Delta R\uparrow: K_C\uparrow \qquad D/q\, K_U P_S(R)\downarrow.$$
(per unit)

As long as the underage cost savings $(C_U\downarrow)$ exceed the carrying cost losses $(C_{CS}\uparrow)$, the reorder point (R) should be increased:

$$\Delta R\uparrow \qquad \text{for } (C_U\downarrow \geq C_{CS}\uparrow)$$
$$\Delta R\uparrow \qquad \text{for } (D/q\, K_U P_S(R) \geq K_C).$$

For increasing values of R, Figure 15.4 illustrates the relative change in underage cost savings and carrying-cost losses. The underage cost curve is represented by:

$$D/q\, K_U P_S(R).$$

D, q, and K_U are parameter constants. As the safety stock increases $(\Delta R\uparrow)$, the probability of a stockout $P_S(R)$ decreases rapidly. The underage cost savings diminishes proportionally to the rapidly decreasing probability of a stockout. On the other hand, the carrying-cost losses for an additional unit of safety stock remain constant. Since underage cost savings will eventually fall below carrying cost losses, the reorder point should be increased to the intersection of the carrying-cost and the underage cost curves (Figure 15.4)—to the point where

---

An Economic Reorder Point Model for Probabilistic Demand   501

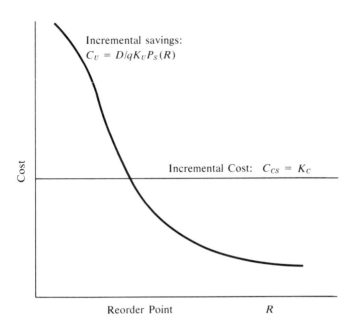

Incremental savings:
$C_U = D/qK_UP_S(R)$

Incremental Cost: $C_{CS} = K_C$

Cost

Reorder Point R

FIGURE 15.4
Incremental Safety Stock Costs

marginal costs equal marginal savings. The optimal value of R will be where:

marginal costs = marginal savings
$$K_C = D/q\ K_U P_S(R).$$

Solving in terms of parameter inputs, the *economic reorder point model* (*ERP*) becomes:

$$P_S(R) = \frac{K_C q}{K_U D}.$$

The reorder point will be optimal when the probability of a stockout equals this specified relationship between the parameters. Since the parameters will be known, the *ERP* model provides a direct determination of the required probability of a stockout for the best reorder point. With reference to the probability distribution of lead time demand, the exact location of the optimal reorder point will be uniquely defined.

Normally Distributed Demand

Under conditions of demand uncertainty, the decision variables can now be obtained directly. The steps for determining the proper decision variables are:

1. Determine the order quantity from the *economic order quantity model:*

$$q = \sqrt{\frac{2K_O D}{K_C}}.$$

2. Using the derived order quantity, determine the probability of a stockout that will minimize safety stock costs from the *economic reorder point model:*

$$P_S(R) = \frac{K_C q}{K_U D}.$$

3. Using the probability distribution of lead time demand, set the reorder point to correspond with the *ERP* model probability of a stockout.

An application will demonstrate the obtainment of the decision variables. A stockkeeping unit (*SKU*) has the following parameters:

$$D = 2,500$$
$$K_O = \$2 \qquad K_U = \$2$$
$$K_C = \$1 \qquad L_T = 5 \text{ days.}$$

There is a 250-day work year. The demand during the lead time is assumed to be *normally distributed*, with a mean ($\bar{D}_L$) of 50 and a standard deviation (σ_L) of 1.5.

In determining the decision variables, the order quantity is:

$$q = \sqrt{\frac{2K_O D}{K_C}}$$

$$= \sqrt{\frac{2(2)(2,500)}{1}}$$

$$= 100.$$

The safety stock level that minimizes total safety stock costs will have a probability of a stockout of:

$$P_S(R) = \frac{K_C q}{K_U D}$$

$$= \frac{1(100)}{2(2,500)}$$

$$= .02.$$

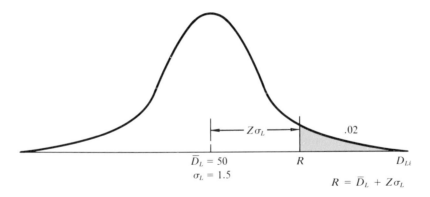

FIGURE 15.5

The Reorder Point with Normally Distributed Demand

The location of the reorder point that provides a 2 percent probability of a stockout is presented in Figure 15.5.

The area under the normal curve is measured in standardized units (Z)—the number of standard deviations away from the mean. Since 2 percent of the area lies to the right of R, reference to the normal distribution table (Appendix I) indicates that R must be 2.5 standard deviations to the right of the mean. The value of R is equal to the mean $(\bar{D}_L)$ plus 2.5 standard deviations:

$R = \bar{D}_L + Z\sigma_L$
$R = 50 + 2.5(1.5)$
$R = 53.75.$

The reorder point should be set at 54 units.

The policy decision for the SKU is to place orders for 100 items when the stock reaches a level of 54. There will be a safety stock of 4 units $(R - \bar{D}_L)$, allowing only a 2 percent probability of a stockout.[6] The inventory will progress through 25 cycles (D/q) during the year.

Normally Distributed Demand with a Specified Service Level

A second application will demonstrate the obtainment of the decision variables when there is a specified service level. A stockkeeping unit in a parts department has the following parameters:

$D = 3{,}200$
$K_O = \$8$
$K_C = \$2.$

---

[6] The level of safety stock is also equal to $Z\sigma_L$.

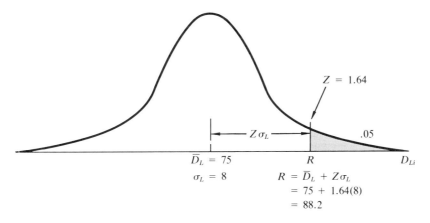

$Z = 1.64$

$Z\sigma_L$

$.05$

$\bar{D}_L = 75$

$\sigma_L = 8$

R

D_{Li}

$R = \bar{D}_L + Z\sigma_L$

$= 75 + 1.64(8)$

$= 88.2$

FIGURE 15.6

The Reorder Point with a 95 Percent Service Level

There is a 250-day work year. The lead time (L_T) is 6 days. The demand during the lead time is assumed to be normally distributed, with a mean $(\bar{D}_L)$ of 75 and a standard deviation (σ_L) of 8. The service level has been specified at 95 percent.

The order quantity is obtained from the *EOQ* model:

$$q = \sqrt{\frac{2K_O D}{K_C}}$$

$$= \sqrt{\frac{2(8)(3,200)}{2}}$$

$$= 160.$$

The probability of a stockout is set to correspond with the service level:

$$P_S(R) = .05.$$

With reference to the normal distribution table (Appendix I), a 5 percent area in the right tail has an associated Z of 1.64. The optimal order point (R^*) is 1.64 standard deviations to the right of the mean (Figure 15.6):

$$R = \bar{D}_L + Z\sigma_L$$
$$= 75 + 1.64(8)$$
$$= 88.2.$$

Service Level (%)	Standard Deviation from the Mean (Z)	Safety Stock ($Z\sigma_L$)	Carrying Cost of Safety Stock
60	.25	2.00	$4.00
70	.52	4.16	8.32
75	.68	5.44	10.88
80	.84	6.72	13.44
85	1.04	8.32	16.64
90	1.28	10.26	20.52
95	1.64	13.12	26.24
98	2.05	16.40	32.80
99	2.33	18.64	37.28
99.5	2.57	20.56	41.12
99.9	3.09	24.72	49.44
99.99	3.71	29.68	59.36

TABLE 15.6

Carrying Costs for Alternative Service Level Policy

The inventory policy decision to maintain a 95 percent service level is:

$q = 160$
$R = 88.$

There will be 13 units of safety stock ($R - \bar{D}_L$ or $Z\sigma_L$). The inventory will progress through 20 cycles annually (D/q).

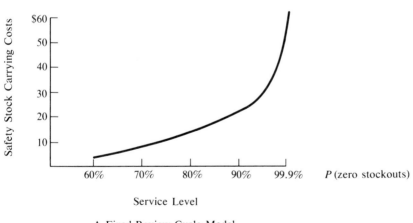

A Fixed-Review Cycle Model

FIGURE 15.7

Service-Cost Tradeoff

If the parts department manager is concerned with the appropriateness of the service level, service-cost tradeoff information is readily available. Table 15.6 and Figure 15.7 provide this information. As the service level increases, the carrying cost increases more than proportionally. Even minor service level improvements above 95 percent are extremely costly.

A FIXED-REVIEW CYCLE MODEL

Previously, the inventory systems have been *fixed-quantity variable-reorder cycle systems* (Figure 15.8). The order quantity q is fixed. The timing of the reorder varies with the level of stock. Another commonly used inventory system is a *variable-quantity fixed-reorder cycle system* (Figure 15.9). The reorder period is specified. The order quantity varies with demand conditions.

A *variable-quantity fixed-reorder cycle system* has several potential advantages. The fixed review and reorder period may allow batch processing and joint product shipments from suppliers. It is no longer necessary to record and compare each transaction with the reorder point level. Also, the ability to adjust the order quantity to changing demand conditions often substantially improves control and flexibility. To take full advantage of this system, however,

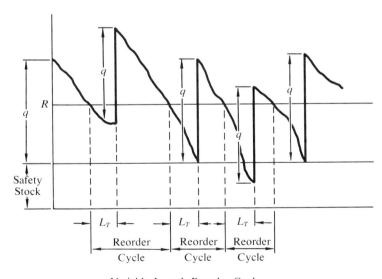

Variable Length Reorder Cycle

FIGURE 15.8
Fixed-Quantity Variable-Reorder Cycle System

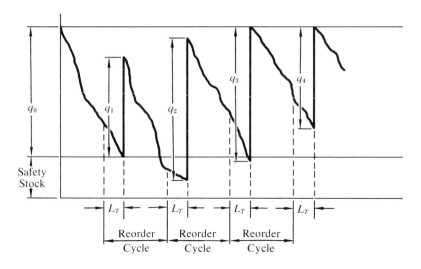

FIGURE 15.9

A Variable-Quantity Fixed-Reorder Cycle System

generally requires computer support and a heavy reliance on good short-term forecasting.

A variable-quantity fixed-reorder cycle system has two analogous decision variables: (1) *the duration of the reorder cycle* (T) and (2) *the fixed-target level of inventory* (q_T). Although there are numerous variations, the following system assumes a normally distributed demand with a constant lead time.

The inventory system is represented in Figure 15.10. The order is placed at the beginning of the lead time period. The order quantity will fluctuate with the amount of stock on hand. The *inventory on hand* (I) consists of supplies to satisfy lead time demand and the level of safety stock. The *quantity ordered* (q) *will adjust the inventory on hand* (I) *to the target quantity* (q_T):

inventory on hand + order quantity = target quantity

$$I \quad + \quad q \quad = \quad q_T \quad .$$

The quantity ordered, therefore, is represented by:

order quantity = target quantity − inventory on hand

$$q \quad = \quad q_T \quad - \quad I \quad .$$

The uncertainty of demand will cause the inventory at the reorder point to fluctuate with demand conditions. The order quantity (q) will adaptively adjust the inventory to the target level (q_T).

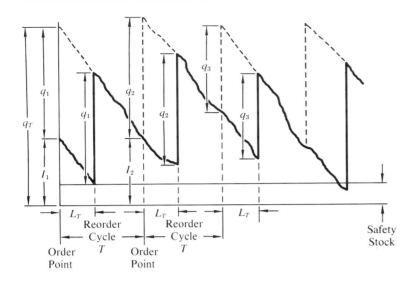

FIGURE 15.10

The Components of the Fixed-Reorder Cycle System

Proceeding through the series of inventory cycles presented in Figure 15.10, the order quantity of q_1 items will replenish the inventory supply at the end of the lead time. This new supply will be depleted until the end of the reorder cycle. The I_2 items on hand will then be adjusted to the target quantity by an order for q_2 items. The new order will not be received until the end of the lead time, when variations in lead time demand are less than the expected level. The excessive supply will be absorbed by a reduction in the forthcoming order quantity (q_3) at the reorder point.

Two essential components of the inventory system should be clarified. The *demand during the reorder cycle* of duration T consists of two subcomponents: (1) *demand during the lead time* and (2) *demand during the period from the receipt of the ordered quantity to the new reorder point.* These subcomponents are labeled A and B respectively in Figure 15.11a. These two subcomponents are connected in Figure 15.11b. Ignoring the effects of random variations, the total demand during the reorder cycle ($A + B$) will equal the order quantity (q):

order quantity = demand during the reorder cycle.

The second essential component is the *planning period* (P_P). *The planning period is defined as the reorder cycle plus the lead time.* The total duration will be:

planning-period duration = reorder cycle + lead time
$$P_P \qquad = \qquad T \quad + \quad L_T \quad .$$

A Fixed-Review Cycle Model

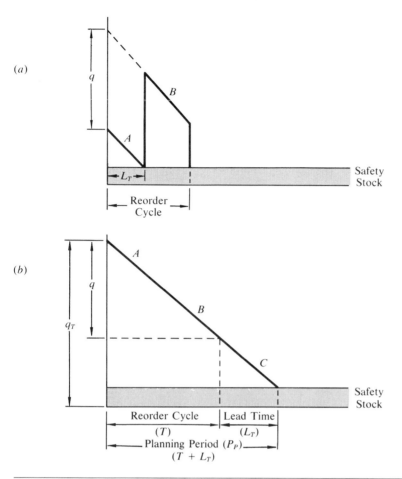

FIGURE 15.11

Expected Demand for Reorder Cycle and Planning Period

Therefore, as illustrated in Figure 15.11b, the expected demand for the planning period will be the demand during the reorder cycle ($A + B$) plus the lead time (C). With the addition of the safety stock buffer for demand uncertainties, the expected demand for the planning period is equal to the target quantity (q_T):

target quantity = expected planning-period demand + safety stock.

Once the componentry of the system is understood, models can be constructed to define the optimal decision variables (T, q_T). The criterion for evaluation is still the minimization of total inventory related costs. The values of T and q_T follow the same logic as the determination of q and R in the variable-cycle system considered earlier.

Inventory Control: Stochastic Models

For the variable-cycle system, total inventory related costs were separated into two components:

$$T_C = \text{cycle costs} + \text{safety stock costs.}$$

With the assumption of the independence between the decision variables, the order quantity (q) required to minimize cycle costs was derived as:

$$q = \sqrt{\frac{2K_O D}{K_C}}.$$

With this q, the position of R required to minimize safety stock costs was defined by the probability of a stockout:

$$P_S(R) = \frac{K_C q}{K_U D}.$$

For a normal distribution of lead time demand with this probability of a stockout, the specific position of R is:

$$R = \bar{D}_L + Z\sigma_L.$$

R is equal to the expected lead time demand plus the least-cost level of safety stock ($Z\sigma_L$).

The derivation of T and q_T proceeds analogously. *The value of T required to minimize cycle costs is determined from an economic order cycle mode!* (*EOC*). With this calculated T, the position of q_T required to minimize safety stock costs is expressed by the probability of a stockout ($P_S(q_T)$). With the normal distribution of lead time demand and this least-cost probability of a stockout, the location of the target quantity is:

$$q_T = \bar{D}_P + Z\sigma_P.$$

The target quantity is equal to the expected demand during the *planning period* ($\bar{D}_P$) plus the least-cost level of safety stock ($Z\sigma_P$).

The logic used to develop the decision variables for the fixed-cycle system (*EOC*, $P_S[q_T]$) is the same as the logic used earlier to develop the decision variables for the variable-cycle system (*EOQ*, $P_S[R]$). To avoid a lengthy development, a simple adjustment will convert one into the other. In the variable-cycle system considered earlier, the annual number of cycles is represented by:

$$\text{number of cycles} = D/q.$$

In the fixed-cycle system, T represents the annual duration of a cycle. The number of cycles will be:[7]

number of cycles $= 1/T$.

Therefore, *the two systems have the common equivalence:*

$1/T = D/q$.

More usefully stated,

$T = q/D$ or $q = DT$.

Substituting DT for q in the EOQ model, the EOC counterpart becomes:

$$q = \sqrt{\frac{2K_O D}{K_C}}$$

$$DT = \sqrt{\frac{2K_O D}{K_C}}$$

$$EOC: T = \sqrt{\frac{2K_O}{K_C D}}.$$

Substituting T for q/D into $P_S(R)$, the $P_S(q_T)$ counterpart becomes:

$$P_S(R) = \frac{K_C q}{K_U D}$$

$$P_S(q_T) = \frac{K_C T}{K_U}.$$

An application will more fully demonstrate the fixed-reorder cycle system. A product has a yearly demand of 600, an order cost of $12, an annual carrying cost of $4, and a stockout cost of $16:

$D = 600$ $K_C = \$4$
$K_O = \$12$ $K_U = \$16$.

The lead time between placing and receiving an order is 5 days. There are 250 working days per year. Daily demand is normally distributed, with a mean of 2.4 and a standard deviation of .8.

---

[7] For example, if there are five cycles per year, the annual duration of a cycle (T) will be one-fifth of a year.

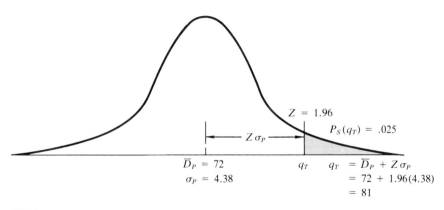

The economic order cycle in years will be:

$$T = \sqrt{\frac{2K_O}{K_C D}}$$

$$= \sqrt{\frac{2(12)}{4(600)}}$$

$$= .10 \text{ years.}$$

The least-cost target quantity will have a probability of stockout of:

$$P_S(q_T) = \frac{K_C T}{K_U}$$

$$= \frac{4(.10)}{16}$$

$$= .025.$$

The right tail of the probability distribution of demand over the planning period is .025 (Figure 15.12).

The mean $(\bar{D}_P)$ and standard deviation (σ_P) for the planning period must be determined. As demonstrated in Figure 15.11b, the planning period consists of the reorder cycle plus the lead time: the duration is $T + L_T$. The expected demand for the planning period $(\bar{D}_P)$ will be the number of days in $T + L_T$ multiplied by the daily demand:

expected planning-period demand $(\bar{D}_P) = (T + L_T)(\text{demand per day}).$

With a calculated T of .10 years, or 25 days, and a lead time of 5 days, the duration of the planning period is 30 days. Given an expected daily demand of 2.4 units, the expected demand over the planning period becomes:

$$\bar{D}_P = (25 + 5)(2.4)$$
$$= 72.$$

The standard deviation for the planning period is obtained directly from the daily standard deviation. The variance of the sum of n independent random variables equals the sum of the variances:

$$\text{Var}(X_1 + X_2 + \cdots + X_n) = \text{Var}(X_1) + \text{Var}(X_2) + \cdots + \text{Var}(X_n).$$

If the planning period contains 30 independent daily demands, each with a variance of $(.80)^2$, the variance for the 30-day period becomes:

$$\text{Var(planning period)} = 30(.80)^2.$$

Since it is the square root of the variance, the standard deviation of the planning period will be:[8]

$$\sigma_P = \sqrt{30}\,(.8)$$
$$= 4.38.$$

With the two parameters $(\bar{D}_P, \sigma_P)$ for the normal distribution of demand for the planning period (Figure 15.12), the magnitude of q_T can be determined. From the normal distribution table (Appendix I), the .025 probability of a stockout in the right tail of the distribution has an associated Z value of 1.96. The target quantity will be:

$$q_T = \bar{D}_P + Z\sigma_P$$
$$q_T = 72 + 1.96(4.38)$$
$$\simeq 81.$$

The safety stock represents the inventory exceeding the expected level of demand: $Z\sigma_P = 9$.

The fixed-reorder cycle decision variables are:

$$T = .10 \text{ years}$$
$$= 25 \text{ days}$$
$$q_T = 81.$$

---

[8] In general, where σ_d represents the daily standard deviation, the standard deviation for the planning period is derived by:

$$\sigma_P = \sqrt{T + L_T}\,\sigma_d.$$

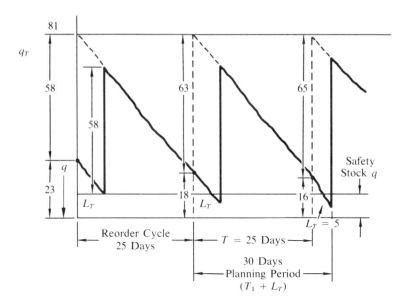

FIGURE 15.13
An Exemplary Fixed-Order Cycle System

Orders will be placed every 25 days for a quantity sufficient to maintain the target level of 81. If the inventory contains 23 items at the reorder point in time, the order will be placed for 58 items. With exemplary inventories of 18 and 16 for the next two 25-day spaced reorder periods, the components of the fixed-order cycle system are represented numerically in Figure 15.13.

A final example will solidify the concepts. A wholesaler is open for 280 days during the year and places orders for items in a certain product group in fixed intervals of 28 days. The lead time to receive an order is 4 days. After an extensive analysis of several representative products, the *service level* for all items in the product group has been specified at 90 percent. Demand has been assumed to be approximately normally distributed. Products in this group are seasonal. For the specific product under consideration, a reliable short-term forecasting model has estimated expected demand over the next 32-day planning period to be 120 units, with a standard deviation of 10.8. The inventory policy decision is required.

In this case, the models to determine T and $P_S(q_T)$ are not required—*both have been specified*. The reorder cycle duration (T) is specified by the fixed 28-day reorder period. The probability of a stockout is specified by the 90 percent service level. Moreover, with these specifications, estimations of K_O, K_C, and K_U are no longer essential.

The target level of inventory, however, is still required. The target quantity is designed to satisfy the demand over the planning period—the demand from

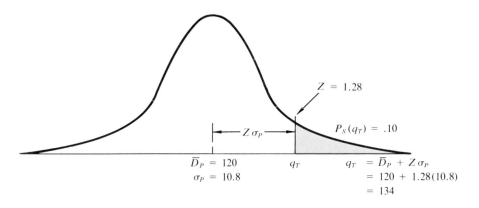

$Z = 1.28$

$P_s(q_T) = .10$

$-Z\sigma_P-$

$\bar{D}_P = 120$ q_T $q_T = \bar{D}_P + Z\sigma_P$
$\sigma_P = 10.8$ $= 120 + 1.28(10.8)$
                                 $= 134$

FIGURE 15.14

The Target Quantity from Forecasted Demand

the placement of one order to the receipt of the next. The anticipated distribution of demand over the planning period is provided in Figure 15.14. The mean and standard deviation are provided by the forecasting model. The right tail probability of stockout is designated by the service level. It specifically defines the location of the target quantity and the level of safety stock. With a 10 percent probability of stockout, q_T must be 1.28 standard deviations to the right of the mean. The required target quantity will be:

$$q_T = \bar{D}_P + Z\sigma_P$$
$$= 120 + 1.28(10.8)$$
$$= 134.$$

To satisfy the demand and safety stock requirements of the forthcoming planning period, the target quantity should be set at 134 units. The associated 14 units of safety stock will maintain the service level specifications. If the level of inventory at the reorder point is 30 items, the order quantity will be 104. With the forthcoming forecast of sales for the next planning period, the target quantity can be adjusted adaptively to the requirements of demand expectations.

SUMMARY

By including the uncertainty of demand, the deterministic inventory system is extended to a stochastic inventory system. The inventory problem is still the determination of two decision variables: an optimal order quantity (q) and an optimal reorder point (R). The criterion for the selection of these variables is still the minimization of inventory related costs.

The deterministic inventory system contains two cycle costs: ordering costs (C_O) and carrying costs (C_C). The uncertainty of demand in the stochastic inventory system produces the requirement that a safety stock be carried to prevent excessive shortages. This adds two safety stock costs: underage costs (C_U) for shortages and safety stock carrying costs (C_{CS}) for surpluses. The decision variables in the stochastic system are selected to minimize the total inventory costs for all four cost components.

With the reasonable assumption of independence between the decision variables, the deterministic EOQ model will define a proper order quantity (q) that minimizes the two cycle costs. With this order quantity, the ERP model will define the reorder point (R) that minimizes the two safety stock costs.

An important extension of the basic stochastic inventory system is the fixed-review cycle system. The length of the review and order cycle is fixed. The order quantity is adjusted to the specific requirements of demand conditions. The decision variables are the reorder cycle (T) and the target quantity (q_T). The model constructs for these decision variables are analogous to those of the basic stochastic inventory system.

Arrow, K., S. Karlin, and H. Scarf. *Studies in the Mathematical Theory of Inventory and Production*. Stanford, Cal.: Stanford University Press, 1958.

Bierman, H., Jr., C. P. Bonini, and W. H. Hausman. *Quantitative Analysis for Business Decisions*. Homewood, Ill.: Richard D. Irwin, 1973.

Bock, R. H., and W. K. Holstein. *Production Planning and Control*. Columbus, Ohio: Charles E. Merrill Books, 1963.

Bowman, E. H., and R. B. Fetter. *Analysis of Production and Operations Management*. Homewood, Ill.: Richard D. Irwin, 1967.

Broom, H. N. *Production Management*. Homewood, Ill.: Richard D. Irwin, 1962.

Buchan, J., and E. Koenigsberg. *Scientific Inventory Management*. Englewood Cliffs, N.J.: Prentice-Hall, 1963.

Buffa, E. S. *Models for Production and Operations Management*. New York: John Wiley & Sons, 1963.

————. *Operations Management: Problems and Models*. New York: John Wiley & Sons, 1968.

————, and W. H. Taubert. *Production Inventory Systems: Planning and Control*. Homewood, Ill.: Richard D. Irwin, 1972.

Groff, G. K., and J. F. Muth. *Operations Management Analysis for Decisions*. Homewood, Ill.: Richard D. Irwin, 1972.

Hadley, G., and T. Whitin. *Analysis of Inventory Systems*. Englewood Cliffs, N.J.: Prentice-Hall, 1963.

Hanssmann, F. *Operations Research in Production and Inventory Control*. New York: John Wiley & Sons, 1962.

Hillier, F. S., and G. T. Lieberman. *Introduction to Operations Research*. San Francisco: Holden-Day, 1974.

Holt, C., F. Modigliani, J. Muth, and H. Simon. *Planning Production, Inventories, and Work Force*. Englewood Cliffs, N.J.: Prentice-Hall, 1960.

Killeen, L. M. *Techniques of Inventory Management*. New York: American Management Association, 1969.

Levin, R. I., and C. A. Kirkpatrick. *Quantitative Approaches to Management*. New York: McGraw-Hill Book Co., 1975.

Magee, J. F. *Production Planning and Inventory Control*. New York: McGraw-Hill Book Co., 1958.

————, and D. M. Boodman. *Production Planning and Inventory Control*. New York: McGraw-Hill Book Co., 1967.

Morris, W. T. *Analysis for Materials Handling Management*. Homewood, Ill.: Richard D. Irwin, 1962.

Naddor, E. *Inventory Systems*. New York: John Wiley & Sons, 1968.

Paik, C. M. *Quantitative Methods for Managerial Decisions*. New York: McGraw-Hill Book Co., 1973.

Prichard, J. W., and R. H. Eagle. *Modern Inventory Management*. New York: John Wiley & Sons, 1965.

Starr, M. K., and D. W. Miller. *Inventory Control: Theory and Practice*. Englewood Cliffs, N.J.: Prentice-Hall, 1962.

Stockton, R. *Basic Inventory Systems: Concepts and Analysis*. Boston: Allyn and Bacon, 1965.

Thierauf, R. J., and R. C. Klekamp. *Decision Making Through Operations Research*. New York: John Wiley & Sons, 1975.

Wagner, H. M. *Principles of Operations Research with Applications to Managerial Decisions*. Englewood Cliffs, N.J.: Prentice-Hall, 1969.

15.1. An item maintained in inventory has an associated stockout cost of $10 per unit. If the demand during the lead time period turns out to be 114 units, and the reorder point has been established at 106 units, what will be the resulting stockout cost for the inventory cycle?

15.2. A stockkeeping unit has a reorder point of 40 units and an expected lead time demand of 36 units. If the annual carrying cost is $4 per unit, what is the safety stock carrying cost to provide a buffer against stockouts?

15.3. When stochastic demand is included in the development of an inventory model, what additional cost components are introduced? These additional cost components focus on what basic element in the stochastic inventory system?

15.4. A stockkeeping unit has the following parameters, expressed in annual terms:

$D = 10,000$
$K_O = \$16$
$K_C = \$2$
$K_U = \$10$
$L_T = 4$ days
250 working days per year
Lead time demand: normally distributed ($\bar{D}_L = 160$; $\sigma_L = 8.6$)

What are the proper values for the inventory decision variables?

15.5. An item in inventory has a normally distributed lead time demand, with a mean of 140 and a standard deviation of 9.4. The annual cost of carrying a unit in safety stock is $4. If the company maintains a service level policy of 80 percent, what is the associated carrying cost of the safety stock? What is it for a service level of 90 percent? For a service level of 92 percent?

15.6. Accounting records and market forecasts provide the basis for the following information regarding a product under inventory management:

annual demand $= 1,200$
annual carrying cost $= \$16$
order cost $= \$24$
stockout costs $= \$40$
lead time $= 10$ days
working days per year $= 300$

Demand during the lead time	Probability
38	.10
39	.20
40	.38
41	.24
42	.08

Determine the decision variables for proper inventory management of the item.

15.7. For the inventory item represented in Problem 15.6, management has decided to adopt a 90 percent service level policy. How will the decision variables change, if at all?

15.8. A stockkeeping unit has the following parameters:

annual demand = 4,800
ordering cost = $12
annual carrying cost = $6
underage cost = $30
lead time = 4 days
300 working days per year
Demand during the lead time: normally distributed, with a mean of 64 and a
standard deviation of 3.4.

Determine the optimal order quantity and reorder point policy. What number of units will provide the buffer safety stock? What is the probability of a stockout? How many stockouts are to be expected during the year? What is the annual expected cost of stockouts? What is the annual cost of providing the buffer stock?

15.9. For the stockkeeping unit specified in Problem 15.8, management has decided to maintain a service level policy of 92 percent. What will be the new reorder point? How many units will be maintained as a safety stock? What will be the expected number of stockouts annually? What will be the annual expected cost of stockout items?

15.10. An organization uses a fixed-reorder cycle inventory system for stockkeeping units. For one of the inventory items, the relevant information, expressed in annual terms, is:

$D = 12,000$
$K_O = \$20$
$K_C = \$2$
$K_U = \$40$
$L_T = 3$ days

Daily demand is normally distributed, with a mean of 40 and a standard deviation of 8.7. There are 300 working days per year.

Determine the economic order cycle in days. How many days are in the planning period? What is the expected demand for the planning period?

Determine the target quantity. What is the required level of safety stock? What is the annual cost of carrying the safety stock?

If there are 104 items in inventory at the reorder point in time, what will be the appropriate order quantity?

15.11. Orders for an inventory item are made every 30 days. The lead time is 4 days. Demand is assumed to be normally distributed, with a seasonally adjusted daily estimate of 4.8 items, with a standard deviation of 1.2. Annual inventory carrying costs are $4 an item. The underage cost for stockouts is estimated at $20. There are 300 working days per year.

With the specified reorder cycle, determine the target quantity. How many items should be maintained in safety stock?

15.12. A stockkeeping units has a demand of 4,000 units for the 250-day work year. The lead time to receive orders is 5 days. Demand is normally distributed at an average rate of 16 per day, with a standard deviation of 3.4 units. The cost parameters are: $K_O = \$8$; $K_C = \$6$; and $K_U = \$24$. For items in this product grouping, the company has a specified service level of 95 percent.

If inventory is maintained on a fixed reorder cycle, what are the values for the inventory policy decision variables?

15.13. A product is ordered on 13 evenly spaced 28 day periods throughout the year. The lead time to receive orders is 4 days. The organization applies a specified service level policy of 98 percent to all items in this product group. The short-term forecast for the product over the planning period is for 260 units with a standard deviation of 8.2. Determine the proper fixed-reorder cycle inventory policy decision.

16

Queuing Models

When the demand for a service facility exceeds the supply, lines form. Waiting lines or queues are all too familiar. They occur everywhere imaginable. Motorists wait for traffic lights, commuters wait for buses, skiers wait for lift lines, and golfers wait for starting times. In industry, airplanes wait for runways, computer jobs wait for computer time, and production waits for materials. Investors wait for capital, workers wait for work orders and pay checks, and so on, ad infinitum. As a result of *uncertainty* and the *expense of service facilities*, momentary excesses in demand frequently must await a restricted supply.

Fortunately, most queuing problems can be adequately resolved through experience and experimentation. Given time to adjust to the requirements of demand, gas stations tend to provide enough pumps, grocery stores enough check-out counters, and banks enough tellers. The avid tennis buff soon learns when and where to play.

Many problems, however, cannot be so easily resolved. A trial-and-error movement toward an adequate solution may be too costly or too time-consuming. Adding another set of gas pumps, a second elevator, or more lanes to a freeway may double or triple the initial installation costs. A more effective approach is needed to facilitate the proper design of service facilities.

As might be expected, quantitative models have evolved to help a decision maker solve *waiting line* or *queuing problems*. Apart from the pioneering work done by A. K. Erlang in the first quarter of the century, most of the work on queuing systems was done after World War II. The present literature on queuing theory is extensive.

THE BASIC STRUCTURE OF THE QUEUING SYSTEM

A queuing system contains several basic components (Figure 16.1). Units enter the system from an *input source* or *calling population*. Members of the calling

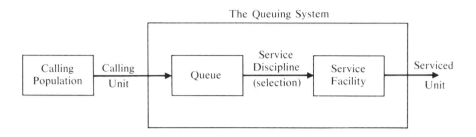

FIGURE 16.1

Components of the Queuing System

population arrive at the facility for service. These *calling units* produce the demand for service. If the service facility is not available for service, the calling units will form a *queue*. Members of the queue are serviced according to the prescribed rules of a *queue discipline* or *service discipline*. Service is performed by a *service mechanism* or *service facility*. Finally, *serviced units* leave the system.

Each of the components of the queuing system has special properties. The *calling population* is assumed to be either *infinite* or *finite*. When the calling population is very large and not easily identified, it is typically assumed to be *infinite*. This greatly simplifies model construction with a negligible loss of accuracy. Many small and easily identified calling populations, however, must be accounted for exactly. When the arrival of one calling unit discernibly alters the probability of another arrival, the calling population is assumed to be *finite*.

The *calling units* are specified by their *arrival rate*. The arrival rate is assumed to be either *constant*, *random*, or in *groups*. In turn, these attributes may vary in intensity and homogeneity. Most commonly, the calling units are assumed to have either a constant or a random arrival rate.

The *service discipline* is specified by *the order for servicing calling units*, *the willingness of calling units to stay in the system*, and *the time and space limitations imposed on the queue*. In the simplest case, calling units would receive service in their order of arrival. They would remain in the system until they had received service. And there would be no limitations on the queue. There are several common variations. The service discipline may specify priority of service. Special customers may not have to wait. Customers may refuse to join an excessively long queue. They may *voluntarily truncate* the length of the queue. A management decision or a legal restriction may *involuntarily truncate* the queue. For service facilities such as parking lots, hotels, car rentals, or theater seats, the depletion of service units may *absolutely truncate* the queue.

The *queuing system* is in either a *transient state* or a *steady-state*. When a system is started, it progresses through a series of changes. Eventually, it attains

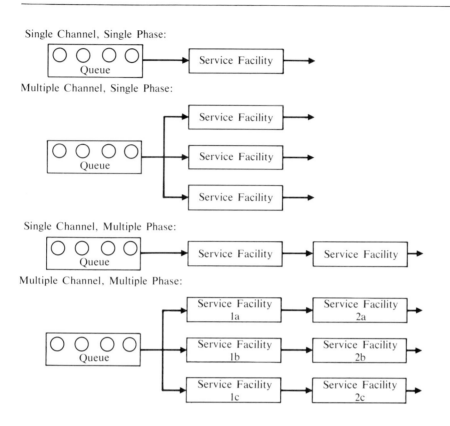

FIGURE 16.2
Standard Types of Service Facilities

stability. In the starting position, the system is greatly influenced by the starting condition and by the amount of elapsed time. This period of rapid transition is termed a *transient state*. After sufficient time has passed, the system becomes essentially independent of the starting condition and the elapsed time. This stable condition is termed a *steady-state*. Because most systems are in a steady-state most of the time and most transient states are considerably more complex, queuing systems are typically assumed to be steady-state.

The *service facility* has two important properties: (1) *the type of facility* and (2) *the service rate*. A service facility can have one or more *parallel service channels* or a sequence of *service channels in series* (Figure 16.2). The *service time* or *service rate* is assumed to be either constant, random, or batch processing.

The permutative system componentry is numerous. The queuing theory literature is extensive.

THE QUEUING PROBLEM

The queuing problem is a matter of economics. The decision maker is concerned with determining the most economical queuing system. The system contains service facilities to satisfy a *calling population* who must often wait for service. A key consideration is the inference of *most economical*. On one hand, almost all waiting could be theoretically eliminated by providing an abundance of service facilities. The unpleasantness, irritation, and frequent tangible dollar losses caused by waiting could be eliminated. On the other hand, the provision of service facilities entails installation, operation, and maintenance costs—also economically unpleasant. The queuing problem is concerned with balancing these opposing costs—*the expected waiting costs $E(W_C)$* and *the expected service costs $E(S_C)$. The objective is to determine the queuing system that minimizes the expected total cost $(E(T_C))$* (Figure 16.3):[1]

$$\text{minimize } E(T_C) = E(W_C) + E(S_C).$$

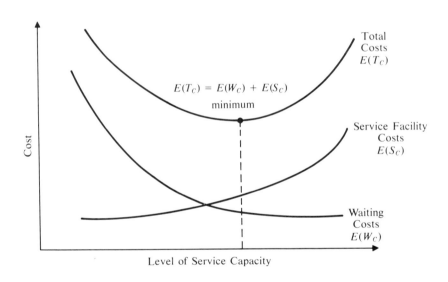

FIGURE 16.3

The Queuing Problem: A Balance of Waiting and Service Facility Costs

---

[1] The expected value notation (*e.g.*, $E(W_C)$, expected waiting cost) is required to include the consideration of random arrival rates and random service times.

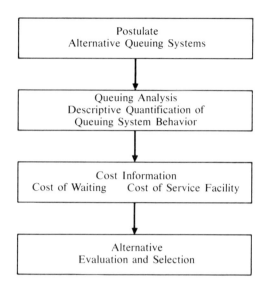

FIGURE 16.4
Selecting the Proper Queuing System

An Approach for Selecting the Proper Queuing System

The proper queuing system is most easily determined from an adapted form of the *basic model for decision making:*

1. List the alternative queuing systems.

2. Evaluate these queuing systems.

3. Select the best queuing system.

These three steps provide the structure needed to incorporate the remaining specifics of the queuing system.

Refer to the extension in Figure 16.4. First, alternative queuing systems are postulated. A change in any component of the system will represent an alternative system. A change in the service facility, for example, would include variations in three major *decision variables:*

(1) the number of servers (s) at a service facility,

(2) the rate of service (μ) of the servers, and

(3) the number of service facilities (S).

Second, *queuing models* are used to provide the *descriptive behavior* of the queuing systems. They will quantify the effect the decision variables have on expected waiting times and expected queue length. With this queuing model information and both waiting cost and service cost information, the alternative queuing systems are evaluated. The criterion for evaluation is the minimization of expected total service facility costs.

Finally, the service facility that offers the minimum expected total cost is selected.

A DETERMINISTIC MODEL: UNIFORM ARRIVALS AND UNIFORM SERVICE

The most basic queuing system is a single-service deterministic system. Members of the calling population arrive for service at a constant rate and are serviced at a constant rate. The machined parts on a production line will illustrate this case.

The parts arrive on a conveyor at the final assembly operation. As long as the arrival rate and the service rate are constant, only three situations can occur:

1. The arrival rate (λ) will equal the service rate (μ) or ($\lambda = \mu$).

2. The arrival rate will be less than the service rate ($\lambda < \mu$).

3. The arrival rate will exceed the service rate ($\lambda > \mu$).

In the first situation ($\lambda = \mu$), the machined parts arrive for service every 10 minutes with an arrival rate (λ) of six per hour. The final assembly machine can also provide service in 10 minutes (μ = six per hour). With λ and μ equal, the assembly service facility will complete service of one part just as the next one arrives. The process will run smoothly with no parts awaiting assembly and no idle assembly capacity.

In the second situation ($\lambda < \mu$), a new assembly machine is installed with an accelerated service rate (μ) of 10 per hour or one every 6 minutes. The arrival rate (λ) remains 6 per hour or one every 10 minutes. When the first machined part arrives for assembly service, the assembly machine will operate for 6 minutes before discharging the assembled product. Four minutes later, a second machined part will arrive, to be discharged 6 minutes later. The process will be repeated over a 10 minute cycle. During this interval the assembly machine will be in operation for 6 minutes and idle for 4—idle 40 percent of the time.

Finally, the machining process is modified to produce parts for final assembly every 4 minutes ($\lambda = 15$). The assembly service rate is still one every 6 minutes ($\mu = 10$). When the first part arrives, the assembly will take 6 minutes. At the end of the fourth minute, a second part arrives for assembly. Since the

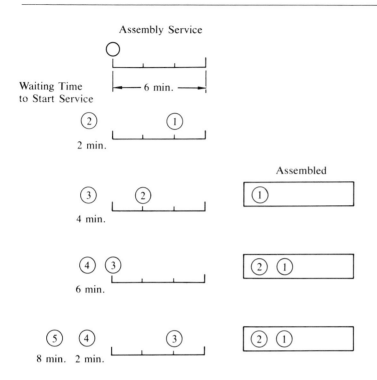

FIGURE 16.5

Assembly Service ($\lambda = 15$, $\mu = 10$) in Four-Minute Intervals Starting with the First Arrival

assembly machine is already in operation, the second part must wait for 2 minutes before service can start. In the next 4-minute interval, the first product will be assembled; the second will be 2 minutes into the assembly; and a third part will have just arrived, to wait 4 minutes before starting assembly. At the end of 4 more minutes, two parts will be serviced, one will be entering service, and one will be waiting 6 minutes to start service (Figure 16.5).

Since the service rate is slower than the arrival rate, a queue will form indefinitely. One hour after the first arrival, 10 parts will be assembled, one part will be entering service, and a queue of four parts will have formed (Figure 16.6). The first part in the queue will have to wait 6 minutes before beginning assembly service. The last part must wait 24 minutes before service starts and 30 minutes to leave the system.

The behavior of a single-service deterministic system is readily defined. If the arrival and service rates are equal ($\lambda = \mu$), there is no waiting for service and no idle capacity for the service facility. If the arrival rate is less than the service rate ($\lambda < \mu$), there is no waiting and the service facility will have idle time. If the arrival rate exceeds the service rate ($\lambda > \mu$), the service facility will be used to capacity and a queue will form indefinitely.

Queuing Models

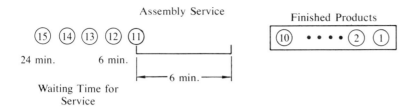

Assembly Service

Finished Products

(15) (14) (13) (12) (11)   (10) • • • • (2) (1)

24 min.   6 min.

← 6 min. →

Waiting Time for
Service

FIGURE 16.6

Assembly Service ($\lambda = 15$, $\mu = 10$) One Hour After First Arrival

An Economic Service Rate: An Optimal Size Assembly Team

A highly integrated production line periodically encounters a difficulty. One of the five-member assembly team cannot always be available for assembly operations. Without being replaced, he is called away around one day in five for special jobs at other plants. The problem is that the production process is conveyor paced. With the five-man assembly team, the production rate (λ) and final assembly service rate (μ) correspond exactly to 20 items per hour. If the one member is absent, the items arrive for assembly faster than they can be serviced. Items begin to back up on the conveyor. Once the maximum allowable queue of 7 items has formed, the production line must be stopped to await assembly. In essence, once the queue contains 7 items, the production line must reduce output to the service rate of the assembly team.

The production manager is considering increasing the assembly team to six men. This will entail the added cost of the new worker, but it will also guarantee that the production line will operate smoothly at full capacity. The following information is available. Items arrive for assembly service at a rate of 20 per hour ($\lambda = 20$). The service rate for the five-man team is 20 per hour ($\mu_5 = 20$). If one man is absent, the service rate for the four-man team is 16 per hour ($\mu_4 = 16$). If the team is increased to six men, the service rate will be 24 per hour ($\mu_6 = 24$). The assembly workers are paid \$32 for an eight-hour day. Items not produced because of slowdowns have an assessed worth of \$20 each.

The production manager would like to choose between two alternatives:

A_1: A five-man assembly team
A_2: A six-man assembly team.

The criterion for alternative selection is the minimum expected total cost ($E(T_C)$). The important cost components are the expected waiting costs ($E(W_C)$) associated with production slowdowns and the expected assembly service facility costs ($E(S_C)$). Therefore, the criterion becomes:

$$\text{minimum } E(T_C) = \quad E(W_C) \quad + \quad E(S_C)$$
$$\qquad\qquad\qquad \text{waiting cost} \qquad \text{service cost.}$$

The assembly service facility costs are more easily evaluated. If alternative 1 is selected, 80 percent of the time there will be a five-member team costing $160 per day (5 men · $32 per day). The remaining 20 percent of the time, there will be a team of four costing $128. The expected daily service facility cost will be:

$$E(S_{C_1}) = .80(\$160) + .20(\$128)$$
$$= \$153.60.$$

For alternative 2, with one extra man:

$$E(S_{C_2}) = .80(\$192) + .20(\$160)$$
$$= \$185.60$$

or

$$E(S_{C_2}) = \$153.60 + \$32.00$$
$$= \$185.60.$$

The waiting costs are also relatively straightforward. The simplest to calculate is the cost for the second alternative. The constant arrival rate (λ) of items to be assembled is 20 per hour. With a six-man team, the uniform service rate (μ) is 24 per hour. Since $\lambda < \mu$, the assembly facility can service all items. There will be no production slowdowns, no waiting time, and no waiting cost. If one member is absent, the resulting five-man team has a service rate of 20. The arrival rate (λ) and service rate (μ) will be equal. The assembly service facility will keep pace smoothly with the production line. Again there will be no waiting time or waiting costs. Therefore, for alternative 2:

$$E(W_{C_2}) = .80(\$0) + .20(\$0)$$
$$= \$0.$$

Alternative 1 requires more careful consideration. If the entire five-man team is present, the arrival rate and service rate will both be 20. With $\lambda = \mu$, no production slowdowns will occur. However, if one member is absent, the service rate will be reduced to 16 per hour. The service facility will be unable to handle the 20 arrivals per hour. A queue will begin to form. Once the queue reaches 7 items, a production slowdown will occur with costs for lost production.

After the first hour in the morning, 20 items will have arrived and 16 will have been assembled. One item will have just entered the assembly service area. Three items will have backed up on the conveyor, forming a queue. At the end of the second hour, 4 additional items will not have been serviced ($\lambda - \mu = 20 - 16$). There will be 7 items in the queue and 1 item entering the assembly area (Figure 16.7). By now the queue will be backed up on the conveyor so far that the production line must wait until there is room for the next item. The

First Hour:

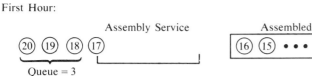

Queue = 3

Second Hour:

Queue = 7

FIGURE 16.7

The Queue Formed When λ of 20 > μ of 16

conveyor will be stopped until the assembly team can reduce the queue to fewer than 7 items. For the remaining six hours of the work day, the production line will be assembly team paced. Instead of having an output of 20 per hour, it will be restricted to the assembly service level of 16 per hour. Four fewer units will be produced for each of the remaining six hours:

$$\begin{array}{ccc} & \text{unit/hr} & \text{no. hrs} \\ \text{lost production} = & 4 & (6) \\ & = 24 \text{ units.} \end{array}$$

At an estimated cost of $20 per unit, the slowdown waiting costs from an insufficient service facility is:

$$\begin{array}{rl} \text{waiting cost} = & \$20(24 \text{ units}) \\ = & \$480. \end{array}$$

The expected waiting cost for alternative 1 can now be calculated. If the fifth man is available, the production arrival rate and assembly service coincide exactly ($\lambda = \mu = 20$). The production line will flow smoothly with no waiting costs. On the other hand, if the fifth man is absent, the assembly facility cannot keep pace with production. There will be an associated slowdown costing $480. Since the assembler will be absent one-fifth of the time, the expected waiting costs will be:

$$\begin{array}{rl} E(W_{C_1}) = & .80(\$0) + .20(\$480) \\ = & \$0 + \$96. \end{array}$$

The expected total cost evaluations of the alternatives are:

A_1 (five-man team):

$$E(T_C) = E(S_{C_1}) + E(W_{C_1})$$
$$= \$153.60 + \$96.00$$
$$= \$249.60.$$

A_2 (six-man team):

$$E(T_C) = E(S_{C_2}) + E(W_{C_2})$$
$$= \$185.60 + \$0$$
$$= \$185.60.$$

Alternative 2, with the minimum expected total cost, is the best choice.

A STOCHASTIC MODEL: RANDOM ARRIVALS AND RANDOM SERVICE RATE

Since demand and service supply are both known with certainty in the deterministic case, selection of a proper service facility is greatly simplified. For example, a small tennis club wants to determine the proper number of indoor courts to construct. A deterministic situation is assumed to prevail. Two tennis players for singles or four players for doubles always arrive every 15 minutes for a court. Their play always lasts exactly one hour. The obvious number of courts to construct will be four. This number will always exactly satisfy demand. If more than four tennis courts are constructed ($\lambda < \mu$), there will always be excess courts available. If fewer than four courts are constructed, they will quickly fill, and in time a growing queue will form.

The major complication in service facility decisions is uncertainty. Neither the demands for service nor the service times typically occur with strict regularity. If court access is on a first come–first served basis, tennis players will not arrive every 15 minutes and play for exactly one hour.

The following example will illustrate the complications that uncertainty introduces into a queuing system. Four tennis courts have been constructed to satisfy total demand. For the first several hours, players have been arriving at approximately 15-minute intervals and have played for the restricted limit of one hour. There has been a smooth flow of players to and from the courts. Then, during a lunch hour, only two pairs of players arrive at half-hour intervals—two courts are left idle. In the following hour, six pairs of players arrive at 10-minute intervals. Since there are only four courts, the last two groups of players must wait 20 minutes each. Moreover, when four players arrive during the next hour, at 15-minute intervals, they will have to wait 20, 15, 30, and 25 minutes, respectively (Table 16.1). A queue has formed. The two idle court hours during the lunch period could not be used later to relieve the excess demand. Whenever court hours are lost, they are lost forever.

	Court #1	Court #2	Court #3	Court #4
	11:00 - 12:00	11:15 - 12:15	11:30 - 12:30	11:45 - 12:45
	12:00 - 1:00 (g_1)	Empty	12:30 - 1:30 (g_2)	Empty
	1:00 - 2:00 (g_3)	1:10 - 2:10 (g_4)	1:30 - 2:30 (g_6)	1:20 - 2:20 (g_5)
	2:00 - 3:00 (g_7)	2:10 - 3:10 (g_8)	2:30 - 3:30 (g_{10})	2:20 - 3:20 (g_9)
	3:00 - 4:00 (g_{11})	3:10 - 4:10 (g_{12})		

Arrival Time
of Players

g_7: 1:40
g_8: 1:50
g_9: 2:00
g_{10}: 2:15
g_{11}: 2:30
g_{12}: 2:45

TABLE 16.1

Uncertainty Produces Lost Service Time and Causes Queues to Form

One fact should be apparent. *If the queuing system contains any uncertainties that allow idle service capacity to be lost forever, the service rate must exceed the arrival rate or the queue will form indefinitely.* Moreover, even when the service capacity exceeds the arrival rate, uncertainties may still require customers to wait for some time before receiving service.

Under conditions of uncertainty, the service facility decision is more complex. The critical complication is the measurement of the effect of uncertainty on the waiting time components of the queuing system. Queuing models have been constructed to provide this measurement. They incorporate and measure the effect of uncertainty on the behavior of the queuing system.

Descriptive Characteristics of a Queuing System

To measure the waiting time components in service facility decisions, several descriptive statistics are important. First, the basic input information is represented by:

λ = the average arrival rate per unit of time
μ = the average service rate per unit of time.

With standard notation, the four descriptive characteristics of the system are:

L = the average number in the system (waiting and in service).
L_q = the average number in the queue.
W = the average waiting time in the system.
W_q = the average waiting time in the queue.

Once the system has achieved a steady-state, an important set of relationships is formed among the four descriptive characteristics of the system. Simple logic will relate the average number in the system (L) to the average wait (W). Calling units arrive for service at an average rate of λ per unit of time. On the average, a unit will wait a time W in the system. Therefore, by the time an *average* unit leaves the system, λW new units will enter the system:

$$\text{New Units} = \underset{\text{arrival rate}}{\lambda} \cdot \underset{\text{time period.}}{W}$$

Therefore, if λW units enter the system behind every average discharged unit, the system must average λW units. With L designating the average number of units in the system, the length of the system (L) and waiting time in the system (W) are functionally related:

$$L = \lambda W.$$

When this same reasoning is applied to the waiting line, the average number in the queue (L_q) and the average waiting time in the queue (W_q) are related by:

$$L_q = \lambda W_q.$$

A relationship can also be formed between W and W_q. The average service rate is μ per unit of time. Therefore, the expected time to be serviced will be $1/\mu$. If the average service rate (μ) is 10 per hour, the expected service time ($1/\mu$) for one unit will be 1/10 hour. Furthermore, the expected time in the system (W) will equal the expected time in the queue (W_q) plus the expected service time ($1/\mu$). The relationship becomes:

$$W = W_q + \frac{1}{\mu}.$$

In summary, *once the system has attained a steady-state, the important descriptive measurements are all interrelated:*

$$L = \lambda W$$
$$L_q = \lambda W_q$$
$$W = W_q + \frac{1}{\mu}.$$

Knowledge of *any one* of these will allow the immediate derivation of the others. Since some of these values are often much more easily derived than others, their functional interrelationships are frequently quite helpful.

The Basic Single-Service Facility Model

The most basic stochastic queuing system is the *single-server* or single-channel system. Calling units arrive randomly for service from an infinite population. The service discipline is first-come-first-served where arrivals must join the line. That is, there is no balking or going elsewhere for service. The service times are also assumed to be random.[2]

With these properties, random arrivals are characterized by a discrete *Poisson distribution* and random service times by a continuous *exponential distribution*. The Poisson and exponential distributions are functionally related.[3] The major difference is the particular aspects being described. The Poisson distribution provides probability measurements of *the number of arrivals over a fixed time interval*. The exponential distribution provides probability measurements of *the length of time intervals for service between successive arrivals*.

The Descriptive System Characteristics

The descriptive measures of the single-channel Poisson arrival exponential service system are developed in the Appendix and are provided below. These models assume a steady-state.

With n calling units in the system, the probabilities of state behavior are:

$$P_0 = 1 - \frac{\lambda}{\mu}$$

and

$$P_n = \left(\frac{\lambda}{\mu} \right)^n P_0.$$

Since P_0 represents the probability that zero units are in the system, it also represents the probability that the service facility is idle.

The expected number of calling units in the system is derived in the Appendix as:

$$L = \frac{\lambda}{\mu - \lambda}.$$

Since one of the fundamental system characteristics is known, the others are easily derived from the set of system interrelationships considered earlier.

---

[2] The arrivals are assumed to be independent of each other, as are the service times. Both arrivals and service times maintain the same averages of λ and μ through time.

[3] In fact, both arrivals and service times can be appropriately expressed by the exponential distribution.

Using the result derived above

$$L = \frac{\lambda}{\mu - \lambda}$$

and the system relationship

$$L = \lambda W,$$

the average waiting time in the system becomes:

$$W = \frac{1}{\mu - \lambda}.$$

With W known, the average waiting time in the queue (W_q) is determined. The system relationship is:

$$W_q = W - \frac{1}{\mu}.$$

Therefore, substituting $1/(\mu - \lambda)$ for W:

$$W_q = \frac{1}{\mu - \lambda} - \frac{1}{\mu}.$$

Rearranging algebraically,

$$W_q = \frac{\lambda}{\mu(\mu - \lambda)}.$$

With W_q known, the average length of the queue (L_q) is determined. The system relationship is:

$$L_q = \lambda W_q.$$

Using the derived W_q,

$$L_q = \lambda \frac{\lambda}{\mu(\mu - \lambda)}$$

or

$$L_q = \frac{\lambda^2}{\mu(\mu - \lambda)}.$$

Given one system characteristic, the others are easily obtained. In terms of the input parameters of λ and μ:

$$L = \frac{\lambda}{\mu - \lambda}$$

$$L_q = \frac{\lambda^2}{\mu(\mu - \lambda)}$$

$$W = \frac{1}{\mu - \lambda}$$

and

$$W_q = \frac{\lambda}{\mu(\mu - \lambda)}.$$

Along with the two probability formulas, these descriptive measures of system behavior provide the critical information required to compare alternative service facilities.

Single-Channel Minimum-Cost Service Rate

The selection of an optimal service rate will illustrate the use of one of the descriptive queuing models. A major food chain has trucks unload goods at a central warehouse for storage, regrouping, and later delivery to retail stores. Throughout the evening, trucks arrive randomly for unloading and storage at an average of two per hour. On the average, the present three man team services three trucks an hour. The service rate is assumed to be adequately approximated by an exponential distribution. If the number of workers on the team is increased, the service rate is increased proportionately. Each member of the work team receives \$5 an hour for the eight-hour night shift. The idle time cost of having the truck driver wait for service is estimated at \$20 per hour. The management of the warehouse facility would like to determine the size of the service team that will minimize company costs.

The critical *decision variable* in this queuing system is the service rate provided by different size unloading teams. Several alternative service rate systems are postulated:

A_1: 3-man team ($\lambda = 2$; $\mu = 3$)
A_2: 4-man team ($\lambda = 2$; $\mu = 4$)
A_3: 5-man team ($\lambda = 2$; $\mu = 5$)
A_4: 6-man team ($\lambda = 2$; $\mu = 6$).

The criterion for evaluation is the minimization of the expected total costs for the queuing system. This will include expected waiting time costs and expected service costs:

$$E(T_C) = E(W_C) + E(S_C).$$

The expected service costs for the alternatives are easily derived. Every member of the unloading team receives $5 an hour for an eight-hour shift:

unloading salary = $5 (8 hours)
= $40.

Therefore, alternative 1, with a three man team, will have a nightly service cost of $120. The other alternatives are adjusted by $40 per additional team member.

The expected waiting cost will require an estimate of the expected waiting time. This information is furnished by one of the queuing models. The average waiting time in the system is:

$$W = \frac{1}{\mu - \lambda}.$$

Since they have different service rates, the respective alternatives have different expected waiting times. With the subscript denoting the alternative:

$$W_1 = \frac{1}{(3 - 2)} = 1 \text{ hour}$$

$$W_2 = \frac{1}{(4 - 2)} = \frac{1}{2} \text{ hour}$$

$$W_3 = \frac{1}{(5 - 2)} = \frac{1}{3} \text{ hour}$$

$$W_4 = \frac{1}{(6 - 2)} = \frac{1}{4} \text{ hour.}$$

The expected waiting cost depends on the number of arrivals, the length of time each must wait, and the waiting cost. For alternative 1:

	arrivals	wait in system (hrs)	cost/hr
$E(W_{C_1}) =$	2	(8)	(1)	($20)
	($\lambda = 2$/hr)	(8 hrs)	W_1	
	= $320.			

Similar evaluations for the other alternatives are provided in Table 16.2.

Alternative Service Levels	Size of Unloading Team	Expected Wait in System: $W = \dfrac{1}{\mu - \lambda}$	Average # of Arrivals $8\lambda = 16$	Expected Waiting Cost at $20/hr $E(W_C)$	Expected Service Cost at $40/man day $E(S_C)$	Expected Total Cost of Alternative $E(T_C) = E(W_C) + E(S_C)$
$A_1(\lambda=2; \mu=3)$	3	1 hour	16	$320	$120	$440
$A_2(\lambda=2; \mu=4)$	4	½ hour	16	$160	$160	$320
$A_3(\lambda=2; \mu=5)$	5	⅓ hour	16	$106.67	$200	$306.67*
$A_4(\lambda=2; \mu=6)$	6	¼ hour	16	$ 80	$240	$320

TABLE 16.2

Evaluation of Alternative Service Levels

The expected total costs of the alternatives are evaluated in Table 16.2. Alternative 3, with a five-man team, has the lowest expected total cost. It is the most economical size for the unloading team.

A Single-Server Poisson-Exponential System with Finite Calling Population

An important variation of the basic single-server Poisson-exponential system occurs when there is a finite calling population of size M. If the calling population is not large, calling units already in the system influence the probability of additional arrivals. The queuing models that describe this more complex situation with n members in the system are:

$$P_0 = 1 \Bigg/ \sum_{n=0}^{M} \left[\frac{M!}{(M-n)!} \left(\frac{\lambda}{\mu} \right)^n \right]$$

$$P_n = \frac{M!}{(M-n)!} \left(\frac{\lambda}{\mu} \right)^n P_0 \qquad \text{if } n = 1, 2, \ldots, M.$$

Also,

$$L = M - \frac{\mu}{\lambda} (1 - P_0)$$

$$L_q = M - \frac{\lambda + \mu}{\lambda} (1 - P_0)$$

$$W = \frac{1}{\mu} \left(\frac{M}{1 - P_0} - \frac{\lambda + \mu}{\lambda} \right) + \frac{1}{\mu}$$

and

$$W_q = \frac{1}{\mu} \left(\frac{M}{1 - P_0} - \frac{\lambda + \mu}{\lambda} \right).$$

For example, a single typist is serving two managers. The average arrival rate (λ) of reports and memos requiring typing is 6 per day. The average service rate (μ) is 10 per day. Since the typist appears idle for a good part of the day, management is considering adding a third manager with proportionate service requirements to the typing pool.

Using the queuing formulas, the characteristics of the present typing pool ($M = 2$) can be measured. The probability of zero units in the system is:

$$P_0 = 1 \Big/ \left[\sum_{n=0}^{M} \frac{M!}{(M - n)!} \left(\frac{\lambda}{\mu} \right)^n \right]$$

$$P_0 = 1 \Big/ \left[1 + \frac{2!}{1!} \left(\frac{6}{10} \right)^1 + \frac{2!}{0!} \left(\frac{6}{10} \right)^2 \right]$$

$$= .3424.$$

About one-third of the time, no calling units will be in the system—the typist will be idle.

The probability of one unit in the system is:

$$P_n = \frac{M!}{(M - n)!} \left(\frac{\lambda}{\mu} \right)^n P_0$$

$$P_1 = \frac{2!}{(2 - 1)!} \left(\frac{6}{10} \right)^1 (.3424)$$

$$P_1 = .4108.$$

About 40 percent of the time, the typist will be working on a project with no other work waiting.

Since the sum of the probabilities for the system states must be one, the probability of two calling units is more easily determined by:

$$P_2 = 1 - (P_0 + P_1)$$
$$P_2 = 1 - (.3424 + .4108)$$
$$= .2468.$$

One-fourth of the time, the typist will be busy on one project and have a second project waiting for service.

The average length of the system and of the queue are:

$$L = M - \frac{\mu}{\lambda} (1 - P_0)$$

$$= 2 - \frac{10}{6} (1 - .3424)$$

$$= .904$$

$$L_q = M - \frac{\lambda + \mu}{\lambda} (1 - P_0)$$

$$= 2 - \frac{6 + 10}{6} (1 - .3424)$$

$$= .2464.$$

An average of .904 calling units will be in the system with .2464 in the queue.
In terms of waiting times:

$$W = \frac{1}{\mu} \left(\frac{M}{1 - P_0} - \frac{\lambda + \mu}{\lambda} \right) + \frac{1}{\mu}$$

$$= \frac{1}{10} \left(\frac{2}{1 - .3424} - \frac{6 + 10}{6} \right) + \frac{1}{10}$$

$$= .1375.$$

Since W_q is the same as W minus the average service time $(1/\mu)$:

$$W_q = W - \frac{1}{\mu}$$

$$= .1375 = \frac{1}{10}$$

$$= .0375.$$

A manager who arrives with a report will have to wait an average of one hour and 6 minutes (.1375 days) for the typed report. Reports will wait on the typist's desk an average of 18 minutes before typing starts.

Since the waiting time for the typist to begin a report is reasonably short and the managers can start work on other projects, management's critical concern is the excessive idle time for the typist—almost three hours in an eight-hour day. The proposal to add a third manager to the typist's lax schedule is investigated. The value of M is increased to three, and the average arrival rate is increased from six to nine per day. The proposed new system will have the following characteristics. The probability of an unused typing facility:

$$P_0 = 1 \bigg/ \left[1 + \frac{3!}{2!} \left(\frac{9}{10} \right)^1 + \frac{3!}{1!} \left(\frac{9}{10} \right)^2 + \frac{3!}{0!} \left(\frac{9}{10} \right)^3 \right]$$

$$= .0952.$$

The typist will still be idle about 10 percent of the day, or 46 minutes. The average length of the system and queue are:

$$L = 3 - \frac{10}{9} (1 - .0952)$$

$$= 1.995$$

$$L_q = 3 - \frac{9 + 10}{9} (1 - .0952)$$

$$= 1.090.$$

On the average, the typist will be working on a report with a second report waiting.

The average waiting time in the system and queue are:

$$W = \frac{1}{10} \left(\frac{3}{1 - .0952} - \frac{9 + 10}{9} \right) + \frac{1}{10}$$

$$= .2205$$

$$W_q = .2205 - \frac{1}{10}$$

$$= .1205.$$

A report arriving for typing will average 58 minutes (.1205 days) in the queue and one hour and 46 minutes in the system.

The proposed new system will reduce the typist's idle time from two hours and 45 minutes to 46 minutes. This should just allow time for a couple of coffee breaks and time to keep the service area orderly. The waiting time in the queue has tripled—from 18 minutes to 58 minutes. However, the overall average time for service has increased by only 40 minutes—from one hour and 6 minutes to one hour and 46 minutes. Since the increased total service wait remains acceptable, the management will increase the typing pool to include the third manager. The addition of a fourth manager is not evaluated. If a fourth manager were added, the arrival rate would be increased beyond the service rate ($\lambda > \mu$). Demands would exceed service capacity supplies, and a queue would form indefinitely.

The Single-Server Poisson-Exponential System with Truncated Queue

Another common exception to the basic stochastic single-service Poisson-exponential system occurs when the length of the queue restricts additional arrivals. The queue length may be restricted by physical space, limited capacity, or the unwillingness of the calling population to wait excessively long. Such restrictions affect the probability of the number of calling units in the system, the average length of the queue or system, and the average waiting time in the queue or system.

Restricting the system to a maximum of M calling units alters the descriptive system characteristics to:

$$P_0 = \frac{1 - (\lambda/\mu)}{1 - (\lambda/\mu)^{M+1}}$$

$$P_n = \left(\frac{\lambda}{\mu}\right)^n P_0$$

$$L = \frac{\lambda}{\mu - \lambda} - \frac{(M + 1)(\lambda/\mu)^{M+1}}{1 - (\lambda/\mu)^{M+1}}$$

$$L_q = L - (1 - P_0).$$

The derivation of the waiting times is most easily obtained from the earlier basic relationships. As was stated previously,

$$L = \lambda W$$

or

$$W = \frac{L}{\lambda}.$$

Since calling units take their business elsewhere when the system has reached capacity, the arrival rate must be expressed in terms of units entering the system. The proper *effective arrival rate* (λ_e) will be the arrival rate multiplied by the proportionate time the system is not at full capacity:

Probability at full capacity
(Fraction of customers lost) $= P_M$

$$\text{Effective arrival rate } \lambda_e = \underset{\text{arrival rate}}{\lambda} \cdot \underset{\substack{\text{probability not} \\ \text{at full capacity}}}{(1 - P_M)}$$

Therefore, specified in terms of arrivals entering into the system, the expected waiting time for arrivals in the system becomes:

$$W = \frac{L}{\lambda_e} = \frac{L}{\lambda(1 - P_M)}.$$

Similarly,

$$W_q = \frac{L_q}{\lambda_e} = \frac{L_q}{\lambda(1 - P_M)}.$$

Uniquely in the truncated queuing system, *the service rate μ need not exceed the arrival rate*. A steady-state will result for any relationship between λ and μ. If the arrival rate is much larger than the service rate, the system becomes saturated with a length approximating the maximum M. If the arrival rate is smaller than the service rate, the formulas given above apply. And as might be expected, if M is very large, the system converges to the basic model without truncation. If the arrival rate and service rate are equal, all states in the system are equally probable. The formulation becomes:

$$P_0 = \frac{1}{M + 1} \qquad \frac{\lambda}{\mu} = 1$$

$$P_n = \frac{1}{M + 1} \qquad \frac{\lambda}{\mu} = 1$$

and

$$L = \frac{M}{2} \qquad \frac{\lambda}{\mu} = 1.$$

To illustrate the application of these formulas, consider the following problem. A barber has a small shop in a prime downtown location. The estimated arrival rate is three customers per hour. Once three persons are in the system, no additional customers will bother to stop. The barber provides a quality razor cut for $7. His present service rate is two per hour. The barber shop is physically limited to one chair and potential customers are being lost daily. The barber would like to analyze the possibility of increasing the service rate with a compensating reduction in price.

If he works slightly faster, he can increase the service rate to three per hour and nearly maintain quality. If he gives more of a scissors cut, he can increase the service rate to four per hour at a minor noticeable reduction in quality. To maintain the present arrival rate, the new service rates will be repriced at $6 and $5, respectively.

$$P_0 = \frac{1 - \lambda/\mu}{1 - (\lambda/\mu)^{M+1}} = \frac{1 - 3/2}{1 - (3/2)^{3+1}} = .1231$$

$$P_1 = (\lambda/\mu)^1 P_0 = (3/2)^1(.1231) = .1846$$

$$P_2 = (\lambda/\mu)^2 P_0 = (3/2)^2(.1231) = .2769$$

$$P_3 = (\lambda/\mu)^3 P_0 = (3/2)^3(.1231) = .4154$$

$$L = \frac{\lambda}{\mu - \lambda} - \frac{(M+1)(\lambda/\mu)^{M+1}}{1 - (\lambda/\mu)^{M+1}} = \frac{3}{2 - 3} - \frac{(4)(3/2)^{3+1}}{1 - (3/2)^{3+1}} = 1.985$$

$$L_q = L - (1 - P_0) = 1.985 - (1 - .1231) = 1.108$$

$$W = \frac{L}{\lambda(1 - P_M)} = \frac{1.985}{3(1 - .4154)} = 1.132$$

$$W_q = \frac{L_q}{\lambda(1 - P_M)} = \frac{1.108}{3(1 - .4154)} = .632$$

TABLE 16.3
Service Rate s_1 ($\lambda = 3$; $\mu = 2$; $M = 3$)

To aid in the analysis of the service policies, Tables 16.3 and 16.4 demonstrate the calculations of the descriptive system characteristics. Table 16.5 summarizes this information for the three service levels.

$$\lambda = \mu$$

$$P_0 = \frac{1}{M+1} = \frac{1}{3+1} = .250$$

$$P_1 = (\lambda/\mu)^n P_0 = (3/3)^1(.25) = .250$$

$$P_2 = P_3 = (1)^n P_0 = P_0 = .250$$

$$L = \frac{M}{2} = \frac{3}{2} = 1.500$$

$$L_q = L - (1 - P_0) = 1.50 - (1 - .25) = .750$$

$$W = \frac{L}{\lambda(1 - P_M)} = \frac{1.50}{3(1 - .25)} = .667$$

$$W_q = \frac{L_q}{\lambda(1 - P_M)} = \frac{.750}{3(1 - .25)} = .333$$

TABLE 16.4
Service Rate s_2 ($\lambda = 3$; $\mu = 3$; $M = 3$)

	$7 s_1: $\mu=2$	$6 s_2: $\mu=3$	$5 s_3: $\mu=4$
P_0	.1231	.2500	.3657
P_1	.1846	.2500	.2743
P_2	.2769	.2500	.2057
P_3	.4154	.2500	.1543
L	1.985	1.500	1.851
L_q	1.108	.750	1.217
W	1.132	.667	.690
W_q	.632	.333	.476

TABLE 16.5

Descriptive System Characteristics ($\lambda = 3$; $\mu = 3$)

The barber notices several interesting statistics. In the low service rate, $7 system ($s_1$), the amount of idle time (P_O) is 12.31 percent, compared to 36.57 percent for the high service rate, $5 system ($s_3$). The $7 system ($s_1$) indicates a 41.54 percent loss in potential customers (P_M). The $5 system ($s_3$) is at full capacity with lost customers only 15.43 percent of the time. The waiting time in the queue is about half as long for the $6 system ($s_2$) as it is for the $7 system ($s_1$).

After considerable thought, the barber isolates three important considerations for the selection of a service policy: (1) total daily profits (P), (2) the amount of idle time (I_T), and (3) the time the customer must wait in the queue (C_{WM}). Each will be measured in terms of assessed dollar benefit. The idle time between customers is assigned a subjective worth of $4 per hour. Considering the long-run effect on the arrival rate and the potential market not being serviced, the amount of time a customer must wait in the queue for service is assigned a subjective loss of $2 per hour. The waiting time in the system is not considered—most customers do not mind waiting while being serviced.

The criterion for alternative selection, therefore, becomes the maximization of expected total benefit ($E(T_B)$) from the service policy:

$$\text{maximization } E(T_B) = \underset{\text{expected profit}}{E(P)} + \underset{\substack{\text{expected idle} \\ \text{time benefit}}}{E(I_W)} + \underset{\substack{\text{expected customer} \\ \text{waiting time loss}}}{E(C_{WM})}.$$

The expected profit $E(P)$ will be the expected number serviced multiplied by the service charge. For system s_1, the expected idle time is .1231. Therefore, the proportion of time spent serving customers will be:

$$\text{expected service time} = 1 - P_0$$
$$= 1 - .1231$$
$$= .8769.$$

System s_1 has a service rate of two per hour for an eight-hour day. The average number of customers serviced will be:

$$\text{average number of customers per day} = .8769 \ (2/\text{hr})(8 \ \text{hr/day})$$
$$= 14.03.$$

With a service charge of $7, the expected profit will be:

$$E(P) = \$7(14.03)$$
$$= \$98.21.$$

Again for s_1, the expected idle time monetary equivalent ($E(I_M)$) will be the idle time hours multiplied by the idle time benefit:

$$\text{expected idle time} = P_0$$
$$\text{expected idle time monetary equivalent} = (8 \ \text{hrs}) \ P_0$$
$$E(I_M) = (8)(.1231)$$
$$= \$3.94.$$

The expected customer waiting time loss is the average number of customers in the queue multiplied by the average wait and cost per hour. The expected customer waiting loss for s_1 will be:

$$\text{expected customer waiting monetary equivalent} = (\text{cost/hr})(\text{average no. of customers}) \ W_q$$
$$E(C_{WM}) = (\$2)(14.03)(.632)$$
$$= \$17.73.$$

The expected total benefit for the $7 s_1 system is:

$$E(T_B) = E(P) + E(I_M) + E(C_{WM})$$
$$= 98.21 + 3.94 - 17.73$$
$$= \$84.42.$$

The other two service levels are evaluated in Table 16.6. The policy with a service rate of three (s_2) provides the maximum expected benefit of $104 per day. This policy offers a daily improved benefit of $18.84 over s_1 and $10.09 over s_3. In relative terms, s_2 provides respective improvements of 18.11 and 9.70 percent.

Alternative Service Policy	Average # Serviced (n) $(1-P_0)(\mu)(8)$	Expected Profit $(E(P))$ Service Cost (n)	Idle Time $(E(I_M))$ $\$4(8\text{ hr})P_0$	Waiting Cost $(E(C_{WM}))$ $\$2nW_q$	Expected Total Benefit $E(T_B) = E(P)+E(I_M)+E(C_{WM})$
s_1: $\mu=2$	$(1-.1231)(2)(8)$ $= 14.03$	$\$7(14.03)$ $= 98.21$	$4(8)(.1231)$ $= 3.94$	$\$2(14.03)(.632)$ $= -17.73$	$E(T_B) = 98.21 + 3.94 - 17.73$ $= \$84.41$
s_2: $\mu=3$	$(1-.2500)(3)(8)$ $= 18.00$	$\$6(18.00)$ $= 108.00$	$4(8)(.2500)$ $= 8.00$	$\$2(.333)(18.00)$ $= -12.00$	$E(T_B) = 108.00 + 8.00 - 12.00$ $= \$104.00**$
s_3: $\mu=4$	$(1-.3653)(4)(8)$ $= 20.31$	$\$5(20.31)$ $= 101.55$	$4(8)(.3653)$ $= 11.70$	$\$2(.476)(20.31)$ $= -19.34$	$E(T_B) = 101.55 + 11.70 - 19.34$ $= \$93.91$

TABLE 16.6

Evaluation of Alternative Service Policies

The Single-Channel Poisson Arrivals: Any Service Time System

The preceding stochastic queuing models were based on the assumption of Poisson arrivals and exponential service rates. As long as arrivals are not scheduled or carefully regulated, for many situations, both intuition and empirical evidence support the reasonableness of independent random arrivals (Poisson). Especially when services are very similar, however, the assumption of an exponential service rate is less tenable. Service times often depart substantially from an exponential distribution.

Because of the mathematical complexity, only a few models have departed from the basic exponential service time assumption. One important development has been a general model for Poisson arrivals with no restriction on the distribution for the service times. Besides the standard assumptions of independent service times and the same probability distribution through time, the general model requires only the mean $(1/\mu)$ and variance (σ^2) of the service time distribution. As long as $\lambda/\mu < 1$, the steady-state descriptive measures for the general model are:

$$P_0 = 1 - \frac{\lambda}{\mu}$$

$$L_q = \frac{(\lambda/\mu)^2 + \lambda^2\sigma^2}{2[1 - (\lambda/\mu)]}.$$

Using the basic functional relationships among the descriptive system characteristics:

$$L = L_q + \frac{\mu}{\lambda}$$

$$W_q = \frac{L_q}{\lambda}$$

$$W = W_q + \frac{1}{\mu}.$$

Service rate variability has a direct effect on the entire queuing system. Refer to the expression for L_q and note the effect of σ^2. Now refer to the effect of L_q on each of the other descriptive system characteristics. Service rate variability will directly effect the length of the queue and the system. It will also directly affect the wait in the queue and the system.

Two special cases of the general model warrant consideration. First, the service rate will be assumed exponential with the associated variance of $\sigma^2 = 1/\mu^2$. The value of P_0 is the same for the general and the Poisson-exponential systems:

$$P_0 = 1 - \frac{\lambda}{\mu}.$$

The value of L_q for the general model is:

$$L_q = \frac{(\lambda/\mu)^2 + \lambda^2\sigma^2}{2[1 - (\lambda/\mu)]}.$$

Substituting the exponential variance ($\sigma^2 = 1/\mu^2$):

$$L_q = \frac{(\lambda/\mu)^2 + \lambda^2(1/\mu^2)}{2[1 - (\lambda/\mu)]}.$$

Reexpressing:

$$L_q = \frac{(\lambda/\mu)^2}{[1 - (\lambda/\mu)]}$$

or

$$L_q = \frac{\lambda^2}{\mu(\mu - \lambda)}.$$

This is the Poisson-exponential system formulation. The exponential service rate is a special case of the general model.

The second special case has Poisson arrivals and constant service times ($\sigma^2 = 0$). Substituting $\sigma^2 = 0$ into the general expression:

$$L_q = \frac{(\lambda/\mu)^2 + \lambda^2(0)}{2[1 - (\lambda/\mu)]}$$

$$= \frac{(\lambda/\mu)^2}{2[1 - (\lambda/\mu)]}.$$

or

$$L_q = \frac{\lambda^2}{2\mu(\mu - \lambda)}.$$

This leads to an important conclusion. The queue for the constant service rate system is only *half* the length of the queue for the exponential service system. If variability in the service rate is reduced, the length of the queue will be reduced considerably. In turn, the associated waiting time and waiting time costs will also be reduced considerably.

These two special cases provide a decision maker with an added tool. The exponential distribution is typically classified as a fairly high variance distribution. That is, few service rate distributions will contain a larger variance. Therefore, the exponential service rate system ($\sigma^2 = 1/\mu^2$) will provide a reasonable upper bound for service rate distributions. The constant service system ($\sigma^2 = 0$) will provide an absolute lower bound. These boundaries will indicate the potential sensitivity of alternative systems to variability in the service rate.

The Constant and Exponential Service Systems Compared

To demonstrate further the adverse effect of variability in the service rate, the constant service rate and exponential service rate systems will be compared. In two different suburbs of a large metropolitan area, two car wash facilities operate on Sundays. In both cases the arrivals are Poisson, occurring randomly every five minutes. The service time for both facilities averages four minutes.

		Coed Wash Poisson-Exponential ($\lambda = 12$; $\mu = 15$)	Machine Paced Poisson-Constant ($\lambda = 12$; $\mu = 15$)
P_0	$= 1 - \lambda/\mu$	$P_0 = 1 - 12/15$ $= .20$	$P_0 = 1 - 12/15$ $= .20$
		$\sigma^2 = 1/15^2$	$\sigma^2 = 0$
L_q	$= \dfrac{(\lambda/\mu)^2 + \lambda^2\sigma^2}{2(1 - \lambda/\mu)}$	$L_q = \dfrac{(12/15)^2 + 12^2(1/15^2)}{2(1 - 12/15)}$ $= 3.200$	$L_q = \dfrac{(12/15)^2 + 12^2(0)^2}{2(1 - 12/15)}$ $= 1.600$
L	$= L_q + \lambda/\mu$	$L = 3.200 + .8000$ $= 4.00$	$L = 1.600 + .800$ $= 2.40$
W_q	$= \dfrac{L_q}{\lambda}$	$W_q = \dfrac{3.200}{12}$ $= .2667$	$W_q = \dfrac{1.600}{12}$ $= .1333$
W	$= W_q + \dfrac{1}{\mu}$	$W = .2667 + 1/15$ $= .934$	$W = .1333 + 1/15$ $= .800$

TABLE 16.7

Exponential and Constant Service System Behavior

Queuing Models

The facilities differ, however, in the variability of the service times. The northern facility is operated by a sorority consisting of a team of five coeds. The service rate is closely approximated by an exponential distribution. The southern facility is machine paced with a constant service rate.

The behavior of these two systems with identical λ and μ (in hours) is provided in Table 16.7. The exponential system will average 3.2 cars in the queue, while the constant system will average 1.6—only half as many. On the average, the exponential system requires customers to wait in line .2667 hours, or 16 minutes, while the constant system requires only an 8-minute wait. The service variance effects on the length of the queue and the waiting time in the queue are often important considerations in service facility design. They are especially important when the facility has balking customers or other forms of truncation.

THE MULTIPLE CHANNEL QUEUING SYSTEM

In many situations, an important controllable decision variable is the number of service channels. Examples of multiple-channel facilities are check-out counters, toll booths, bank tellers, airport runways, and multilane freeways. By increasing the number of servicing units, the length of the queue and the waiting time are reduced.

The most common and basic multichannel system contains parallel stations serving a single queue on a first-come-first-served basis. The service stations all provide the same service. The single queue may separate into shorter queues in front of the respective service stations. Also, when it is advantageous, calling units can shift from one queue to another. Arrivals are Poisson and service times are exponential.

With the number of calling units represented by n and the number of service stations by S, the descriptive characteristics of the multichannel system are summarized by:

$$P_0 = 1 \left/ \left[\sum_{n=0}^{S-1} \frac{1}{n!} \left(\frac{\lambda}{\mu} \right)^n + \frac{1}{S!} \left(\frac{\lambda}{\mu} \right)^S \frac{1}{[1 - (\lambda/S\mu)]} \right] \right.$$

$$P_n = \begin{cases} \dfrac{(\lambda/\mu)^n}{n!} P_0, & \text{if } 0 \leq n < S \\[2em] \dfrac{(\lambda/\mu)^n}{S! \, S^{n-S}} P_0, & \text{if } n > S \end{cases}$$

$$L_q = \frac{(\lambda/\mu)^{S+1}}{(S-1)! \, [S - (\lambda/\mu)^2]} P_0.$$

Using the basic relationships,

$$W_q = \frac{L_q}{\lambda}$$

$$W = W_q + \frac{1}{\mu}$$

$$L = \lambda W$$

or

$$L = \lambda W = \lambda W_q + \frac{\lambda}{\mu} = L_q + \frac{\lambda}{\mu}.$$

The average proportion of server idle time can also be developed. The number of active servers must equal the number of calling units in the system: $L - L_q$. Therefore, the average proportion of active servers will be $(L - L_q)/S$. Thus,

$$\text{average proportion of time the servers are idle} = 1 - \frac{L - L_q}{S}.$$

Since the basic relationships indicate $L - L_q = \lambda/\mu$,

$$\text{average proportion of time the servers are idle} = 1 - \frac{\lambda/\mu}{S}.$$

With input parameters, server idle time is easily determined.

Selecting the Proper Number of Channels

Multiple-channel models equip the decision maker with a means for measuring the effects of different numbers of service stations. They provide a means for determining the appropriate number of service stations. For example, the number of tellers must be determined for the outside step-up window of a bank. The step-up window is designed to provide added service during hours when the bank is otherwise closed. Because the bank's policy emphasizes service, the customers' waiting time is subjectively assessed at a loss of $5 per hour. The tellers are salaried at $4 per hour. The arrivals are essentially random and average 40 per hour. The service rate is exponential and averages two minutes ($\mu = 30/hr$).

Since the arrival rate (λ) of 40 exceeds the service rate (μ) of 30, a single server cannot possibly service the arrivals—a queue will form indefinitely. The number of service stations must exceed one. The alternative service systems will consist of two, three, or four servers in parallel. With S representing the number of channels, the alternatives are:

A_1	A_2	A_3
$S = 2$	$S = 3$	$S = 4$.

The criterion used to evaluate the alternatives will be the minimum expected total cost. The systems will contain two opposing cost considerations: (1) waiting time costs for calling units and (2) service facility costs for servers. As the number of servers is increased, the expected customer waiting cost ($E(W_C)$) will decrease, and the server costs (S_C) will increase:

$$\Delta S\uparrow : E(W_C)\downarrow \quad S_C\uparrow$$

The desired system will balance these opposing costs to minimize the expected total cost:

$$\text{minimum } E(T_C) = E(W_C) + S_C.$$

The expected waiting costs for calling units ($E(W_C)$) is determined by multiplying the expected total waiting time by the waiting costs:

$$E(W_C) = \text{waiting cost} \cdot \text{expected waiting time.}$$

The expected waiting time will be the average number of arrivals (λ) multiplied by the average time each arrival must wait in the system (W):

$$\text{expected waiting time} = \underset{\substack{\text{average} \\ \text{arrivals}}}{\lambda} \quad \cdot \quad \underset{\substack{\text{average wait} \\ \text{in system}}}{W} .$$

With a waiting cost of $5 per hour, the expected waiting cost becomes:[4]

$$E(W_C) = \$5\,\lambda W.$$

The server costs are easily determined. The cost of providing the service facility is the number of servers (S) multiplied by the server costs ($4 per hour):

$$S_C = \$4\,S.$$

---

[4] Note, since $L = \lambda W$, $E(W_C)$ can also be expressed as $5L$.

In order to evaluate the alternative systems, the expected waiting time in the system (W) is required. Referring to the descriptive models of system behavior, the calculations for alternative one ($S = 2$) are:

$$P_0 = 1 \Bigg/ \left[\sum_{n=0}^{S-1} \frac{1}{n!} \left(\frac{\lambda}{\mu} \right)^n + \frac{1}{S!} \left(\frac{\lambda}{\mu} \right)^S \frac{1}{[1 - (\lambda/S\mu)]} \right]$$

$$= 1 \Bigg/ \left[\frac{1}{0!} \left(\frac{40}{30} \right)^0 + \frac{1}{1!} \left(\frac{40}{30} \right)^1 + \frac{1}{2!} \left(\frac{40}{30} \right)^2 \frac{1}{[1 - 40/2(30)]} \right]$$

$$= \frac{1}{1 + 1.333 + 2.667}$$

$$= .200$$

$$L_q = \frac{(\lambda/\mu)^{S+1}}{(S-1)! \, [S - (\lambda/\mu)^2]} P_0$$

$$= \frac{(\frac{40}{30})^{2+1}}{(2-1)! \, (2 - \frac{40}{30})^2} (.200)$$

$$= 1.067$$

$$L = L_q + \frac{\lambda}{\mu}$$

$$= 1.067 + \frac{40}{30}$$

$$= 2.400$$

$$W_q = \frac{L_q}{\lambda}$$

$$= \frac{1.067}{40}$$

$$= .0267$$

$$W = W_q + \frac{1}{\mu}$$

$$= .0267 + \frac{1}{30}$$

$$= .0600.$$

On the average, the system is idle 20 percent of the time (P_0). The queue length is just over 1 customer (L_q). An average of 2.4 customers are in the system (L). On the average, a customer must wait .0267 hours (1.6 minutes) in the queue (W_q) and .0600 hours (3.6 minutes) in the system (W).

	$S = 2$	$S = 3$	$S = 4$
P_0	.200	.254	.262
L_q	1.067	.145	.015
L	2.400	1.478	1.348
W_q	.0267	.0036	.0004
W	.0600	.0369	.0337

TABLE 16.8

Multichannel System Characteristics

A summary of the system characteristics for each alternative is provided in Table 16.8. With the known values of λ and S, the calculated W from Table 16.8 will allow the evaluation of the alternatives. Table 16.9 provides the complete evaluation. The three server system is most economical.

	Expected Waiting Cost $E(W_C) = \$5\lambda W$	Service Facility Cost $S_C = \$4S$	Expected Total Cost $T_C = E(W_C) + S_C$
A_1: $S = 2$	$5(40)(.0600) = 12.00$	$4(2) = 8$	20.00
A_2: $S = 3$	$5(40)(.0369) = 7.39$	$4(3) = 12$	19.39**
A_3: $S = 4$	$5(40)(.0337) = 6.72$	$4(4) = 16$	22.72

TABLE 16.9

Multichannel System Evaluation

OTHER QUEUING SYSTEMS

Although they are beyond the scope of this introductory presentation, the queuing literature considers many other important models. Models have been constructed for the multichannel system with a finite calling population and for the multichannel system with a truncated queue. Intermediate service time variance models (Erlang distributions) have been constructed for both the single-server and the multiple-server systems. Models have been constructed for single and multiple-server systems with nonPoisson arrivals and exponential service times.

In many situations, the mean service rate or the mean arrival rate may not remain constant. As the queue lengthens, empirical evidence indicates that servers tend to increase the rate of service. As the queue lengthens, customers begin to balk and return another time. Also, when there is no queue, customers may enter an otherwise unattractive system. State dependent service systems and state dependent arrival systems have been constructed.

In many situations, certain special members of a calling population may have service priority. Emergency patients in hospitals, firetrucks in traffic, and seniors in registration lines receive priority over other members of the calling population. Single and multiple-server priority discipline queuing models have been constructed.

In other situations, the calling units may proceed through a series of sequential services before leaving the system. Calling units may receive service from one or more service facilities in an entire *queuing network*. Although they are limited, models have been constructed for a network of service systems with Poisson arrivals and exponential service times.

The types of probability distributions for arrivals and service times are often unknown. And when they are known, their parameters are often unknown. Even over short periods, the arrival rate and service rate may not remain constant. The *transient states* of some systems may be as important as the *steady state*.

A queuing system may be multiple channel with truncated queues. It may be state dependent with a finite calling population. The arrival rate and service time distributions may be complex with unknown and changing parameters. In turn, this queuing system may be part of a more complex network of dependent queuing systems. Queuing systems can be complex. And unfortunately, complex systems are not always the exception. They are too commonly the rule.

As soon as the queuing system departs materially from the basic models, a strict mathematical modeling[5] often becomes untenable. For more complex nonstandard queuing situations, the decision maker must usually rely on the flexibility offered by simulation. This exceedingly adaptive modeling procedure will be the topic of the next two chapters.

SUMMARY

The uncertainty of arrivals, the uncertainty of service times, and the cost of service facilities frequently cause the demand for service to exceed the service supply. When this happens, queues form. Queues are a virtually unavoidable phenomenon.

While queuing problems may not be avoidable, better solutions can surely be found. In a queuing problem, the decision maker is concerned with determining the most economical queuing system. Alternative queuing systems are

---

[5] Accompanied by sensitivity tests for special attributes, the basic models will typically provide sufficient information for proper service facility design decisions.

postulated. They are then evaluated. And finally, the most economical queuing system is selected.

Alternative queuing systems are provided by changing any component of the queuing system. The major decision variables relate to changes in the arrival rate, changes in the service rate, changes in the uncertainty of the arrival rate, changes in the uncertainty of the service rate, and changes in the service facility.

The evaluation of alternative queuing systems consists primarily of balancing two opposing costs: (1) the expected cost of having calling units wait in the queue and the system and (2) the expected cost of providing the service facility. The major difficulty in measuring these expected costs is the incorporation of the uncertainty from arrival variations and service time variations.

Queuing models have been developed to incorporate these uncertainties into descriptive measures of the important queuing system characteristics. Queuing models provide probabilities for the states of the system (P_0, P_n); the amount of expected idle facility time (P_0, P_n); measures of the average length of the queue or the system (L, L_q); and quantification of the average waiting time in the queue or the system (W, W_q). Fortunately, the last four characteristics (L, L_q, W, and W_q) are functionally related. If one is obtained for a specific system, the others are easily determined.

The most basic queuing systems and resulting queuing models are for the single-server or multiple-server facilities with Poisson arrivals and exponential service times. Important extensions include the modeling of systems with a finite calling population, a truncated queue, and nonexponential service times. Many more complex extensions have been developed. When the queuing system becomes overcomplex, however, the mathematical models tend to become intractable. Simulation may offer a better modeling approach.

DERIVATION OF THE DESCRIPTIVE MODELS FOR THE SINGLE-SERVER POISSON-EXPONENTIAL SYSTEM

In the development of the descriptive characteristics of the single-server Poisson-exponential queuing system, the implicit assumptions are random arrivals and random service times. Time is measured in terms of a unit time interval subdivided into n very small subintervals of width Δt. The probabilities of an arrival or service completion during a subinterval are p_a and p_s, respectively. Because Δt is very small, the probabilities p_a and p_s will also be extremely small. Moreover, the subinterval Δt is so small that the probability of more than one arrival or more than one service completion in a subinterval is negligible.

STEADY-STATE PROBABILITIES

The queuing system is assumed to be in a steady-state at time t. The objective will be to develop probability models that define the probability distribution for the number of calling units in the system at time t. Defining $P_n(t)$ as n units in the system at time t, the probability information desired will be: $P_0(t)$, $P_1(t)$, $P_2(t)$, $\cdots$, $P_k(t)$.

In order to produce required relationships, the steady-state queuing system at time t is assumed to progress one subinterval Δt in time. The probability of n units being in the system at time $t + \Delta t$ will be determined:

$P_n(t + \Delta t)$.

Since only one arrival or one service completion can occur over a subinterval Δt, there are only four ways the system can contain n units at time $t + \Delta t$:

1. The system contains n items, in state S_n, at time t; there are no arrivals and no service completions.

2. The system is in state S_n at time t; there is one arrival and one unit serviced.

3. The system is in state S_{n+1} at time t; there are no arrivals and one departure.

Possible Ways to be in State n Events	State of System at Time t	Arrivals in Subinterval Δt	Units Serviced in Subinterval Δt	State of System at Time $t + \Delta t$
1	S_n	0	0	S_n
2	S_n	1	1	S_n
3	S_{n+1}	0	1	S_n
4	S_{n-1}	1	0	S_n

TABLE 16A.1

Events Leading to n Units in the System at Time $t + \Delta t$

4. The system is in state S_{n-1} at time t; there is one arrival and no departures.

These four ways are illustrated in Table 16A.1.

The probability of finding the system in state n will be expressed by the basic probability model for compound events (Chapter 2). With A representing an arrival, S a service completion, and the intersection ($\cap$) for AND, the probability becomes:

$$P_n(t + \Delta t) = P(P_n(t) \cap 0A \cap 0S \text{ OR } P_n(t) \cap 1A \cap 1S$$
$$\text{OR } P_{n+1}(t) \cap 0A \cap 1S \text{ OR } P_{n-1}(t) \cap 1A \cap 0S).$$

With p_a the probability of an arrival and p_s the probability of a service completion, the application of probability rules provides:

$$P_n(t + \Delta t) = P_n(t)(1 - p_a)(1 - p_s) + P_n(t)p_a p_s$$
$$+ P_{n+1}(t)(1 - p_a)p_s + P_{n-1}(t)p_a(1 - p_s)$$
$$= (1 - p_a - p_s + 2p_a p_s)P_n(t) + (p_s - p_a p_s)P_{n+1}(t)$$
$$+ (p_a - p_a p_s)P_{n-1}(t).$$

Since the subinterval Δt is very small, the probability of an arrival p_a and the probability of a service completion p_s are also very small. The probability of *both* an arrival and a service completion in a single subinterval is negligibly small. For example, if p_a is .0001 and p_s is .0002, the probability of *both* an arrival and a service completion will be:

$$P(1A \cap 1S) = p_a p_s$$
$$= (.0001)(.0002)$$
$$= .00000002.$$

Ignoring the probability $p_a p_s$:

$$P_n(t + \Delta t) = (1 - p_a - p_s)P_n(t) + p_s P_{n+1}(t) + p_a P_{n-1}(t).$$

In the steady-state, the state of the system is independent of the elapsed time. Therefore, over the very small interval Δt, the probability of the state of the system will remain unchanged. At steady-state:

$$P_n(t + \Delta t) = P_n(t).$$

Therefore, substituting $P_n(t)$ for $P_n(t + \Delta t)$:

$$P_n(t) = (1 - p_a - p_s)P_n(t) + p_sP_{n+1}(t) + p_aP_{n-1}(t)$$

and solving for $P_n(t)$:

$$P_n(t) = \frac{p_s}{(p_a + p_s)} P_{n+1}(t) + \frac{p_a}{(p_a + p_s)} P_{n-1}(t).$$

This defines one set of required relationships for the steady-state system. The probability of finding the system in state n depends on the probability that the system is in state $n + 1$ and state $n - 1$ at time t. Also, since a departure is possible, the value of n must be positive.

With p_a and p_s known parameters of the system, the other two state probabilities are required to determine $P_n(t)$. This will be accomplished by forming another set of required relationships. The probability that the system is in state 0 at time $t + \Delta t$ will be formed:

$$P_0(t + \Delta t).$$

There are two ways the system will be in state 0 at $t + \Delta t$ (Table 16A.2):

(1) S_0 at time t and no arrivals, or

(2) S_1 at time t and no arrivals and one service completion.

Possible Ways to be in State n Events	State of System at Time t	Arrivals in Subinterval Δt	Units Serviced in Subinterval Δt	State of System at Time $t + \Delta t$
1	S_0	1	–	S_0
2	S_1	0	1	S_0

TABLE 16A.2

A System State of Zero at Time $t + \Delta t$

The probability for the compound events is:

$$P_0(t + \Delta t) = P(P_0(t) \cap 0A \text{ OR } P_1(t) \cap 0A \cap 1S)$$

or

$$P_0(t + \Delta t) = P_0(t)(1 - p_a) + P_1(t)(1 - p_a)(p_s).$$

Reexpressing,

$$P_0(t + \Delta t) = (1 - p_a)P_0(t) + (p_s - p_a p_s)P_1(t).$$

The term with $p_a p_s$ is negligibly small. The probability requirements are:

$$P_0(t + \Delta t) = (1 - p_a)P_0(t) + p_s P_1(t).$$

For the steady-state:

$$P_0(t + \Delta t) = P_0(t).$$

Substituting $P_0(t)$ for $P_0(t + \Delta t)$ and rearranging terms:

$$P_0(t) = \frac{p_s}{p_a} P_1(t)$$

or

$$P_1(t) = \frac{p_a}{p_s} P_0(t).$$

With these relationships, the other possible states will be derived by substitutions into the general requirements for $P_n(t)$. Inserting 1 for n,

$$P_n(t) = \frac{p_s}{(p_a + p_s)} P_{n+1}(t) + \frac{p_a}{(p_a + p_s)} P_{n-1}(t)$$

becomes

$$P_1(t) = \frac{p_s}{(p_a + p_s)} P_2(t) + \frac{p_a}{(p_a + p_s)} P_0(t).$$

Substituting

$$P_0(t) = \frac{p_s}{p_a} P_1(t)$$

Appendix: Steady-State Probabilities

561

into the equation and solving for $P_1(t)$:

$$P_1(t) = \frac{p_s}{p_a} P_2(t)$$

or

$$P_2(t) = \frac{p_a}{p_s} P_1(t).$$

Inserting the $P_0(t)$ relation for $P_1(t)$:

$$P_2(t) = \left(\frac{p_a}{p_s}\right)^2 P_0(t).$$

Inserting 2 for n in the general requirements for $P_n(t)$ and following the same succession of steps, the results are:

$$P_3(t) = \frac{p_a}{p_s} P_2(t)$$

which in turn provides

$$P_3(t) = \left(\frac{p_a}{p_s}\right)^3 P_0(t).$$

Continually repeating this sequence with an incremented n and the latest results, the general relationship between $P_n(t)$ and $P_0(t)$ is established:

$$P_n(t) = \left(\frac{p_a}{p_s}\right)^n P_0(t).$$

All probability states will be obtainable with the determination of $P_0(t)$.

The value of $P_0(t)$ will be derived by starting with the basic relationship that requires the sum of the probabilities for all events to be one:

$$\sum_{n=0}^{\infty} P_n(t) = 1.$$

Using the previously determined relationship between $P_n(t)$ and $P_0(t)$:

$$\sum_{n=0}^{\infty} \left(\frac{p_a}{p_s}\right)^n P_0(t) = 1$$

Queuing Models

or

$$P_0(t) \sum_{n=0}^{\infty} \left(\frac{p_a}{p_s} \right)^n = 1.$$

Fortunately,

$$\sum_{n=0}^{\infty} \left(\frac{p_a}{p_s} \right)^n$$

follows a common infinite series expansion:

$$\sum_{n=0}^{\infty} a^n = a^0 + a^1 + a^2 + \cdots = \frac{1}{1-a}.$$

With $[a]$ equal to:

$$a = \frac{p_a}{p_s}$$

the summation becomes:

$$\sum_{n=0}^{\infty} \left(\frac{p_a}{p_s} \right)^n = \frac{1}{1 - (p_a/p_s)}.$$

Therefore,

$$P_0(t) \sum_{n=0}^{\infty} \left(\frac{p_a}{p_s} \right)^n = P_0(t) \frac{1}{1 - (p_a/p_s)} = 1$$

and solving for $P_0(t)$:

$$P_0(t) = 1 - \frac{p_a}{p_s}.$$

Since the descriptive characteristics of the queuing system are traditionally expressed in terms of the parameters λ and μ, the probabilities over a subinterval will be converted to parameter equivalence. Time was initially defined in terms of a *unit time interval* containing n subintervals of width Δt. The expected number of arrivals (λ) over a *unit time interval* is equal to the number of subintervals (n) multiplied by the probability of an arrival in a subinterval (p_a):[1]

$$\lambda = np_a.$$

Similarly, with p_s the probability of a service completion in a subinterval, the expected service completion time (μ) is equal to:

$$\mu = np_s.$$

Expressing the subinterval probabilities in terms of the parameters:

$$p_a = \frac{\lambda}{n} \qquad p_s = \frac{\mu}{n}.$$

Substituting these values into the state probability relationships:

$$P_0(t) = 1 - \frac{p_a}{p_s} \qquad\qquad P_n(t) = \left(\frac{p_a}{p_s}\right)^n P_0(t)$$

$$= 1 - \frac{\lambda/n}{\mu/n} \qquad\qquad = \left(\frac{\lambda/n}{\mu/n}\right)^n P_0(t)$$

$$= 1 - \frac{\lambda}{\mu} \qquad\qquad = \left(\frac{\lambda}{\mu}\right)^n P_0(t).$$

The final state probabilities are:

$$P_0(t) = 1 - \frac{\lambda}{\mu}$$

$$P_n(t) = \left(\frac{\lambda}{\mu}\right)^n P_0(t).$$

With known parameters (λ, μ), the probability distribution for the number of units in a single-server Poisson-exponential system will be obtained readily from the two state probability expressions given above.

---

[1] This relationship infers that the subintervals are *independent*. It is essentially the assumption of a Poisson distribution: the interval Δt is so small that the probability of more than one arrival per interval is negligible.

SYSTEM CHARACTERISTICS

The behavior of queuing systems is typically expressed in terms of four basic descriptive characteristics:

L = expected number in the system
L_q = expected number in the queue
W = expected waiting time in the system
W_q = expected waiting time in the queue.

These four characteristics are functionally related. If one is determined for a specified queuing system, the others can be obtained from the relationships:[2]

$$L = \lambda W \qquad W = W_q + \frac{1}{\mu}.$$
$$L_q = \lambda W_q$$

The expected number in the system (L) will be determined. The *expected value* of the random variable X is defined as:

$$E(X) = \sum_i X_i P(X_i).$$

Therefore, the *expected number* in the system will be represented as:

$$L = \sum_{n=0}^{\infty} n P_n(t).$$

Using the state probability expressions,

$$L = \sum_{n=0}^{\infty} n \left(\frac{\lambda}{\mu} \right)^n \left(1 - \frac{\lambda}{\mu} \right)$$

$$= \left(1 - \frac{\lambda}{\mu} \right) \sum_{n=0}^{\infty} n \left(\frac{\lambda}{\mu} \right)^n.$$

With a minor adjustment,

$$L = \left(1 - \frac{\lambda}{\mu} \right) \sum_{n=0}^{\infty} n \left(\frac{\lambda}{\mu} \right) \left(\frac{\lambda}{\mu} \right)^{n-1}$$

$$= \left(1 - \frac{\lambda}{\mu} \right) \left(\frac{\lambda}{\mu} \right) \sum_{n=0}^{\infty} n \left(\frac{\lambda}{\mu} \right)^{n-1}.$$

---

[2] The development of the relationships is provided in the chapter.

The quantity in the summation can be expressed as a well-known series expansion:[3]

$$\sum_{n=0}^{\infty} n \left(\frac{\lambda}{\mu} \right)^{n-1} = \frac{1}{1 - (\lambda/\mu)^2}.$$

Substituting this result,

$$L = \left(1 - \frac{\lambda}{\mu} \right) \left(\frac{\lambda}{\mu} \right) \frac{1}{1 - (\lambda/\mu)^2}$$

which reduces to:

$$L = \frac{\lambda}{\mu - \lambda}.$$

With the expected number in the system determined, the other three characteristics are derived directly from the relationship. For W,

$$W = \frac{L}{\lambda}$$

$$= \frac{\lambda/(\mu - \lambda)}{\lambda}$$

$$= \frac{1}{\mu - \lambda}.$$

---

[3] The geometric series is:

$$\sum_{n=0}^{\infty} x^n = \frac{1}{1 - x}.$$

The derivative is:

$$\frac{d}{dx} \left(\sum_{n=0}^{\infty} x^n \right) = \sum_{n=0}^{\infty} nx^{n-1} = \frac{d}{dx} \left[\frac{1}{1 - x} \right] = \frac{1}{(1 - x)^2}.$$

Therefore, the derivative of the geometric series provides the desired series expansion:

$$\frac{d}{dx} \left(\sum_{n=0}^{\infty} x^n \right) = \frac{1}{(1 - x)^2}.$$

W_q is obtained as easily:

$$W_q = W - \frac{1}{\mu}$$

$$= \frac{1}{\mu - \lambda} - \frac{1}{\mu}$$

$$= \frac{\lambda}{\mu(\mu - \lambda)}.$$

Finally, the average length of the queue becomes:

$$L_q = \lambda W_q$$

$$= \lambda \frac{\lambda}{\mu(\mu - \lambda)}$$

$$= \frac{\lambda^2}{\mu(\mu - \lambda)}.$$

These are the descriptive characteristics for the single-server Poisson-exponential queuing system. Other systems follow a similar development.

Bierman, H., Jr., C. P. Bonini, and W. H. Hausman. *Quantitative Analysis for Business Decisions*. Homewood, Ill.: Richard D. Irwin, 1973.

Cooper, R. B. *Introduction to Queuing Theory*. New York: The Macmillan Co., 1972.

Hillier, F. S., and G. T. Lieberman. *Introduction to Operations Research*. San Francisco, Cal.: Holden-Day, 1974.

Lee, A. *Applied Queuing Theory*. New York: St. Martin's Press, 1966.

Morse, P. M. *Queues, Inventories, and Maintenance*. New York: John Wiley & Sons, 1958.

Newell, G. F. *Applications of Queuing Theory*. London: Chapman and Hall, 1971.

Panico, J. A. *Queuing Theory: A Study of Waiting Lines for Business, Economics, and Science*. Englewood Cliffs, N.J.: Prentice-Hall, 1969.

Plane, D. R., and G. A. Kochenberger. *Operations Research for Managerial Decisions*. Homewood, Ill.: Richard D. Irwin, 1972.

Prabhu, N. U. *Queues and Inventories*. New York: John Wiley & Sons, 1965.

Richmond, S. B. *Operations Research*. New York: The Ronald Press Co., 1968.

Riordan, J. *Stochastic Service Systems*. New York: John Wiley & Sons, 1965.

Saaty, T. L. *Elements of Queuing Theory with Applications*. New York: McGraw-Hill Book Co., 1961.

Takocs, L. *Introduction to the Theory of Queues*. New York: Oxford University Press, 1962.

Thierauf, R. J., and R. C. Klekamp. *Decision Making Through Operations Research*. New York: John Wiley & Sons, 1975.

Trueman, R. E. *An Introduction to Quantitative Methods for Decision Making*. New York: Holt, Rinehart and Winston, 1974.

16.1. A single-channel queuing system has random arrivals at a rate of 9 per hour and a random service rate of 10 per hour. Determine the following system characteristics: P_0, L, L_q, W, and W_q.

16.2. A service facility has the capacity to service 20 items per hour. If items arrive for service uniformly at a rate of 10 per hour, what is the state of the service system after the first 30 minutes? Assume that an item is awaiting service at the beginning of the time period. Also, if the arrival rate is increased to 30 per hour, find the number waiting for service, being serviced, and already serviced after 30 minutes.

16.3. A single-channel Poisson arrival-exponential service queuing system has the following parameters: $\lambda = 2$ and $\mu = 5$.

1. What is the probability that the system is idle?
2. What is the probability that there will be two calling units in the system?
3. Construct the probability distribution for the number of units in the system.
4. What will be the expected number of calling units in the system?
5. What will be the expected waiting time in the queue for a calling unit?
6. What will be the average length of the queue?

16.4. The research department of a large organization has recently installed a new computer system. As a reasonable approximation, computer jobs are assumed to arrive randomly with a mean time of 12 minutes. The processing is assumed to be exponentially distributed with an average of 10 minutes.

1. What proportion of the time will the computer system be idle?
2. What is the average wait in the queue and in the computer system?
3. How long is the average queue of computer jobs awaiting service?

16.5. A public park and picnic area has a single tennis court. On weekends during the summer, twosomes for singles and foursomes for doubles arrive randomly at an average rate of .75 per hour. The duration of play is exponential with an average of one hour and 15 minutes.

Upon arriving at the courts on a warm summer weekend, what is the probability that players will find the court empty? If arriving players all patiently await access to the court, how many groups will be waiting to play? How long will the average group have to wait? What will arriving players probably do?

16.6. A medical clinic has a secretary who answers phone calls from patients for a group of doctors. On the average, about 12 patients call per hour. The average duration of a call is four minutes. The phone will allow two callers to be put on hold. The calls and the service time are considered random.

When a patient phones, what is the probability of obtaining direct service, of being put on hold, and of finding the line busy?

Once the call goes through, how long will the average caller have to wait for service?

16.7. The secretaries for five departments in a university must periodically copy material on a single Xerox machine. The arrival rate is Poisson with $\lambda = 4$ per hour. The service time is exponential with $\mu = 6$.

What is the probability that the machine will be idle? What is the probability that three secretaries will all need to use the Xerox at once? What is the average number of secretaries using the Xerox?

16.8. Refer to the tennis court queuing system in Problem 16.5. The Public Parks and Recreation management has imposed a court rule limiting play to 40 minutes. Assume that the duration of play remains exponentially distributed with a mean equal to the time limit. Upon arriving at the court, what is the probability that players will find the court empty? What will be the average length of the queue and the average waiting time to get on the court?

If play is extended to one hour, what will be the values for P_0, P_1, L_q, and W_q?

If all players use the court for *exactly* the time limit, how will these answers change?

16.9. A single pump gas station has the following operating information. The average arrival rate is one customer every four minutes. One attendant can service a customer in 4 minutes. Two attendants at the same pump can provide service in 2 1/2 minutes. Each customer will provide an economic benefit of 70 cents. Arrivals and service rates are assumed Poisson and exponential, respectively. Not more than two customers will wait in the line for service. The station is open for fifteen hours a day.

Compare the two-attendant, one-pump system with the alternative of a two pump system. Should the second pump be installed?

16.10. During peak hours, a barber has customers randomly arriving at an average rate of one every 25 minutes. He has recorded the hair cutting time for over a hundred customers. In hours, the mean was 3.0 and the standard deviation .092.

During peak hours, how large a queue is expected to form?

After talking with a customer who was taking a quantitative course at the university, the barber decides to eliminate all of the service variance by pacing himself with the wall clock. If haircutting time can be controlled to exactly 20 minutes per hair cut, how large a queue will be expected to form?

If the barber has sufficient business to accept only appointments at 25-minute intervals, and if he further controls cutting time to exactly 20 minutes, how large a queue will form? What kind of a queuing system will this be?

16.11. A seven-man night crew for a large warehousing operation consists of a three-man team that loads items on pallets for a four-man team to transport and selectively unload into storage. When the crew arrives, two pallets will already be filled. The crew will also leave two filled pallets for another shift. The loading and warehousing operations occur uniformly at a rate of five per hour for the eight-hour night shift. The transporting operation is facilitated by two battery powered pallet-lifting machines.

About one-fourth of the time, one of the battery powered pallet lifters fails to take a full charge. When this happens, it breaks down within the first hour of use. When it is restricted to only one transporting machine, the storage operation is less efficient. Since loading room is limited, however, part of the loading crew will help in the storage operation. Nevertheless, the storage service rate will be reduced to four pallets an hour.

If the machine is not fully charged, how many hours at normal productivity will be lost for the entire crew? How many hours will be lost at the one-machine rate?

The night crew members are paid $5 an hour and time-and-one-half for overtime. If the night crew must work overtime to accomplish a normal night's work, what is the added cost of the machine failure? What is the expected cost of not having the machine repaired before the night crew arrives?

16.12. A large garage repairs and services automobiles. When one of the many mechanics needs a particular body or engine part, the item can be obtained from an adjoining parts department. Mechanics arrive randomly for service at the parts department window at a rate of 10 per hour. The parts department attendant provides randomly distributed service at a rate of 12 mechanics per hour. The mechanics' time is valued at $7 per hour profit contribution to the garage.

Because mechanics have been complaining, the garage is considering hiring assistance for the parts attendant. One assistant is expected to improve the service rate by 50 percent. A second assistant can improve the initial service rate by 80 percent. An assistant, however, will cost $36 per day.

Does the situation economically warrant hiring assistance? If so, how many assistants should be hired?

16.1.3 An old single pump gas station has a prime location and a policy of excellent service. On the average, a customer arrives every five minutes. A single attendant can provide complete service in four minutes. A customer typically provides a dollar toward overhead, salaries, and profits. It has been discovered that customers are unwilling to wait when there are already three cars in the system. The station is open from 7 A.M. to 10 P.M.

Assuming that the arrival rate and service rate are applicable for all hours the station is open, what is the daily expected contribution to profits (overhead, salaries, and profits)? If customers were willing to wait in line, what would be the expected daily profits?

The station owner's son, home from college, notices the frequency of the queues and the potential customers that drive right on by. He recommends the hiring of a second attendant. With two attendants, the average service rate can be reduced to 2 1/2 minutes. If the attendants' wage is $2.50 an hour, should the attendant be hired?

Along with hiring an attendant, the station owner's son also recommends lowering the price of gas by 2 cents to stimulate arrivals with the new attendant. The price reduction is expected to draw an arrival every three minutes. However, profit per customer will drop by 30 cents. Should the price be reduced? What will be the anticipated daily change in profits for the new pricing policy with the added attendant?

16.14. A small grocery store in a resort town does most of its business during the summer months. The store is presently being expanded to meet next summer's needs. Last summer, during peak hours, the arrival rate at the checkout counter reached 70 customers per hour (Poisson). With adequate box boy support for the check-out counter clerks, the average service rate was two minutes a customer (exponential).

To maintain customer satisfaction and continued patronage, the store manager does not want an average of more than three customers waiting for service at any check-out counter. As an implied assumption, customers will shift to shorter lines. Moreover, clerks will not leave the check-out counters until all waiting customers are being serviced.

How many check-out counters will be required to maintain the store manager's policy with anticipated summer needs?

SIMULATION

PART FOUR

17

Monte Carlo Simulation

Whether they are intuitive expressions or mathematical algorithms, forms of structured logic—*models*—are a central theme of decision making. Broadly defined, models are the decision maker's attempt to more clearly describe, explain, or predict reality—to more fully understand and more effectively cope with the complex behavior of the real world. In a few meaningful relationships, models ideally *abstract* from a richly complex environment the inherent essential behavior. They provide the decision maker with a *simplification*. And as *simplifying abstractions*, models do not duplicate reality—they merely *simulate* reality.

In this chapter and the next, the modeling procedure is *simulation*. While there is a broader inference, simulation will be restricted to information-based systems used in decision making. Simulation will provide the decision maker with *a structured duplication of the essential behavior of a decision environment*. It will provide the decision maker with a means to understand complex interreactions in the decision environment and with an experimental testing ground to measure the anticipated effects of change.

Of all of the quantitative models, simulation is the *most general*. This is its exceptional power. In a single statement: *if a problem can be solved, simulation will provide an approximate optimal solution*. If other models cannot be successfully applied, simulation provides a potentially successful procedure.

The application of simulation is not without restriction: (1) the problem must be solvable and (2) the solution of the problem must warrant the necessary expenditure of time, effort, and resources. For a problem to be solvable, each of the essential elements of the decision process must be available (Chapter 1). There must be conceptualized alternatives, information to define the alternatives, an acceptable value system, and structured logic to evaluate and sort the alternatives. The adequacy with which these requirements are satisfied will define the solvability of the problem. This is predominantly a matter of expending sufficient time, effort, and resources.

In general, simulation is a method of duplicating the essential behavior of a real-world system. The assumptions, parameters, inputs, stimuli, and structure of the model can be manipulated to determine their effect on the behavior of the model. If the model is a good duplication of the real world, the effects on the model should duplicate the effects on the real world.

By duplicating real-world system behavior, a simulation model offers *a wealth of information through experimentation*. While an organization encounters a unique experience of last year's operating conditions and performance, simulation provides a means for generating *an entire history of operating conditions with measured performance*. Last year can be relived any number of times under any hypothesized conditions. Without the real-world unretractable commitment of time and expense, simulation provides a testing ground for altering the system. A decision maker can live with a system and experience behavioral changes without paying the price of real-world experimentation.

An approach that is very similar to simulation is commonly used to solve problems. In fact, it is the means by which most problems are pragmatically solved. When a decision maker needs to select a course of action in a repetitive situation, he or she selects an alternative, experiences the effect of the selection, and then selects an improved alternative. Time after time, this trial-and-error movement to increasingly improved selections is repeated. After enough adjustments have been made through time, after enough experience has been gained through experimentation, the decision maker's selection will become acceptably close to the optimal solution.

Although the final selection will be good, this approach is highly inefficient. The initial selections will entail an excessive cost—the cost of the difference between the actual returns and those obtainable from the best selection. In the gradual movement toward the best selection, the series of nonoptimal selections produces a series of *opportunity losses*.

Simulation provides a similar trial-and-error movement toward the optimal solution. The decision maker selects an alternative, experiences the effect of the selection, and then improves the selection. In this way, the selection is adjusted until it approximates the optimal solution. The critical difference: simulation allows a selection to be tried and measured without the cost of real-world experimentation. When the best selection is found, it can be used in the first application. A simulation *avoids the sum of all of the opportunity cost*. Simulation provides the decision maker with a means *to dry-lab test real-world implications*.

MONTE CARLO SIMULATION

Because of its exceptionally adaptive structure, simulation has taken many forms. One form of considerable importance is *Monte Carlo simulation*.[1] It is

---

[1] The method was originally developed as part of a secret project at the end of World War II. The project, code-named Monte Carlo, used a roulette device to simulate the probabilistic behavior of neutron diffusion.

a frequently applied procedure that duplicates stochastic behavior. An *artificial probability distribution* is constructed *to duplicate the probability distribution for a stochastic element in a real-world system.* Samples are then drawn from the artificial distribution to substitute for samples drawn from the real-world counterpart. When the sample becomes large, it will tend to duplicate the stochastic behavior of the real-world system.

This chapter will develop the modeling properties of Monte Carlo simulation. Simple decision environments will be used to develop the modeling procedure. The next chapter will extend the application to more complex and more realistic decision environments.

The Simulation of a Stochastic Process

The Monte Carlo technique will be demonstrated by a simplified example. One important component of a more complex decision environment is a political decision on Capitol Hill. Legislation will be either signed into law or vetoed by the president. (If it is vetoed, the veto will not be overridden.) The associated subjective probabilities and anticipated returns are provided in Table 17.1. The objective will be to measure the expected return (or average return) for the legislation decision. An exact measure of the expected return is provided by the *EMV* in Table 17.1. Instead of using a mathematical model, however, this same measure of worth will be sought by simulation.

The simulation of a stochastic process is *a sampling technique.* The probability distribution for the legislation decision is represented in Figure 17.1. *Random samples* will be drawn from this distribution to form several *sampling distributions.* These sampling distributions will be used to demonstrate the statistical concept underlying Monte Carlo simulation.

Figure 17.2 contains several sampling distributions of increasing sample size. For a sample of 2—if this same environment is encountered two times— there are three possible average returns that could occur: $-100,000$, $100,000$, or $200,000$. The associated probabilities of obtaining these results are .25, .50, and .25, respectively. Similarly, for samples of 4 and 10, the sampling distributions represent the average returns that could occur from the samples. Note, *the average return from the sample may not be the same as the actual average return (EMV)* for the legislation decision (Table 17.1, Figure 17.2).

Events (e_i)	$p(e_i)$	Payoff ($\$_i$)
Law: L	½	$200,000
Veto: V	½	$-100,000
	1.00	$EMV = \$50,000$

TABLE 17.1

The Legislation Decision

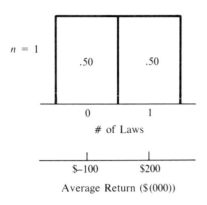

n = 1

.50   .50

0   1

\# of Laws

$-100 $200

Average Return ($(000))

FIGURE 17.1

The Probability Distribution for the
Legislation Decision

Also note, *as the sample size increases, the probability that the sample average return will depart materially from the actual average return decreases.*

With the actual average return determined (Table 17.1), the *error* in the sample average estimates *due to random variations* will be measured. The actual average return is $50,000. For a sample of 2, the probability of obtaining a sample with this average is .00. It is not a possibility. The probability of obtaining a sample with an average return that differs from the actual average return by as much as $100,000 is .50. If the sample is increased to 4, the probability of obtaining a sample with the actual average return is .375. The probability of obtaining a sample that errs by more than $100,000 is reduced to .1250. For a sample of 10, this same probability is reduced much further to .0034.

Figure 17.3 contains the sampling distribution of the average returns for a sample of 100. It demonstrates an important statistical concept. The probability of obtaining an average return that deviates by more than $100,000 from the actual average return is .000000. Pragmatically, all average returns are within $40,000 of the actual average return. *As the sample is increased, the average returns for the sampling distribution converge to the actual average return. The probability of any material departure becomes virtually nonexistent.*

Since a large sample will very closely approximate the actual population characteristic, the simulation of the legislation decision is easily devised. An artificial probability distribution is constructed to duplicate the essential behavior of the legislation decision. Samples are then drawn from this artificial distribution to replicate sample-legislation decisions. These sample outcomes will provide the basis for calculating an average return. If the sample is large, this average return will accurately approximate the actual average return.

To facilitate the *random selection* of sample outcomes from the artificial distribution, *random numbers* will be used. Random numbers have the character-

Monte Carlo Simulation

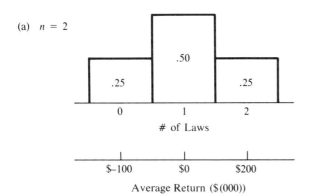

(a) $n = 2$

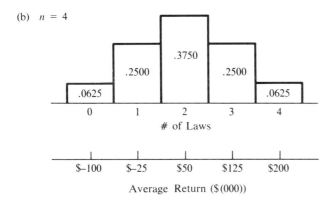

(b) $n = 4$

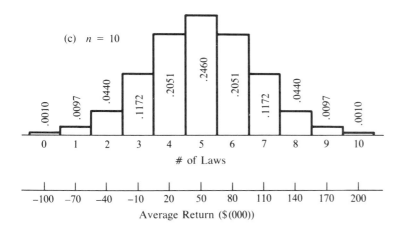

(c) $n = 10$

FIGURE 17 2

Sampling Distributions for the Legislation Decision

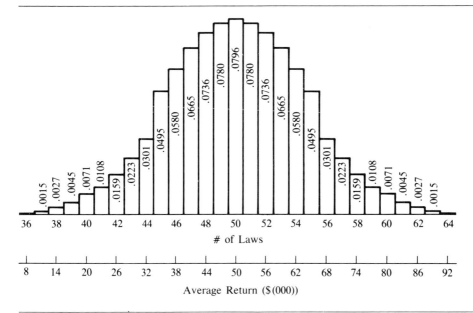

# of Laws

Average Return ($(000))

FIGURE 17.3

Sampling Distribution ($n = 100$)

istic of being drawn independently from a uniform distribution of equally likely and mutually exclusive events. Therefore, a one-digit random number with values of only zero or one would have the uniform distribution indicated in Figure 17.4.

Note, the probability distribution for the legislation decision (Figure 17.1) and the probability distribution for the two-state, one-digit random number (Figure 17.4) are identical. Samples from these identical probability distributions will have *identical sampling distributions*. A sample that depicts an actual legislation decision will be generated as reliably by determining the state of a two-state, one-digit random number.

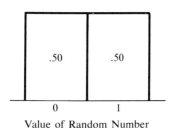

Value of Random Number

FIGURE 17.4

The Probability Distribution for a
One-Digit Random Number

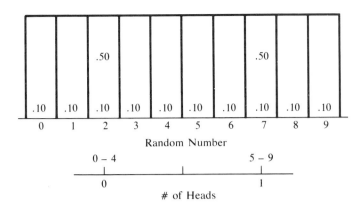

FIGURE 17.5
Ten-State, One-Digit Random Numbers

Since random-number tables and random-number generating devices are typically ten-state, one-digit numbers, one of several conventions will be used. Since the ten-state numbers possess the same characteristics as the two-state numbers, the lowest five numbers will be assigned the outcome *veto* and the largest five assigned the outcome *law* (Figure 17.5):

Event	Random Number (RN)
Veto	0–4
Law	5–9

Instead of generating a series of random numbers, the decision maker can refer to random numbers already generated in a random-numbers table.[2] Appendix 2 reproduces one page of such a table with 2,500 random digits. It will be used to generate the sample for the legislation decision. Reading by rows from the upper left-hand corner, the first random digits[3] are 0, 3, 9, 9.

---

[2] The Rand Corporation has a published volume with 1 million random digits: The Rand Corporation, *A Million Random Digits with 100,000 Normal Deviates*. Glencoe, Ill.: Free Press, 1955.

[3] Technically, for a published series or a computer generated series, the term "random numbers" is a misnomer. If digits are read in the same way from the same page of a printed table, or if the same "seed" or initiating value is used for a computer generated series, the digits are reproducible and exactly predictable. In the strict sense, they are not truly random. For simulation purposes, however, these "pseudorandom numbers" satisfy the requirements for random numbers. They also have the added advantage of allowing the replication of the same series to provide common comparative environments.

Sample Number (n)	RN	Event	Payoff ($\$_i$(000))	Total Payoff $\Sigma \$_i$(000)	Average Return $\overline{\Sigma \$_i}$(000)
1	0	Law	200	200	200
2	3	Law	200	400	200
3	9	Veto	−100	300	100
4	9	Veto	−100	200	50
5	1	Law	200	400	80
6	1	Law	−200	600	100
.	.	.	.	.	.
.	.	.	.	.	.
.	.	.	.	.	.
10	1	Law	200	1100	110
.	.	.	.	.	.
.	.	.	.	.	.
.	.	.	.	.	.
20	4	Law	200	1300	65
.	.	.	.	.	.
.	.	.	.	.	.
40	4	Law	200	6300	157.5
.	.	.	.	.	.
.	.	.	.	.	.
100	6	Veto	−100	3800	38
.	.	.	.	.	.
.	.	.	.	.	.
200	0	Law	200	10,600	53
.	.	.	.	.	.
.	.	.	.	.	.
400	7	Veto	−100	22,100	55.25
.	.	.	.	.	.
.	.	.	.	.	.
.	.	.	.	.	.
500	1	Law	200	76,850	153.7
.	.	.	.	.	.
.	.	.	.	.	.
.	.	.	.	.	.
1000	2	Law	200	53,000	53.0
.	.	.	.	.	.
.	.	.	.	.	.
2000	6	Veto	−100	102,400	51.20
.	.	.	.	.	.
.	.	.	.	.	.
2500	5	Veto	−100	125,500	50.20

TABLE 17.2

A Simulation of n Legislative Decisions

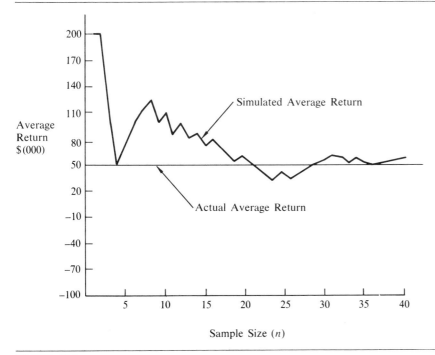

FIGURE 17.6
Stability Chart

This corresponds to:

Random Number	Outcome
0	Law
3	Law
9	Veto
9	Veto

The estimated average returns from the simulated samples are provided in Table 17.2. Very small samples produce wide variations in the estimates. *As the sample increases, the variations progressively dampen and the estimates more closely approach the actual value.* For a sample of 100, the estimate is within $12,000 of the actual value. When the sample reaches 2,500, the sample average return is within only $240 of the actual average return.

Figure 17.6 provides a *stability chart* of the estimates as the sample size increases. The potential change in the estimates become progressively smaller and smaller with each added sample. They eventually stabilize at the actual average return. A stability chart will indicate the adequacy of the sample size for any acceptable level of accuracy.

EVALUATING THE WORTH OF AN OPPORTUNITY

The application of the Monte Carlo technique will be further demonstrated with a problem from Chapter 3. A realtor has the opportunity to invest $1,000 in a project for one year. The return depends on one of three possible future economic environments. Table 17.3 summarizes the important information with the evaluating statistic (EMV = $90). While the mathematical procedure for evaluating the opportunity is far more efficient, this example will demonstrate the applicability of simulation to this general category of problems.

Economic Environmental States (S_i)		$p(S_i)$	Associated Payoffs
Optimistic:	S_1	.20	$400
Normal:	S_2	.50	200
Pessimistic:	S_3	.30	−300
			EMV = $ 90

TABLE 17.3

An Investment Opportunity

The simulation process will generate a sample representation of the stochastic investment opportunity. With the information from a large sample, the average return for the investment opportunity will be calculated. This process will be equivalent to letting the decision maker enter into the investment a large number of times and discover the desirability of the opportunity. The advantage of simulation, again, is that all this can be done on paper without risking a single cent. When the opportunity is found to be desirable, the decision maker can then make an actual commitment.

The first step in the simulation is to assign random numbers to each state of nature in accordance with the associated probabilities (Table 17.4). Because it has a probability of .20, state of nature S_1 is assigned 2 of 10 possible one-digit

State of Nature (S_i)	$p(S_i)$	Random Number
S_1	.20	0-1
S_2	.50	2-6
S_3	.30	7-9

TABLE 17.4

Random Number Assignment to States of Nature

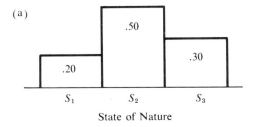

Probability Distribution for States of Nature

(a)

Probability Distribution for Grouped Random Numbers

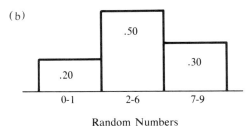

(b)

FIGURE 17.7

(a) Probability Distribution for States of Nature
(b) Probability Distribution for Grouped Random Numbers

random numbers (0, 1). Similarly, S_2 is assigned 5 of the 10 possible random numbers (2–6). The remaining 3 random numbers (7–9) are assigned to S_3. Since each random number has an equal probability (.10), the probabilities for the random-number will exactly correspond to those for the states of nature. As indicated in Figure 17.7, the probability distributions for the random numbers and states of nature are identical. Both distributions will have identical sampling distributions—a sample can be generated as appropriately from either distribution.

A sample that duplicates real-world investments is easily developed. A random number is selected from a random-number table or generated by a computer. The random number will define the state of nature and the associated return. If the first random number is a 2, state of nature S_2 (Table 17.5) is assumed to occur with a return of $200. This process can be repeated until the sample is large enough to measure the expected return accurately.

Random numbers will be taken from Appendix 2. As an arbitrary procedure, the random numbers are read in groups of five down the last column. For samples larger than a single column, the columns are then read consecutively right-to-left. The measure of investment desirability is the average return or expected monetary value. The simulation with associated measure of average

Sample Size (n)	RN	State (S_i)	Payoff ($\$_i$)	Accumulated Payoff $\Sigma \$_i$	Average Monetary Return $\Sigma \$_i/n$
1	2	S_2	200	200	200
2	5	S_2	200	400	200
3	5	S_2	200	600	200
4	9	S_3	−300	300	75
5	3	S_2	200	500	100
6	4	S_2	200	700	116.67
.	.	.	.	.	.
.	.	.	.	.	.
.	.	.	.	.	.
10	6	S_2	200	1000	100
.	.	.	.	.	.
.	.	.	.	.	.
.	.	.	.	.	.
20	0	S_1	400	2800	140
.	.	.	.	.	.
.	.	.	.	.	.
.	.	.	.	.	.
40	7	S_3	−300	4200	105
.	.	.	.	.	.
.	.	.	.	.	.
.	.	.	.	.	.
50	1	S_1	400	5700	114
.	.	.	.	.	.
.	.	.	.	.	.
100	8	S_3	−300	8600	86
.	.	.	.	.	.
.	.	.	.	.	.
.	.	.	.	.	.
250	5	S_2	200	26700	106.80
.	.	.	.	.	.
.	.	.	.	.	.
.	.	.	.	.	.
500	4	S_2	200	46300	92.60
.	.	.	.	.	.
.	.	.	.	.	.
.	.	.	.	.	.
1000	8	S_3	−300	87200	87.20
.	.	.	.	.	.
.	.	.	.	.	.
.	.	.	.	.	.
2500	2	S_2	200	223900	89.56

TABLE 17.5

Simulating a Stochastic Investment Opportunity

Monte Carlo Simulation

returns for various size samples is provided in Table 17.5. Using the entire table of 2,500 random numbers, the simulated average return is $89.56. Compared with the exact mathematically derived value of $90.00 (Table 17.3)—it is a close approximation. With the use of a computer, the sample size could easily be increased to produce any desired degree of accuracy.

SIMULATING A DECISION TREE

A final problem involving a sequence of dependent stochastic events will illustrate the simulating of a stochastic process. A small private investor has an opportunity to enter into two forthcoming investments. Both investments involve a group purchase of land. Both are based on speculation that the land will be favorably rezoned by the city planning commission.

In order to participate in the first purchase, the investor must have $40,000 available within two days. If the area is rezoned industrial, the group's strategy is a quick resale with large gains to be used for another similar investment. If the area remains residential, the quick resale will result in a substantial loss. The quantification of the essential elements of the decision environment for this single investment is provided in Table 17.6.

States of Nature	Probabilities	Return
Rezone Industrial	.60	$10,000
Remain Residential	.40	–$20,000

TABLE 17.6
Investment 1 ($40,000)

Four months hence, after the first purchase has been resold, and just before the planning commission makes a new rezoning decision, the group will purchase a second parcel of land. This parcel is presently zoned residential. There is an exceedingly good chance, however, that it will be rezoned industrial or light industrial. In this case, the group will enjoy the benefits of a quick resale. Table 17.7 provides the quantitative assessment of this second situation.

The small investor's decision is constrained by the amount of capital required to participate. The first investment will require $40,000 and the second, $50,000. By liquidating certain assets commensurate with a small loan, the small investor can raise the $40,000. If he considers the second investment separately from the first, he sees no prospect of raising the necessary $50,000 within the next four months.

States of Nature	Probabilities	Return
Rezone Industrial	.50	$20,000
Rezone Light Industrial	.40	$10,000
Remain Residential	.10	–$10,000

TABLE 17.7
Investment 2 ($50,000)

Since the investor is extremely interested in the second investment, he considers the prospect of entering into the first investment in order to generate enough income to enter the second investment. If the first parcel is rezoned industrial, a quick resale will return the $40,000 invested plus the anticipated profit of $10,000—enough to enter into the second speculative venture.

The tree diagram in Figure 17.8 descriptively illustrates the decision environment. The simulation of the decision environment for the investor's decision rule (to enter into both investments) will consist of three steps. First, a model will be constructed to duplicate the essential behavior of the decision environment. Second, the decision rule will be tested in the simulated environment and the results recorded. Since the decision environment contains stochastic

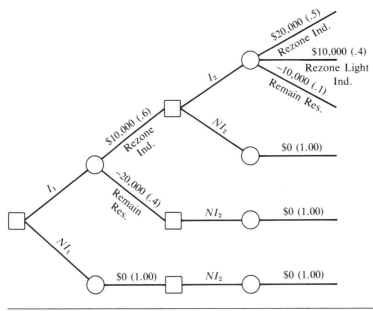

FIGURE 17.8
The Decision Environment

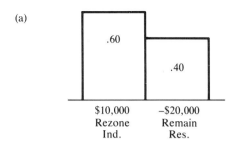

Duplicating the First Stochastic Process
Investment 1

(a)

.60

.40

$10,000
Rezone
Ind.

–$20,000
Remain
Res.

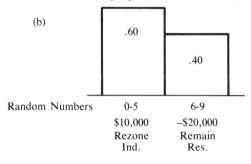

Artificial Sampling Distribution for Investment 1

(b)

.60

.40

Random Numbers   0-5   6-9

$10,000   –$20,000
Rezone   Remain
Ind.   Res.

FIGURE 17.9

(a) Duplicating the First Stochastic Process
    Investment 1
(b) Artificial Sampling for Investment 1

elements, the results will contain variability. A large sample will be required to allow the joint stochastic influences (from both investments) to be adequately represented in terms of relative frequencies of results. Third, with sufficient sampling information, the results will be aggregated to measure the decision rule.

In the construction of a model that duplicates the essential behavior of the first investment opportunity, there are two states of nature: rezone industrial or remain residential (Figure 17.9a). Random numbers are assigned in proportion to their probabilities (Table 17.8). As indicated in Figure 17.9b, an

States of Nature	Probabilities	Random Numbers
Rezone Industrial	.60	0-5
Remain Residential	.40	6-9

TABLE 17.8

Random Number Assignment (I_1)

Simulating a Decision Tree

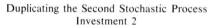

Duplicating the Second Stochastic Process
Investment 2

(a)

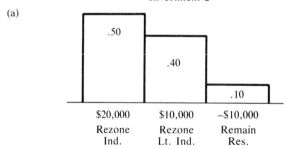

.50

.40

.10

$20,000 $10,000   −$10,000
Rezone   Rezone   Remain
Ind.   Lt. Ind.   Res.

Artificial Sampling Distribution for Investment 2

(b)

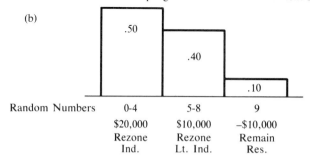

.50

.40

.10

Random Numbers   0-4   5-8   9

$20,000 $10,000   −$10,000
Rezone   Rezone   Remain
Ind.   Lt. Ind.   Res.

FIGURE 17.10

(a) Duplicating the Second Stochastic Process
Investment 2
(b) Artificial Sampling Distribution for Investment 2

artificial sampling distribution with random numbers specifying the outcomes exactly duplicates the original investment distribution.

The second investment is considered in the same way. The second investment decision has the probability distribution indicated in Figure 17.10a. By assigning random numbers in concurrence with the respective probabilities (Table 17.9), an identical artificial sampling distribution is constructed (Figure 17.10b).

States of Nature	Probabilities	Random Numbers
Rezone Industrial	.50	0-4
Rezone Light Industrial	.40	5-8
Remain Residential	.10	9

TABLE 17.9

Random Number Assignment (I_2)

A series of random numbers can now be drawn to represent a corresponding series of outcomes for investment 2.

With the two stochastic elements represented by outcome associated random numbers, the decision rule is ready to be tested in a simulated environment. Two random numbers are selected from Appendix 2. The first random number (RN_1) will represent the first investment rezoning outcome. The second random number (RN_2) will represent the second investment rezoning outcome. Each number also represents the anticipated return on the associated investment. Reading down the columns, the first set of two numbers is 03. The corresponding environmental associates are:

RN_1	State of Nature	Return on I_1	RN_2	State of Nature	Return on I_2
0	Rezone Industrial	$10,000	3	Rezone Industrial	$20,000

The first simulated behavior of the decision environment produced a return of $30,000. For the sample of size one, the decision rule (to enter both investments) is performing admirably.

To make sure that the inference drawn from the sample was not merely due to random causes, the sampling procedure will be conducted many times.[4] Table 17.10 provides the first 10 outcomes associated with the decision rule.

RN_1	State of Nature	Payoff I_1	RN_2	State of Nature	Payoff I_2	Total (I_1, I_2)
0	Rezone Ind.	$10,000	3	Rezone Ind.	$20,000	$30,000
3	Rezone Ind.	10,000	8	Rezone L. Ind.	10,000	20,000
1	Rezone Ind.	10,000	7	Rezone L. Ind.	10,000	20,000
3	Rezone Ind.	10,000	2	Rezone Ind.	20,000	30,000
6	Remain Res.	−20,000	—			−20,000
2	Rezone Ind.	10,000	4	Rezone Ind.	20,000	30,000
6	Remain Res.	−20,000	—			−20,000
3	Rezone Ind.	10,000	0	Rezone Ind.	20,000	30,000
0	Rezone Ind.	10,000	3	Rezone Ind.	20,000	30,000
4	Rezone Ind.	10,000	8	Rezone L. Ind.	10,000	20,000

TABLE 17.10

Simulated Decision Environments, Decision Rule (I_1, I_2)

[4] Sampling should be sufficient to allow an adequate numerical interplay of the two joint stochastic events. A stability chart could be used.

Simulating a Decision Tree

Sample Size (n)	Average Return for I_1 & I_2
1	$30,000
2	25,000
$\vdots$	$\vdots$
10	17,000
$\vdots$	$\vdots$
20	7,000
$\vdots$	$\vdots$
50	8,000
$\vdots$	$\vdots$
100	6,400
$\vdots$	$\vdots$
200	4,800
$\vdots$	$\vdots$
300	3,800
$\vdots$	$\vdots$
400	4,350
$\vdots$	$\vdots$
500	4,420

TABLE 17.11

Average Return for the Simulated Decision Rule
(I_1, I_2)

Table 17.11 provides the average return for the decision rule for various sample sizes from 1 to 500. Although the final sample is still far from stability of expected result, the sample average returns strongly support the efficacy of the decision rule. From the sample of size 500, the estimated expected return is $4,420.

For comparison, the exact expected return is provided by the mathematical procedure of *averaging out and folding back*. (Figure 17.11). The expected return for the decision rule is $5,800.

The mathematical modeling counterpart demonstrates two important properties of simulation. First, while a mathematical model provides a computationally efficient exact solution, *simulation provides an inefficient approximate solution*. Simulation tends to replace a few calculations by a few thousand calculations, although with the advent of high-speed computers, the drawback of computational inefficiency is becoming less and less serious. Second, while a mathematical model requires a sophisticated set of highly structured logic, *simulation duplicates the essence of the decision environment with simple logical constructs*. By separating the decision environment into its most basic components, simulation provides a means of descriptively interrelating complex phenomena.

For a decision maker who is confronted with a complex problem, there is an important corollary. If the complex set of logic for a mathematical model

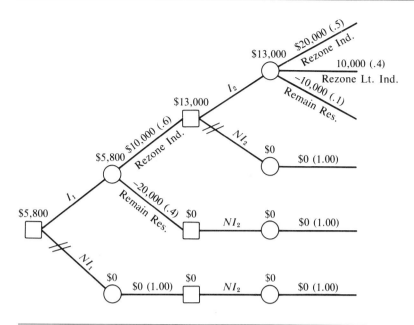

The Mathematical Model: Averaging Out and Folding Back

has not been structured or is not known by the decision maker, simulation will provide a conceptually simple way to solve the problem. The more complexly intractable the mathematical structuring of the decision environment, the more appealing an approximate simulation solution.

SUMMARY

Simulation is an exceptionally adaptive modeling technique. It is a process of duplicating the essential behavior of the decision environment. Once this model has been constructed, a computer presents the duplicated decision environment. It numerically presents the interactive effects of the model's componentry. Any component of this model—any assumption, parameter, structure, stimuli, or decision rule—can be manipulated with measured effect on the entire sysstem. Alternative courses of action can be tested, modified, and progressively improved.

An important attribute of simulation is its general applicability. It can be used to solve *any* solvable problem—even for the most complex decision environments. Stochastic elements—uncertainties—are often complicating factors in the decision environment. The Monte Carlo technique provides a simple means to incorporate these stochastic elements into a modeled duplication of the decision environment. The process typically separates each of the stochastic elements. For each of these, an artificial probability distribution is constructed identical to the probability distribution for stochastic behavior. Samples are then drawn from the artificial distribution to form a sampling distribution of stochastic behavior. With the use of a computer, very large samples are taken. This will produce the information needed to measure the influence of the stochastic element of any component in the entire system.

Although it is significantly less efficient computationally than a well-structured mathematical model, the Monte Carlo technique provides an alternative approach for measuring the influences of stochastic elements in a decision environment. As the stochastic elements become more complex, however, pure mathematical modeling quickly becomes too untractable. Monte Carlo simulation provides a conceptually straightforward way.

Earlier in the text, problems containing uncertainty were solved by Bayes' decision rule, a conditional profit table, a conditional opportunity loss table, or a decision tree. These problems can also be solved by Monte Carlo simulation. More complex stochastic systems were introduced later in inventory models and queuing systems. The next chapter will demonstrate the application of simulation to these and more complex decision environments.

Bonini, C. P. *Simulation of Information and Decision Systems in the Firm.* Englewood Cliffs, N.J.: Prentice-Hall, 1963.

Evans, G. W., G. F. Wallace, and S. L. Sutherland. *Simulation Using Digital Computers.* Englewood Cliffs, N.J.: Prentice-Hall, 1967.

Forrester, Jay W. *Industrial Dynamics.* Cambridge, Mass.: M.I.T. Press, 1961.

———. *World Dynamics.* Cambridge, Mass.: Wright-Allen Press, 1971.

Hillier, F. S., and G. J. Lieberman. *Introduction to Operations Research.* San Francisco: Holden-Day, 1974.

McMillan, C., and R. F. Gonzalez. *Systems Analysis: A Computer Approach to Decision Models.* Homewood, Ill.: Richard D. Irwin, 1968.

Meier, R. C., W. P. Newall, and H. L. Poger. *Simulation in Business and Economics.* Englewood Cliffs, N.J.: Prentice-Hall, 1969.

Mize, J. H., and J. S. Cox. *Essentials of Simulation.* Englewood Cliffs, N.J.: Prentice-Hall, 1968.

Naylor, T. H. *Computer Simulation Experiments with Models of Economic Systems.* New York: John Wiley & Sons, 1971.

Naylor, T. H., J. L. Balintfy, D. S. Burdick, and K. Chu. *Computer Simulation Techniques.* New York: John Wiley & Sons, 1966.

The Rand Corporation. *A Million Random Digits with 100,000 Normal Deviates.* Glencoe, Ill.: Free Press, 1955.

Schmidt, J. W., and R. E. Taylor. *Simulation and Analysis of Industrial Systems.* Homewood, Ill.: Richard D. Irwin, 1970.

Thierauf, R. J., and R. C. Klekamp. *Decision Making Through Operations Research.* New York: John Wiley & Sons, 1975.

17.1. A short-term investment opportunity offers potential returns of $20,000, $4,000, or $-10,000$. The subjective probability assessments are .30, .50, and .20. Using Monte Carlo simulation, evaluate the expected worth of this opportunity to an *EMV*'er.

17.2. In the gambling resort at Monte Carlo, the game of roulette is played as follows. The wheel is numbered from 0 to 36. A bet can be placed on one of the numbers. If the number appears, the player wins 35 times the amount of the bet. If another number appears, the stake is lost.

Using the random numbers in Table 17.2, simulate 400 plays of one dollar bet on number 4. From the simulation data, what is the expected value of the game? What is the true mathematical expectation?

17.3.

C_1	C_2	C_3
$5 $10 $10 $20	$5 $5 $5 $50	$1 $1 $1 $1 $100

A game is played by tossing a coin and drawing a bill from one of two containers. If a head appears, the bill will be drawn from container 1. If a tail appears, the bill will be drawn from container 2.

As a second alternative, a bill can be drawn directly from container 3.

Use simulation to select the best alternative. Generate information from 200 samples for each alternative and compare the simulated result with the calculated mathematical expectations.

17.4. A manager is contemplating involvement in a decision environment containing three sequentially related two-state decisions (D_1, D_2, D_3). If he makes the right decision in each case, the return will be $80,000. If he makes the wrong decision in D_1, he will lose $1,000 and the other options will be terminated. If he makes the wrong decision in D_2, he will lose $10,000, and again the other options will be terminated. If he makes the wrong decision in D_3, he must make another two-state decision immediately. While a correct decision here produces no loss, a wrong decision will be costly. If the manager (an EMV'er) must make equally likely guesses for each decision, what is the maximum tolerable loss?

Set up the simulation to duplicate the decision environment. Without solving, indicate a method for approximating the solution.

17.5.

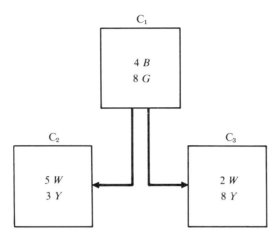

An item is drawn from container 1. If it is blue (B), a second item is drawn from container 2. If it is green (G), the second item is drawn from container 3.

Use simulation to duplicate the stochastic process of selection for 200 sets of selections. From the simulation data:

1. What is the probability of drawing a yellow item (Y) on the second draw?
2. What is the probability of drawing a blue item (B) and a white item (W) in sequence?
3. If the second draw is white (W), what is the probability that the first draw was green (G)?
4. Construct a joint probability table.

17.6. A private investor in stocks and bonds on the New York Stock Exchange anticipates that within the next three days a major bank will announce a one-point reduction in the prime lending rate. He speculates that this will create a sizeable fluctuation in the market value of three prospective stock purchase options. As a result of other cash flow commitments, the stock will be purchased for resale within four days. If the prime rate is reduced, the projected profits for the present bull market are:

Stock 1	Stock 2	Stock 3
$1,050	$1,400	$1,750.

If the prime rate is not reduced, the profit projections are:

Stock 1	Stock 2	Stock 3
$200	$100	$ − 150.

The assessed likelihood of the prime rate cut is .70.

Use simulation to determine which of the three stock options appears most favorable.

17.7. An organization produces a number of different consumer goods. Most of the products are influenced by seasonal factors. One of the products has the following deseasonalized monthly demand projection over the three-month summer period with accompanying seasonal indexes. From the following data, use simulation to determine the expected level of sales for the three-month summer period.

Monthly Demand (000)	Probability of Demand	Seasonal Index (% of normal)
6	.02	June: 1 12%
7	.05	July: 1 18%
8	.12	August: 1 24%
9	.19	
10	.27	
11	.17	
12	.11	
13	.04	
14	.02	
15	.01	

17.8. The following problem was presented (4.4) in Chapter 4. An individual has $80,000 to invest. There will be two known opportunities, one at the beginning of each of the next two months:

Investment	Cost	Payoff	Probability
Inv. 1	$ 80,000	$ − 40,000	.60
		20,000	.40
Inv. 2	100,000	20,000	.20
		40,000	.30
		60,000	.40
		− 20,000	.10

The initial investment, plus the payoff, will be refunded at the end of the month. *No money can be borrowed.*

Use a decision tree to indicate the decision environment. Use simulation to determine: (1) the proper decision, (2) the expected return, and (3) the maximum an *EMV*'er would pay for the opportunity to borrow $20,000. Then determine each of these by the previously developed mathematical models.

17.9. On the basis of all available information, a marketing manager subjectively assesses the chance that a new product will be successful at .75. To confirm this feeling, he conducts a market research project to test consumer reaction. If the product really will be successful, there is a .85 chance that the survey will so indicate. If the product will not be successful, there is a .25 chance that the survey will indicate success anyway.

Construct a probability tree representing the decision environment. With the aid of the decision tree, construct a simulation model that represents the stochastic elements of the decision environment.

With a simulated sample of 250, answer the following questions:

1. If the survey is conducted and the research project indicates a successful product, what is the marketing manager's revised probability that the product really will be successful?
2. If the survey indicates an unsuccessful product, what is the marketing manager's revised probability that the product will be successful anyway?

Now answer these two questions using the probability models provided in Chapter 2.

18

Simulation of Complex Systems

The process of modeling begins with an *abstraction of the essential behavior* of a more complex decision environment. In many situations, the essential behavior of the decision environment may contain a number of complicating special characteristics. When it contains nonlinearity, stochastic subsystems, and transient components, for example, pure mathematical modeling may often become intractable. When the essential behavior is highly complex, the decision maker may prefer to rely on the more adaptive modeling technique of simulation.

In Chapter 17, simulation was used to solve problems that contained simple stochastic elements. In this chapter, simulation will be extended to more complex decision environments. Simulation will first be used to solve a queuing problem. It will then be used to solve an inventory problem. And finally, simulation will be demonstrated as a means to structurally duplicate and test the complex behavior of an entire organization.

SIMULATION OF QUEUING SYSTEMS

Queuing systems often illustrate the difficulty of constructing a mathematical model that contains all the important elements of the decision environment. The basic descriptive queuing models are for single-channel and multiple-channel systems with Poisson arrivals and exponential service times. They further assume an infinite calling population, the obtainment of a steady-state, a first-come-first-served service discipline, no customer balking, and no truncated queue. Such simplifying assumptions typically do not distort the model's representation of the queuing system sufficiently to prevent their effective use for reliable decision making.

In many situations, however, the queuing system may have important special characteristics. It may have several transient, as well as steady-state, conditions. It may be state-dependent or it may be part of an entire network of interdependent service facilities. It may have service priorities or it may have balking customers from finite calling populations. The exclusion of such special characteristics may significantly distort the true nature of the system. They need to be incorporated into the model representation of the system of behavior.

If there are several important special characteristics, however, a complete mathematical modeling may be intractable. In such cases, the more flexible structure of simulation is required for effective modeling of the decision environment.

Simulation of a Queuing System

A queuing problem will demonstrate the relative ease with which special characteristics may be incorporated into a simulation model. A major food chain unloads trucks at a central warehouse. The unloaded items are stored, regrouped, and then delivered to retail outlets. The night unloading crew consists of three men working an eight-hour shift from 9:00 P.M. to 5:30 A.M. Unless they have already begun to unload a truck, the night crew takes a half-hour lunch break at 1:00 A.M. Otherwise, they take the break after they have finished unloading the truck. The union workers on the crew receive $4.20 per hour plus an 80-cent night premium. The unloading dock opens at 9:00 P.M. and receives trucks until 5:30 A.M. The unloading crew services all trucks received. If overtime is required, the members of the crew receive time-and-one-half pay. The idle-time cost for the driver, truck, and rig has been assessed at $20 per hour.

When the unloading dock opens for service at 9:00 P.M., frequently one or more trucks have already arrived. From past records of the number of trucks awaiting service, it is possible to make relative frequency estimates of the

Number (n) of trucks waiting for opening	Probability of n	Cumulative Probability: $P(n$ or less$)$	Random Number Assignment (RN)
0	.57	.57	01-57
1	.32	.89	58-89
2	.07	.96	90-96
3	.03	.99	97-99
4	.01	1.00	00

TABLE 18.1

Relative Frequency Probability Estimates of Trucks Awaiting Opening of Facility

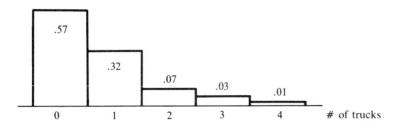

FIGURE 18.1

Probability Distribution of Trucks Awaiting Opening of Facility

Arrival Time (T_A)	Probability of Arrival Time: $P(T_A)$	Cumulative Probability: $P(\text{time} \leq T_A)$	Random Number Assignment
15 min.	.02	.02	01-02
20	.04	.06	03-06
25	.09	.15	07-15
30	.16	.31	16-31
35	.22	.53	32-53
40	.19	.72	54-72
45	.11	.83	73-83
50	.07	.90	84-90
55	.03	.93	91-93
60	.04	.97	94-97
65	.02	.99	98-99
70	.01	1.00	00

TABLE 18.2

Probabilities of Time Between Truck Arrivals

probability distribution for trucks awaiting the opening of the facility. These are provided in Table 18.! and Figure 18.1. Once the facility has opened for operation, empirical records also provide information that can be used to construct the probability distribution of the time between arrivals (Table 18.2 and Figure 18.2). The service time distribution for the three-man night crew is summarized in Table 18.3 and Figure 18.3.

With this descriptive information, the unloading facility will be structurally duplicated by a model, and then night shifts will be be simulated. There are three stochastic elements that require the Monte Carlo technique: the number of

Simulation of Complex Systems

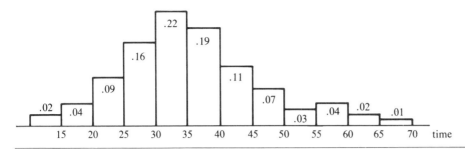

FIGURE 18.2

Probability Distribution of Time Between Arrivals

Service Times (T_S)	Probability of Service Times: $P(T_S)$	Cumulative Probability: $P(\text{time} \le T_S)$	Random Number Assignment
20	.02	.02	01-02
25	.06	.08	03-08
30	.14	.22	09-22
35	.32	.54	23-54
40	.20	.74	55-74
45	.07	.81	75-81
50	.02	.83	82-83
55	.10	.93	84-93
60	.04	.97	94-97
65	.02	.99	98-99
70	.01	1.00	00

TABLE 18.3

Probabilities of Service Time for Three-Man Night Crew

trucks awaiting service when the facility opens; the time between truck arrivals; and the time required for the unloading crew to provide service. For each stochastic system, random numbers will be assigned consecutively in direct proportion to the probabilities (Tables 18.1, 18.2, 18.3). For example, in Table 18.1, the probability that zero trucks will be waiting is .57. The two-digit random numbers from 01 to 57 are assigned to this outcome. The probability that one truck will be waiting is .32. The next 32 random numbers (58–89) are assigned to this outcome.

Note, the random numbers are assigned in direct proportion to the probabilities of the stochastic element. This will produce a sampling distribution for

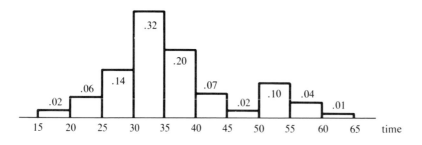

the random numbers *identical* to the sampling distribution for the stochastic element. Since both sampling distributions are identical, samples can be drawn interchangeably from either one—the random-number distribution being much more convenient.

To provide the stochastic elements for the night shift, random numbers will be taken from Appendix 2. The first event is the number of trucks awaiting the opening of the facility. A two-digit random number is selected (the last two of the five digits in the last row of the first column).[1] The random number is 82. From Table 18.1, there will be one truck waiting when the facility opens at 9:00 P.M.

To determine the service time for the truck, the random number is taken from the first two digits in the first row of the second column Appendix 2.[2]

The first service time random number is 10. The sampled service time is 30 minutes (Table 18.3).

After the facility is open for service, the time between successive arrivals will be determined by taking the first two digits of the random number in the first row of the first column (Appendix 2).[3] This random number is 03. The time between the opening and the first arrival will be 20 minutes (Tables 17.2 and 18.3).

There are two ways to synchronize the arrivals and the service times. The state of the system can be *stepped through time* by either: (1) *fixed-time incrementing* or (2) *next-event incrementing*. Both procedures advance the system for all events that occur over *specified* increments of time. Both procedures use a *simulation clock* to record the progressive movements in time. The procedures differ in the way in which increments are specified.

In *fixed-time incrementing*, the simulation clock is advanced by increments

---

[1] Additional starting condition random numbers continue up this column.
[2] Additional service time random numbers continue down this column.
[3] These random numbers will proceed down the column.

Simulation of Complex Systems

that are equivalent to actual times for the system. For example, time may be advanced by increments of five minutes. When the simulation clock is advanced by one unit in time, the system is updated for all events that occurred over the five-minute time interval. The system is now at a new state and ready for the process to be repeated.

In *next-event incrementing*, the simulation clock is advanced by the time between events. For example, if the time between the fourth event and the fifth event is 30 minutes, the simulation clock is advanced by the elapsed time of 30 minutes and the system is updated for the fifth event. This procedure will be applied to the unloading dock problem.[4]

A sample of the night shift unloading operation is simulated in Table 18.4. At 9:00 P.M., when the facility opens, one truck is waiting for service ($RN = 82$; Table 18.1). Service starts at 9:00 P.M. and continues for 30 minutes ($RN = 10$; Table 18.3). The next arrival occurs 20 minutes after opening ($RN = 03$; Table 18.2). The arrival time clock is therefore moved forward to 9:20. The service time for this truck is 60 minutes ($RN = 95$; Table 18.3). The earliest starting time for the next arrival is therefore 10:30. At 9:20, when the first truck arrives after opening, one truck has already been waiting 10 minutes for service.

Arrival Time Random Number	Time for Arrival	Arrival Time	Service Starting Time	Service Time Random Number	Service Time	Service Completion Time	Team Idle	Driver & Truck Idle in Queue	Length of Queue
		9:00	9:00	10	30 min.	9:30			1
03	20 min.	9:20	9:30	95	60	10:30	—	10 min.	1
38	35	9:55	10:30	73	40	11:10	—	35	1
17	30	10:25	11:10	52	35	11:45	—	45	2
32	35	11:00	11:45	68	40	12:25	—	45	2
69	40	11:40	12:25	66	40	1:05	—	45	2
24	30	12:10	1:35	30	30	2:05	—	85	2
61	40	12:50	2:05	21	30	2:35	—	75	2
30	30	1:20	2:35	97	60	3:35	—	75	3
03	20	1:40	3:35	63	40	4:15	—	115	3
48	35	2:15	4:15	19	30	4:45	—	120	3
88	50	3:05	4:45	23	35	5:20	—	100	3
71	40	3:45	5:20	58	40	6:00	—	95	3
27	30	4:15	6:00	00	70	7:10	—	105	3
80	45	5:00	7:10	60	40	7:50	—	130	3

TABLE 18.4

Simulation of Night Unloading Operations

---

[4] Next-event or significant-event incrementing has the added advantage of conserving computer time by jumping over periods of inactivity.

Throughout the night operations, both the time between arrivals and the service times are determined from random numbers. After each event the associated "event clock" is updated. At the first completed service after 1:00 A.M., the night crew takes its half-hour lunch break from 1:05 to 1:35 A.M. From 1:20 A.M. on, the waiting time for trucks becomes excessive. There are always three trucks forming a queue for service. To service the last truck, which arrives at 5:00 A.M., the night crew is held over to 7:50 A.M.—two hours and 20 minutes at overtime pay.

The total cost (T_C) for the simulated night unloading operation is derived from the cost information given earlier:

$$T_C = \text{Service facility cost } (S_C) + \text{Trucker waiting cost } (W_C).$$

The service facility cost consists of:

$$S_C = \text{Regular salary } (R_S) + \text{Overtime salary } (O_S).$$

Specifically,

$$S_C = \underset{\substack{\text{cost per} \\ \text{hour}}}{\$5} \cdot \underset{\substack{\text{no. of} \\ \text{hours}}}{(8)} \cdot \underset{\substack{\text{no. in} \\ \text{crew}}}{(3)} + \underset{\substack{\text{overtime} \\ \text{per hour}}}{\$7.50} \underset{\substack{\text{no. of} \\ \text{hours}}}{(2.33)} \underset{\substack{\text{no. in} \\ \text{crew}}}{(3)} \; .$$

$$S_C = \$120 + \$52.45.$$

The service facility costs for the three-man night crew are $172.45.

The cost associated with delaying the truck, driver, and rig in the service facility (W_C) consists of:

$$\text{Trucker waiting cost } (W_C) = \text{Service time cost } (S_{TC}) + \text{queue time cost } (q_{TC}).$$

$$W_C = \underset{\substack{\text{cost per} \\ \text{hour}}}{\$20} \cdot \underset{\substack{\text{total service} \\ \text{hours}}}{10.33} + \underset{\substack{\text{cost per} \\ \text{hour}}}{\$20} \cdot \underset{\substack{\text{total queue} \\ \text{hours}}}{16}$$

$$= \$206.67 + \$360.$$

The trucker cost for waiting in the system is $566.67.

For the simulated night shift, the total cost for the three-man unloading operations becomes:

$$\begin{aligned} T_C &= S_C + W_C \\ &= R_S + O_S + S_{TC} + q_{TC} \\ &= 120 + 52.45 + 206.67 + 360 \\ &= \$739.12. \end{aligned}$$

| Night | Service Facility Costs (S_C) | | Waiting-Time Costs (W_C) | | Total Cost: |
	Regular (R_S)	Overtime (O_S)	Service (S_{TC})	Queue (q_{TC})	$T_C = S_C + W_C$
1	$120.00	$52.45	$206.67	$360.00	$739.12
2	120.00	39.38	185.00	113.33	457.71
3	120.00	7.49	160.00	101.66	389.15
4	120.00	0	145.00	21.66	286.86
5	120.00	31.87	165.00	98.32	415.19
Five Night Average	$120.00	$26.24	$172.33	$138.99	$457.56

TABLE 18.5

A Five-Night Simulation of Night Unloading Operations

Although this is only a single simulation of night crew operations, the resulting operating information is significant. Trucks are waiting an inordinate time. Waiting-time costs are more than triple service facility costs. The waiting time in the queue exceeds the service time. Moreover, about one-third of the service costs are overtime payments.

To increase the reliability of the sample information, four additional night crew operations were simulated.[5] The operation cost information is provided in Table 18.5. For the five-night average, trucker waiting costs were 68 percent of the total costs, and overtime was 18 percent of the service facility costs. Detaining trucks appears to be a problem area.

To reduce this problem, the possibility of using several larger night crews will be explored:

A_1: three-man crew
A_2: four-man crew
A_3: five-man crew
A_4: six-man crew.

As the night crew is increased, there is an assumed proportionate reduction in expected service times (Figure 18.3 and 18.4).

The five nights of operations that were simulated for the three-man crew (Table 18.5) will be reproduced for each of the other alternatives. All of the alternatives will then be compared under identical conditions.[6]

---

[5] To replicate these four simulations, the previously defined random-number selection procedure should be continued.

[6] Pseudo-random numbers allow the reproduction of the same stochastic variations.

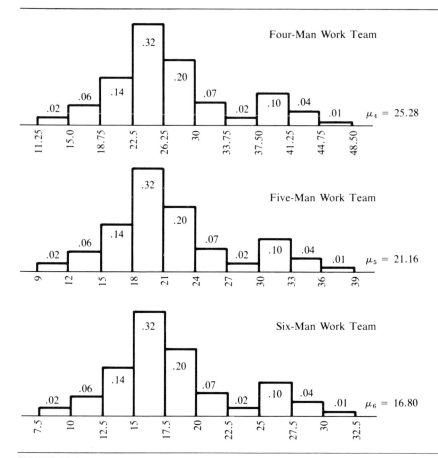

FIGURE 18.4

Probability Distribution of Service Times Proportionate to Crew Size

Table 18.6 provides the comparable simulation of the first night for the four-man crew. As indicated in Figures 18.5 and 18.6, the four-man crew significantly reduces (1) service time, (2) queue time, and (3) overtime. A complete cost breakdown for each of the alternatives for the first two nights and the five-night average is provided in Table 18.7. The nightly total costs and average total cost for each alternative are provided in Table 18.8.

The experience of living with the simulated unloading operation for only one simulated week suggests several ways to improve efficiency. The present three-man crew is inadequate to provide economical unloading service to the truckers. A four-man or five-man crew will be more economical. To consider adequately the variation in night crew operations produced from the three stochastic elements in the system,[7] a large sample of simulated operations is

[7] The three jointly interactive stochastic elements are the trucks awaiting the opening of the facility, truck arrivals, and unloading service times.

Simulation of Complex Systems

Arrival Time Random Number	Time for Arrival	Arrival Time	Service Starting Time	Service Time Random Number	Service Time	Service Completion Time	Team Idle	Driver & Truck Idle in Queue	Length of Queue
		9:00	9:00	10	22.5	9:22.5	—	—	—
03	20 min.	9:20	9:22.5	95	45	10:07.5	—	2.5 min.	1
38	35	9:55	10:09.5	73	30	10:37.5	—	12.5	1
17	30	10:25	10:37.5	52	26.25	10:53.75	—	12.5	1
32	35	11:00	11:00	68	30	11:30	6.25	—	—
69	40	11:40	11:40	66	30	12:20	10	—	—
24	30	12:10	12:10	30	22.50	12:32.5	—	10	1
61	40	12:50	12:50	21	22.50	1:12.5	—	—	—
30	30	1:20	1:42.5	97	45	2:27.5	—	22.5	1
03	20	1:40	2:27.5	63	30	2:57.5	—	47.5	2
48	35	2:15	2:57.5	19	22.5	3:20	—	42.5	2
88	50	3:05	3:20	23	26.25	3:46.25	—	15	1
71	40	3:45	3:46.25	58	30	4:16.25	—	1.25	1
27	30	4:15	4:16.25	00	52.50	5:08.75	—	1.25	1
80	45	5:00	5:08.75	60	30	5:38.75	—	8.75	1

TABLE 18.6

Simulation of Night Unloading Operations with Four-Man Team

required. With computer support, however, the simulation of several years of operations for each alternative would be available in a matter of minutes.

The simulation also provides other information that is useful for improving unloading operations. From Tables 18.4 and 18.6 and Figures 18.5 and 18.6, the increased length of the queue of truckers during and shortly after the night crew's lunch period is quite apparent. Lunch period policy options to reduce trucker waiting costs could be considered. For example, crews of four or more might be split into two groups to take alternating lunch breaks. Whenever the service time is less than one half hour,[8] trucker waiting time will be reduced.

This policy option will be illustrated for a six-man crew. Under the present system, a truck arrives just as the entire crew departs for a half-hour lunch break. The truck has a 20-minute service requirement. It will not be able to depart, however, for 50 minutes—30 minutes waiting for service plus 20 minutes of service time (Figure 18.7). Under the new two-group lunch policy, one group will begin service on the truck while the other goes to lunch. In the half-hour lunch period, the first three-member working crew will provide 15 minutes of service at the 6-man rate. They will then go to lunch while the other three take over. In 10 minutes this second crew will provide the remaining 5 minutes of service (Figure 18.7). The truck will be fully serviced in 40 minutes. It can be on its way 10 minutes earlier.

---

[8] For a six-man team, this will occur 99 percent of the time (Figure 18.4)

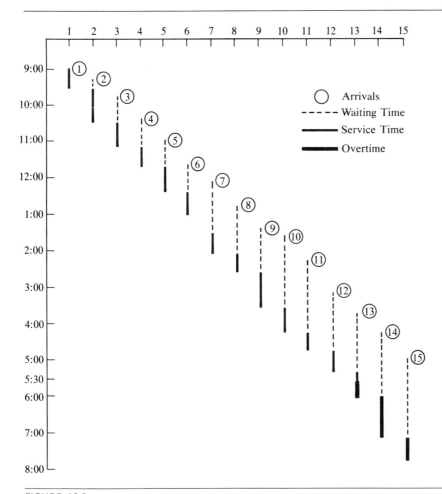

FIGURE 18.5
Simulated Unloading Operations with Three-Man Team

Once empirical data have been accumulated, monthly, nightly, and hourly variations in arrivals can be incorporated into the simulation of the operating system. The stochastic effects of a crew member's absence, a truck strike, or the breakdown of a pallet transporting machine can be made a part of the operating environment. Policy decisions can be experimentally tested. The system can be reconstructed and experienced in a dry lab of system behavior.

SIMULATION OF INVENTORY SYSTEMS

Inventory systems often contain several jointly interactive stochastic components. When these components are important, their inclusion in a mathemat-

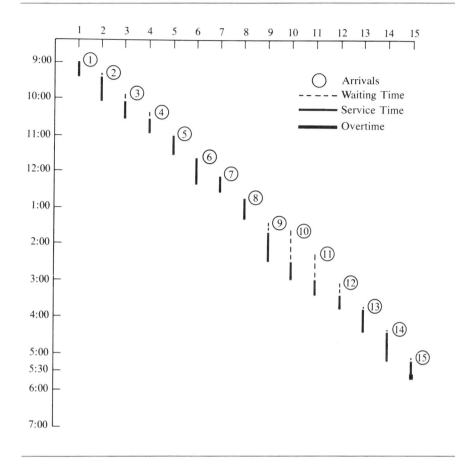

FIGURE 18.6
Simulated Unloading Operations with Four-Man Team

ical model adds considerably to the model's complexity. The basic deterministic inventory model (Chapter 14) assumed a known demand with a constant rate of depletion; a known, fixed, lead time period; an infinite production rate; no stockouts or backordering; and known linear ordering and carrying-cost parameters. When random demand variations were added to the inventory model (Chapter 15), the basic stochastic inventory model became distinctly more sophisticated. Inventory systems, however, contain many more complicating stochastic components. Besides random demand variations, inventory items typically have complicating variations due to a trend, seasonal influences, or nonstationarity. The lead time between placing and receiving an order may be stochastic. There may be partial backordering. The items may be perishable or partially integrated with other products in a product line. Ordering costs, stockout costs, and carrying costs may be difficult to estimate. These parameters may also be nonlinear. If many of these complications are important to the

Alternatives	Service Cost (S_C)		Waiting Cost (W_C)		Total Cost
	Regular	Overtime	Service	Queue	$T_C = S_C + W_C$
night #1					
A_1	$120.00	$52.45	$206.67	$360.00	$739.12
A_2	160.00	4.37	149.17	58.75	372.29
A_3	200.00	0.00	116.67	17.33	334.00
A_4	240.00	0.00	103.33	16.66	360.00
night #2					
A_1	$120.00	$39.38	$185.00	$113.33	$457.71
A_2	160.00	20.63	138.41	19.17	338.21
A_3	200.00	20.63	111.00	9.33	340.96
A_4	240.00	3.44	91.83	6.67	341.94
5-night average					
A_1	$120.00	$26.24	$172.33	$138.99	$457.56
A_2	160.00	9.13	129.43	27.12	325.68
A_3	200.00	7.13	103.86	9.53	320.52
A_4	240.00	2.42	86.47	7.17	336.07

TABLE 18.7
Alternative Systems Cost Comparisons

inventory system, a strictly mathematical model may become intractable. A computer supported simulation model may be more effective.

Simulation of an Inventory System

The selection of the decision variables for an inventory item will further demonstrate the adaptivity of simulation modeling. The inventory system will be *fixed-quantity variable reorder cycle*. The required decision variables are the order quantity (q) and reorder point (R) that will minimize total inventory related costs:

Total cost (T_C) = ordering cost (C_O) + carrying cost ($C_C + C_{CS}$)
+ underage cost (C_U).

The stockkeeping unit of interest has the following cost estimates:

ordering cost (K_O per order) = $36
annual carrying cost (K_C per unit) = $6
underage cost (K_U per item) = $8.

Alternatives	1st	2nd	3rd	4th	5th	average
A_1 (3 man)	$739.12	$457.71	$389.15	$286.66	$415.19	$457.57
A_2 (4 man)	372.29	338.21	325.66	268.92	321.37	325.67
A_3 (5 man)	334.00	340.96	327.95	289.32	310.38	320.52
A_4 (6 man)	360.00	341.94	337.34	309.87	330.46	336.08

TABLE 18.8

Total Cost Comparisons for Alternative Crew Sizes

A Two-Group Lunch Policy

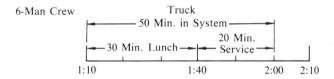

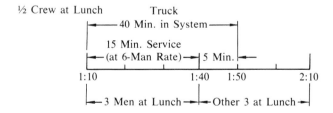

FIGURE 18.7

A Two-Group Lunch Policy

The estimated weekly demand, represented in Table 18.9, is assumed normally distributed with a mean of 20 and standard deviation of 4. Extending the stochastic model in Chapter 15, the lead time period will be subject to random variation (Table 18.9), and weekly demand will be subject to seasonal influences (Table 18.10).

Weekly Demand (DD)	Probability (DD)	Random Number	Lead Time (L_I)	Probability (L_I)	Random Number
8 or less	.0000	——	0	.000	——
9	.0023	0000-0022	1	.062	000-061
10	.0045	0023-0067	2	.249	062-310
11	.0081	0068-0148	3	.378	311-688
12	.0137	0149-0285	4	.249	689-937
13	.0219	0286-0504	5	.062	938-999
14	.0327	0505-0831	6	.000	——
15	.0461	0832-1292			
16	.0602	1293-1893			
17	.0754	1894-2648			
18	.0881	2649-3529			
19	.0965	3530-4494			
20	.1010	4495-5504			
21	.0965	5505-6469			
22	.0881	6470-7350			
23	.0754	7351-8104			
24	.0602	8105-8706			
25	.0461	8707-9167			
26	.0327	9168-9494			
27	.0219	9495-9713			
28	.0137	9714-9850			
29	.0081	9851-9931			
30	.0045	9932-9976			
31	.0083	9977-9999			
32 or more	.0000	——			

TABLE 18.9

Random Demand and Random Lead Time

In the simulation solution to this problem, there will be three separate procedural steps. First, a simulation model will be constructed to duplicate the essential behavior of the inventory system. Second, different values of the decision variables (q, R) will be tested in simulated duplications of the inventory system. Third, from this information, the values of the decision variables will be progressively improved.

In the construction of the simulation model, the separate components of the inventory system are related in the natural sequence of occurrence. The inventory system will begin with a specified inventory. Weekly demand will deplete the inventory. At a defined reorder point, an order for a specified quantity of items will be placed with a supplier. After a lead time period, the ordered items will arrive and replenish the inventory stock. When this cycle has been completed, the process is repeated.

Jan. 1	1.	.97	12.	1.11	23.	.94	34.	.98	45.	.92
	2.	.97	13.	1.10	24.	.94	35.	1.10	46.	.93
	3.	.97	14.	1.09	25.	.94	36.	1.20	47.	.91
	4.	.98	15.	1.09	26.	.94	37.	1.23	48.	.92
	5.	.99	16.	1.09	27.	.94	38.	1.23	49.	.93
	6.	1.01	17.	1.08	28.	.94	39.	1.00	50.	.95
	7.	1.03	18.	1.04	29.	.94	40.	.92	51.	.92
	8.	1.04	19.	1.01	30.	.94	41.	.89	52.	.90
	9.	1.06	20.	1.01	31.	.95	42.	.89		
	10.	1.10	21.	1.01	32.	.96	43.	.89		
	11.	1.11	22.	.96	33.	.96	44.	.91		

TABLE 18.10
Weekly Seasonal Index

The structuring of the process will not be any more complex than the sequencing of these separate components. The process will start on January 1 with the order quantity (q) in inventory. The week's demand is defined by a computer generated[9] four-digit random number. The demand is seasonally adjusted by referring to the seasonal index. The seasonally adjusted demand is used to deplete the level of inventory. This process is conducted each week. The end-of-the-week closing inventory is compared to the reorder point (R). If the reorder point has been reached, an order for q items is placed to arrive within the period of time specified by another four-digit random number. When the order quantity arrives from the supplier, the inventory is adjusted correspondingly.

To measure the system's performance for the selected decision variables (q, R), the components of the total inventory related cost are accumulated. Each time an order is requisitioned, the order is recorded with an associated ordering cost of K_O. The average weekly inventory level can be approximated by adding half of the beginning inventory to half of the ending inventory.[10] Summing this weekly inventory level and multiplying it by the weekly carrying cost will provide the total carrying cost. At the end of each cycle, the stockouts, if any, are multiplied by the underage cost (K_U). Their sum over all cycles will provide the total underage cost.

The following example will clarify the process. Table 18.11 contains the random numbers that produce the seasonally adjusted demand for the first 14 weekly periods and the lead times for four cycles. Using decision variables of $q = 120$ and $R = 80$, Table 18.12 and Figure 18.8 illustrate the first 14 simulated weeks. The inventory started with 120 items. The demand for the

---

[9] A table of random numbers could also be used.
[10] If a stockout occurs, a proportionate adjustment is made for the period with no inventory.

Week	Random Number	Demand	Seasonal Adjustment	Seasonally Adjusted Demand	Order Cycle	Random Number	Lead Time
1	3576	19	.97	18	1	8044	4
2	2996	18	.97	17	2	7889	4
3	9398	26	.97	25	3	5313	3
4	8435	24	.98	24	4	6552	3
5	7702	22	.99	22			
6	0116	11	1.01	11			
7	3000	18	1.03	19			
8	8557	24	1.04	25			
9	1438	16	1.06	17			
10	8333	24	1.10	26			
11	4950	20	1.11	22			
12	3358	18	1.11	20			
13	7912	23	1.10	25			
14	4698	20	1.09	22			
15	2791	18	1.09	20			

TABLE 18.11

Stochastic Demand and Lead Times

Week	Beginning Inventory	Seasonally Adjusted Demand	Ending Inventory	Stockout	Order	Inventory Carried
1	120	18	102			111.0
2	102	17	85			93.5
3	85	25	60		R_4	72.5
4	60	24	36			48.0
5	36	22	14			25.0
6	14	11	3			8.5
7	3	19	0	16		.2
8	104	25	79		R_4	91.5
9	79	17	62			70.5
10	62	26	36			49.0
11	36	22	14			25.0
12	14	20	0	6		5.0
13	114	25	89			101.5
14	89	22	67		R_3	78.0

TABLE 18.12

Simulated Inventory ($q = 120$, $R = 80$)

Simulation of Complex Systems

Total Cost = $C_O + C_C + C_{CS} + C_U$			
Order Cost (C_O) (# order · · · cost per order)	Carrying Cost (C_c) + C_{CS} (# items · · · cost per item per week)	Underage Cost (C_U) (# stockouts · · · cost of stockouts)	Total Cost
3 ($36) = $108	779.2 ($.115) = $89.61	22 ($8) = $176	$373.61

TABLE 18.13

Total Inventory Related Costs

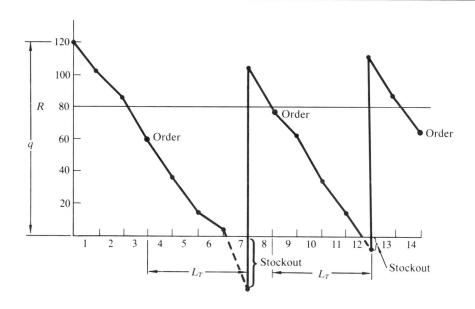

FIGURE 18.8

Simulated Inventory ($q = 120$, $R = 80$)

first week was 18, reducing the inventory to 102. The average inventory carried for the week was $(120 + 102)/2 = 111$. At the end of the third week, the inventory level had fallen below the reorder point. An order was placed to arrive in 4 weeks. During the seventh week, the beginning inventory contained only 3 items. Since there was a demand for 19 items, a stockout of 16 items occurred. At the beginning of the eighth week, the order quantity of 120 items arrived to replenish the depleted inventory. Sixteen of these items were used immediately to fill waiting backorders. The total cost for the first 14 weeks was $373.61 (Table 18.13).

The duplicated inventory system provides the structure for experimentally testing the performance of selected values of the decision variables (q, R). A

Order Quantity (q)	Reorder Point (R)	Order Cost (C_O)	Carrying Cost ($C_C + C_{CS}$)	Underage Cost (C_u)	Total Cost
115	70	295.20	414.33	875.28	1584.81
	75	302.40	442.48	611.93	1356.82
	80	310.60	462.26	412.76	1184.62
	85	316.80	489.49	269.18	1075.47
	90	316.80	505.35	269.18	1091.33
	95	316.80	541.48	200.14	1058.43
	100	324.00	579.43	114.38	1017.82
120	70	288.00	422.41	875.71	1586.12
	75	295.20	447.60	657.20	1400.00
	80	295.20	486.09	415.72	1197.00
	85	302.40	494.18	221.08	1017.67
	90	302.40	525.65	190.88	1018.93
	95	309.60	555.87	117.04	982.51
	100	309.60	591.64	58.67	959.92
125	70	280.80	444.39	821.40	1546.60
	75	280.80	459.42	743.56	1483.79
	80	288.00	485.18	378.83	1152.02
	85	288.00	523.92	276.55	1088.28
	90	295.20	551.44	146.44	993.09
	95	295.20	560.46	117.24	972.91
	100	295.20	601.29	37.45	939.95
130	70	266.40	458.81	725.29	1450.51
	75	266.40	482.88	673.35	1422.84
	80	273.60	511.48	505.21	1290.30
	85	273.60	523.29	404.08	1201.47
	90	280.80	562.57	276.86	1120.24
	95	280.80	528.74	201.60	1061.14
	100	288.00	612.82	108.22	1009.04

TABLE 18.14

Initial Information to Improve (q, R)

general approach will be used to search for appropriate values for these decision variables. First, select reasonable estimates of appropriate values. Measure their performance on the simulated inventory system. Use this information to improve the estimates. Measure their performance, and use the new information to improve them. Continue these improved adjustments until sufficiently optimal values for the decision variables have been isolated.

Since q and R are jointly interactive, four initial values of q are selected, each having seven accompanying values of R. The q's are evenly spaced from 115 to 130. The accompanying R's are from 70 to 100. These twenty-eight sets

Order Quantity (q)	Reorder Point (R)	Order Cost (C_o)	Carrying Cost ($C_C + C_{CS}$)	Underage Cost (C_u)	Total Cost
120	90*	302.40	525.65	190.88	1018.93
	95*	309.60	555.87	117.04	982.51
	100*	309.60	591.64	58.67	959.92
	105	309.60	617.66	29.84	957.10
	110	309.60	648.00	29.84	987.44
	115	309.60	680.22	0.00	989.82
125	90*	295.20	551.44	146.44	993.09
	95*	295.20	560.46	117.24	972.91
	100*	295.20	607.29	37.45	939.95
	105	295.20	639.89	37.45	972.55
	110	302.40	662.23	7.31	971.94
	115	302.40	698.15	0.00	1000.55

*From initial information

TABLE 18.15

Second Set of Information to Improve (q, R)

of decision variables are tested over five years of simulated inventory operations. Expressed in average annual costs, the measured performance of the decision variables is provided in Table 18.14.

The lowest total costs are associated with the q's of 120 and 125. The desired q should be somewhere within this range. For the q's of 120 and 125, the best accompanying R's are for the largest value tested. To gather information about larger values of R, three larger R's are tested with q's of 120 and 125. The measured performance is provided in Table 18.15. The desired R should be somewhere in the neighborhood of 95 to 105.

The search for the desired combination of q and R is now restricted to q's from 121 to 124 with accompanying R's of 95 to 101. If the the R's of 101 do not indicate an upturn in total costs,[11] then R's of 102 to 105 will be tested. The twenty-eight new sets of decision variables are tested over the five years of simulated inventory operations. The measured performance is provided in Table 18.16. From this information, the lowest total cost decision variables are $q = 122$ and $R = 96$ with a total annual cost of $911.75.

Once the simulation model has been constructed to duplicate the operating behavior of the system, it can easily be used to improve other components of

[11] For increases in R, the total costs tend to decrease to a lowest value and then increase. They should follow the shape of the total cost curve presented in Figure 14.2. These total cost measures of performance will, of course, be distorted by the random variations in demand and lead times.

Order Quantity (q)	Reorder Point (R)	Order Cost (C_o)	Carrying Cost ($C_C + C_{CS}$)	Underage Cost (C_u)	Total Cost
121	95	302.40	554.26	106.12	962.79
	96	302.40	559.83	106.12	968.35
	97	302.40	570.95	106.12	979.48
	98	302.40	582.08	106.12	990.61
	99	309.60	587.41	93.36	990.37
	100	309.60	599.73	57.84	967.17
	101	309.60	602.52	57.84	969.96
122	95	302.40	550.73	106.75	959.88
	96	302.40	562.43	46.92	911.75
	97	302.40	565.23	46.92	914.56
	98	302.40	573.64	46.92	922.97
	99	302.40	584.86	46.92	934.19
	100	302.40	596.08	46.92	945.41
	101	302.40	604.50	46.92	953.82
123	95	295.20	561.77	76.76	940.93
	96	295.20	564.59	76.76	943.76
	97	302.40	569.04	76.76	948.21
	98	302.40	571.04	47.28	920.72
	99	302.40	576.70	47.28	926.38
	100	302.40	582.35	47.28	932.03
	101	302.40	593.66	47.28	943.34
124	95	295.20	569.79	93.45	958.44
	96	295.20	579.25	106.11	980.56
	97	295.20	587.31	63.31	953.02
	98	295.20	587.31	63.31	953.02
	99	295.20	590.16	63.31	955.87
	100	295.20	604.41	63.31	970.02
	101	295.20	609.24	63.31	974.95

TABLE 18.16

Approximation of the Optimal Decision Variables

the system. What is the anticipated reduction in total costs of reducing the average lead time by one week? What is the worth of a guaranteed delivery date? What is the worth of reducing ordering costs by 40 percent? If inventory carrying costs increase by 20 percent, how should the system be adjusted? With computer support, a simulation model will provide the information needed for adaptive improvements—for optimal system design.

SIMULATION OF COMPLEX INTERRELATED FEEDBACK SYSTEMS

Once methods have been developed to solve an abstracted part of the decision environment, there is a natural tendency for the decision maker to increase the scope of inquiry—to increase the abstraction. Computer supported simulation modeling is no exception. Important separate components of the decision environment have been optimally solved by mathematical models. Simulation is increasingly being used to interrelate these separate components. It has been focused on modeling the dynamic interplay of many components—on providing a more global model of total system behavior.

In the marketing decisions surrounding the introduction of a new product, for example, the product design, pricing, promotion, and distribution strategies are interrelated. Instead of developing a model for each of these critical dimensions in isolation, the entire marketing mix for the product can be viewed as an integrated system. Moreover, each of the components of a production system, (orders, scheduling, acquisition of materials, assignment of resources, inventories, etc.) can be viewed as an entire system of interrelated behavior. The area of financial transactions constitutes another system with major subcomponent parts. In turn, marketing, production, and financial systems are subsystems of organizational behavior. An organization is a subsystem in an industry of the social community. And this, in turn, is a subsystem in an expanding set of synergistic systems of complex, dynamic, interrelated behavior.

Marketing systems, production systems, financial systems, organizations, economies, and even the world environment have been structured by simulation models. As long as the essential behavioral components are known, the required information is available, and the task warrants a sufficient expenditure of time, effort, and resources, the behavior of a system can be structured by simulation.

The Simulation of an Organization

As early as 1961, Jay W. Forrester expertly illustrated the essential properties and application of a large-scale simulation model in *Industrial Dynamics*.[12] In this classic work, Forrester constructs a simulation model for an entire organization. The model was developed for *industrial design*. It demonstrates how the dynamic interrelated behavior of decisions, policies, structures, and delays affects the major corporate objectives of profits, growth, and stability. It provides the information needed by management to make better, more integrated decisions in such areas as policy formulation, organizational structuring, and investment selection.

This section will provide a simplified overview of the industrial dynamics modeling procedure. With considerations restricted to providing goods to consumers,[13] Figure 18.9 illustrates the major sectors of an organization's production-distribution system. The internal components of each of these major sectors are expressed by interrelating networks of orders, money, materials, personnel, and capital equipment. In turn, these networks are interconnected by an information network (Figure 18.10).

---

[12] Jay W. Forrester, *Industrial Dynamics* (Cambridge, Mass.: M.I.T. Press, 1961).
[13] The full model considers all major systems (e.g., thel abor flow system, the cash flow system).

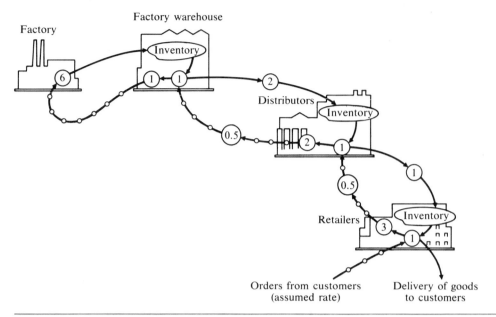

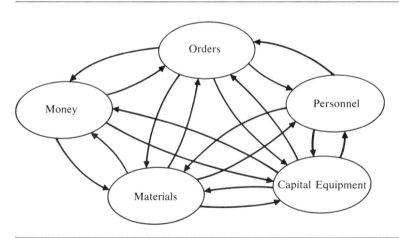

FIGURE 18.10
Basic Networks Interconnected by an Information Network

The structure is expressed by *levels, flow rates,* and *decisions. Levels* represent different forms of accumulations. Examples are inventories, bank balances, and number of employees. *Flow rates* represent activity that changes the state of a level. Examples are additions to inventories, bank balance with-

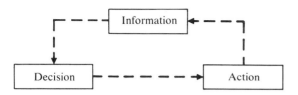

FIGURE 18.11
An Information Feedback System

drawals, and employee assignments. *Decisions* represent the definition of action. They define the flow rates that act on the levels. They are represented functionally by *flow rate equations* that express decision rules and policy statements. Examples are order requisitions, materials purchases, and employee hiring. The basic structure, therefore, consists of *a network of levels interconnected by controlled flows*.

The states of the system are progressively updated by increments of time. *Time* is divided into small intervals of equal length Δt. These intervals are small enough to allow linear segments to approximate any curve.

In this complex, interrelated network of information channels, *management* has the special function of decision making. It converts information into action. The flow of decisions from management occupied decision points is considered in the framework of an *information-feedback system* (Figure 18.11). Information is the input into a decision point that determines action, which, in turn, produces information.[14] Each of the components may contain delays, amplifications, and distortions.

Figure 18.12 illustrates a small part of the retail-consumer sector of the production-distribution system shown in Figure 18.9. *UOR* (unfilled orders at retail), *IAR* (inventory actual at retail), and *SSR* (shipments sent from retail) are *levels* at time K. The *UOR flow rate equation* from time J to time K is provided in Table 18.17. The equation adjusts the *UOR* at time J for the inflow and outflow of orders during the time interval from J to K:

Flow Rate Equation

adjusted level		previous level		time	inflow		outflow
$UOR.K$	$=$	$UOR.J$	$+$	DT	$\cdot$ $(RRR.JK$	$-$	$SSR.JK)$
level time K		level time J		time interval	level change J to K		level change J to K

The length of time DT is multiplied by the inflow rate $RRR.JK$ to define the new orders received from J to K. $DT(SRR.JK)$ defines the orders filled from

---

[14] This statement might be reconsidered in terms of the structural components. Information about levels is provided to decision makers, who adjust the flow rates leading into the levels, which, in turn, produces new levels.

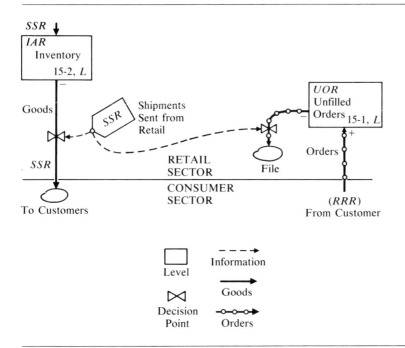

FIGURE 18.12

Beginning of Flow Diagram of Retail Sector: Reprinted from *Industrial Dynamics* by Jay W. Forrester by permission of the M.I.T. Press, Cambridge, Massachusetts. (Copyright 1961, All rights reserved.)

J to *K*. The new level *UOR. K* now moves to the right side of the equation for the next adjustment over the time interval from *K* to *L*.

When the other components have been added, Figure 18.13 illustrates the flow diagram for the consumer-retail sector. To complete the *production-distribution sector*, similar flow relationships are formed for the distribution-retail sector and the factory-distribution sector. In turn, each of the other

---

$$UOR.K = UOR.J + (DT)(RRR.JK - SSR.JK) \qquad 15\text{-}1, L$$

UOR   Unfilled Orders at Retail   (measured in units
          of goods on order)

RRR   Requisitions (orders) Received at Retail
          (units/week)

SSR   Shipments Sent from Retail   (units/week)

DT   Delta Time   (weeks), the time interval between
          solutions of the equations

TABLE 18.17

Flow Rate Equation for *UOR*: Reprinted from *Industrial Dynamics* by Jay W. Forrester by permission of the M.I.T. Press, Cambridge, Massachusetts. (Copyright 1961, All rights reserved.)

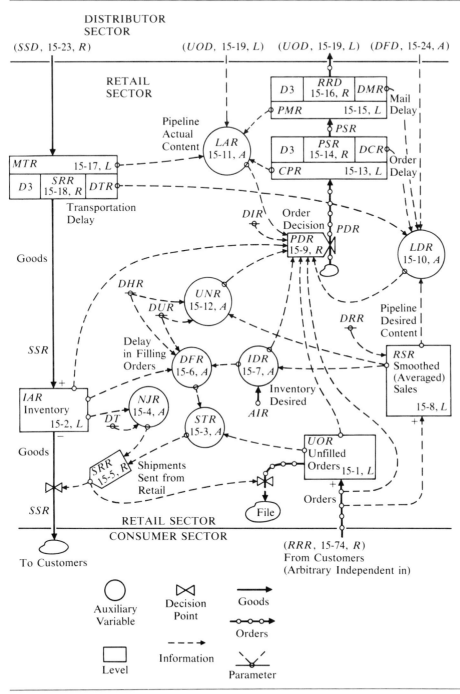

Simulation of Complex Interrelated Feedback Systems

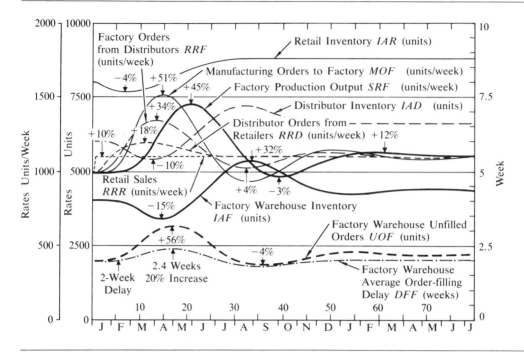

major sectors (*e.g.*, cash flow, personnel flow, materials flow, capital equipment flow) has a similar flow structure.

The fully constructed model traces the state of the entire system through time. Through a constant flow of finite time intervals, it demonstrates how the environment (levels) stimulates decisions (selecting flow rates), which produce action (flow rates), which, in turn, reacts on the environment (levels). It demonstrates the interactive behavior of a complex, dynamic, interrelated feedback system.

With a simulation model of the scope of the entire organizational system, management is elegantly equipped with an exceedingly powerful projective instrument. Scenarios can be stepped through time to reveal total system performance. For example, given an assumed 10 percent increase in retail sales, Forrester's model (Figure 18.14) plots the dynamic repercussions in retail inventory, distribution inventory, factory inventory, and factory orders.[15]

Equipped with such a model, management has a tool for experiencing and experimenting with a system—a tool for improved organizational design. The

---

[15] Note the excessively amplified peak in factory orders 15 weeks later, and the factory output 21 weeks and 40 weeks ahead.

model can unveil the potential for better policies and better structure. It can indicate where the system is sensitive or vulnerable. With computer support, the consequences of a policy decision can be resolved in a matter of minutes—a decision over which a group of top executives might argue *inconclusively* for weeks, months, or years. The management laboratory becomes a possibility.

SUMMARY

Simulation is an exceedingly flexible approach to modeling. In fact, it is more of an approach than a well-structured technique. It provides a straightforward method for structurally duplicating the essential behavior of a decision environment. The decision environment is defined in terms of easily understood separate components. These components are then combined in their natural order of occurrence. The model building is reduced to the construction of a logical flow of naturally ordered events. In the simulated duplication of the system's behavior itself, the computer numerically presents the complex interactive effects of the system's separate components.

By considering only easily understood separate components and allowing the simulation data to reveal the complex interactive effects of total system behavior, simulation simplifies the definition of complex system behavior. Stochastic, nonlinear, and transient behavior can be incorporated into a simulation model with relative ease. Highly complex, mathematically intractable decision environments can be explored with simulation.

The ease with which complex components can be incorporated into a simulation model significantly extends the horizons of formal modeling. A marketing problem can be viewed in the context of a marketing system, and the marketing system in the context of an organizational system. Financial problems, production problems, and personnel problems can be viewed in the full dimension of synergistic expansions.

By structurally duplicating the essential behavior of the decision environment, simulation provides the decision maker with a descriptive, experimental tool. It provides a means for making changes and observing their effects. Any component of the system, any alternative course of action, can be altered with a measure of total system performance. A decision maker can live with the system and gather experience through dry-lab experimentation.

BIBLIOGRAPHY

Bonini, C. P. *Simulation of Information and Decision Systems in the Firm.* Englewood Cliffs, N.J.: Prentice-Hall, 1963.

Evans, G. W., G. F. Wallace, and S. L. Sutherland. *Simulation Using Digital Computers.* Englewood Cliffs, N.J.: Prentice-Hall, 1967.

Forrester, Jay W. *Industrial Dynamics.* Cambridge, Mass.: M.I.T. Press, 1961.

————. *World Dynamics.* Cambridge, Mass.: Wright-Allen Press, 1971.

Hillier, F. S., and G. J. Lieberman. *Introduction to Operations Research.* San Francisco: Holden-Day, 1974.

McMillan, C., and R. F. Gonzalez. *Systems Analysis: A Computer Approach to Decision Models.* Homewood, Ill.: Richard D. Irwin, 1968.

Meier, R. C., W. P. Newall, and H. L. Poger. *Simulation in Business and Economics.* Englewood Ciffs, N.J.: Prentice-Hall, 1969.

Mize, J. H., and J. S. Cox. *Essentials of Simulation.* Englewood Cliffs, N.J.: Prentice-Hall, 1968.

Naylor, T. H. *Computer Simulation Experiments with Models of Economic Systems.* New York: John Wiley & Sons, 1971.

Naylor, T. H., J. L. Balintfy, D. S. Burdick, and K. Chu. *Computer Simulation Techniques.* New York: John Wiley & Sons, 1966.

The Rand Corporation. *A Million Random Digits with 100,000 Normal Deviates.* Glencoe, Ill.: Free Press, 1955.

Schmidt, J. W., and R. E. Taylor. *Simulation and Analysis of Industrial Systems.* Homewood, Ill.: Richard D. Irwin, 1970.

Thierauf, R. J., and R. C. Klekamp. *Decision Making Through Operations Research.* New York: John Wiley & Sons, 1975.

18.1. In the game of craps, a pair of dice is rolled. One play is the "field bet." If a total of 3, 4, 9, 10, or 11 appears, the player wins the amount bet. If a total of 5, 6, 7, or 8 appears, the player loses the amount bet. If a total of 2 (snake eyes) appears, the player wins double the amount bet. If a total of 12 (boxcars) appears, depending on the casino, the player wins *either* double or triple the amount bet.

A player makes at least one hundred $5 bets on the field in an evening. Use simulation to approximate the minimum expected worth of playing at a casino that pays triple for boxcars.

18.2. A tennis player is allowed two attempts to serve a ball into the opponent's service square. The particular player has the option of using a hard, potent, flat serve or a slower, consistent, spin serve. The probability that he will deliver the hard, flat serve successfully is .40. If he starts play with the hard, flat serve, the probability that he will eventually win the point is .75. The probability that he will sucessfully deliver the slower, spin serve is .85. In this case, the probability that he will win the point is only .50.

The player is contemplating three possible strategies for service play: (1) hard first serve, hard second serve; (2) hard first serve, spin second serve; or (3) spin first serve, spin second serve. Use simulation to determine which service strategy will maximize the player's chance of winning his serve.

18.3. In roulette, one bet is made on either *red* or *black*. There are 18 red, 18 black, and 1 green number on the wheel. If a player bets on a color and the color appears, he or she wins the amount bet. If the other color appears, however, the player loses the amount bet. If the green appears, the wheel is spun until a nongreen appears. If this color is the color bet, the player neither wins nor loses. Otherwise, the amount bet is lost.

Two players use different strategies. One player simply bets $1 on red each time. The other player uses a progression betting scheme. He starts by betting $1 on red. If he wins, he bets another dollar. However, if he loses, he bets $2 next time. If he loses again, he bets $4. The player keeps doubling his bet up to the table limit of $250. If he loses with $250 down, he starts over with $1 again.

Each player arrives with $250. Simulate the first 500 plays for each. Which do you think is the more favorable strategy? What conclusions can you draw regarding the progression betting scheme?

18.4.

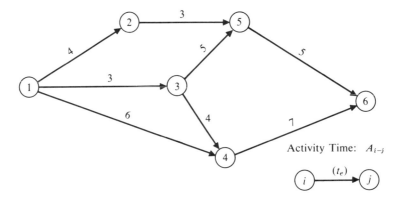

Activity Time: A_{i-j}

Refer to the network structuring of a small project shown above. Simulate the duration of the respective paths through the network. With this information, determine the minimum duration of the project, the critical path, and the slack paths.

18.5. The weekly allocation of two machines to perform two activities has been formulated as a linear programming problem:

$f_{max} = 24X_1 + 20X_2$
subject to: $4X_1 + 2X_2 \leq 16$ machine 1
$\ 2X_1 + 6X_2 \leq 24$ machine 2
$\ X_1 \geq 0; X_2 \geq 0$

Use simulation to find the optimal solution to this linear programming problem. Note, the optimal solution must be at a corner point.

18.6. A stockkeeping unit has the following probability distribution for daily demand and lead time:

Daily Demand (DD)	Probability	Lead Time	Probability
0	.07	2	.23
1	.14	3	.52
2	.22	4	.21
3	.31	5	.04
4	.17		
5	.07		
6	.02		

For an inventory policy of an order quantity (q) of 50 and reorder point (R) of 16, provide a 60-day simulation of demand and inventory levels. Represent the simulation information graphically. The starting inventory level is 42 items. All unsatisfied

       Simulation of Complex Systems

customers will place backorders to be satisfied immediately upon receipt of the order quantity.

Repeat this process with an inventory rule of $q = 50$ and $R = 6$.

18.7. An inventory item has the following probability distributions for demand and lead time:

Daily Demand (DD)	Probability	Lead Time	Probability
15	.01	1	.60
16	.03	2	.30
17	.06	3	.10
18	.14		
19	.18		
20	.24		
21	.16		
22	.11		
23	.05		
24	.02		

If items are not available upon request, customers will await the arrival of the new shipment for only a limited time. Backorders have the following probability distribution:

Backorder: Waiting Time (days)	Probability
0	.42
1	.16
2	.24
3	.18

The inventory item has the following cost information:

ordering cost $(K_O) = \$12$ per order
carrying cost $(K_C) = \$6$ per year
cost of lost sales and customer dissatisfaction for nonbackorders $= \$30$
underage cost for backorders $(K_U) = \$10$
work year $= 250$ days.

The starting inventory level is 100 items. The order quantity (q) and reorder point policy (R) are $q = 100$ and $R = 35$. Simulate the first 24 days for the inventory item. Provide a tabular and graphic representation for the level of inventory and stockouts for each day. Calculate the total cost for the inventory policy $(q = 100, R = 35)$.

Rework this problem providing tabular, graphic, and total-cost information for each of the following inventory policies:

(a) $q = 100$ (b) $q = 140$
    $R = 35$ $R = 35$.

From the limited simulation, which of the four inventory policies has the lowest total cost?

Briefly outline a procedure for obtaining the optimal inventory policy decision variables.

18.8. On weekends during the summer, a tennis club uses its six available courts in various ways. The arrival rates of twosomes for singles and foursomes for doubles differ throughout the day. From sign-in time registers for representative periods last year, the following probability distributions were constructed:

	Time Periods				
Time Between	7:40 AM–	8:30 AM–	12:30 PM–	4:30 PM–	6:30 PM–
Arrivals (T_A)	8:29 AM	12:29 PM	4:29 PM	6:29 PM	8:00 PM
(minutes)	$P(T_A)$	$P(T_A)$	$P(T_A)$	$P(T_A)$	$P(T_A)$
5	.50	.20	.10	.15	.05
10	.30	.25	.20	.25	.15
15	.15	.40	.25	.30	.20
20	.05	.10	.20	.20	.30
25		.05	.15	.10	.15
30			.10		.10
35					.05

If players are waiting for a court, the club has a rule limiting play to one hour and 10 minutes.

With this information, simulate one day of court use. Determine the total number of twosomes or foursomes that will be required to wait for a court. Determine the average waiting time, the total waiting time for a day, and the longest time any players had to wait for a court. Determine the number of idle courts and how long they remain idle.

From this limited information, does the tennis club have enough courts to meet the needs of peak weekend demand?

Using the earlier simulated arrivals for a day, generate comparable waiting and idle facility information for eight courts.

18.9. For some time, the manager of a service station in a prime location has been collecting information regarding arrivals and service times. On weekday morning shifts, the time between arrivals fluctuates substantially, as shown below:

Time Between Arrivals (T_A) (minutes)	7:00 AM–8:39 AM $P(T_A)$	8:40 AM–11:59 AM $P(T_A)$
1	.09	.02
2	.17	.08
3	.32	.14
4	.14	.21
5	.11	.19
6	.09	.14
7	.05	.07
8	.02	.05
9	.01	.04
10		.02
11		.01
12		.01
13		.01
14		.01
15		

Moreover, if two customers are already waiting for service, no more customers will enter the station.

The gas station has two two-pump units, which provide ethyl and regular gasoline. Several attendants may be simultaneously employed. If any attendant is not busy, he will help other busy attendants. Moreover, once they have started serving a car, all the attendants involved will finish serving that car before they start serving a new car.

The manager's estimates of service times are as follows:

Service Time (T_S) (minutes)	One Attendant Probability of Service Time	Two Attendants $P(T_S)$
1	.01	.06
2	.05	.36
3	.20	.42
4	.40	.12
5	.20	.03
6	.11	.01
7	.02	
8	.01	

Each customer provides an estimated profit contribution of 70 cents. Attendants cost $2.50 an hour.

Given one attendant, simulate one hour of both morning periods. Determine the total attendant cost, total profit contribution, and profit contribution lost from an excessive queue.

For the same time, replicate the samples given two attendants. From a total profit perspective, does the limited simulation data favor one or two attendants? Briefly indicate another attendant policy worth considering.

19

Quantitative Business Analysis:
Perspective and Viewpoint

Man is confronted with a continual flow of alternative courses of action—with a continual flow of decisions. There is no escape from this reality. Once there is a presumption of purposeful direction, some courses of action will be better than others. Therefore, if man is concerned with successful achievement, he will have minimal freedom to make a random selection of behavior. Man is predestined to become a *decision maker* who seeks purposeful behavior.

The decision maker is confronted with the richly complex nature of the decision environment. It often contains many unknown and uncontrollable influences. The decision maker will not be capable of considering all of its inherent complexities. He or she must often contend with imponderables.

There is a natural conflict. The decision maker seeks purposeful behavior. The entire decision environment is irresolvably complex. The fundamental question: *How can the decision maker best resolve this basic conflict?*

MODELING THE DECISION ENVIRONMENT

Since the complexity of the entire decision environment is far beyond the capabilities of the decision maker, the decision maker does the best that he or she can to cope with the situation. The decision maker simplifies the irresolvable complexities by considering only part of the entire decision environment. In turn, this part may also be exceedingly complex. The decision maker simplifies again. Through simplifying and simplifying further, the decision maker reduces the complexities to manageable proportions. The decision maker considers a problem that is within his or her potential capabilities.

The decision maker uses his or her time, effort, and resources to acquire additional capabilities to understand and to cope with this *simplified* decision environment. He or she acquires additional knowledge, experience, logic, and information to relate uncontrollable environmental influences and controllable decision variables. The decision maker structures a model of behavior. The model serves as a means to describe, explain, and predict behavior. With a personal definition of purpose, it provides a means for testing, evaluating, and sorting alternative courses of action—for selecting purposeful behavior for the simplified part.

If the model of the simplified part is a good representation of the essential behavior of the decision environment, then the model should provide a good selection of an appropriate course of action for the decision environment. If the simplified part excludes an important aspect of the decision environment, the decision maker must either expand the simplified part to include this aspect or risk a poor selection of an appropriate course of action.

The decision maker attempts to resolve the conflict between restricted capabilities and irresolvable complexities in his or her search for purposeful action. The decision maker simplifies the decision environment by focusing on *a specific problem. The problem is then related back to the entire decision environment in terms of essential relationships only.* In essence, the whole is simplified to a manageable part. The part is adjusted back to the whole. From the myriad of information and relationships, the decision maker selects purposeful action by abstracting and modeling only the essential[1] behavior of the decision environment.

DETERMINING THE MODELING PROCEDURE

Unless he or she is willing to risk poor decisions, the decision maker needs to take the essential parts of the decision environment into consideration. This is done with a model. The model integrates relevant information into a value oriented, structured search for purposeful action.

A critical question: *How should the decision maker model the essential parts of a decision environment?* There are three general approaches for modeling all or part of a decision environment:

1. *Use acquired personal experience models.*

---

[1] The term *essential* has an important meaning. It reflects the decision maker's evaluation of the *opportunity cost* for further expansion of the model. The opportunity cost has three components. First, the decision maker will perceive a cost in time, effort, and resources to expand the model. Second, the decision maker will perceive a benefit in improved selection of purposeful action from the model expansion. Third, the net benefit (benefit minus cost) from model expansion must compete with all other net benefits for the decision maker's perceived use of his or her restricted time, effort, and resources.

2. *Construct a new model.*

3. *Use an internalized reference model.*

The proper approach to modeling is defined in terms of *cost-benefit*. Different approaches require different *costs*—the decision maker's expenditure of time, effort, and resources. Different approaches produce different *benefits*—the likelihood of obtaining an appropriate course of action. The proper approach to modeling provides the decision maker with the greatest net benefit.

The least costly approach to modeling is for the decision maker to rely on personal experience models. Since they require little time, effort, or resources, personal experience models provide the decision maker with *a simple way to resolve most problems*. As long as the decision maker's intuition, judgement, wisdom—*acquired personal experience models*—indicate appropriate courses of action, this approach to modeling may be very good indeed.

Occasionally, however, the decision maker encounters an important problem in a complex situation. The decision maker's personal experience may not be inclusive enough. The decision maker's personal experience models may not indicate sufficiently appropriate courses of action.

In fact, the more complex the situation, the less likely it is that the decision maker will have internalized an acceptably accurate personal experience model. The decision maker may be confronted with an important problem without having an acceptable model to provide a solution. In this case, there is always the possibility of structuring a new model for the situation. This approach, however, typically requires an excessive expenditure of time, effort, and resources. In some cases, there may be the added restrictive requirement of considerable insight, ingenuity, and possibly even a little genius. Structuring an entirely new model is a possibility. The costs, however, too frequently prohibit this approach.

Thus, when a decision maker is confronted with an important problem in a complex situation, he or she may be faced with the unpleasant choice between (1) a low-cost model that will probably indicate a poor course of action or (2) a high-cost model that will possibly indicate a good course of action. Fortunately, there is the possibility of a third choice. The decision maker may use *an internalized reference model*—a formal model that has already been constructed by others.

This third approach to modeling has profound importance. For most problems, *decision models have already been constructed that provide excellent solutions*. Instead of relying on limited personal experience, the decision maker can rely on the *collective experience of mankind*. Instead of utilizing excessive time, effort, and resources in an attempt to "invent the wheel" anew, the decision maker can use the models already developed and proven by others. He or she can transform others' experience into an increased endowment of personal experience. And in this process, the decision maker can remove the shackling constraints of a single individual's limitations. The decision maker can become *educated in mankind's collective efforts in modeling*.

INTERNALIZED REFERENCE MODELS

When an *educated decision maker* has an important problem warranting formal modeling, he or she will usually be able to fit the specific problem into the general structure of one or more internalized reference models. The decision maker will be able to obtain a *low-cost, high-benefit* solution to the problem.

The accumulated body of knowledge on formal modeling is extensive. In the course of making innumerable important decisions throughout a professional career, a wise decision maker will have little choice but to become educated in many of the readily available modeling techniques. The costs of acquisition are minimal. The potential personal and professional lifetime benefits are great.

A prime objective of this text has been the introduction of many important internalized reference models. To provide perspective, these powerful modeling techniques are summarized below.

Stochastic Behavior

The desirability of many decisions today depends on uncertain events tomorrow. The most general classification of the decision environment is uncertainty. Fortunately, in many situations, a decision maker can appropriately exclude the complicating stochastic elements from the essential behavior of the decision environment. In many cases, however, uncertainty is an inherent part of the essential behavior. A decision maker must consider the complicating stochastic elements.

Besides the entire disciplines of probability and statistics, a wide assortment of stochastic models have been developed to incorporate uncertainty into the essential behavior of the decision environment. This text has presented several: *Bayes' decision rule*; *the conditional profit table*; *the conditional opportunity loss table*; *the decision tree*; *game theory*; *inventory models*; *queuing models*; and *Monte Carlo simulation*. There are many internalized reference models for the decision maker who is concerned with a proper course of action in an environment of uncertainty.

An Environment of Competition

A decision environment of competition (or conflict) literally pervades a market system of exchange. Such basic market processes as buying, selling, pricing, and bargaining are attempts to resolve a conflict of interests. And for the parties involved in a cooperative effort, the distribution of the returns from the cooperative participation produces an environment of conflict. Competition (or conflict) is often an essential part of the decision environment. In these cases, the decision maker must somehow take it into consideration.

Decision environments of competition are often exceedingly complex. They frequently produce difficulties in formal modeling. *Game theory*, *linear programming*, and *simulation*, however, can help a decision maker to cope more appropriately with these complexities.

Allocating Resources

The allocation of resources to competing activities is an exceptionally general problem area. Virtually all managerial decisions involve some form of resource allocations. A decision maker can use *linear programming* to help in these decisions.

For the resource related part of the decision environment, linear programming (with a few nonrestrictive assumptions) answers the resource allocation question. In a linear programming solution, the resource related components are *formulated* in a formal linear structure. Once the resource relationships have been formulated, the *simplex method* can then be used to define the best possible allocation of the resources.

Linear programming provides a decision maker with much more than an optimal allocation of the resources. The formulation of the problem contains all essential resource related information. The *simplex tableaus* and minor adjustments of the simplex tableaus (*sensitivity analysis*) provide a decision maker with *any desired resource related information. Any component* of this decision environment can be changed with measured effects on all other components. A decision maker who is educated in this powerful model will be equipped with the information necessary to make rational, intelligent, informed resource allocation decisions.

Project Planning, Scheduling, and Controlling

Another common problem area is the planning, scheduling, and controlling of large-scale projects. Here a decision maker has *PERT* and *CPM*. By separating a complex project into clearly defined time, cost, and resource requirements; relating all activities in a single time dimension; and isolating critical and subcritical activities, these models provide project management with essential information. They provide management with a means for coordinating and synchronizing the myriad of subcomponent parts with the requirements of the total project. And by this process of readily relating individual and team efforts to total project requirements, they facilitate communication and cooperation between diverse parts of the total project. They keep management constantly informed of the project's progress. They produce essential information for reallocating resources and isolating potential trouble areas. PERT and CPM provide the information management needs to facilitate a smoothly coordinated, on-time completion of vastly complex, one-time projects.

Inventory Management

As cooperative systems increase in size, interdependence, and complexity, a common problem is the economic maintenance and control of inventories. The scope of inventory problems extends far beyond the classical prototype of the storage of physical goods. The efficient handling, storage, and retrieval of information or the acquisition, training; and advancement of employees can be considered as inventory problems.

Inventory theory offers a decision maker access to an extensive body of collective knowledge on inventory systems. Ranging from simple deterministic forms to highly sophisticated stochastic ones, it offers a decision maker a wide assortment of formal models for better inventory management.

Waiting Lines

Waiting lines or queues are another general problem area. The cost of providing service facilities, the uncertainty of arrivals for service, and the uncertainty in service times frequently cause the demands for service to exceed the service facilities' supply. When this happens, queues form to await service. Decision makers are frequently concerned with designing economic queuing systems—with properly balancing the cost of providing service and the cost of having items or individuals wait for service.

Queuing theory provides a decision maker with descriptive models of queuing system behavior. These models can significantly aid a decision maker with optimal queuing system design. An extensive literature awaits the interested decision maker.

Complex Interrelated Systems

Organizations are complex interrelated systems. Important decisions for part of the system cannot be made in isolation. A new product decision, for example, requires the decision maker to consider the entire interrelated marketing mix of product design, pricing, promotion, and distribution. In turn, these affect the personnel, production, and financial systems. A decision maker often needs a formal model of this complex interrelated behavior.

Combining the computational capabilities of computers and the simple model structuring of simulation, *computer simulation models* are being used to reveal the complex behavior of dynamic, interrelated, feedback systems. Marketing systems, financial systems, ecological systems, urban systems, and organizational systems have been structured into computer simulation models of complex system behavior. These models provide a decision maker with an experimental testing ground to discover cause and effect. Any component of the system can be changed with a measure of total system performance. A decision maker thus equipped has an exceptionally powerful decision making tool.

AN EXTENDED PERSPECTIVE OF INTERNALIZED REFERENCE MODELS

Man's collective modeling experience is extensive. The previous section on internalized reference models is only an introduction to evolving methods of formal modeling. While there are still many problems beyond the present endowment of collective human experience, a progressive decision maker needs to stay informed on available and evolving modeling developments. A summary of several extensions in two modeling areas will indicate some of what is already available and some of the emerging pathways of pioneering efforts.

Linear Programming Extended

Linear programming is a powerful modeling procedure. Its importance is summed up in the problem it solves: the allocation of resources to competing uses for optimal objective obtainment. As early as 1958, a published bibliography[2] contained over one thousand articles describing the developments and successful applications of linear programming.

For a formulated problem (Chapter 8), several algorithms provide an optimal solution. The most generally recognized approach is the *simplex method* (Chapter 9). For problems that would normally contain artificial variables, the *dual-simplex method* (Chapter 10, Appendix) improves computational efficiency. Also, not considered earlier, a *composite simplex method*[3] allows negative valued variables in the movement to the optimal solution.

Two extensions not considered in earlier chapters can significantly improve the computational efficiency of the simplex method: *the decomposition method*[4] and *the revised simplex method.*[5] In the decomposition method, a large problem is divided into subcomponent parts. These are solved separately. They are then recombined in accordance with total system requirements by means of "penalties" and "bonuses." In the revised simplex method, movements are made from

---

[2] V. Riley and S. I. Gass, *Bibliography on Linear Programming and Related Techniques* (Baltimore: The Johns Hopkins Press, 1958).

[3] P. Wolfe, "The Composite Simplex Algorithm," *SIAM Review* 7 (1969): 42–54.

[4] G. B. Dantzig, *Linear Programming and Extensions* (Princeton, N.J.: Princeton University Press, 1963). Also, C. Kim, "Decomposition of Planning Systems," *Decision Sciences* 1 (1972): 397–422.

[5] N. P. Loomba and E. Turbin, *Applied Programming for Management* (New York: Holt, Rinehart & Winston, Inc., 1974).

tableau to improved tableau with minimal information and computation requirements. This substantially improves the efficiency with which large-scale problems can be solved. It is the method used in most computer programs.

Duality and *sensitivity analysis* (Chapters 10 and 11) add considerable flexibility and important decision-making information to a linear programming solution. Every linear programming problem can be formulated and solved in two distinct ways: as the *primal* problem or as the *dual* problem. Sensitivity analysis provides algorithms for measuring the effects on the total system produced by a change in any component of a formulated linear programming problem. When these algorithms have been programmed on a computer, a decision maker has available a tremendous wealth of information—virtually all information on resource allocations and all information on the implications of any change that could be suggested.

Special decision environments are solvable by improved special-purpose algorithms. The *transportation problem* is solvable by a streamlined version of the simplex tableau: *the transportation model* (Chapter 12). Other special decision environments with special-purpose algorithms include *the assignment problem, the transshipment problem*, and the *multitime period transportation problem*.[6]

Although they require a unique formulation, several major problem areas are solvable by linear programming. Both *game theory* (Chapter 7) and *network models* (Chapter 13) fit this category.

The applicability of linear programming is determined primarily by the closeness with which the decision environment maintains several inherent assumptions. Linear programming assumes a *fixed time period* for a *deterministic* decision environment. Resource relationships and objective contributions are assumed *proportional* and *additive*. Activities are assumed *divisible*. Any substantial deviation from these assumptions may produce an appreciable difference between the actual and the calculated optimal solutions. Fortunately, when these assumptions are not adequately maintained, linear programming extensions have been developed and are being further developed to consider the added complexities.

Linear programming assumes the possibility of a partial completion of an activity with proportional effects: a *divisibility* of activity levels. For example, any fractional part of a product that is produced in one time period can be completed in the next. If entirely completed activities are required, however, *integer programming* and *mixed integer programming*[7] provide an optimal solution.

Linear programming assumes *proportionality* and *additivity*. A change in the availability of the resources will produce a proportional change in the activity levels—constant returns to scale. Additivity infers an independence of

---

[6] F. S. Hillier and G. J. Lieberman, *Introduction to Operations Research* (San Francisco: Holden-Day, Inc., 1974).

[7] H. A. Taha, *Integer Programming: Theory, Applications, and Computations* (New York: Academic Press, 1975).

activity utilization rates and contribution rates. In combination, proportionality and additivity require the objective function and the structural constraints to be *linear equations*. If these properties are not maintained, *nonlinear programming*,[8] *quadratic programming*,[9] and *separable programming*[10] provide optimizing procedures.

Linear programming assumes a *deterministic* decision environment: the parameters are known constants. Since linear programming is typically used to select a future course of action, the parameters infer projected conditions with an implication of uncertainty. While this makes the deterministic assumption theoretically imprecise, it is usually quite sound pragmatically. In certain situations with considerable uncertainty, however, other modeling procedures may be required. *Stochastic programming* and *chance-constrained programming models*[11] provide means for directly incorporating uncertainties into the analysis.

Linear programming also assumes *a fixed point in time*. Many situations, however, are dynamic in nature. *Multistage linear programming*[12] and *dynamic programming*[13] *models* entend linear programming for dynamic situations.

Almost all problems in some way concern the allocation of resources. The problem area is extensive. The decision making implications of a successful resolution are significant. While they are still evolving, linear programming developments and extensions have been bountiful. The fertile area abounds with a wealth of reference models.

Simulation Extended

Simulation is an exceedingly flexible modeling procedure. Of all the formally structured models, it has the most adaptive structure for modeling the decision environment. If sufficient time, effort, and resources, are available, computer supported simulation can be used to structure and solve virtually any solvable problem.

The extensions in the application of simulation will be demonstrated by a new generation of simulation models of world system scope. Sponsored by the Club of Rome and a grant from the Volkswagen Foundation, Jay Forrester extended his industrial dynamics and his subsequent urban dynamics to world

---

[8] Dantzig, *op. cit.* and Loomba and Turbin, *op. cit.*
[9] J. C. G. Boot, *Quadratic Programming* (Skokie, Ill.: Rand McNally, 1964). Also, Loomba and Turbin, *op. cit.*
[10] G. Hadley, *Nonlinear and Dynamic Programming* (Reading, Mass.: Addison-Wesley, 1964).
[11] Dantzig, *op. cit.* Also, A. Charnes and W. W. Cooper, *Management Models and Industrial Application of Linear Programming* (New York: John Wiley & Sons, Inc., 1960).
[12] Dantzig, *op. cit.*
[13] R. Bellman, *Dynamic Programming* (Princeton, N.J.: Princeton University Press, 1963). Also, G. L. Nemhauser, *Introduction to Dynamic Programming* (New York: John Wiley & Sons, Inc., 1966).

dynamics.[14] In another classic work, the important behavioral forces affecting the world environment are modeled in terms of their dynamic interrelated effects.

The world environment is separated into the interreactive systems of:

(1) Population,

(2) Natural Resources,

(3) Capital Investment, and

(4) Pollution.

Each of these major systems, in turn, contains subsystems that are related to the other major systems. A new dimension, the Quality of Life, is used as a measure of total system performance.

Man's social, technical, and natural environment (the socio-technical-natural system) is structured into a model of world system behavior. For the model's specified assumptions, any subsystem change can be studied in terms of the interreactive growth and stress throughout the entire system. Scenarios can be stepped through time to unfold the dynamics of behavioral consequences, Alternative futures can be tested and compared.

A scenario representing the effects of a depletion in natural resources is provided in figure 19.1. In summary, the system effects are:

Natural Resources↓ → Effectiveness of Capital↓ → Investment↓
→ Material Standard of Living↓ → Population↓

While these projections are not universally accepted,[15] the model provides an indication of the direction of the total system based on the underlying set of assumptions.

Although global modeling is still in an early stage of development, the analysis made thus far leads to several important conclusions regarding the plight of mankind. The world environment is in a transition from world growth to world equilibrium. Exponential growth rates cannot continue forever. The question is not whether growth will cease—just when and how. The challenge confronting mankind is to choose the best available transition from the past dynamics of growth to a future condition of world equilibrium.

———

[14] Jay W. Forrester, *World Dynamics* (Cambridge, Mass.: Wright-Allen Press, Inc., 1971).
[15] Experts such as Herman Kahn of the Hudson Institute feel that many of the assumptions underlying the structural components of the model are questionable and significantly underestimate the dynamism and flexibility of capitalism. See Herman Kahn, "Our Global Growing Pains," *Nation's Business* July, 1973, pp. 32–38. Some critics may argue that not enough is known to construct social models. Can these same critics believe enough is known to directly design new social systems by passing laws and developing new social programs? See Forrester, *op. cit.*, pp. 123–28.

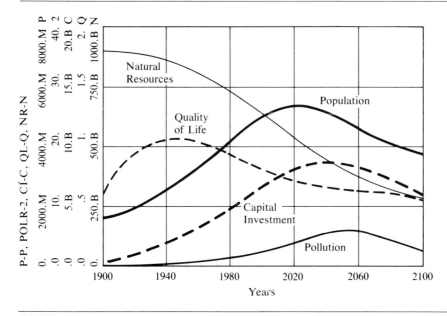

FIGURE 19.1

Population Decline Imposed by Depletion of Natural Resources: Reprinted from *World Dynamics* (Second Edition) by Jay W. Forrester by permission of the Wright-Allen Press, Cambridge, Massachusetts, 02142, U.S.A. (Copyright 1973, All rights reserved.)

Since good solutions for dynamic behavior are often counter-intuitive and short-run solutions often burden the system with long-run depressants, a passage from Forrester's epilogue is worth reflection:[16]

People are in the position of a wild animal running from its pursuers. We still have some space, natural resources, and agricultural land left. We can avoid the question of rising population as long as we can flee into this bountiful reservoir that nature provided. But the reservoir is limited. Exponential growth cannot continue. The wild animal flees until he is cornered, until he has no more space. Then he turns to fight, but he no longer has room to maneuver. He is less able to forestall disaster than if he fought in the open while there was still room to yield and to dodge. The world is running away from its long-term threats by trying to relieve social pressures as they arise. But, if we persist in treating the symptoms and not the causes, the result will be to increase the magnitude of the ultimate threat and reduce our capability to respond when we no longer have more space and resources to invade.

In the decades that follow, decision makers will be confronted with difficult social, political, and economic problems. The need for better solutions to these pressing problems will stimulate new and improved models to help them better understand and cope with reality—to help decision makers more successfully guide the course of mankind.

_____
[16] Ibid, pp. 124.

THE STANDARD NORMAL DISTRIBUTION

The entry in the table corresponds to the shaded area from $z = 0$ to z units from the mean.

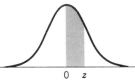

z	.00	.01	.02	.03	.04	.05	.06	.07	.08	.09
0.0	.0000	.0040	.0080	.0120	.0160	.0199	.0239	.0279	.0319	.0359
0.1	.0398	.0438	.0478	.0517	.0557	.0596	.0636	.0675	.0714	.0753
0.2	.0793	.0832	.0871	.0910	.0948	.0987	.1026	.1064	.1103	.1141
0.3	.1179	.1217	.1255	.1293	.1331	.1368	.1406	.1443	.1480	.1517
0.4	.1554	.1591	.1628	.1664	.1700	.1736	.1772	.1808	.1844	.1879
0.5	.1915	.1950	.1985	.2019	.2054	.2088	.2123	.2157	.2190	.2224
0.6	.2257	.2291	.2324	.2357	.2389	.2422	.2454	.2486	.2517	.2549
0.7	.2580	.2611	.2642	.2673	.2703	.2734	.2764	.2794	.2823	.2852
0.8	.2881	.2910	.2939	.2967	.2995	.3023	.3051	.3078	.3106	.3133
0.9	.3159	.3186	.3212	.3238	.3264	.3289	.3315	.3340	.3365	.3389
1.0	.3413	.3438	.3461	.3485	.3508	.3531	.3554	.3577	.3599	.3621
1.1	.3643	.3665	.3686	.3708	.3729	.3749	.3770	.3790	.3810	.3830
1.2	.3849	.3869	.3888	.3907	.3925	.3944	.3962	.3980	.3997	.4015
1.3	.4032	.4049	.4066	.4082	.4099	.4115	.4131	.4147	.4162	.4177
1.4	.4192	.4207	.4222	.4236	.4251	.4265	.4279	.4292	.4306	.4319
1.5	.4332	.4345	.4357	.4370	.4382	.4394	.4406	.4418	.4429	.4441
1.6	.4452	.4463	.4474	.4484	.4495	.4505	.4515	.4525	.4535	.4545
1.7	.4554	.4564	.4573	.4582	.4591	.4599	.4608	.4616	.4625	.4633
1.8	.4641	.4649	.4656	.4664	.4671	.4678	.4686	.4693	.4699	.4706
1.9	.4713	.4719	.4726	.4732	.4738	.4744	.4750	.4756	.4761	.4767
2.0	.4772	.4778	.4783	.4788	.4793	.4798	.4803	.4808	.4812	.4817
2.1	.4821	.4826	.4830	.4834	.4838	.4842	.4846	.4850	.4854	.4857
2.2	.4861	.4864	.4868	.4871	.4875	.4878	.4881	.4884	.4887	.4890
2.3	.4893	.4896	.4898	.4901	.4904	.4906	.4909	.4911	.4913	.4916
2.4	.4918	.4920	.4922	.4925	.4927	.4929	.4931	.4932	.4934	.4936
2.5	.4938	.4940	.4941	.4943	.4945	.4946	.4948	.4949	.4951	.4952
2.6	.4953	.4955	.4956	.4957	.4959	.4960	.4961	.4962	.4963	.4964
2.7	.4965	.4966	.4967	.4968	.4969	.4970	.4971	.4972	.4973	.4974
2.8	.4974	.4975	.4976	.4977	.4977	.4978	.4979	.4979	.4980	.4981
2.9	.4981	.4982	.4982	.4983	.4984	.4984	.4985	.4985	.4986	.4986
3.0	.4987	.4987	.4987	.4988	.4988	.4989	.4989	.4989	.4990	.4990

APPENDIX 2

2500 RANDOM DIGITS

03991	10461	93716	16894	98953	73231	39528	72484	82474	25593
38555	95554	32886	59780	09958	18065	81616	18711	53342	44276
17546	73704	92052	46215	15917	06253	07586	16120	82641	22820
32643	52861	95819	06831	19640	99413	90767	04235	13574	17200
69572	68777	39510	35905	85244	35159	40188	28193	29593	88627
24122	66591	27699	06494	03152	19121	34414	82157	86887	55087
61196	30231	92962	61773	22109	78508	63439	75363	44989	16822
30532	21704	10274	12202	94205	20380	67049	09070	93399	45547
03788	97599	75867	20717	82037	10268	79495	04146	52162	90286
48228	63379	85783	47619	87481	37220	91704	30552	04737	21031
88618	19161	41290	67312	71857	15957	48545	35247	18619	13674
71299	23853	05870	01119	92784	26340	75122	11724	74627	73707
27954	58909	82444	99005	04921	73701	92904	13141	32392	19763
80863	00514	20247	81759	45197	25332	69902	63742	78464	22501
33564	60780	48460	85558	15191	18782	94972	11598	62095	36787
90899	75754	60833	25983	01291	41349	19152	00023	12302	80783
78038	70267	43529	06318	38384	74761	36024	00867	76378	41605
55986	66485	88722	56736	66164	49431	94458	74284	05041	49807
87539	08823	94813	31900	54155	83436	54158	34243	46978	35482
16818	60311	74457	90561	72848	11834	75051	93029	47665	64382
34677	58300	74910	64345	19325	81549	60365	94653	35075	33949
45305	07521	61318	31855	14413	70951	83799	42402	56623	34442
59747	67277	76503	34513	39663	77544	32960	07405	36409	83232
16520	69676	11654	99893	02181	68161	19322	53845	57620	52606
68652	27376	92852	55866	88448	03584	11220	94747	07399	37408
79375	95220	01159	63267	10622	48391	31751	57260	68980	05339
33521	26665	55823	47641	86225	31704	88492	99382	14454	04504
59589	49067	66821	41575	49767	04037	30934	47744	07481	83828
20554	91409	96277	48257	50816	97616	22888	48893	27499	98748
59404	72059	43947	51680	43852	59693	78212	16993	35902	91386
42614	29297	01918	28316	25163	01889	70014	15021	68971	11403
34994	41374	70071	14736	65251	07629	37239	33295	18477	65622
99385	41600	11133	07586	36815	43625	18637	37509	14707	93997
66497	68646	78138	66559	64397	11692	05327	82162	83745	22567
48509	23929	27482	45476	04515	25624	95096	67946	16930	33361
15470	48355	88651	22596	83761	60873	43253	84145	20368	07126
20094	98977	74843	93413	14387	06345	80854	09279	41196	37480
73788	06533	28597	20405	51321	92246	80088	77074	66919	31678
60530	45128	74022	84617	72472	00008	80890	18002	35352	54131
44372	15486	65741	14014	05466	55306	93128	18464	79982	68416
18611	19241	66083	24653	84609	58232	41849	84547	46850	52326
58319	15997	08355	60860	29735	47762	46352	33049	69248	93460
61199	67940	55121	29281	59076	07936	11087	96294	14013	31792
18627	90872	00911	98936	76355	93779	52701	08337	56303	87315
00441	58997	14060	40619	29549	69616	57275	36898	81304	48585
32624	68691	14845	46672	61958	77100	20857	73156	70284	24326
65961	73488	41839	55382	17267	70943	15633	84924	90415	93614
20288	34060	39685	23309	10061	68829	92694	48297	39904	02115
59362	95938	74416	53166	35208	33374	77613	19019	88152	00080
99782	93478	53152	67433	35663	52972	38688	32486	45134	63545

2500 RANDOM DIGITS

03991	10461	93716	16894	98953	73231	39528	72484	82474	25593
38555	95554	32886	59780	09958	18065	81616	18711	53342	44276
17546	73704	92052	46215	15917	06253	07586	16120	82641	22820
32643	52861	95819	06831	19640	99413	90767	04235	13574	17200
69572	68777	39510	35905	85244	35159	40188	28193	29593	88627
24122	66591	27699	06494	03152	19121	34414	82157	86887	55087
61196	30231	92962	61773	22109	78508	63439	75363	44989	16822
30532	21704	10274	12202	94205	20380	67049	09070	93399	45547
03788	97599	75867	20717	82037	10268	79495	04146	52162	90286
48228	63379	85783	47619	87481	37220	91704	30552	04737	21031
88618	19161	41290	67312	71857	15957	48545	35247	18619	13674
71299	23853	05870	01119	92784	26340	75122	11724	74627	73707
27954	58909	82444	99005	04921	73701	92904	13141	32392	19763
80863	00514	20247	81759	45197	25332	69902	63742	78464	22501
33564	60780	48460	85558	15191	18782	94972	11598	62095	36787
90899	75754	60833	25983	01291	41349	19152	00023	12302	80783
78038	70267	43529	06318	38384	74761	36024	00867	76378	41605
55986	66485	88722	56736	66164	49431	94458	74284	05041	49807
87539	08823	94813	31900	54155	83436	54158	34243	46978	35482
16818	60311	74457	90561	72848	11834	75051	93029	47665	64382
34677	58300	74910	64345	19325	81549	60365	94653	35075	33949
45305	07521	61318	31855	14413	70951	83799	42402	56623	34442
59747	67277	76503	34513	39663	77544	32960	07405	36409	83232
16520	69676	11654	99893	02181	68161	19322	53845	57620	52606
68652	27376	92852	55866	88448	03584	11220	94747	07399	37408
79375	95220	01159	63267	10622	48391	31751	57260	68980	05339
33521	26665	55823	47641	86225	31704	88492	99382	14454	04504
59589	49067	66821	41575	49767	04037	30934	47744	07481	83828
20554	91409	96277	48257	50816	97616	22888	48893	27499	98748
59404	72059	43947	51680	43852	59693	78212	16993	35902	91386
42614	29297	01918	28316	25163	01889	70014	15021	68971	11403
34994	41374	70071	14736	65251	07629	37239	33295	18477	65622
99385	41600	11133	07586	36815	43625	18637	37509	14707	93997
66497	68646	78138	66559	64397	11692	05327	82162	83745	22567
48509	23929	27482	45476	04515	25624	95096	67946	16930	33361
15470	48355	88651	22596	83761	60873	43253	84145	20368	07126
20094	98977	74843	93413	14387	06345	80854	09279	41196	37480
73788	06533	28597	20405	51321	92246	80088	77074	66919	31678
60530	45128	74022	84617	72472	00008	80890	18002	35352	54131
44372	15486	65741	14014	05466	55306	93128	18464	79982	68416
18611	19241	66083	24653	84609	58232	41849	84547	46850	52326
58319	15997	08355	60860	29735	47762	46352	33049	69248	93460
61199	67940	55121	29281	59076	07936	11087	96294	14013	31792
!8627	90872	00911	98936	76355	93779	52701	08337	56303	87315
00441	58997	14060	40619	29549	69616	57275	36898	81304	48585
32624	68691	14845	46672	61958	77100	20857	73156	70284	24326
65961	73488	41839	55382	17267	70943	15633	84924	90415	93614
20288	34060	39685	23309	10061	68829	92694	48297	39904	02115
59362	95938	74416	53166	35208	33374	77613	19019	88152	00080
99782	93478	53152	67433	35663	52972	38688	32486	45134	63545

Index